GAMBLING BEHAVIOR AND PROBLEM GAMBLING

GAMBLING BEHAVIOR AND PROBLEM GAMBLING

EDITED BY

William R. Eadington
Professor of Economics and Director
Institute for the Study of Gambling and Commercial Gaming
College of Business Administration
University of Nevada, Reno

Judy A. Cornelius
Associate Director
Institute for the Study of Gambling and Commercial Gaming
College of Business Administration
University of Nevada, Reno

ISBN 0-942828-33-X

Institute for the Study of Gambling and Commercial Gaming
College of Business Administration
University of Nevada, Reno
Reno, Nevada 89557 USA

Book design and layout by Diane Chester Berg
Computer Support Services of Northern Nevada
Carson City, Nevada

Dust jacket artwork and design by
Communication by Design
Reno, Nevada

Printed in the United States of America

For my family:
Margaret Ann Dean Eadington
Diana Elizabeth Eadington
Michael Travis Eadington

For my Reno family:
Curious Gato
Creme Kitty

Gambling Behavior and Problem Gambling

Contents

V
Gambling and Youth

Contributors

VÍCTOR MORENO AGUADO, PH.D.

Professor of Biostatistics
Laboratory of Biostatistics and Epidemiology
Autonomous University of Barcelona
Spain

ALEX BLASZCZYNSKI, PH.D.

Professor
Academic Mental Health Unit
University of New South Wales
Liverpool Hospital
Australia

MICHAEL D. BOSTON, NCAC II, CAS, CSAC

St. Mary's Hospital
Reno, Nevada

DR. JOHANNES C. BRENGELMANN, PH.D.

Professor
Max-Planck-Institute for Psychiatry
Munich, Germany

R. IAIN F. BROWN

Department of Psychology
University of Glasgow
Glasgow, Scotland

BASIL R. BROWNE

Assistant Professor
Department of Sociology
Queens College
Flushing, New York

KENNY R. COVENTRY, PH.D.

Department of Psychology
University of Dundee
Dundee, Scotland

JOHN CROSS

Department of Sociology
Oklahoma State University

ROBERT L. CUSTER, M.D.

Washington, D.C.

MARK DICKERSON

Associate Professor
Department of Psychology
University of Western Sydney, Macarthur
Australia

THOMAS FABIAN, DR. PHIL.

Bremer Institut für Gerichts Psychologie
Universität Bremen
Germany

SUSAN FISHER, PH.D.

University of Plymouth
United Kingdom

MICHAEL L. FRANK

Associate Professor of Psychology
Stockton State College
Pomona, New Jersey

ANNE GABOURY, M.PS.

Ecole de Psychologie
Université Laval
Quebéc, Canada

JAMES D. GRAY

Readjustment Counselor
Veterans Administration Vet Center
Sioux City, Iowa

MARK GRIFFITHS, B.SC., PH.D., C. PSYCHOL.

Department of Psychology
University of Plymouth
United Kingdom

JOSÉ LUIS GUIRAO, M.B.A.

Casinos de Catalunya
Barcelona, Spain

MARY HEINEMAN, MSW, CGC

Family Therapist
South Oaks Hospital
Amityville, New York

JOSEPH HRABA

Professor of Sociology
Iowa State University
Ames, Iowa

DAVID HUFF

Graduate Student
Department of Sociology
Iowa State University
Ames, Iowa

DURAND F. JACOBS, PH.D., ABPP

Clinical Professor of Psychiatry
Loma Linda University Medical School
Loma Linda, California

ROBERT LADOUCEUR, PH.D.

Ecole de Psychologie
Université Laval
Quebéc, Canada

HENRY R. LESIEUR

Professor and Chairperson
Department of Criminal Justice Sciences
Illinois State University
Normal, Illinois
(Formerly of St. John's University)

VALERIE C. LORENZ, PH.D.

Executive Director
Compulsive Gambling Center, Inc.
Baltimore, Maryland

MARIE MARK

St. John's University
Jamaica, New York

MIGUEL MARTÍN MATEO

Professor of Biostatistics
Laboratory of Biostatistics and Epidemiology
Autonomous University of Barcelona
Spain

NEIL MCCONAGHY, D.SC.

Visiting Professor
School of Psychiatry
University of New South Wales
Kensington, Australia

LAWRENCE MELAMED, PH.D.

Kent State University
Kent, Ohio

GERHARD MEYER, PH.D.

Studiengang Psychologie
Universität Bremen
Germany

WAIMAN P. MOK

Graduate Student
Department of Sociology
University of Wisconsin
Madison, Wisconsin

DR. EMANUEL MORAN

Chairman
U.K. National Council on Gambling
and
Consultant Psychiatrist
Grovelands Priory Hospital
London

KAREN MOSELEY

University of North Texas

ANGEL MARTÍNEZ PINA, PH.D.

Professor of Psychiatry
Autonomous University of Barcelona
Spain

XAVIER SERRAT PLANAS, PH.D.

Psychiatrist
Autonomous University of Barcelona
Spain

ROBERT M. POLITZER

Director of Research
Washington Center for Pathological Gambling, Inc.
College Park, Maryland

SEONAID ROBERTSON

Graduate Student
Department of Clinical Psychology
University of Edinburgh
Edinburgh, Scotland

RICHARD J. ROSENTHAL, M.D.

Assistant Clinical Professor of Psychiatry
UCLA School of Medicine
Los Angeles, California

GARRY RUBENSTEIN

University of Nevada, Reno
Reno, Nevada

LOREEN J. RUGLE, PH.D.

Gambling Treatment Program
Brecksville Veterans Administration Medical Center
Brecksville, Ohio

GARY J. SCRIMGEOUR, PH.D.

Editor
College of Engineering
University of Nevada, Reno
Reno, Nevada

DAVID SHEWAN

Glasgow Caledonian University
Glasgow, Scotland

JAMES R. SMITH

Chief, Psychology Services
Department of Veterans Affairs - Domiciliary
White City, Oregon

MARVIN A. STEINBERG, PH.D.

Assistant Director
Hamden Mental Health Service
Hamden, Connecticut

SHARON A. STEIN, ED.D.

Assistant Attending Psychologist
McLean Hospital, Belmont, Massachusetts
and
Instructor in Psychology
Harvard Medical School

MARY LOU STRACHAN, B.A.

Independent Researcher
Phoenix, Arizona

JULIAN I. TABER

Staff Psychologist
Department of Veterans Affairs - Domiciliary
White City, Oregon

RAFAEL FUSTÉ I VALLVERDÚ, PH.D.

Psychiatrist
Autonomous University of Barcelona
Spain

RACHEL A. VOLBERG, PH.D.

President
Gemini Research
Albany, New York

MICHAEL B. WALKER, PH.D.

Department of Psychology
University of Sydney
Australia

MICHAEL WELCH

Department of Sociology and Anthropology
St. John's University
Jamaica, New York

CAROLYN WHITE

Director of Alcoholism Services
Canton-Potsdam Hospital
Potsdam, New York

ROBERT A. YAFFEE, PH.D.

Director of Research
Compulsive Gambling Center, Inc.
and
Consultant
Academic Computing Facility
Courant Institute of Mathematical Sciences
New York University

Preface

The world-wide spread of commercial gaming industries from the 1960s into the mid-1990s can only be described as phenomenal. Gambling in many forms — lotteries, casinos, charitable gambling, parimutuel wagering, Indian gaming — has changed the way people gamble and think about gambling. Gambling has become big business, and much of the population is along for the ride.

Accompanying the spread of gambling has been an increasing concern about the social consequences associated with improved access to commercial gaming opportunities. Though it is clear that most people who participate in gambling activities treat it responsibly as a recreational pursuit, there is a small but significant portion of the population for whom gambling becomes an obsession, a compulsion, or a pathology — in a word, a "problem." Why this occurs, who is affected by problem gambling, and what can be done about it are the major themes of this book.

There are many reasons to believe that, as commercial gaming continues to become more acceptable among the general public, problem gambling will spread as well. From a public policy perspective, it is important to understand the proliferation of gambling and how it is changing the role gambling plays in modern society. It is also important to comprehend the linkages between normal gambling behavior and problem gambling.

The most important change regarding legal commercial gaming in the past thirty years has been the improved access of the general public to gambling that has followed legalization. Consider the North American experience, for example. As late as 1964, there were no legal lotteries in the United States or Canada. Legal casinos were only to be found in Nevada. Though thoroughbred race tracks existed in many urban areas, one had to visit the track to bet legally. Thus, there was limited gambling product, both in terms of geographic presence and in the variety of options available to the potential gambler.

However, in slightly more than a generation — by 1993 — the world of gambling had changed drastically. Lotteries had spread to every Canadian province and, in the U.S., to 37 states and the District of Columbia. More than 80% of the U.S. population lived in states where lotteries were legally available. Lottery sales in the U.S. — before payment of prizes — exceeded $20 billion in 1991, with over $10 million retained by lottery commissions after payment of prizes.

Similar changes in the legal status of casinos had begun in the late 1980s. At the beginning of 1989, casino gaming could only be found in Nevada and Atlantic City, and in so-called charitable casinos in a few Western Canadian cities. By early 1993, one could legally gamble in casinos in over fifteen states and four provinces, with more on the way.

A variety of types of casinos had emerged. There were destination resort hotel casinos, as found in Nevada and Atlantic City; riverboat or dockside casinos, such as those operating in Iowa, Illinois, and Mississippi, and in the planning stages in Louisiana and Missouri; and limited stakes mining town casinos, such as those to be found in Deadwood, South Dakota, and in Cripple Creek, Central City, and Blackhawk, Colorado. There were Indian owned casinos in the states of Connecticut, Michigan, Wisconsin, Minnesota, South Dakota, Colorado, Washington State, Arizona, and California. One could even find a government owned and operated casino in Winnipeg, Manitoba; and "charity" casinos — where the major beneficiaries were not-for-profit organizations — in British Columbia, Alberta, and Saskatchewan. Furthermore, significant plans were underway in 1993 for the development of urban casinos — land-based or on riverboats — in New Orleans, Kansas City, St. Louis, Montreal, and Windsor.

By 1993, other gaming industries had also become well entrenched. Charitable or church sponsored gaming, in the form of bingo, pull-tab tickets, low stakes blackjack, or "Las Vegas" nights, had become major revenue generators in many states and provinces. In Minnesota, for example, charitable gaming in 1991 generated gross winnings of about $230 million. Pari-mutuel wagering could also be found in many jurisdictions, associated with thoroughbred racing, harness racing, dog racing, and jai alai. The pari-mutuel industry had evolved considerably over the past three decades, both with legalization into new jurisdictions and with the introduction of such developments as off-track betting, intertrack wagering, and teletrack theaters in many locales, as well as slot machines at some racetracks.

In total, commercial gaming industries in the United States had gross revenues of about $26 billion in 1991, about 0.6% of the country's disposable income. Yet, in comparison to other countries with more accessible gambling, the United States might still have a long way to go. For example, in New South Wales, Australia's largest state, per capita gaming expenditures in 1990/91 were 2.6% of disposable income, of which about two-thirds came from non-casino slot machines or video poker machines. As slot machine gambling spreads in America, through casinos, video lottery terminals, or other non-casino venues, it is quite possible that the U.S. will experience similar spending patterns on gambling.

But access through legislative authorization has not been the only reason for the strong growth of gambling activity. Technology, competitive pressures, new gambling products, and more exciting forms of gambling have added to the popularity and allure of gambling in society. There has been substantial development of gambling activities which has enhanced entertainment values and excitement factors. Sophisticated marketing and player development strategies have been introduced to match potential customers with the correct mix of gambling product and other amenities.

Legitimization of commercial gaming has occurred as a bi-product to legalization. This has opened the door to capital investment, technological innovations, and a wide variety of marketing and management tools that have made the gaming industries among the most dynamic in the economy.

Perhaps the best way to appreciate the strength of gambling as an economic force is by examining the recent history of casino gaming in Las Vegas. That city has remained one of the fastest growing metropolitan areas in America since the 1960s, predominantly because of growth in its casino-based tourism industry. By 1994, Las Vegas will have the ten largest hotels in the world, and will have over 85,000 hotel and motel rooms, more than Manhattan and London combined. There are also numerous man-made creations whose primary purpose is to attract visitors to the destination resort so that they will spend their money, gamble, and generally have a good time. Major amusement parks are being linked to casinos at the MGM Grand and the Circus Circus. Las Vegas provides a wide variety of live entertainment, mainly in casino showrooms. The Las Vegas casino industry boasts some of the architectural wonders of the late 20th century, such as the volcano at the Mirage, the Forum Shops area at Caesars Palace, and the pyramid which is the new Luxor Casino Hotel. Las Vegas boasts the world's finest large convention facilities with its convention center and hotel-casino meeting areas. In effect, Las Vegas has grown like no other area in the country with the exception of Orlando, Florida, and it has done so with casinos that are adult variations of Disney World. And gambling remains the lifeblood of Las Vegas casinos.

The development of gaming product has also affected lotteries. Lotteries have evolved from relatively uninteresting passive games into activities that capture much of the excitement that casino gaming can generate. Multi-million dollar prized Lotto draws, ubiquitously placed video lottery terminals, sports parlay wagering cards, and keno games with five-minute draws have all become part of the modern lottery scene. In their search for new markets, lotteries have moved closer and closer to casino-style gaming to attract a broader base of customers and to increase spend per capita from their markets.

These expansions in the presence and type of commercial gaming have probably permanently displaced the prior prohibitions against virtually all forms of gambling that prevailed until quite recently. Commercial gaming will undoubtedly have a greater presence in the lives of future generations than it has ever had in the past. And all indications point toward a continuing expansion in these trends.

Interestingly, gambling was prohibited or severely constrained in many countries of the world for centuries for a variety of reasons, one of the most important of which was the fear of problem gambling and its social consequences. Now that it seems gambling will be everywhere, it is important for society to analyze the issue of problem gambling in a far more scientific light than it has ever done before. Why do some people become problem gamblers? Is the problem one that stems from physiological roots, from psychological deficiencies, or from personality disorders? Are there different causes for problem gambling, and if so, are there different cures? How can society mitigate the social consequences that will follow from greater commercial gaming? And what are the responsibilities of commercial gaming industries, regulatory bodies, and other beneficiaries of the growth of commercial gaming to address the negative side-effects that accompanies the expansion?

Answers to these questions will not come easily. One cannot tally up the social damage from a new gaming industry with the same ease that one can count jobs created, new investments made, or taxes paid. Yet such costs can be just as real, and can carry important long term implications for the stability of society. The articles in this book are an attempt to improve the understanding of problem gambling, whether it is an obsession, a compulsion, or a pathology.

This book, along with its two companion books, *Gambling and Public Policy: International Perspectives*, and *Gambling and Commercial Gaming: Essays in Business, Economics, Philosophy and Science*, present "state of the art" knowledge and research concerning gambling and its implications for society. The books are the outgrowth of research conducted for, and papers presented at the Eighth International Conference on Risk and Gambling, held in London, England, in August, 1990. The Conference brought together a diverse and interesting group of about 240 scholars, regulators, entrepreneurs, consultants, gamblers, and writers, who share a common interest in the rapidly changing and hyper-dynamic world of gambling and commercial gaming. More than a dozen countries were represented, and issues brought up at the conference covered the gamut of public policy, social scientific, psychological, business, and analytic topics relevant to the study of gambling today. The participants, and their interests, point out just how much similarity there is in different parts of the world at this point in time to the processes of gambling legalization, regulation, and entrepreneurial development, as well as the variety of social and political implications that more widespread presence of gambling entails.

The conference was the continuation of a series of such gatherings, all sponsored and organized through the University of Nevada, Reno, ranging back to 1974. These have resulted in a number of publications, including *Gambling and Society* (Eadington, 1976), *The Gambling Papers* (Eadington, 1982), *The Gambling Studies* (Eadington, 1985), and *Gambling Research* (Eadington, 1988). These collections have contributed to the broad understanding of gambling as an increasing commercial presence in many countries. They have formed important building blocks for much of the policy analysis which has taken place in the last few years, as the momentum of commercial gaming industries spread into new markets and new jurisdictions has accelerated.

The conferences have benefitted by contributions from most of the outstanding researchers and participants in their respective fields and areas of expertise who have worked on gambling topics over the last twenty years. Most notable at this point are some of the major pioneers who played important roles in the formation of public policy and attitudes toward gambling and commercial gaming, but who have passed on. Among those are Dr. Robert Custer, who was a dominant influence in increasing the level of understanding of compulsive and pathological gambling; Dr. Alida M. Glen, who was one of the founders of the Brecksville V.A. program with Dr. Custer; and Ken Uston, who almost single-handedly made card counting at casino blackjack a commercial activity for expert players, and an area of concern and chagrin for casinos and their regulators.

Also worth noting in this context is John Rosecrance, formerly on the faculty at the University of Nevada, Reno, who, prior to a near-fatal automobile accident in Australia in 1988, was a major contributing scholar to the professional literature that tries to explain why people gamble, how they interact with other gamblers, and how they cope with adverse financial situations that emerge when they become heavy losers. It is our hope that some day John Rosecrance will recover enough from his injuries so that he will once again be able to make major contributions to this field.

ACKNOWLEDGEMENTS

This book, and the conference from which it emanated, benefitted immensely from a number of people whose help was most welcome. In London, Nigel Kent-Lemon, David Spanier, Jack Dowie, Helen Fitzpatrick, and Jackie Vere Nicholl all contributed time and effort to bring the Conference into reality. Leonard Steinberg of the United Kingdom, José Guirao and Enrique Muro of Spain, Jan McMillen and Mark Dickerson of Australia, David Clark and Ron Sheppard of Canada, Bernard Polders of the Netherlands, and Iain Brown of Scotland all contributed their expertise and advice in shaping the Conference and bringing the conference delegates together. Mike Carr and Betty Mercer of the Michigan State Lottery, Howard Shaffer of the Norman E. Zinberg Center for Addiction Studies at Harvard, Eugene Christiansen of Christiansen\Cummings & Associates in New York, and Henry Lesieur of Illinois State University were invaluable in providing organizational support. During the conference, Ian R.T. Ellis and Denise Entecott of Top Rank Ltd. and Ina Bartram of Germany volunteered their services for which we are grateful.

Thanks are also extended to The Open University — United Kingdom; Asociacion Emprsarial Española de Casino de Juego — Spain; Casinos de Catalunya — Spain; The Boyd Group — Las Vegas, Nevada; Top Rank Ltd. — United Kingdom; Stoy Hayward — United Kingdom; Crystal Casino — Manitoba, Canada; Raad Voor de Casinospelen — The Netherlands; Holland Casinos — The Netherlands; National Association for Gambling Studies — Australia; The Society for the Study of Gambling — United Kingdom; *International Gaming and Wagering Business* — New York; North American Gaming Regulators Association; Association Internationale des Loteries d'Etat; North American Association of State & Provincial Lotteries; British Casino Association; National Council on Problem Gambling, Inc. — U.S.A.; Casino Association of New Jersey; and Casinos Austria for their support and sponsorships of the conference.

And the staff of the University of Nevada, Reno, Laurie Adams Decker and Marvin Small II, along with Diane Chester Berg and Larry Berg of Computer Support Services of Northern Nevada worked well beyond the call of duty to produce a most stimulating and valuable record of the conference. Diane Berg in particular provided invaluable assistance in the completion of the manuscripts, design and layout of the books. It has been with Diane's assistance and guidance that we have been able to produce truly professional publications and attain a level of quality of which we are extremely proud. We would also like to thank Patty Atcheson of Communication by Design for her creative talent and artwork for the dust jackets. Undoubtedly, the contributors to this and the other volumes are the foundation of the Conference and the books. It is from their ideas, opinions, and observations that future policies, practices, and directions will be shaped.

William R. Eadington

Judy A. Cornelius

May, 1993

Post-script:

A special thank you to Dr. Julian I. Taber — Jules, to his friends — who began this project as our third co-editor. Jules assisted us with several of the papers requiring additional technical expertise, but asked to be released from further obligation, in part, to pursue his latest love — flying.

Dr. Taber is, undisputedly, one of the early pioneers in the field of compulsive gambling treatment. He, along with the late Robert Custer, Alida Glen, and others *were* the Brecksville program. Ever controversial, every profession needs a Jules Taber for the purpose of promoting radical ideas and challenges to accepted ways of thinking.

Now, at sixty-something, Dr. Taber has learned to fly airplanes, and is a self-described "Fly-bum." It is a pursuit that is in keeping with his character and which leaves many people shaking their heads. For many others however, it is this characteristic which draws them to him. One has only to read one of Dr. Taber's contributions to this book in Section III to have a glimpse into his character, in particular, when he describes the fundamental tools for living: humility, reflection, simplicity, honesty, responsibility, sensitivity, service, self-denial, self-acceptance, perseverance, reverence for life, tolerance and love.

GAMBLING BEHAVIOR AND PROBLEM GAMBLING

I

Gambling Behavior Attributes and Observations

Internal and External Determinants of Persistent Gambling: Problems in Generalizing From One Form of Gambling to Another

Mark Dickerson

Recent studies focussing on poker machine players are reviewed and some tentative conclusions drawn concerning the importance of learning, cognition and arousal in persistent play. Some preliminary data was presented concerning off-course betting illustrating that the psychological processes underlying persistence and impaired control for this form of gambling may be very different from those determining similar phenomena in poker machine players. The implications for general theories of gambling are discussed.

During the last seven years a sequence of interrelated studies into the most common and preferred forms of gambling in Australia, poker machines (slots) and off-course betting, has been supported by grants from the Australian Research Council. The research has focussed on real gamblers, volunteers from the local community, who have been observed and assessed while gambling in social clubs, and off-course agencies. A major series of direct-observation studies of poker-machine players has recently been completed (Dickerson, Cunningham, Legg England and Hinchy, 1991; Dickerson, Hinchy, Cunningham and Legg England, 1992; Dickerson, Hinchy, Cunningham, Legg England and Fabre, 1992a). In the following sections of this paper the results of this and related work are reviewed.

In the literature on the addictive behaviors there have been a variety of attempts to explore the common characteristics of, and even to propose theoretical models that may account for, all such behaviors when control becomes impaired (Jacobs, 1986; Orford, 1985). The second objective of this work is to emphasize the difficulties in building such general models of the addictions by illustrating that the psychological processes underlying two common forms of gambling may be very different.

ASSUMPTIONS UNDERLYING THE AUSTRALIAN NATIONAL UNIVERSITY RESEARCH PROGRAM

Reviews of the research literature on gambling have lead us to question three common assumptions:

1. That the universe of people who gamble is comprised of two distinct groups, excessive or uncontrolled players and controlled social gamblers.
2. That the results of laboratory-based studies may be generalized to the real world of gambling.
3. That gambling is a homogeneous set of behaviors.

If in this domain of research into addictive behavior we are indeed going to take advantage of the hard-won lessons of the literature on alcoholism (Dickerson, 1987) then it seems preferable to assume that there is a continuum of levels of involvement in gambling, at least until substantive evidence to the contrary has been found. At the present time even if one considers the characteristic central to all addictions, impaired control, then it is clear from Table 1 that this is not an all or nothing characteristic by which one may distinguish excessive or pathological gamblers from other people who gamble. It seems likely that if one took any of the nine DSM III-R criteria (American Psychiatric Association, 1987) a similar picture would appear.

TABLE 1

SUMMARY OF IMPAIRED CONTROL DATA IN GAMBLING STUDIES

Study (gamblers)	**Operational criteria for impaired control**				
Caldwell (1974) (poker machine players) -club members	*Lost more than intended during the last month* 25%				
Dickerson (1984) (off-course bettors)					
	Chasing	*Spending more than planned* *sometimes*	*regularly*	*Spending all cash* *sometimes*	*regularly*
-low frequency	20%	24%	0%	1%	0%
-high frequency	95%	23%	75%	51%	45%
-compulsives	96%	33%	65%	23%	75%

	No desire to reduce spending	*Desire to stop*	*Want to stop*
-regulars	64%	32%	4%
	Never tried stopping	*Tried and was easy*	*Tried and was hard*
-regulars	62%	6%	22%
		Easy to stop	*Hard to stop*
-compulsives		20%	60%

Dickerson et al. (1985)	*Spending more than planned on last 5 occasions* Never	1 or 2	3 or 4	5
-poker machine players	26%	35%	21%	18%
-off-course bettors	62%	22%	10%	4%

Stewart and Brown (1987) Gamblers Anonymous members	*Achieved total abstinence over 2 years*
	7%

Dickerson et al. (1987)	*Never chase*	*Occasionally*	*Usually*	*Always*
-off-course bettors	55.7%	30.4%	12.7%	1.3%

Following on from this argument, one assumption underlying this research has been that the study of the psychological processes leading to impaired control in high-frequency gamblers who have NOT sought treatment will provide theoretical models that may be applied to excessive or pathological gamblers. Rather than study gamblers in treatment using retrospective procedures, the researchers have preferred to use prospective direct-observation methods focussing on volunteer gamblers using their preferred form in their typical real-life setting.

This anticipates the problems of generalizing from the laboratory to the real world of gambling which can be illustrated by the work of Ellen Langer (1975) and Anderson and Brown (1984). Their studies on the illusion of control and arousal respectively provided convincing demonstrations that hypothesized relationships between independent and dependent variables only appeared for real gamblers in realistic gambling environments. For this reason the research at Australian National University (ANU) has preferred a field work approach, and, when using laboratory facilities (Leary and Dickerson, 1985), has used real volunteer gamblers as subjects, using their own money and a poker machine currently in use in the local social clubs.

Implicit in much of the work on excessive or pathological gambling has been the assumption that impaired control arises in a similar fashion whether the person plays poker machines, bets, plays roulette or whatever is their preferred form of gambling. Given the very different stimulus and temporal characteristics of the different forms such an assumption has poor face validity. It is further undermined by the fact that some gamblers use one form exclusively, showing impaired control of that form and that form alone. In our own research we have found it useful to discriminate between what we have called continuous and discontinuous forms. The latter is typified by lotto or lotteries, where there is a considerable period of time between stake and determination or result, whereas the former is associated with the opportunity to have a session comprising many sequences of stake, play and determination, e.g., off-course betting, poker machines, blackjack, roulette, etc.

This distinction may have important considerations for treatment and the maintenance of controlled gambling; this is discussed in greater detail later. From a research perspective, to assume that gambling is a homogeneous set of behaviors may be counterproductive as a detailed consideration of the different characteristics of different forms may permit the identification of the unique ways in which stimulus conditions, and gambler responses may combine to cause impaired control. An illustration of the potential value of this is given below in the section discussing the problems inherent in generalizing from the results for poker machines to off-course betting.

DEFINITIONS OF IMPAIRED CONTROL

This research has used a variety of measures of impaired control, both what might be called direct and indirect. The former are summarized in Table 1 and consist mainly of self statements that indicate an awareness of the way in which a person's gambling does not match some preferred standard and/or an awareness that even with effort such a standard cannot consistently be achieved, e.g., lost more than intended, spent more than planned, found it hard to give up or stop. Although most people who gamble regularly do seem to be able to describe preferred levels of expenditure or limits to their losses, on a cautionary note it must be acknowledged that this is not always the case. We have certainly encountered a few individuals with whom it has been difficult to establish whether they actually have any preferred limits to their gambling and for whom it is debatable whether a standard for the behavior exists.

Impaired control, defined in terms of these difficulties or failures to achieve certain standards, has good face validity but also all the problems of reliability inherent in self-statements. In this research, therefore, other, more reliable, but essentially indirect measures of control have also been used. Throughout all the empirical data runs the common theme that the more a person gambles the more likely they are to report experiencing problems of maintaining control of their behavior. Thus, in one study, level of involvement in gambling (defined in terms of expenditure of cash and time) *per se* accounted for over half the variance in impaired control measured in terms of the perceived likelihood of starting a new session of gambling, or continuing an ongoing one when in debt or losing (Corless and Dickerson, 1989). In the following discussion it is assumed that as the level of involvement in gambling increases so too does the likelihood of overspending and other indications of impaired control.

In the direct-observation studies, the main dependent variables of relevance to impaired control were session duration and persistence when losing. (The latter was derived by computing the area under the curve of cumulative balance for periods when the balance was less than zero, i.e., the player was behind and still losing.) This measure correlated significantly and positively with time and money involvement in gambling (Dickerson et al., 1991).

Although the more reliable indirect measures of impaired control have played an important part in the research, it must be accepted that the factors that determine persistence or level of involvement are not necessarily causes of loss of control. The underlying psychological processes of the person who regularly plays and loses may be quite different from another player who shows similar persistence but reports feeling out of control, spending more than he or she intended.

No discussion of the subjective control of gambling can omit the mention of *chasing*. Typically defined as the continuation of gambling after a sequence of losing, but with increased stakes, the concept is probably best considered as having emotional, cognitive and behavioral components. Although chasing has played a convincing role in theories concerned with explaining the addictive aspects of gambling (Lesieur, 1984), little work has been done on defining or measuring the phenomena in any adequate psychometric fashion. In our research we have attempted to assess the frequency of chasing among off-course bettors and, for poker machine players, the effect of being behind or in debt on the likelihood of continuing a session or starting a *new* one.

IMPAIRED CONTROL IN POKER MACHINE PLAY

A variety of research studies has been completed interviewing, testing and observing over two-hundred poker machine players who volunteered to participate in the research (Dickerson and Adcock, 1987; Fabre and Bayliss, 1985; Dickerson et al., 1991, 1992, 1992a; Leary and Dickerson, 1985). A direct-observation methodology and related equipment was developed that permitted the recording of a variety of data streams on a real-time basis with relatively little intrusion while individual volunteers played their preferred machine in their usual social club setting (Dickerson, Hinchy, Schaefer,

Whitworth and Fabre, 1988). Sessions of up to two hours were recorded. The following discussion attempts to synthesize the findings of these various studies with respect to the factors associated with impaired control.

The following conceptual structure has been adopted:

- to distinguish between the start of a new session and the continuation of an ongoing session (Cameron, 1985);
- to consider both internal factors (cognitions, emotions, personality) and external factors (cues in the environment, machine characteristics); and,
- to focus the discussion on three levels of player involvement, from low/medium frequency, high frequency to problematic or excessive levels of play. (Some of the characteristics of these groups are summarized in Table 2.)

TABLE 2

GAMBLING CHARACTERISTICS OF LOW/MEDIUM, HIGH-FREQUENCY AND PROBLEM POKER MACHINE PLAYERS

		Low/Medium	*HighProblem*
	frequency	*frequency*	*Players*
Playing time (average hours/month)	0.75	7.75	38.0
Session expenditure (range A$)	0.4-20	2-16	25-250
Total expenditure (average A$/month)	6.00	63.00	1,336
Considered a 'big win'	'A$50, or less'	'A$100 or more'	
Way of playing influences chance of winning (% occasionally/usually)	40	60	35
Can predict when payout due	40	35	70
Reasons for playing	'for entertainment' 'to be sociable'	'to forget troubles' 'to win a major payout'	

LOW/MEDIUM FREQUENCY PLAYERS

In the various groups of players that have been studied this category included people who had only played once in their lives to those who regularly played once a month. Although as frequency of play increases some distinguishing characteristics have been found, for the purposes of this discussion of the factors associated with impaired control it is acceptable to take this range of players as a single group.

A. Session START

Given the very infrequent nature of sessions it is not surprising that we have been able to find very few predictors of the onset of a *new* session. Players report using poker machines "to be sociable" and "for entertainment." Compatible with these motives was the finding that negative moods such as frustration and disappointment rendered the start of a session *less* likely. In examining personality variables such as extroversion, neuroticism and sensation seeking we have found no relationships with frequency of sessions although from the latter construct the expectation would be that high sensation seekers would gamble more often.

B. Session PERSIST

When players in this category have been observed they typically have a session length of about 17 minutes but the range is large (5-107 minutes) and session frequency is a significant predictor of session duration with the more frequent players having longer sessions. Furthermore, as frequency and duration increase it seems that the characteristics of the playing change from a rate of playing (i.e., pulling the lever or pressing the button) that is slow, unpredictable from minute to minute and not consistently related to machine events such as payouts, to a faster rate that is fairly consistent from one minute to the next and most important, shows bursts of faster rates of play after a small win (50 credits or less) and slowing after a big win.

Persistence when losing was found to be associated with arousal or excitement experienced prior to or during the earlier stages of the session and with the belief that the machine was about to pay out. Two factors were associated with reduced persistence when losing. These were dysphoric mood and the presence of debts. Actual self-reports of impaired control such as "spending more than planned" occurred at a frequency of 1 in 10 of all subjects observed (i.e., regardless of whether they were low- medium- or high-frequency players). However this result is believed to be a function of the interactive effect of the presence of the observer as other self-report data shows quite consistently that as the frequency of sessions increases so do the reports of over-spending (Dickerson, Fabre and Bayliss, 1985).

HIGH FREQUENCY PLAYERS

A. Session START

Once players reach a level of weekly and more frequent sessions the onset of a *new* session comes to be predictably associated with cues such as the club environment and large cash sums. Regular players also report having a session when they feel lucky and when celebrating.

B. Session PERSIST

Typically high-frequency players have sessions that last just over 40 minutes (range 6-127 minutes) and they play faster, playing one coin every six seconds on average, while low/medium players use one coin every eight seconds. High-frequency players also have a stereotypical pattern of play rate that is very consistent from minute to minute and varies according to the size of the pay-outs. Small wins result in an increased play rate for up to three minutes whereas wins in excess of 50 credits result in a significant decrease in rate. It is interesting to note that neither change in rate is consistently associated with raised or lowered expectations in answer to the question of whether the machine was about to pay out. Furthermore the variations in play rate are not consistently associated with either subjective reports of excitement or heart rate. The researchers' preferred interpretation of these results is that after several hundred hours of play individuals acquire a stereotypical learnt pattern of play that is consistently associated with the reinforcement contingencies of the poker machine being played. Changes in arousal and expectations of winning seem to account for very little of the variance in play rate. In contrast, the stability of play from one minute to the next, the autoregressive component, and big win/small win may account for over 90% of the within subject variability in play-rate.

Similar levels of predictability were also found for the duration of the session; age and the number of big wins received during the session accounted for 71% of the variance. Although this has good face validity as casual observation of social clubs indicates the ever-present pensioners seeking a "good run for their money," it is not particularly informative on the topic of impaired control.

However persistence when losing increased in association with the belief that the machine was about to pay out and the subjective size of a *big win*, i.e., in answer to the question: What do you consider to be a big win? The larger the dollar figure given, the greater the persistence when losing. In addition, some tentative conclusions were drawn about the effect of different mood states experienced just prior to the onset of a session. In the pilot study which focussed on players who had sessions at least three times a week, it was found that dysphoric mood immediately before the beginning of the session, when the player was already in the club and about to start, was associated with greater persistence when losing (Dickerson et al., 1992a). The second study (Dickerson et al., 1992) failed to replicate this finding but showed a decrease in persistence when losing when there was prior anger and hostility. Similarly the presence of debts was associated with a decrease in persistence when losing.

EXCESSIVE/PROBLEMATIC PLAYERS

These were people for whom poker machine play was their preferred form of gambling and who had entered a program of psychological treatment for their impaired control of their gambling. All satisfied the DSM III-R criteria for pathological gambling. Nonetheless, it is important to emphasize the purely chance factors that two occasions resulted in players being allocated to this group rather than participating as volunteers in the high-frequency group. When establishing the original direct observation studies of volunteer players, the ANU Ethics Committee insisted in its wisdom that before we accepted any volunteer we should ask them whether they wished to receive any treatment or help for their gambling. As was expected, most people found this question irrelevant or indicative of some criticism of their gambling. However, at a later stage in the research, when a minimal intervention project was being run concurrently, two male subjects did change their minds when asked the question and opted into the treatment program instead. In addition, the follow-up of another volunteer player who it was felt was probably losing at a rate that might outstrip his income established that he had in fact stopped playing altogether and that he had done this without seeking any help or treatment.

A. Session START

Problem players typically report gambling "to forget troubles" and "to win a major payout." Congruent with these motives was the fact that the onset of a *new* session was associated with negative moods such as frustration, disappointment, and the presence of debts or recent gambling losses. In addition, large cash sums, being in the club and feeling lucky or celebrating also rendered the onset of a session more likely.

B. Session PERSIST

The researchers have completed no observation studies of problem players. Although, given the similarities of session frequency and duration, it seems likely that their pattern of play rate will be similar to the high frequency players. Certainly their self report data on beliefs about the probability of the machine paying out and concerning subjective size of a *big* win show similar relationships to persistence when losing that were found for high-frequency players. Retrospective reports also suggest that dysphoric mood immediately prior to a session and during the session itself may increase persistence when losing. One difference from high-frequency players was that the problem players reported that they were more likely to continue a losing session when they were already in debt.

ORIGINS OF CONSISTENT IMPAIRED CONTROL IN POKER MACHINE PLAYERS

A. The Role of Learning

In this section an attempt is made to summarize the above results with respect to the development of levels of impaired control that are likely to be associated with the person seeking help. Although previous reviews (Cornish, 1978; Dickerson, 1984, 1989; Orford, 1985) have indicated some of the various factors associated with increased involvement in gambling, it must be stressed that there is no necessary progression from low to higher frequencies. For example, in this study the majority of players in all categories reported playing at their present level for more than a year, and many for much longer. In other words, it is likely that a stable level of playing poker machines may be achieved by most players regardless of whether they are low-, medium-, or high-frequency. Thus, the stereotypical learnt patterns of play *driven* by the machine payout characteristics do not necessarily result in higher and higher levels of involvement. Nevertheless, the strong positive relationship between frequency of play and frequency of reported loss of control does lend support to the argument that habit or learning *per se* is an important factor in the development of impaired control. Furthermore, given that impaired control is more likely to occur within an ongoing session, it is difficult not to assume that for high-frequency players this must be, at least in part, a function of the rhythmic relationship between their speed of play and the size of the machine payouts.

One of the problems of a field-work approach is the failure to control or manipulate crucial variables such as the machine characteristics. The limited information available from the machine manufacturers suggests that both the temporal characteristics, e.g., duration of reel spin, and the frequency of large and small payouts, have been finely tuned to increase machine usage or player persistence (Daley, 1986).

Given Skinner's (1953, 1972) statements about the role of reinforcement schedules in the generation of *pathological* poker machine play, this study's findings and conclusions are hardly a revelation. However, they are important because they pose theoretical problems for the understanding of human learning. How is play rate structure maintained in the absence of wins? How do small wins result in increases in playrate, and why does a combination of big and small wins result in greater persistence? Furthermore, contrary to Skinner's assumption, CONSISTENT impaired control is unlikely to arise from the learnt patterns of play alone. Such learning may be necessary, but the sufficient conditions for regularly losing control seem likely to involve other variables. Furthermore, it is difficult to claim that the machine characteristics result in the onset of a *new* session of play.

B. The Role of Cognitions

Chasing and the illusion of control are two cognitive phenomena that play a central role in persistent gambling on poker machines. The former is typified by statements such as "it (the machine) owes me" and "I've lost the last few times, it must be my turn for a win today." In the very experienced player, the belief that it is the *correct* strategy to continue gambling when significant losses have occurred seems almost rational. If the player stops, then the probability of recouping those losses is zero (i.e., from gambling); whereas if he or she continues, there is at least some chance of winning. Such a belief and the behavior of continued play may in the past have resulted in a major payout. Even one such win may make a significant impact on the strength with which beliefs about chasing are held.

Beliefs about being able to predict when a machine is about to pay out are similar but are probably best categorized under the illusion of control. As illustrated in Table 2, this illusion is concerned with the belief that chance-determined events are in fact somehow under the control of the player. Thus, a typical high-frequency player will have a favorite machine (i.e., one that they believe is more likely to pay out), will believe that the manner in which he or she plays alters the likelihood of winning (eg., playing to a steady rhythm or playing out all credits before putting in more cash and a whole range of what are best described as superstitious behaviors), and, finally, will claim to be able to predict when the machine is about to pay out. These direct observation studies have produced a few illustrations of how a sudden upward fluctuation in a player's estimate of the likelihood of their machine paying out has been immediately followed by a large win. Even one such event must have a strong influence on the player's illusion of control. Indeed, player's claims that they can spot sequences of reel spin results that precede a large pay out may have some validity if recent work on the *errors* in the random nature of the latest generation of poker machines can be replicated (Eisler, 1989).

Player expectations of payouts are not consistently associated with variations in play rate. Even when play rates suddenly fall for the two minutes or so after a big win, this is not associated with a lowering of expectations for future pay-outs. This has lead us to the proposition that it is the machine reinforcement schedule that *drives* the behavior and that the cognitive processes are by-products that provide the player with a verbal *explanation* of the behavior of his or her body. This is not to say that the cognitive processes do not contribute to impaired control; they clearly do, both to persistence when losing and to the onset of a *new* session.

However, two aspects of these cognitions, particularly those involving the illusion of control, merit comment. First, the beliefs are often situation specific, being expressed only during a session of play or even only at certain points during play. In interviews or in surveys completed away from the club setting there is a tendency for subjects not to endorse illusion of control items or possibly not even to believe that they have any control over the machine outcomes. Furthermore, a small minority of players at ALL levels of involvement, including problem players, do not seem to entertain ANY illusory beliefs.

The second point of interest is that although the relationship between enhanced expectations of payouts and persistence when losing has good face, and even theoretical validity, the researchers encountered a variety of idiosyncratic views from high-frequency players that were far from logical. For example, players have stated after a considerable period of play, "I'm bored stiff, but I must play out my credits" and "I know I won't win, but I don't want anyone else to play this machine just yet" and have then gone on to play for a further ten or fifteen minutes. At one time or another, it would seem that players may express almost any reason for continuing to play, and it is this overall perspective to the cognitive aspects of poker machine play that leads us to consider them as the players' attempts to understand the way in which their stereotypical habit has a *life of its own* driven on by the machine events.

If, in the above, the intention has been to question the contribution of cognitive factors to impaired control WITHIN a session, then the conclusions regarding their contribution to the onset of a *new* session is quite the reverse. There is no doubt that as players come to believe that chasing is the *correct* strategy, particularly when they are in debt, these cognitions make it harder for players to resist the urge to start another session. This is one reason why cognitive-behavioral methods of maintaining control may be effective in reducing the number of sessions per week but may have limited effect on reducing persistence when losing once a session has started, and this is discussed in the section on the implications for treatment.

C. The Role of Emotions

Despite the significant role attributed to arousal or excitement in theoretical models of pathological gambling, the present results for poker machine play suggest that excitement may only play a minor role in encouraging the low-frequency player to persist. At all levels of involvement players experience small rises in heart rate and subjective reports of excitement immediately following a big win. Neither measure was consistently associated with changes in play rate. In contrast, for the off-course betters, both self-report and heart rate indicate that excitement is an important and consistent component of each sequence of placing a bet and listening to or watching the race.

Turning to mood states such as dysphoria, frustration, and disappointment, it is important to note that they increase persistence when losing only amongst players with a well established habit, and, in fact, for low-frequency players, such moods are associated with LESS persistence. Although the data is far from convincing, it is interesting to speculate that this difference between low- and high-frequency players suggests that the process underlying the interaction of habit and mood may not be cognitively mediated. Furthermore, if the conceptual frame is altered from addictions to *self-defeating behaviors*, then the association between negative moods and persistence when losing, but not persistence *per se*, suggests that the valence of the outcome (i.e., losing) may contribute to impaired control. This is conceptually very similar to the original psychoanalytic view that the compulsive gambler *wished* to lose (Bergler, 1957).

D. The Role of Personality

The present research has consistently failed to confirm Zuckerman's (1979) prediction that gambling was a sensation seeking activity. In fact, for both forms of gambling that have been studied thus far, it would appear that the participants are lower than the population means per age category on the Sensation Seeking Scale (Form V) (Blaszczynski, Wilson and McConaghy, 1986; Dickerson, Walker, Legg England and Hinchy, 1990). In the present Australian context where betting and poker machine play are legally and readily available in environments that have no obvious sensational qualities, these results are unremarkable. They are a reminder that all forms of gambling are not the same, and Zuckerman's prediction may still hold for casino gaming by premium players and for people who participate in illegal gambling.

However, this study's results do provide some support for an interactionist perspective. As Orford (1984) noted, in the absence of a psychoactive agent, the interaction of personality type with the different gambling games and environments may be an important aspect of the development of problematic or excessive levels of involvement. These researchers have found some support for interactions between scores on the subscales of the SSS and the manner in which the gambler plays or bets (Dickerson, Hinchy and Fabre, 1987; Dickerson and Legg England, 1990).

In conclusion, it has been argued that consistent impaired control of poker machine play may arise from:

1. Habit strength alone — particularly in the context of a person with generally few controlling standards for expenditure of time and money.
2. Habit strength, negative emotional states and cognitions about chasing and control.

Research has yet to investigate whether other factors such as life event stresses, social support and coping style are necessary in the development of excessive or problematic levels of poker machine play.

GENERALIZING TO OTHER FORMS OF GAMBLING

The important question is whether the above results for poker machine play can be validly generalized to other forms of gambling such as betting on horse and dog races, blackjack, roulette, poker and video gambling games such as draw-poker, etc. In the past, most theoretical explanations of excessive gambling have assumed that similar psychological processes will underlie the development of impaired control of all forms of gambling (e.g., Custer, 1982; Moran, 1975). It seems worthwhile to challenge this assumption.

Different forms of gambling vary across a variety of dimensions, the first of which, continuity versus discontinuity, has already been discussed and the importance of the former in the generation of impaired control confirmed. The dimension of skill may also be significantly implicated in persistence and control. Situational factors, such as variability in the gambling sequence such as timing, stake size and the presence of non-gambling stimuli, may all contribute to very different learning situations. Similarly, the subjective experience of the gambler may vary from one form to another. The relationship of the gambler with the machine, the croupier or opponent, as in poker, may have a significant impact on persistence and control.

Very little research has been completed on any of these dimensions, but by considering the available evidence for just two, skill and the subjective experience of excitement, in relation to two forms of gambling, poker machines and horse race betting, the complexities of generalizing can be illustrated.

On a continuum of *no skill* to *all skill*, poker machine play clearly is at the end of the former; whereas, betting on horse races involves both skill and chance determinants of outcomes. If with respect to beliefs about *skill* it can be said that poker machine players hold them weakly (i.e., when away from the machine, they may realize how irrational it is to claim that they can control the machine and predict outcomes) then people who bet may hold very strong beliefs about their skill in pricing a field and selecting a bet. The very fact that it is clear that SOME skill is involved in betting makes such claims acceptable, and the more frequently a person bets, the more will he or she attribute their bet selection to skill — and this holds even when betting has become out of control and excessive (Dickerson, 1984). The point to be made is that if the weakly held beliefs of poker machine players contribute to the development of persistence when losing, then in betting, beliefs about skill may make a more significant impact on control. Furthermore, in recent work developing a measure of betting skill (Solonsch, 1989), it appeared that impaired control leading to debts and other problems was associated not just with poor betting behaviors but also poor cognitive processing of race information. A question of interest is whether, for such a person, good processing skills were never acquired or whether the schedules of reinforcement inherent, for example, in the off-course betting situation (Dickerson, 1979; Saunders, 1981), are the main determinants of impaired control and the processing skills deteriorate as control is eroded.

Turning to the subjective experience of excitement, in contrast to the negative findings for poker machine players, in betting it may be a significant factor in the reinforcement of each betting sequence and contribute to poor bet selection. These researchers' preliminary studies show significant increases in heart rate and subjective reports of excitement for *bet on* races compared with other races broadcast during the same session. Earlier work also suggested that certain individual differences interacted with the off-course betting environment, resulting in greater levels of excitement and impaired control in the form of more frequent reports of chasing (Dickerson, Hinchy and Fabre, 1987).

Without laboring the point further, it has been argued that to assume that the same psychological models will explain impaired control in all forms of gambling is not only naive but runs the risk of not fully exploiting the significant differences between different forms to develop a far richer and informative vein of research.

REFERENCES

American Psychiatric Association (1980). *Diagnostic and Statistical Manual of Mental Disorders*, 3rd edition. Washington, D.C.: American Psychiatric Association.

American Psychiatric Association (1987). *Diagnostic and Statistical Manual of Mental Disorders*, 3rd edition - revised. Washington, D.C.: American Psychiatric Association.

Anderson, G. and Brown, R.I.F. (1984). Real and laboratory gambling, sensation seeking and arousal. *British Journal of Psychology*, 75, 401-410.

Bergler, E. (1957). *The Psychology of Gambling*. New York: Hill and Wang Inc.

Blaszczynski, A.P. (1988). *Clinical studies in pathological gambling*. Ph.D. thesis. University of New South Wales (unpublished).

Blaszczynski, A.P., Wilson, A.C. and McConaghy, N. (1986). Sensation seeking and pathological gambling. *British Journal of Addictions*, 81, 113-117.

Brown, R.I.F. (1987). Models of gambling and gambling addictions as perceptual filters. *Journal of Gambling Behavior*, 3:4, 224-236.

Caldwell, G.T. (1974). The gambling Australian. In D. Edgar (ed.), *Social Change in Australia*. Melbourne: Cheshire.

Cameron, D. (1985). Why alcohol dependence: And why now? In N. Heather, I. Robertson and P. Davies (eds.), *The Misuse of Alcohol*. London: Croom Helm.

Corless, A. and Dickerson, M.G. (1989). Gamblers' self-perceptions of determinants of impaired control. *British Journal of Addiction*, 84, 1527-1537.

Cornish, D.B. (1978). *Gambling: A Review of the Literature and Its Implications for Policy and Research*. London: H.M.S.O.

Culleton, R.P. (1989). The prevalence rates of pathological gambling: A look at methods. *Journal of Gambling Behavior*, 5:1, 22-41.

Custer, R.L. (1982). An overview of compulsive gambling. In P.A. Carone, S.F. Yolles, S.N. Kieffer and L.W. Krinsky (eds.), *Addictive Disorders Update*, 51-93. New York: Human Sciences Press.

Daley, K. (1986). Encouraging habitual gambling on poker machines. In M. Walker (ed.), *Faces of Gambling: Proceedings of the Second National Conference of the National Association for Gambling Studies*. Sydney, Australia: University of Sydney.

Dickerson, M.G. and Hinchy, J. (1990). Minimal treatments and problem gamblers: A preliminary investigation. *Journal of Gambling Behavior*, 6, 87-102.

Dickerson, M.G. (1979). FI schedules and persistence at gambling in the U.K. betting office. *Journal of Applied Behavior Analysis*, 12, 315-23.

Dickerson, M.G., Cunningham, R., Legg England, S., and Hinchy, J. (1991). On the determinants of persistent gambling III: Personality prior mood and poker machine play. *International Journal of the Addictions*, 25, (5), 531-548.

Dickerson, M.G., Hinchy, J., Cunningham. R. and Legg England, S. (1992). On the determinants of persistent gambling II: A comparison of low-, medium -, and high-frequency players. *Australian Journal of Psychology*.

Dickerson, M.G., Hinchy, J., Cunningham, R., Legg England, S. and Fabre, J. (1992a). On the determinants of persistent gambling I: High frequency poker machine players. *British Journal of Psychology*, 83, 237-248.

Dickerson, M.G., Walker, G., Legg England, S. and Hinchy, J. (1990). Demographic, personality, cognitive & behavioral correlates of off-course betting involvement. *Journal of Gambling Studies*, 6(2), 165-182.

Dickerson, M.G. (1984). *Compulsive Gamblers.* London: Longman.

Dickerson, M.G. (1987). The future of gambling research: Learning from the lesson of alcoholism. *Journal of Gambling Behavior*, 3, 248-256.

Dickerson, M.G. and Adcock, S.G. (1987). Mood, arousal and cognitions in persistent gambling: Preliminary investigation of a theoretical model. *Journal of Gambling Behavior*, 3, 3-15.

Dickerson, M.G. and Weeks, D. (1979). Controlled gambling as a therapeutic technique for compulsive gamblers. *Journal of Behavior Therapy and Experimental Psychiatry*, 10, 139-145.

Dickerson, M.G. (1989). Gambling: A dependence without a drug. *International Review Journal of Psychiatry*, 1, 157-172.

Dickerson, M.G., Fabre, J. and Bayliss, D. (1985). A comparison of TAB customers and poker machine players. In J. McMillen (ed.), *Gambling in the 80's.* Brisbane: Griffiths University Reprographics.

Dickerson, M.G., Hinchy, J., Schaefer, M., Whitworth, N. and Fabre, J. (1988). The use of a hand held micro-computer in the collection of physiological, subjective and behavioral data in ecologically valid gambling settings. *Journal of Gambling Behavior*, 4, 92-98.

Dickerson, M.G., Hinchy, J. and Fabre, J. (1987). Chasing, arousal and sensation seeking in off-course gamblers. *British Journal of Addiction*, 82, 673-680.

Eisler, H. (1989). *The Drop-a-Coin Merry-Go-Round.* Paper given at the Fourth National Conference of the National Association for Gambling Studies, Victoria, Australia.

Jacobs, D.F. (1986). A general theory of addictions: A new theoretical model. *Journal of Gambling Behavior*, 2, 15-32.

Langer, E.J. (1975). The illusion of control. *Journal of Personality and Social Psychology*, 32, 311-328.

Leary, K. and Dickerson, M.G. (1985). Levels of arousal in high- and low-frequency gamblers. *Behavior Research Therapy*, 23, 635-640.

Lesieur, H.R. and Blume, S.B. (1987). The South Oaks Gambling Screen (SOGS): A new instrument for the identification of pathological gamblers. *American Journal of Psychiatry*, 144, 1184-1185.

Lesieur, H.R. (1984). *The Chase: Career of the Compulsive Gambler.* Cambridge, MA: Schenkman.

Lesieur, H.R. (1988b). *Report on Pathological Gambling in New Jersey.* New Jersey: Governor's Advisory Commission.

Lesieur, H.R. (1989). Altering the DSM III criteria for pathological gambling. *Journal of Gambling Behavior*, 4, 38-47.

Marlatt, G.A. (1979). Alcohol use and problem drinking: A cognitive-behavioral analysis. In P.C. Kendall and S.D. Hollen (eds.), *Cognitive Behavioral Interventions, Theory Research and Procedures*, pp. 319-356. London: Academic Press.

McConaghy, N., Armstrong, M., Blaszczynski, A. and Alcock, C. (1983). Controlled comparison of aversion therapy and imaginal desensitization in compulsive gambling. *British Journal of Psychiatry*, 142, 366-372.

Miller, W.R. (ed.), (1980). *The Addictive Behaviors: Treatment of Alcoholism, Drug Abuse, Smoking and Obesity.* Oxford: Pergamon Press.

Moran, E. (1975). Pathological gambling. In *British Journal of Psychiatry, Special Publication No. 9: Contemporary Psychiatry.* London: Royal College of Psychiatrists.

Orford, J. (1985). *Excessive Appetites: A Psychological View of Addictions.* New York: Wiley.

Orford, J. (1988). Pathological gambling and its treatment. *British Medical Journal*, 296, 729-730.

Rankin, H. (1982). Control rather than abstinence as a goal in the treatment of excessive gambling. *Behavior Research Therapy*, 20, 185-187.

Saunders, D.M. (1981). The late betting phenomenon in relation to type of bet and type of race. *Behavioral Psychotherapy*, 9, 330-37.

Seager, C.P. (1970). Treatment of compulsive gamblers using electrical aversion. *British Journal of Psychiatry*, 117, 545-553.

Skinner, B.F. (1972). *Beyond Freedom & Dignity?* London: Cape.

Skinner, B.F. (1953). *Science and Human Behavior.* New York: Free Press.

Solonsch, M. (1989). *The conceptualization and evaluation of the concept of skill in gambling.* Honors Thesis. Department of Psychology, Australian National University, unpublished.

Stewart, R.M. and Brown, R.I.F. (1987). An outcome study of Gamblers Anonymous. *British Journal of Psychiatry*, 152, 284-288.

Zuckerman, M. (1979). *Sensation Seeking: Beyond the Optimal Level of Arousal.* New York: John Wiley.

Sensation Seeking in Gamblers and Non-Gamblers and its Relation To Preference for Gambling Activities, Chasing, Arousal and Loss of Control in Regular Gamblers©

Kenny R. Coventry and R. Iain F. Brown

It has been observed that a central feature of all gambling is the subjective excitement or arousal it appears to engender (Boyd, 1976). This observation is supported by reports from questionnaires and surveys that excitement is a main reason cited by gamblers as to why they gamble (Anderson and Brown, 1984; Scarne, 1975; Commission on the Review of National Policy Towards Gambling In America, 1976).

This study attempts to link sensation seeking behavior in gamblers to a number of commonly observed behaviors, such as chasing, arousal, and loss of control. It also examines the sensation seeking propensities of non-gamblers as a control.

© This article is based substantially on the following paper that has appeared in *Addiction* (1993): Sensation seeking, gambling, and gambling addictions. We gratefully acknowledge permission to reprint this article from the publishers, the Society for the Study of Addiction.

Furthermore, it explores some of the contributing factors among gamblers in determining preference for gambling activities.

SENSATION SEEKING, AROUSAL AND GAMBLING

The existence of increases in arousal while gambling has received extensive empirical support, (Anderson and Brown, 1984; Leary and Dickerson, 1985; Dickerson and Adcock, 1987; Coventry and Taggart, 1987). Anderson and Brown, for example, found increases in heart-rate of up to 58 beats per minute for frequent gamblers during blackjack play in a casino. The size of the observed increases supports the importance of arousal as a variable in the explanation of gambling behavior (Brown, 1986). There is also evidence to suggest that higher arousal is associated with greater persistence (Dickerson and Adcock, 1987), and more withdrawal symptoms when trying to abstain (Wray and Dickerson 1981).

Zuckerman's Sensation Seeking Scale is based on the theory that individual differences exist in the need for optimal levels of stimulation. He postulated sensation seeking to be a biologically based personality dimension, with sensation seekers identified as those who seek varied, novel or complex sensations or experiences. High sensation seekers appraise risk to be less, and anticipate arousal as more positive, than low sensation seekers, i.e., the *surgency-elation effect* (Zuckerman, 1979, 1983).

Alone among theories of individual differences, Zuckerman's (1979) account of sensation seeking makes explicit predictions concerning a person's preference for gambling. Studies have shown significant associations between sensation seeking scores and drug abuse, sex experience, involvement in risky sports, and volunteering for such activities as sensory deprivation experiments, encounter groups, and gambling instruction. Zuckerman suggested a relationship between gambling and the trait of sensation seeking in which:

> ". . . individuals entertain the risk of monetary loss for the positive reinforcement produced by states of high arousal during the period of uncertainty, as well as the positive arousal produced by winning" (Zuckerman, 1979, p. 211).

The evidence for Zuckerman's hypothesis is, however, not clear cut.

Anderson and Brown (1984) found higher *Sensation Seeking Scale* (SSS) scores to positively correlate with greater increases in heart-rate and bet size during blackjack play, although as a group, the mean scores of the blackjack players did not differ significantly from a non-gambling control group of students. Kuley and Jacobs (1987) point out that the lack of significant differences between the gamblers and controls in the Anderson and Brown study could be a result of the lack of control for the variable of age. Anderson and Brown reported that their sample of gamblers were between the ages of 20 and 48 years and the controls ranged from 21 to 28 years; the mean age was not reported. As sensation seeking scores have been found to correlate negatively with age (Zuckerman, 1978), then the relationship between sensation seeking and gambling must remain inconclusive from Anderson and Brown's study. However, Leary and Dickerson's findings of significantly greater increases in arousal during poker machine play in high-frequency gamblers as compared with low-frequency gamblers adds extra support for the hypothesis that gambling is positively related to sensation seeking.

NEUROBIOLOGICAL SUBSTRATES OF GAMBLING

Zuckerman (1983) has attempted to elucidate the relationships of serotonin levels, brain mono-amines, mono-amine oxidase (MAO), and endorphins to variations in scores on the Sensation Seeking Scale without reaching striking clarity. In a more recent study dealing with features of the brain chemistry of addicted gamblers, Roy and others (Roy et al., 1988) measured levels of noradrenaline, monoamine metabolites and peptides in cerebrospinal fluid, plasma and urine. They expected to find low levels of serotonin metabolite, which would have indicated that addicted gamblers had poor impulse control. Instead, they found a pattern of biochemical indicators which pointed towards a significantly different pattern of levels of noradrenalin metabolites, indicating "a functional disturbance of the noradrenergic system" which, they noted, had been postulated to underlie sensation seeking behaviors.

Roy's study did not include a direct measurement of sensation seeking, but extraversion, as measured by Eysenck's *Extraversion and Psychoticism Quotient* — or EPQ — (Eysenck, 1967), was found in the same sample to be "highly significantly correlated with indexes of adrenergic function" in pathological gamblers. Roy concluded that this suggested that the disturbance in the central noradrenergic system in pathological gamblers may be partly reflected in their personality" (Roy, de Jong and Linnoila, 1989).

It appears that the early psychological work on the role of arousal in persistent regular gambling has been corroborated by the psychobiologists. Gambling problems are addictions rather than disorders of impulse control, and the existence of a role of arousal linked with possible personality features of sensation seeking or extraversion within the development of the addiction has been affirmed.

The relationship between Eysenck's extraversion and psychoticism scales (EPQ) and Zuckerman's Sensation Seeking Scale (SSS) is complex. Both sensation seeking and extraversion have been related to the construct of an "optimal level of stimulation" (Eysenck, 1967; Zuckerman 1969, 1974) but sensation-seeking has been found to correlate moderately but highly significantly with both Eysenck's extraversion and his psychoticism superfactors (Eysenck and Zuckerman, 1978). Zuckerman (1979) has interpreted these relationships as indicating that sensation seeking may relate more directly to a rotation of the factors in Eysenck's psychological space and therefore to Gray's separate reward and punishment systems (Gray, 1971), as well as to his concepts of biological pessimism and optimism (Brown, 1986). More recently (Zuckerman, Kuhlman and Camac, 1988), sensation seeking has come to be seen as closer to Eysenck's psychoticism rather than his extraversion; in accordance with this, pathological gamblers were found to have psychoticism scores (Roy, Custer, Lorenz and Linnoila, 1989).

Within a learning theory conceptualization of persistent betting, arousal has been hypothesized to act as reinforcer on a fixed interval schedule (Dickerson, 1977, 1979, 1984; Sanders, 1981), together with the more commonly hypothesized variable schedule of cash won (Skinner, 1953; Knapp, 1976). The relationship of arousal and chasing suggests that arousal as a reinforcer may be a more important determinant of loss of control (Dickerson, Hinchy and Fabre, 1987; Blaszczynski, Wilson and McConaghy, 1986). The learning theory conceptualization, however, is unable to account for the fact that only a small percentage of gamblers lose control to the point where their gambling becomes problematic (Commission on the Review of National Policy Toward Gambling, 1976; Kallic, Suits, Dielman and Hybels, 1979). Brown (1986) has attempted to integrate the roles of arousal and sensation-seeking among many other factors in the development of an individual's gambling frequency from low through regular to excessive gambling. Blaszczynski and McConaghy

(1989) developed this still further with the addition of factors such as stress reactions and behavior completion mechanisms.

PROBLEMS IN ANY SIMPLE RELATIONSHIP BETWEEN SENSATION SEEKING AND GAMBLING

More recent studies suggest that Zuckerman's simple predicted relationship between gambling and sensation-seeking cannot have been accurate. Blaszczynski et al. (1986) found that a group of male pathological gamblers presenting for treatment had significantly lower than average SSS total scores. Although it can be argued that the questionnaire responses of persons in crisis may differ significantly from their typical responses, the Blaszczynski data matched existent norms with respect to age and extroversion, which lends support to the validity of their findings.

Dickerson, Hinchy and Fabre (1987) found lower than average SSS scores in a sample of non-treatment seeking off-course betters. They suggest that off-course betting is favored by low sensation seekers because:

> ". . .in the late 1960s in the U.S., when gambling might typically be associated with a trip to Las Vegas or illegal gambling, then to predict that this activity would be a more likely choice for the sensation seeker is understandable. However, in the 1980s (in Australia) where the state concerned has many readily accessible forms of legalized gambling one might well predict the opposite. Sensation seekers might well prefer to choose from a wide range of sporting and social activities rather than bet in an off-course agency commonly set in a shopping center, or play poker machines at their local social club."

They point out that casino gambling, card clubs, betting at the race track and some illegal forms of gambling may remain exceptions to a general relationship between sensation seeking and gambling diametrically opposed to that proposed by Zuckerman. This confirms the need for researchers not to assume that gambling is a homogeneous activity. This need is further confirmed by a study in personality differences as measured by the *Minnesota Multiphasic Personality Inventory* (MMPI) between gamblers participating in games of luck and those gamblers participating in games of skill, suggesting that different personality types choose different forms of gambling (Adkins, Kreudelbach, Toohig, and Rugle, 1988).

Starr and Potashner (1985) suggest that some forms of gambling activity may be more easily substituted for one another. They found, through cluster analysis of protocols from 197 adult subjects, that gambling activities group into four distinct quadrants, with the two dimensions being casino versus non-casino and serious versus recreational.

Blaszczynski, Winter and McConaghy (1985) found that specifically horse-race addicts had significantly lower baseline Beta-endorphin levels as compared to poker-machine players and controls. They too concluded that this suggests that distinct subgroups of gamblers exist and raises the possibility that different etiological factors may characterize each subgroup.

Factors reviewed above suggest that it may be useful to distinguish, after Cornish (1978), those determinants of gambling which govern the choice of type or form of gambling from those governing the way in which a particular form is used by the individual.

Kuley and Jacobs (1987) found that problem gamblers scored significantly higher than social gamblers on the Sensation Seeking Scale total score and on the Disinhibition, Experience Seeking and Boredom Susceptibility subscales. There was no control for the type or form of gambling participated in, and it is possible that the results relate sensation seeking to the wide range of differences in the choice of form among their sample rather than to the way in which all forms were used.

Dickerson, Hinchy and Fabre (1987) found that total SSS scores and subscale scores on Experience Seeking and Disinhibition were associated with greater expenditures of time and money, and other general measures of involvement in betting. Boredom susceptibility subscale scores were also found to be linked to subjective reports of arousal while betting. They speculate that these sensation seeking characteristics in off-course gamblers may be a "possible predisposing route to loss of control of betting and eventual problematic or pathological gambling." These possible predisposing factors in the sensation seeking of off-course bettors, which may lead them to loss of control and gambling to excess, were summarized by Dickerson, Hinchey and Fabre (see Figure 1).

The present study is in part a near replication of Dickerson, Hinchy and Fabre's work examining chasing, arousal and sensation seeking in off-course gamblers. In addition, an attempt is made to examine the relationship between sensation seeking and preference for gambling activities in a sample of the general population.

Attempts were also made to control for another possible confounding factor in the Dickerson, Hinchy and Fabre study, the lack of control for other possible forms of gambling that the off-course bettors may have participated in.

FIGURE 1

Schema of Variables that may Contribute to Loss of Control of Betting

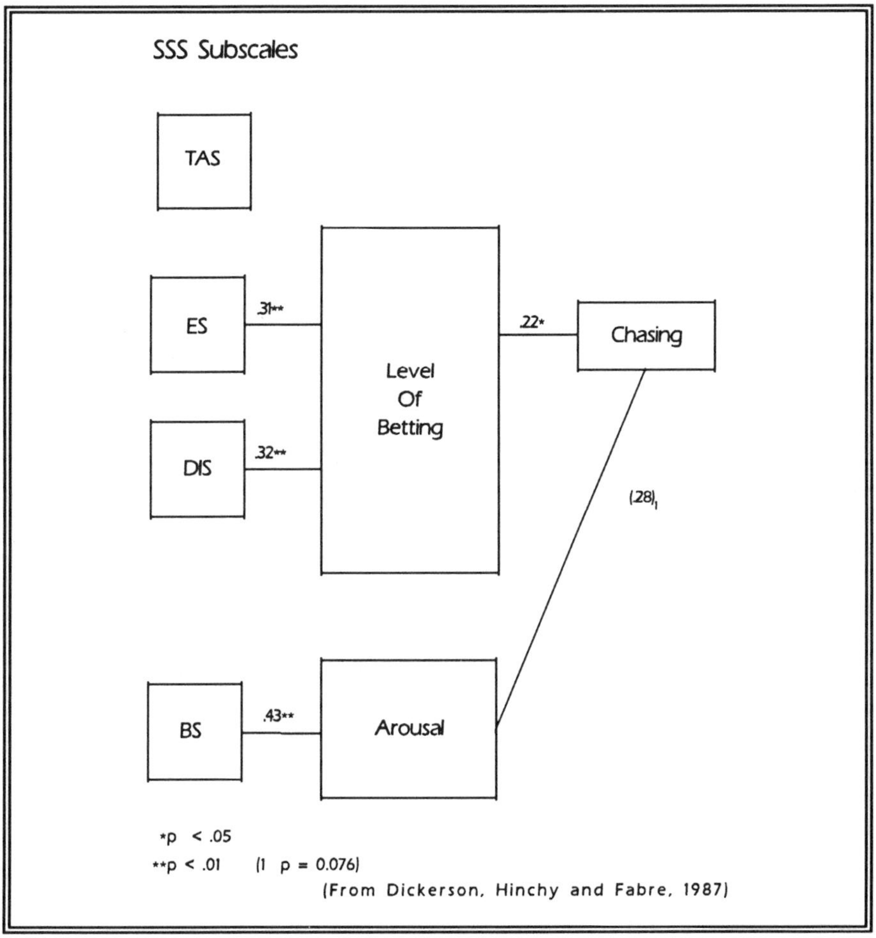

Past studies investigating the relationship between gambling and sensation seeking have compared the scores of gamblers to those of the general population. But Downes et al. (1976) estimated that 27% of men and 7% of women in the United Kingdom bet at least occasionally in betting offices, and that 17% of men and 2% of women bet there regularly (not to mention the people who gamble on other forms). Hence, gamblers have in the past been compared to a general population sample containing a significant proportion of gamblers plus the non-gamblers with whom they are being compared.

METHOD

There were two groups of subjects: a group of gamblers (N=79) from off-course betting offices, and a sample of the general population of the city of Glasgow (N=96). All subjects were male.

- A six page battery of questionnaires was used comprising:
- the *Sensation Seeking Scale* (SSS) Form V (Zuckerman, 1979);
- questions concerning frequency of gambling behavior and the number of different forms of gambling participated in;
- demographic data on sex, marital status, age and employment;
- a four-item subscale for the state portion of the *State-Trait Anxiety Inventory* (Speilberger et al., 1970), used previously by Dickerson (Leary and Dickerson, 1985; Dickerson and Adcock, 1986) and especially by Dickerson, Hinchy and Fabre (1986) as a measure of subjective arousal. Subjects were asked to answer about how they usually felt when waiting for the result of a race on which they had bet to be announced;
- a version of the *Awareness of Autonomic Activity* (AAA) scale. This is an eleven item scale developed by Mandler et al. (Mandler, Mandler and Uviller, 1958; Mandler, Mandler, Kremen and Sholiton, 1961; Mandler and Kremen, 1958), and adopted by Kissen, Brown and Kissen (1969). It was included as a measure of subjective awareness of arousal in addition to the State Trait Anxiety Inventory, but also to compare with it, because it seemed to be extremely easy to complete, and therefore it was hoped that there would be few blank returns. (Only 50% of off-course betters that returned questionnaires in the Dickerson, Hinchy and Fabre study completed the four-item Speilberger subscale);

- a question concerning chasing: "When you are behind or losing, how often do you attempt to chase your losses? In other words, how often do you start placing more bets once you've had a few losers? Never, occasionally, usually, nearly always?"
- questions concerning betting behavior which have been associated with loss of control. These include items which have been used and associated with out of control betting behavior before (Dickerson, 1977, 1979, 1984; Dickerson, Hinchy and Fabre, 1987; Kuley and Jacobs, 1987; Custer, Meeland and Krug, 1985, etc.); and
- questions relating to cash involvement in betting, including bet size and amount of expenditure on one day on gambling.

PROCEDURE: OFF-COURSE BETTORS SAMPLE

The sample of off-course bettors came from eight off-course betting agencies in the Glasgow area, selected to cover different types of location — city center, shopping center and industrial — to ensure a wide selection of bettors from different areas of Glasgow, and including both large chain and private offices. All agencies were approached beforehand and the co-operation of staff was secured, with the exception of one agency which refused to allow the study to take place for fears of adverse publicity. This agency was replaced by one which was similarly situated. Times of day and days of the week were systematically chosen to ensure that lunchtime, afternoon and week-end customers were sampled.

Bettors were selected as those people who entered the office after the data collector, or people who were already in the office if the number was small enough to avoid experimenter bias. They were never approached during the races themselves (i.e., during race commentary) or while placing bets, as it would be more of an invasion of privacy as these stages have been seen as central in the betting process (Dickerson, 1977, 1979, 1984). Thus, they were approached either when leaving the office or between races.

If the subject agreed to take a questionnaire, he was instructed to return it to the data collector or to hand it in behind the counter in that particular office the next time he was in. The data collectors consisted of one psychology student and three regular gamblers well acquainted with the agencies in question. The staff behind the counter in each office were all aware of the methods of data collection, and helped to encourage high return rates from the bettors they were acquainted with.

PROCEDURE: SAMPLE OF THE GENERAL POPULATION

A random sample of two hundred males of the general population of Glasgow was selected from the Glasgow Electoral Voters' Register by selecting every 2437th name, ensuring representatives from all 66 electoral wards; the number from each ward varied depending on the size of the ward. If the name at the number reached was female, the male name nearest to that position in the role was selected.

Although it has been estimated that over 80% of the population are reachable by phone (Belson, 1986), the possibility of selecting names from the telephone directory and phoning a random sample was ruled out due to possible confounding variables (such as experimenter bias manifested in alterations in pitch, etc.), unnecessary expense (it was estimated that each call would last 20 minutes), and for the simple reason that there are more people registered as voters than there are people who have phones.

Once the names were selected, questionnaires were posted out to each subject with a stamped addressed envelope for return.

Each of the addressed envelopes were secretly encoded inside in order that the sample could be examined to see if it was a representative sample of the Glasgow population with respect to wards covered, and to allow the analysis of social class factors. For ethical reasons, the original names chosen from the electoral role were left out, and only the ward areas were recorded by code.

RESULTS

Of the 143 male off-course bettors approached, ten refused, and 79 (55%) returned a questionnaire. The mean age was 40.7 years (Standard Deviation =17.3, range 19-74). Ninety-four percent reported betting once a week or more often.

Of the bettors sampled, 33.9% reported themselves as never chasing; 26% as occasionally; 16.8% as usually; and 23.4% as nearly always. Table 1 illustrates the relationship between chasing and questions relating to loss of control of gambling and gambling expenditure.

TABLE 1

PEARSON PRODUCT-MOMENT CORRELATIONS BETWEEN CHASING AND ITEMS RELATED TO LOSS OF CONTROL (Two-Tailed Significance)

Questionnaire Items	Q7	Q8	Q9	Q10	Q11	Q12	Q13	Q14	Q15
Q7 Chasing	1.00	0.53^{***}	0.63^{***}	0.54^{***}	0.48^{***}	0.37^{***}	0.37^{***}	0.55^{***}	0.52^{***}
Q8 Gambling Longer Than Planned		1.00	0.60^{***}	0.78^{***}	0.31^{**}	0.17	0.49^{***}	0.35^{***}	0.48^{***}
Q9 Gamble Till All Spare Cash Gone			1.00	0.65^{***}	0.31^{**}	0.34^{**}	0.40^{***}	0.54^{***}	0.60^{***}
Q10 Spend More Than Intended				1.00	0.47^{***}	0.32^{**}	0.42^{***}	0.43^{***}	0.59^{***}
Q11 Do You Have A Problem Controlling Level of Gambling					1.00	0.51^{***}	0.58^{***}	0.47^{***}	0.44^{***}
Q12 Previously Tried Stopping						1.00	0.58^{***}	0.41^{***}	0.35^{***}
Q13 Like to Reduce Amount You Spend							1.00	0.52^{***}	0.45^{***}
Q14 Must Return After Losing								1.00	0.55^{***}
Q15 Must Return to Win More After Winning									1.00

$^{*}p < .05$ $^{**}p < .01$ $^{***}p < .001$

TABLE 2

Pearson Product-Moment Correlations Between Sensation Seeking, Chasing, Arousal, Frequency of Betting, Age, Bet Size, Expenditure on Betting, Loss of Control, and Number of Other Gambling Forms Participated in (Two-Tailed Significance)

Variable	TAS	ES	Dis.	BS	TOTAL	CHSING	SPIEL.	AAA	AGE	BET SIZE	EXPEND-ITURE	LOSS OF CONTROL	NO OTHER FORMS	FREQUENCY BETTING
SSS TAS	1	0.42***	0.56***	0.19	0.74***	0.19	0.18	0.22*	-0.61***	0.23*	0.26*	0.19	0.17	-0.18
ES		1	0.59***	0.25*	0.74***	0.09	0.05	0.32**	-0.42***	0.27*	0.28*	0.06	0.23*	-0.13
Dis.			1	0.43***	0.87***	0.29***	0.15	0.32**	-0.67***	0.53***	0.61***	0.36***	0.35**	-0.14
BS				1	0.62***	0.22*	0.05	0.28*	-0.25*	0.26*	0.34**	0.40***	0.36***	0.23*
TOTAL					1	0.26*	0.15	0.38***	-0.67***	0.43***	0.49***	0.37***	0.36***	-0.09
CHASING						1	0.2	0.45***	-0.43***	0.46***	0.41***	0.65***	0.44***	0.14
AROUSAL (SPIEL.)							1	0.49***	-0.30**	0.19	0.17	0.38***	0.13	0.02
AROUSAL (AAA)								1	-0.36***	0.51***	0.47***	0.57***	0.41***	0.11
AGE									1	-0.40***	-0.44***	-0.33**	-0.37***	0.16
BET SIZE										1	0.88***	0.51***	0.39***	0.09
EXPENDITURE											1	0.48***	0.42***	0.08
LOSS OF CONTROL												1	0.49***	0.28*
NO OTHER FORMS													1	0.19
FREQUENCY OF BETTING														1

The short form of the state portion of the State-Trait Anxiety Questionnaire was fully completed by only 56 subjects. The remainder checked only one or two of the subscales, and their records were excluded on this component. The mean score of those completing the scale was 8.61 (SD = 3.89, range 4-16), which is similar to that reported by poker machine players while betting (Dickerson and Adcock, 1986) and off-course bettors from Australia while betting (Dickerson, Hinchy and Fabre, 1987).

The other measure of subjective arousal used, the Awareness of Autonomic Activity (AAA) scale, was fully completed by 73 subjects. The remainder left several of the items blank, and their records were excluded on this component. The mean score of those completing the scale was 15.6 (SD = 6.14, range 11-38). The Pearson Product-Moment correlation between the AAA scale and the Speilberger subscale was 0.485 ($p < 0.001$).

All 79 of the off-course bettors completed Zuckerman's Sensation Seeking Scale. The mean total score was 16.86 (SD = 7.38, range 2-39), with mean subscale scores of 4.25 for TAS (Thrill and Adventure Seeking) (SD = 2.74, range 0-10), 4.10 for Experience Seeking (SD = 2.04, range 1-9), 4.59 for Disinhibition (SD = 2.91, range 0-10), and 3.91 for Boredom Susceptibility (SD = 2.24, range 0-10). Significant negative correlations of the SSS total and subscale scores with age were found, with the strongest relationship for the total scale score ($r = -0.675$, $p < 0.001$) and the Disinhibition subscale ($r = -0.6742$, $p < 0.001$). Correlations for the Experience Seeking and Boredom Susceptibility subscales were $r = 0.421$ ($p < 0.001$) and $r = -0.250$ ($p < 0.05$) and the correlation for TAS subscale was $r = -0.61$ ($p < 0.001$).

The relationship between sensation seeking and other variables of interest central to the study is illustrated in Table 2. A measure of frequency of betting was derived by multiplying the reported frequency of betting each week with the time spent during each episode of betting. *Loss of control* refers to a score which resulted from the summation of questions relating to loss of control.

From the random sample of the male population of Glasgow, 52% of the questionnaires which reached the subjects who had not moved houses or could be located by the Post Office were returned. The return rate did not differ significantly from ward to ward. The mean age of the subjects who returned questionnaires was 38.82 years (SD = 17.46, range 18-76). No significant differences in social class were apparent when comparing data from the sample to figures for the whole of the Glasgow population, as given in the ward profiles introduction to the electoral register.

All of the 96 males who returned questionnaires completed the Sensation Seeking Scale. The mean total SSS score was 17.53 (SD = 7.96, range 2-37), with mean subscale scores of 5.23 for TAS (SD = 7.96, range 0-10), 4.26 for Experience Seeking (SD = 1.96, range 0-9), 4.64 for Disinhibition (SD = 2.73, range 0-10) and 3.48 for Boredom Susceptibility (SD = 2.24, range 0-10). The mean scores of the sample are contrasted with mean scores of English males (Zuckerman, Eysenck and Eysenck, 1978) in Table 3.

The change in sensation seeking subscale scores as a function of age is shown in Figure 2. A greater decline with age was observed for TAS and Disinhibition than for Experience Seeking and Boredom Susceptibility. This is in accordance with previous results (Zuckerman et al., 1978; Zuckerman, 1979, 1984).

The sample of Glaswegian off-course bettors were compared to the sample of the Glaswegian population on the sensation-seeking dimension. The off-course bettors scored significantly lower than the general population on the TAS ($t = 2.118$, $p < 0.05$). The gamblers (i.e., off-course bettors) also scored lower on the total SSS and on the Disinhibition and Experience Seeking subscales (although this trend did not reach significance). The off-course bettors scored higher than the general population on the Boredom Susceptibility subscale (but not significantly).

Since the mean age of the sample of off-course bettors (40.7) did not differ significantly from the mean age of the general population sample (38.8), and the profile of changes in SSS with age was so similar for both samples, it was not judged necessary to perform an analysis of co-variance to demonstrate the independence of differences in sensation seeking between the two samples from age effects.

Of the general population sample, 47% reported gambling on one form or more. Thirty two subjects reported gambling on one form; ten subjects reported gambling on two forms; and three subjects reported gambling on more than two forms. The relationship between sensation seeking, number of gambling activities participated in, and type of gambling in those who gamble in the general population is illustrated in Table 4. There is a trend (not reaching significance), with non-gamblers scoring higher on the SSS total and on all the subscales than those who gamble in the off-course betting office. Gamblers

TABLE 3

Mean Scores of Scottish (Glaswegian) Males and English Males by Age Groups

Ages			*Total Score*		*TAS*		*ES*		*Dis.*		*BS*	
	Scottish	English	Scottish	English	Scottish	English	Scottish	English	Scottish	English	Scottish	English
16-19	6	72	23.8	21.5		7.4	4	4.1	7.7	6.2	4	3.8
20-29	26	119	21.8	19.3	6.7	6.6	5.8	4.4	5.7	4.9	3.7	3.5
30-39	11	25	20.2	18.4	6	5.7	4.5	4.5	6.2	4.6	3.4	3.6
40-49	14	26	15.9	15.8	4.1	4.3	4	4	4.4	4.6	3.4	3
50-59	9	—	11.9	—	4.2	—	2.9	—	2.3		2.4	
60+	14	12	11.9	12.4	3.4	3.2	3.1	2.7	3	3.3	2.4	3.3

FIGURE 2

Change in Sensation Seeking Subscale Scores as a Function of Age

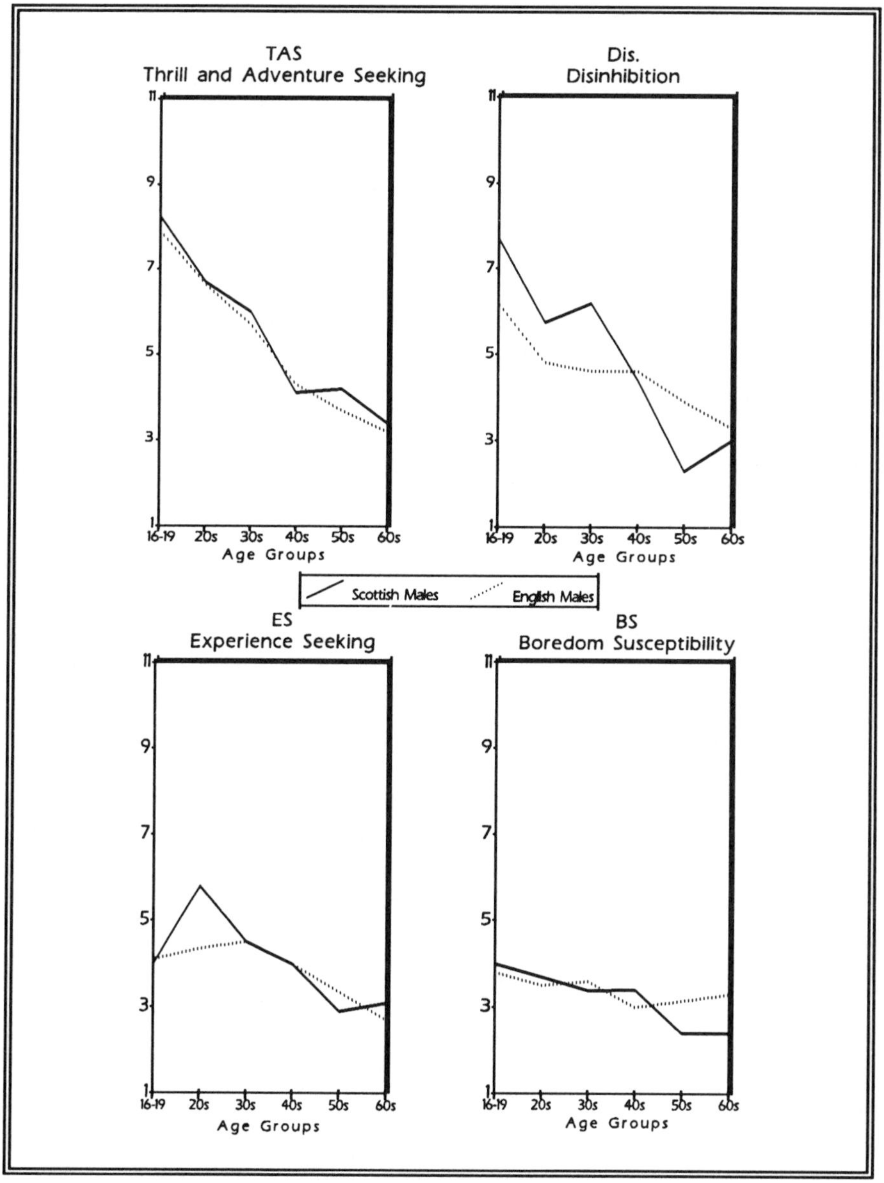

who gamble on two forms of gambling are similarly higher scorers on the SSS total and subscales than non-gamblers (with the exception of the Experience Seeking subscale), but this trend does not reach levels of significance. Those who gamble in the casino scored higher than any of the other groups mentioned on all the SSS subscales and on the total SSS (although, once again not to a significant level).

An analysis of the off-course bettors' sample with respect to other forms of gambling participated in and sensation seeking is shown in Table 5. Similar results were found to those for the general population, with those participating in off-course betting and nothing else scoring lower than the general population on the total SSS and all the subscales. Off-course bettors who gamble on three or more additional forms of gambling, or gamble in the casino or at the race-track, were found to be higher scorers than the general population on the total SSS and on all the subscales.

A principal components varimax factor analysis with orthogonal rotation was carried out on the variables involved in the off-course betting office; hence the off-course bettors' sample was used. The results are displayed in Table 6 with the factor loadings of variables on factor one.

DISCUSSION

The sample, and therefore the findings from it, appear to be broadly representative of the male populations of off-course bettors and non-gamblers in the City of Glasgow. There were very few refusals among the off-course bettors; over half of the questionnaires that reached the general population were returned. Strong relationships of total and subscale scores of the Sensation Seeking Scale to age were found, but with the Boredom Susceptibility scale showing the weakest effect, which is a typical finding in earlier studies (Zuckerman et al., 1978; Zuckerman, 1979; Zuckerman and Neeb, 1980; Blaszczynski et al., 1986; Dickerson et al., 1987). The correlations within the SSS are typical of previous reports. Comparison between returners and non-returners from the general population showed no significant differences in social class, occupation, and areas of return. Furthermore, the SSS scores of the male general sample show the same relationships to age and among the subscales; this provides evidence of concurrent validity for the bettors' sample.

TABLE 4

Gambling in the General Population, and the Relationship to Sensation-Seeking				
	Non-Gamblers (N = 51)	Off-Course Betting (No Other Forms) (N = 15)	Participation in Two Forms (N = 10)	Casino Among Gambling Activities (N = 7)
SSS Total	16.4	14.1	18.4	22.0
TAS	5.3	3.5	6.3	7.2
ES	3.9	3.8	4.4	5.4
Dis	4.1	3.8	5.1	6.2
BS	3.1	3.0	2.6	3.2

TABLE 5

Off-Course Bettors, Other Forms of Gambling Participated in and Sensation-Seeking			
	Off-Course Betting (No Other Forms) (N = 9)	*Off-Course Betting And One Other Form (N = 44)*	*Off-Course Betting And Two Other Forms (N = 18)*
SSS Total	10.9	16	19.1
TAS	2	4.2	5.1
ES	3.6	4	4.3
Dis	2.8	4.2	4.8
BS	2.7	3.4	4.9
	Off-Course Betting And Three Other Forms (N = 6)	*Casino Among Activities (N = 21)*	*Racetrack Among Activities (N = 22)*
SSS Total	24	20.2	21.8
TAS	4.3	4.7	5.1
ES	5.7	5.2	4.9
Dis	8	6.3	5.9
BS	6	3.9	5.9

TABLE 6

Results of Factor Analysis

Factor	*Eigenvalue*	*Percentage of Variance*	*Loading of Variables on Factor 1 (Varimax Rotation)**	
1	8.9796	32.1	Size of Bet	0.86
2	2.54407	9.1	Spending More Than Intended	0.84
3	2.12178	7.6	Expenditure on Gambling	0.79
4	1.79889	6.2	Acknowledge Problems Controlling Levels of Gambling	0.62
5	1.56022	5.6	Spending All Spare Cash	0.56
6	1.36955	4.9	Subjective Arousal While Betting	0.56
7	1.18495	4.2	Spending Longer Than Planned In the Office	0.56
8	1.06104	3.8	After Winning, Want To Return to Win More	0.56
9	0.97599	3.5	Amount of Time Per Day Spent Gambling	0.51
10	0.86242	3.1	Number of Days a Week Spent Gambling	0.47
			SSS Total	0.4
			Chasing	0.36
			*Only loadings over 0.3 are reported	

The results of the general population sample probably generalize quite well to the population of the United Kingdom as a whole. Scottish norms for the SSS have hitherto been drawn from undergraduate populations. This sample covers all age groups randomly and, when compared to existing English general norms (Zuckerman, Eysenck and Eysenck, 1978), it looks very similar indeed (see Figure 2). Since there is no known reason to suspect that Glaswegian off-course bettors are any different from those of the remainder of the United

Kingdom, it is likely that the present findings are broadly representative of the United Kingdom as a whole.

The comparison of SSS scores between the gamblers' sample and the general population shows consistent differences in the direction of lower sensation seeking among the off-course bettors, although the only statistically significant difference is on the TAS subscale. These findings concur with the previous findings of Blaszczynski et al. (1986) and Dickerson et al. (1987).

Closer scrutiny of the data, separating the general population sample out into different groups (including a group of non-gamblers) and separating the off-course bettors into different groups (with reference to the number of other activities participated in, and the nature of those gambling activities) reveals important relationships in sensation seeking between types of gambling participated in and the number of forms of gambling participated in. As Dickerson, Hinchy and Fabre suggested (1987), off-course bettors as a group are lower sensation seekers than the general population. But, by contrast, casino gamblers and gamblers that go to the race-track are higher sensation seekers than the general population.

The number of gambling forms participated in is also an important factor. Involvement in many different forms of gambling is associated with high SSS. The relationship between sensation seeking and the number of gambling forms participated in is summarized in Figure 3 and appears to be linear.

The relationships depicted in Figure 3 bear a close resemblance to predictions from previous research. The preference of high sensation seekers for casino and race-track gambling fits the general picture of the high sensation seeker. It also fits the general picture of the high SSS that he should be more likely to participate in a number of different forms of gambling rather than just one form, as sensation seeking is defined by the "need for varied, novel and complex sensations and experiences" (Zuckerman, 1979). The finding that the only statistically significant difference between off-course bettors and the general population was in the TAS subscale might suggest that low sensation seekers, especially, would shun the more dramatic and extravert forms of sensation seeking, and be more likely to pick off-course betting in a safe, well-controlled environment close to home. Indeed, it is likely that gamblers as a whole, even those with the highest SSS scores, become specialists in their sensation seeking outlets, concentrating all their sensation seeking in just one channel — gambling.

They would thus fail to register the true extent of their commitment to sensation seeking on a scale which simply sums the commitment to a *variety* of sensation seeking activities without weighting the extent of commitment to any single one.

One way of conceiving of the distribution of sensation seekers within gambling forms might be to combine the relationships depicted in Figure 3, (where it might be predicted that the highest sensation seekers should be located towards the outside of the first quadrant, with the lowest sensation seekers located towards the outside of the third quadrant) with the dichotomy made between skill and luck games (Adkins, Kreudelbach, Toohig and Rugle, 1988), or with the serious recreational casino versus non-casino distinctions made by Starr and Potashner (1985). Off-course bettors are different and, from the characteristics of slot machine players depicted by Adkins et al. (1988), slot players can be predicted to be lower sensation seekers also, possibly the lowest of all. Certainly the relationship of sensation seeking to preference for form of gambling activities is more complex than Zuckerman's original prediction suggests, and it now seems an essential requirement of future research methodology in gambling that it should control for the likely differences between forms.

Focussing now on the sample of off-course bettors and the interrelationships between variables involved, the comparison of measures of arousal used showed that the correlation between the AAA scale and the Speilberger was highly significant. However, it is suggested that the AAA is the better measure, both because it is easier to complete (73 subjects completed it as opposed to 56), and because it has a greater ability to detect significant differences in arousal than the subscale of the STAI (possibly due to the higher completion rate). This can be readily observed from Table 2.

The validity of the long entertained assumption that chasing is a central variable of interest in the generation of problematic levels of gambling is supported by the relationships between chasing and aspects of control (illustrated in Table 1) such as spending more than planned, gambling longer than planned, and attempting to stop, as well as with more direct admissions to having problems controlling levels of gambling. Chasing, therefore, may be a central characteristic of a complex of experiences that are concerned with the subjective control of gambling behavior. (These results concur with those of Dickerson, Hinchy and Fabre, (1987).) However, in the present sample, 66% of off-course

FIGURE 3
Sensation Seeking and Gambling Preferences

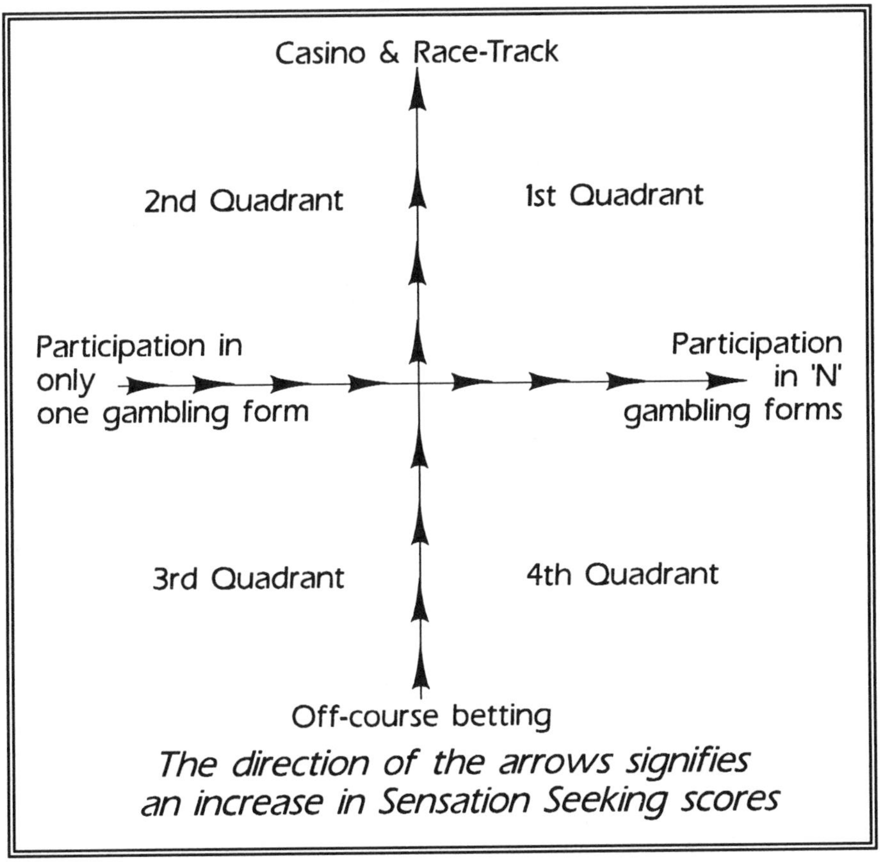

bettors reported chasing at least occasionally. It is therefore unlikely that chasing *per se* leads to problematic levels of gambling. Lesieur (1979) suggested that an additional change in associated cognitions is required so that the gambler comes to believe that chasing is rational before it may become the central feature of a major addiction.

Once inside the off-course betting office, the total SSS is related significantly and positively to subjective awareness of arousal (as measured by the AAA), bet size, expenditure on betting, loss of control, and number of other forms participated in. Sensation seeking therefore seems an important variable involved in high levels of gambling. All the subscales of the SSS relate to arousal (as measured by the AAA), and to bet size and expenditure. No significant relationship was found between the subscale scores of the Speilberger and any Sensation Seeking Scale score, either total or subscales.

Only the first factor emerging from the factor analysis is discussed because, as can be seen from Table 6, it accounts for more than three times the percentage of the total variance than any other factor. The loadings on this factor — as illustrated in Table 6 — include variables associated with loss of control of gambling and frequency of gambling, as well as variables related to expenditure on gambling. This factor might therefore be interpreted as representing a cluster of variables associated with problematic levels of gambling. If this is the case, then this is further evidence for the importance of the variables of chasing and sensation seeking, as they load on this factor.

The results of this study give rise to some problems surrounding Dickerson et al.'s (1987) schema of variables which may contribute to loss of control of betting, mainly because of validation problems with the STAI subscale as a measure of subjective awareness of arousal. Because of this, it may still be too early to speculate about variables involved in the route to loss of control of betting. If the AAA does prove to be an effective measure, then the Sensation Seeking Scale (SSS) subscales and total may well, nevertheless, through their relationships to arousal and level of betting, eventually point to a predisposition to chasing and loss of control. The correlations among variables (see Table 2) lend some support to this.

CONCLUSION

Scrutiny of the evidence from this study suggests that sensation seeking is an important variable in both choice of form of gambling and in the way in which gambling develops. This is confirmed by the psychophysiological and the psychobiological evidence about the neural substrates of both sensation seeking and gambling. But the *optimum level of arousal/optimum level of stimulation* model for understanding the relationship between sensation seeking and gambling — both "normal" and addictive — may be conceptually too simple. A reversal theory framework for explaining the gambler's behavior in terms of the paradoxes of felt arousal as put forward by Apter (1989) may make more sophisticated research and explanation possible. The application of reversal theory to gambling and other addictions (Brown, 1988) leaves the possibility open of subsuming sensation seeking within a reversal theory framework, or vice versa. Nevertheless, the present study has shown the need for continued interest in sensation seeking with respect to explanations of gambling and excessive gambling behavior.

REFERENCES

Adkins, B., N. Kreudelbach, T.M. Toohig and L.J. Rugle (1988). The relationship of gaming preferences to MMPI personality variables. In W.R. Eadington (ed.), *Gambling Research: Proceedings of the Seventh International Conference on Gambling and Risk Taking*, vol. 5. Reno: University of Nevada, Reno.

Anderson, G., and R.I.F. Brown (1984). Real and laboratory gambling, sensation-seeking and arousal. *British Journal of Psychology*, 75, 401-410.

Apter, M.J. (1989). *Reversal Theory Motivation Emotion and Personality.* London: Routledge.

Belson, W.A. (1986). *Validity In Survey Research.* Cambridge: University Press.

Blaszczynski, A.P., S.W. Winter, and N. McConaghy (1985). Plasma endorphin levels in pathological gambling. In W.R. Eadington (ed.), *The Gambling Studies: Proceedings of the Sixth National Conference on Gambling and Risk Taking*, vol. 5. Reno: University of Nevada, Reno.

Blaszczynski, A.P., A.C. Wilson, and N. McConaghy (1986). Sensation Seeking and pathological gambling. *British Journal of Addiction*, 81, 113-117.

Blaszczynski, A.P. and N. McConaghy (1989). Anxiety and/or depression in the pathogenesis of addictive gambling. *International Journal of the Addictions*, 24, 337-350.

Boyd, W.H. (1976). Excitement: The gambler's drug. In W.R. Eadington (ed.), *Gambling and Society.* Springfield, IL: Charles C. Thomas.

Brown, R.I.F. (1986). Arousal and sensation seeking components in the general explanation of gambling and gambling addictions. *International Journal of Addiction*, 21, 1001-1016.

Brown, R.I.F. (1988). Reversal theory and subjective experience in the explanation of addiction and relapse. In M.J. Apter, J.H. Kerr, and M. Cowles (eds.), *Progress in Reversal Theory* Amsterdam: North Holland (Progress in Psychology Series.)

Commission on the Review of National Policy Toward Gambling In America (1976). *Gambling in America.* Washington D.C.: U.S. Government Printing Office.

Cornish, D.B., (1978). *Gambling: A review of the literature and its implications for policy and research.* Home Office Research Study No. 42. London: HMSO.

Coventry, K.R. and P.M. Taggart (1987). *Excitement and gambling in the UK off-course betting office.* Unpublished undergraduate project, University of Glasgow.

Custer, R.L., T. Meeland, and S.E. Krug (1985). Differences between social and pathological gamblers. In W.R. Eadington (ed.), *The Gambling Studies: Proceedings of the Sixth National Conference on Gambling and Risk Taking*, vol. 5. Reno: University of Nevada, Reno.

Dickerson, M.G. (1977). The role of the betting office environment in the training of compulsive gamblers. *Behavioural Psychotherapy*, 1, 24-29.

Dickerson, M.G. (1979). FI schedules and persistence at gambling in the UK betting office. *Journal of Applied Behavior Analysis*, 12, 315-323.

Dickerson, M.G. (1984). *Compulsive Gamblers.* London: Longman.

Dickerson, M.G. and S.G. Adcock (1987). Mood, arousal and cognitions in persistent gambling: Preliminary investigation of a theoretical model. *Journal of Gambling Behavior*, 3, 3-15.

Dickerson, M.G., J. Hinchy, and J. Fabre (1987). Chasing, arousal and sensation seeking in off-course gamblers. *British Journal of Addiction*, 82, 673-680.

Downes, D.M., B.P. Davies, M.E. David, and P. Stone (1976). *Gambling, Work and Leisure: A Study Across Three Areas.* London: Routledge and Kegan Paul.

Draft Electoral Register for Glasgow (1987). Strathclyde Regional Council.

Electoral Register for Glasgow (1986). Strathclyde Regional Council.

Eysenck, H.J. (1967). *The Biological Basis of Personality.* Springfield, IL: Charles C. Thomas.

Eysenck, S., and M. Zuckerman (1978). The relationship between sensation-seeking and Eysenck's dimensions of personality. *British Journal of Psychology*, 69, 483-487.

Gray, J.A. (1972). The psychophysiological nature of introversion/extraversion: A modification of Eysenck's theory. In V.D. Nebylitsyn and J.A. Gray (eds.), *Biological Bases of Individual Behavior.* New York: Academic Press.

Frey, J.H. (1983). *Survey Research By Telephone.* New York: Sage Publications.

Kallick, M., D. Suits, T. Dielman, and J. Hybels (1979). *A Survey of American Gambling Attitudes and Behavior.* Ann Arbor, MI: Survey Research Center, Institute for Social Research, University of Michigan.

Kissen, D.M., R.I.F. Brown, and M. Kissen (1969). A further report on personality and psychosocial factors in lung cancer. *Annals of New York Academy of Science*, 164, 535-545.

Knapp, T.J. (1976). A functional analysis of gambling behavior. In W.R. Eadington (ed.), *Gambling and Society.* Springfield, IL: Charles C. Thomas.

Kuly, N.B., and D.F. Jacobs (1988). The relationship between dissociative-like experiences and sensation-seeking among social and problem gamblers. *Journal of Gambling Behavior*, 4, 197-207.

Leary, K., and M.G. Dickerson (1985). Levels of arousal in high and low frequency gamblers. *Behavior Research and Therapy*, 23, 635-640.

Lesieur, H.R. (1979). The compulsive gambler's spiral of options and involvement. *Psychiatry*, 42(1), 79-87.

Lesieur, H.R. (1984). *The Chase: Career of the Compulsive Gambler.* Cambridge, MA: Schenkman.

Lo, G., and I. Kremen (1958). Autonomic feedback: A correlational study. *Journal of Personality*, 26, 388-399.

Lo, G., J.M. Lo, I. Kremen, and R.D. Sholiton (1961). The response to threat: Relations among verbal and physiological indices. *Psychological Monographs*, 75(9), 513.

Lo, G., J.M. Lo, and E.T. Lo (1958). Autonomic feedback: The perception of autonomic activity. *Journal of Abnormal and Social Psychology*, 56, 367-373.

Roy, A., B. Adinoff, L. Roehrich, D. Lamparski, R. Custer, V. Lorenz, M. Barbaccia, A. Guidotti, E. Costa, and M. Linoila (1988). Pathological gambling: A psychobiological study. *Archives of General Psychiatry*, 45, 369-373.

Roy, A., R. Custer, V. Lorenz, and M. Linnoila (1989). Personality factors and pathological gambling. *Acta Psychiatrica Scandinavia*, 80, 37-39.

Roy, A., J. De Jong, and M. Linnoila (1989). Extraversion in pathological gamblers: Correlates with indexes of noradrenergic function. *Archives of General Psychiatry*, 46, 679-681.

Saunders, D.M. (1981). The late betting phenomenon in relation to type of bet and type of race. *Behavioural Psychotherapy*, 9, 330-337.

Scarne, J. (1983). *Scarne's New Complete Guide to Gambling.* London: Constable.

Skinner. B.F., 1953. *Science and Human Behavior.* New York: Free Press.

Speilberger, C.D., R.L. Gorsuch, and R.E. Lushene (1970). *Manual for the State-Trait Anxiety Inventory (Self-evaluation Questionnaire).* Palo Alto, CA: Consulting Psychologist Press.

Starr, M.W., and M.R. Potashner (1985). The structure of preferences for gambling activities. In W.R. Eadington (ed.), *The Gambling Studies: Proceedings of the Sixth National Conference on Gambling and Risk Taking*, vol. 3. Reno: University of Nevada, Reno.

Wray, I. and M.G. Dickerson (1981). Cessation of high-frequency gambling and withdrawal symptoms. *British Journal of Addiction*, 76, 401-405.

Zuckerman, M. (1969). Theoretical formulations. In J.P. Zubek (ed.), *Sensory Deprivation: Fifteen Years of Research.* New York: Appleton.

Zuckerman, M. (1974). The sensation seeking motive. In B.A. Maher (ed)., *Progress In Experimental Personality Research*, vol. 7. New York: Academic Press.

Zuckerman, M. (1979). *Sensation Seeking: Beyond the Optimal Level of Arousal.* Hillsdale, NJ: Erlbaum.

Zuckerman, M. (1983). *Biological Bases of Sensation Seeking, Impulsivity and Anxiety.* Hillsdale, NJ: Erlbaum.

Zuckerman, M., S. Eysenck, and H.J. Eysenck (1978). Sensation seeking in England and America: Cross-cultural, age and sex comparisons. *Journal of Consulting and Clinical Psychology*, 46, 139-143.

Zuckerman, M., D.M. Kuhlman, and C. Camac (1988). What lies beyond E and N? Factor analysis of scales believed to measure basic dimensions of personality. *Journal of Personality and Social Psychology*, 54, 96-107.

Age and Gambling Behavior: A Declining and Shifting Pattern of Participation©

Waiman P. Mok and Joseph Hraba

The relationship between age and gambling has received little attention in the social sciences. If for no other reason, an aging American population suggests that such research is needed. Chronological age was found to be negatively related to gambling behavior. However, within this trend of general decline, people of different ages were found to be participating in different types of gambling. The general decline across all age categories can be conceptualized as a result of age decline in experimentation for self-identity, age decline in the need for self-presentation, and an historical increase in social acceptance of gambling. People 65 or over gambling less than those under 65 could be a result of a decrease in intellectual

---

© This article was previously published in the *Journal of Gambling Studies* (1991), 7(4), 313-336. New York: Human Sciences Press, Inc. Permission to reprint has been granted by the authors and publisher.

functioning after the age of 65, and being socialized during the Great Depression. The differential rates of participation in different types of gambling could result from differential needs and resources related to different stages of development.

Any connection between gambling behavior and age has received little attention in the social sciences. If for no other reason, an aging American population suggests that such research is needed. An understanding of age differences in gambling behavior would provide rationale for forecasts and future policies regarding gambling.

AGE AND GAMBLING BEHAVIOR

Age differences have been found in many behaviors, including driving ability and perception of accident risk (Matthews and Moran, 1986; Finn and Bragg, 1986), changes in preferred sexual activity (Turner and Adams, 1988), social interaction (Boyd and Dowd, 1988), evaluation and experience of emotions (Sommers and Kosmitzki, 1988), crime rates (Smith, 1986; Sheley and Smith, 1988; Khullar and Wyatt, 1989; Steffensmeier et al., 1989; Shavit and Rettner, 1988), political attitudes and participation (Kiecolt, 1987; Cutler and Kaufman, 1975; Campbell, 1971), work involvement (Lorence, 1987; Loscocco and Kalleberg, 1988; Lorence and Mortimer, 1985), environmental concerns (Mohai and Twight, 1987), and perception of health status (Clarke, 1987). Age differences have also been observed in the relationship between subjective and objective economic well-being (Fletcher and Lorenz, 1985), locus of control (Penk, 1969; Schneider, 1988), and subjective well-being (Shehan et al., 1986; Felton, 1987; Herzog et al., 1982; Gove et al., 1989). Yet, age has received little attention in research on gambling. The only two studies that investigated age and gambling were done in the 1970s. Using data from a 1971 national Gallup survey, Li and Smith (1976) found chronological age to be negatively related to gambling propensity. In 1975, Kallick et al. (1979) conducted a national study on the extent of gambling activity, and found a general decline in gambling participation with chronological age. These age differences in gambling behavior can be attributed to aging and cohort effects (McPherson, 1983).

AGING EFFECTS

Aging effects refer to changes within an individual as she or he develops (McPherson, 1983). Thus, any age differences in gambling behavior could be an aging effect, and several theories suggest such effect.

A. Erikson's Eight Stages of Development

According to Erikson (1963, 1968, 1982), there are eight stages of human development, and each is associated with certain developmental tasks. During the fifth stage, adolescence, individuals seek self-identity through role experimentation. Confronted by the different roles they can play, adolescents test and experiment with role behavior to form their identities. The implication is that adolescents are likely to engage in several types of gambling, particularly those immediately available, such as lotteries, sports and card games. Adolescents experiment with gambling as they do with other role behavior.

The task following adolescence is to develop intimacy and overcome isolation. The experimentation of adolescence is slowly replaced by concerns over mate selection, family formation, and career launching. This is possibly a time when people begin to focus on certain types of gambling, particularly those that bring more financial rewards and risks, and commensurate with the expanding income associated with adulthood. The seventh stage, developing a sense of generativity, occurs around mid-adulthood. This stage is characterized by high productivity, creativity, a concern with self, achievement and power. The middle-aged are likely to continue the gambling focus of young adults.

Life's final stage is to develop ego integrity. The individual becomes more accepting of her or his fate as being inevitable and meaningful. Therefore, older people are less concerned with ego, but are more reflective and accepting of self, and thus have more stable self-concepts. The elderly are less likely to gamble, for they have less need to experiment for self-identity and to take risks for financial success.

The implications for gambling are twofold. First, one could expect a general decline in gambling behavior with age. Second, people in different age categories with different needs and abilities may be attracted to different types of gambling. The middle-aged, who are more financially secure as well as concerned about financial success, could be interested in gambling that brings greater financial rewards and risks, like investment speculation and casinos. The elderly are more likely to participate in games that are less competitive, such as bingo, due to declining mental faculties and less concern over financial success. They gamble not so much for financial rewards or excitement, but for maintaining social relationships. For their part, the young experiment with various forms of gambling.

B. Self-Presentation

Goffman (1967) maintained that social behavior can be understood in the context of self-presentation. Individuals engage in social activities to make a favorable impression on others and thus enhances self-esteem. Participating in action, or risk-taking, is highly valued in American culture and thus a context for favorable self-presentation (Goffman, 1967; Abt et al., 1985; Frey, 1984). By gambling, one can be seen as a big-spender and thus a big-shot. But the routinization of everyday life systematically eliminates opportunities for such action, but gambling is an obvious exception. Gambling is a form of action, in which fateful decisions are made and observed. It breaks out of the routine and an opportunity to display one's confidence and competence to others for self-esteem enhancement (Holtgraves, 1988).

Self-presentation has been found to have a role in gambling. In a study at a horsetrack in Hollywood Park, California, Herman (1967) observed that horse betting served to enhance bettor's self-esteem; they displayed for others that they were making fateful decisions. Zola (1963) made similar observations in his study of bettors at an illegal off-track betting parlor in a New England town. They gambled, making decisions for themselves, and thus enhanced their self-esteem.

Thus, a linear decline in gambling behavior with chronological age would be expected from this perspective. Older people, having more life experiences and more stable and positive self-concepts (McPherson, 1983; Gove et al., 1989), would be less likely than the younger to turn to gambling for self-presentation.

C. Activity, Disengagement, and Continuity Theories

According to activity theory, gambling behavior could increase in later years of life. Changes associated with old age, such as retirement and the loss of friends and spouses, reduce the number of roles that the elderly can play, and they could turn to gambling to replace these lost roles. However, it is hard to imagine the elderly rushing into gambling to replace lost roles. When faced with stress, such as those related to role losses, the elderly use passive, emotion-focused coping strategies rather than active, problem-focused ones (Osgood and Sontz, 1989). That is, older people would be more likely to deal emotionally but passively with stress rather than actively seek consolation from gambling. Moreover, when faced with declining abilities, the elderly lower their standards to maintain self-efficacy (Schulz, 1986). The elderly would not likely turn to gambling for compensations. They simply would readjust their standards to maintain their personal efficacy. It is in this sense that one can imagine the elderly turning to gambling that is social-oriented to compensate for losses in their social networks. Playing bingo with friends in bingo halls or churches provides, for example, the elderly with a social network of support.

Disengagement theory argues that it is often necessary for the elderly to disengage from previous roles. Disengagement is supposed to bring satisfaction to the elderly, as it releases one from normative constraints or pressures, such as work demands (Cumming and Henry, 1961). The elderly may disengage, due to their perception of lower intellectual functioning, in the same manner that they disengage from work (Lachman, 1989; Osgood and Sontz, 1989). Some gambling requires a fair amount of skill, and older people might see themselves as less capable of meeting these skill requirements.

Disengagement theory has come under attack, however, for its claims that disengagement is a universal process and that it produces life satisfaction (McPherson, 1983). Thus, disengagement from gambling may not be universal across all types of gambling. For example, the elderly may remain engaged in bingo and lottery play, while disengaging from horse betting.

Continuity theory maintains that as one ages, she or he strives to maintain her or his previously established life style as long as personal resources permit it (Williams and Wirths, 1965). This is based on the assumption that personality and life style are shaped by early socialization, suggesting that gambling behavior is a cohort-effect. In light of the increasing in social acceptance of gambling since the 1930s, we would expect a general decline in gambling with older cohorts.

COHORT EFFECTS

Cohorts are categories of people born during particular five- or ten-year periods, and cohort effects refer to the impact of specific historical events on different age cohorts (Riley, 1988). Poll results show gambling has been gaining social acceptance. In 1939, 54 percent of a sample of the American population had gambled at least once; in 1950, a Gallup poll estimated that 57 percent of the

American population gambled; in 1975, 61 percent of a sample of 2,000 American adults reported that they gambled in 1974; by April of 1989 a Gallup poll found that 72 percent of the adults surveyed had gambled in the past twelve months; and in April of 1989 an Iowa State University poll found 73 percent of the adult population in the state of Iowa gambled (Rosecrance, 1988; Fact Research Inc., 1976; Kallick et al., 1979; Hugick, 1989; Hraba et al., 1989). Almost every state has legalized gambling, including state-sponsored lotteries, horse and dog racing, casinos, bingo, and riverboat casinos. This trend might be reflected in a general decline in gambling with chronological age. Each consecutive (later) age cohort has been socialized into a less conservative environment about gambling.

OTHER CORRELATES OF GAMBLING

Literature from both aging and cohort effects predicts a decline in gambling behavior with age, as well as a changing pattern of gambling behavior with age. Such relationships might be moderated, however, by other variables that have been found to be correlates of age or gambling behavior. Social class, marital status, employment status, gender, community size, religion, and the social worlds of gambling have been found to be related to age or gambling behavior.

A. Social Class

The theories of anomie, alienation, and decision-making posit that gambling provides opportunity for lower-class persons to relieve frustrations in their efforts to become successful and independent, as well as to gain power and control (Frey, 1984). However, Veblen (1899) argued that gambling serves as a status symbol for the upper class, to conform with other members of the same class, and thus gambling is positively related to class.

Research on class theories of gambling have brought mixed results. On the one hand, both Herman (1967) and Zola (1963) found that horse betting offered gamblers otherwise unavailable opportunities to take control and make decisions in order to enhance their self-esteem. Downes et al. (1976) found a negative relationship between gambling and middle-class values, but the study failed to support the theory of alienation. On the other hand, Li and Smith (1976) reported that social class and gambling behavior were positively related. Kallick et al. (1979) also found that people with higher income and educational attainment were more likely to gamble.

The class-conflict perspective also implies that social class is related to gambling. Hogan (1986) maintained that the middle and upper classes control working-class gambling to prevent the working class from diverting their energy from productive labor and squandering the subsistence to absorb the production surplus. The implication is obvious; the working class is thought to be prone to gambling. In reviewing the history of working-class gambling in England since 1800, Maguire (1987) concluded that working-class people maintain their interests in gambling as an expression of their working-class culture.

Age differences are related to social class, for persons under 25 and over 65 years old are more likely to fall below the poverty line than other age categories (Foner, 1988). An integration of the anomie and age stratification perspectives would predict that persons under 25 or over 65 years old are more likely to gamble because they are otherwise denied access to opportunity. On the other hand, a merger of the age-stratification and the Veblenian perspectives would predict that middle-aged people, who are more likely to be upper-middle and upper class, would gamble more than the young and the old.

B. Marital and Employment Statuses

Kallick et al. (1979) reported that singles and those divorced or separated were more likely to gamble than were the married. Widows were the least likely to gamble. A possible explanation could be that singles and the divorced/separated, usually having fewer family responsibilities, would have more time and means to gamble. Widows would perhaps gamble less, even with diminished family responsibility, since they usually have fewer financial resources.

C. Gender

Psychological differences between females and males are widely acknowledged (Gove et al., 1989). Men are more likely than women to attribute to themselves competitive attributes, for example, but gender differences in competitive attributes are smaller for older age categories (Gove et al., 1989). If competitiveness drives gambling, then women would have a weaker propensity to gamble than men. Kallick et al. (1979) reported that more males said they bet in 1974 than did females (68 versus 55 percent).

Women are less likely than men to gamble in games, such as blackjack and lotteries, but are more likely than men to engage in bingo and raffles (Kallick et al., 1979). This has been attributed to gender-role socialization (Lindgren et al., 1987). Hence, the relationship between gambling behavior, different forms of gambling, and age could be moderated by gender.

D. Community Size

Li and Smith (1976) found that community size was positively related to gambling propensity. Kallick et al. (1979) reported that 72 percent of the suburbanites, and 66 percent of city dwellers, but only 53 percent of people living in small cities or rural areas bet in 1974. One explanation is that metropolitan areas offer more gambling opportunities. Another is that metropolitan areas tend to have younger populations (McPherson, 1983), and thus community size might moderate any age-gambling relationship.

E. Religion

Lieberman (1988) argued that church endorsement of gambling has given respectability to gambling. Catholics were found to be less likely to disapprove of gambling and more likely to gamble than were Protestants and other religious groups (Stark and Bainbridge, 1985; Lieberman, 1988; Kallick et al., 1979). Kallick et al. (1979) reported 80 percent of Catholics, 77 percent of Jews, and 54 percent of Protestants bet in 1974. Thus, religion might be another moderating variable.

F. Social Worlds of Gambling

Social worlds are defined as groups of individuals bound together by communication and share perspectives on reality (Lindesmith et al., 1975). Strauss (1978) maintained that these social worlds are organized with respect to a specific activity. The social world of gambling is obviously organized around gambling. Moreover, the social worlds of horse and sports betting, and casino gambling were found to be the major factor sustaining members' gambling (Rosecrance, 1988).

Instead of being attracted to the game itself, working-class women in England were found to play bingo to fulfill the need to socialize with other women (Dixey, 1987). They preferred bingo, for most other forms of gambling were dominated by males. Many elderly women reported that their bingo clubs were the only places where they had contacts with others. In his study of betting shops in England, Newman (1968) also found that such gambling provided an affective setting that stressed sociability and group-centeredness. People gamble because of the social relationships they develop through gambling, and this can vary with age. For example, younger people might gamble more on sports to sustain their interests and friendships in this social world. The elderly might gravitate toward games like bingo for companionship and support.

This raises an obvious question: Are people of different ages attracted to different types of gambling? In a 1975 national survey, Kallick et al. (1979) found that lotteries and bingo to be the most popular games in all age categories. In addition to lotteries and bingo, horse racing was also popular among those between 25 and 44 years old, and casinos had the lowest popularity (in comparison with bingo, lotteries, and horse racing) in all age categories. Thus, not only is the relationship between age, gambling behavior in general and specific types of gambling studied in this paper, but also the possible moderation of these relationships is investigated.

METHODS

A. Sample

A proportionally stratified (by county population of the most recent census) simple random sample of 3200 households in Iowa with working telephone numbers was obtained. A target of 1,000 respondents was set. The telephone survey was conducted between April and June, 1989 at the microcomputer laboratory of the Department of Sociology at Iowa State University. Calls were made between 6 p.m. and 10 p.m. from Sunday through Thursday.

Interviewers determined the number of adult females and males in households, and selected the appropriate adult respondent according to a set of random selection tables (the Troldahl-Carter-Bryant selection method) to assure age and gender representativeness of the final sample (Lavrakas, 1987). Call-backs were arranged if the selected respondent was not available. A maximum of seven potential call-backs was set.

B. Data Collection

Out of 1275 eligible respondents contacted, 215 refused to participate in the survey, and 49 could not be reached within the time frame of the study. 1011 respondents completed the interview, representing an overall response rate of 79.3%.

The interview guide measured respondents' gambling behavior. Demographic and socio-economic variables included, social class, gender, community size, marital and employment statues, and religions. Each interview took about 20 to 30 minutes.

C. Dependent Variable

Gambling behavior was defined by the scope, frequency, the amount of money wagered, and the amount of leisure time spent on gambling. Scope refers to the number of gambling types in which a respondent engages. A gambling scope score was constructed by adding across questions about different types of gambling, with the answers "frequently" and "sometimes" coded as one and the "never" response coded as zero. This score was then divided by two to standardize it against other gambling behavior measures discussed below.

Gambling frequency was measured by the question, "Since the New Year (January 1), how frequently have you gambled?" Response categories were coded as follows: (1) less than monthly, (2) monthly, (3) weekly, (4) at least twice a week, and (5) daily. To measure wagering, respondents were asked, "Since the New Year, how much money do you usually bet at one time on games, sports, races, and other kinds of gambling?" Response categories were coded as follows: (0) none, (1) $1 to $4, (2) $5 to $10, (3) $11 to $20, (4) $21 to $50, (5) $51 to $100, and (6) more than $100. "How much of your leisure time do you spend on gambling activities?" was asked to measure respondents' leisure time spent on gambling. Responses were coded as follows: (1) almost none, (2) a little, (3) some, (4) most, and (5) nearly all. These variables — scope, frequency, wagering amount, and amount of time spent on gambling — ranged from 0 to 5 (n=992, mean=1.319, SD=1.172), 0 to 5 (n=991, mean=1.327, SD=1.404), 0 to 6 (n=990, mean=0.774, SD=0.966), and 0 to 5 (n=1003, mean=0.903, SD=0.737), respectively.

The above four components were then used to construct an unweighted additive gambling behavior scale. Since some respondents (27.2%) had been determined to be nongamblers in the beginning section of the interview, they were not asked about the last three components (frequency, wagering, and leisure time) of the gambling behavior scale, and their scores on the scale were automatically coded zero. Scores on this gambling behavior scale ranged from 0 to 21 (n=974, mean=4.302, SD=3.579). The reliability coefficient, Cronbach's Alpha, was found to be 0.82 for the whole sample, and 0.65 for the subsample which contains only gamblers.

D. Independent and Control Variables

The independent variable was age category. The age categories were 18-24 years old, 25-34, 35-44, 45-54, 55-64, 65-74, 75-84, and 85 or older. Control variables included social class (personal yearly income and educational attainment were simultaneously controlled in the analyses), marital status, employment status, size of the community in which the respondent resided, gender, religion (religious preferences and frequency of attendance at religious services were controlled in the analyses).

E. Data Analysis

Since control variables are either ordinal or categorical, Multiple Classification Analysis (MCA), a dummy variable regression analysis, was employed in the study (Andrews et al., 1967). It presents mean scores on gambling behavior for each category of the independent variable (age category) both before and after adjusting for the main effects of control variables. Multiple Classification Analysis presents five indicators of the degree and significance of association between the dependent (the Gambling Behavior Scale) and independent variables (ten-year age categories). The first is ETA^2, indicating the proportion of variance in the dependent variable that is explained by the independent variable without controlling for other variables. The second indicator is called $BETA^2$, and can be interpreted just like ETA^2, except that it has been adjusted for the effects of the control variables. The third indicator, R^2, is interpreted just like regular regression analysis, that is, proportion of variance in gambling behavior scale explained by all variables included in the model. The fourth indicator, p-value(age), indicates the probability that there is no relationship between age and gambling behavior. The fifth indicator, p-value(model) or *, indicates the probability that age and other control variables are not related to gambling behavior.

The first step was to analyze the zero-order relationship between age and gambling behavior. In the second step, possible collective effects of control variables (social class, marital status, employment status, gender, community size, and religion) on the relationship between age and gambling behavior were analyzed. In the third step, the age-gambling relationship was investigated when controlling for different types of gambling. In the last step, participation rates of different age categories in different types of gambling were studied.

RESULTS

A. Zero-Order Relationship

Gambling-behavior scale scores decrease with age category (Table 1). The oldest (85 years old or older) and the youngest age category (18-24 years old) have the lowest and the highest score, respectively. Gambling behavior decreases gradually from the youngest category to the 55-64 age category, and then begins to decline more rapidly with the older age categories. Age itself accounts for 0.122 of the variance in gambling behavior. The p-value of age is less than 0.001.

TABLE 1

Mean Scores of Gambling Behavior by Different Age Categories (N=967, Mean=4.31, R^2=0.122, p(age)<0.001)

Age Category (N)	Mean	ETA^2
18-24 (55)	5.89	
25-34 (201)	5.63	
35-44 (196)	4.83	
45-54 (134)	4.39	
55-64 (150)	4.16	
65-74 (130)	3.01	
75-84 (78)	1.78	
≥85 (23)	0.95	
		0.123

B. Effects of Control Variables

Control variables are social class, marital status, employment status, gender, community size and religion. Results from a full model including all the above control variables are presented in Table 2. After collectively adjusting for all control variables, the pattern of decline in gambling behavior across age categories still exists, although differences in group means are less distinct (see Figure 1). The gambling behavior scores of people 18 to 44 years old become smaller when controlling for other variables, whereas scores of those

65 years old or over increase after controlling for other variables. Scores of those between 45 and 64 years old do not change much after adjustment. The explanatory power of age on gambling behavior significantly declines from 0.11 (ETA^2) to 0.05 ($BETA^2$) after adjustment. The same pattern was also found in separate analyses for each control variable.

TABLE 2

Mean Scores of Gambling Behavior of Different Age Categories when Controlling for Social Class, Marital Status, Employment Status, Gender, Community Size, and Religion (N=861, Mean=4.43, R^2=0.248*, p(age)<0.005)

Age Category	Unadjusted Mean	ETA^2	Adjusted Mean	$BETA^2$
18-24	5.89		5.46	
25-34	5.61		5.33	
35-44	4.96		4.75	
45-54	4.37		4.28	
55-64	4.26		4.29	
65-74	3.13		3.59	
75-84	2.04		2.78	
≥85	1.08		2.14	
		0.11		0.05

*Significant at 0.001 level

C. Types of Gambling

The final step was to explore the robustness of the previously found age-gambling relationship for different types of gambling. A general decline in gambling behavior with age may oversimplify this relationship, for gambling behavior may shift across gambling types with age. Gambling types included betting on lotteries, games played at home, games played with others in public places, sports in which the person participates, spectator sporting events, horse or dog races, games in casinos, speculation on stocks and commodities, bingo in public places, and dog or cock fights. Table 3 presents mean scores of gambling behavior for different age categories when controlling for different types of gambling.

FIGURE 1

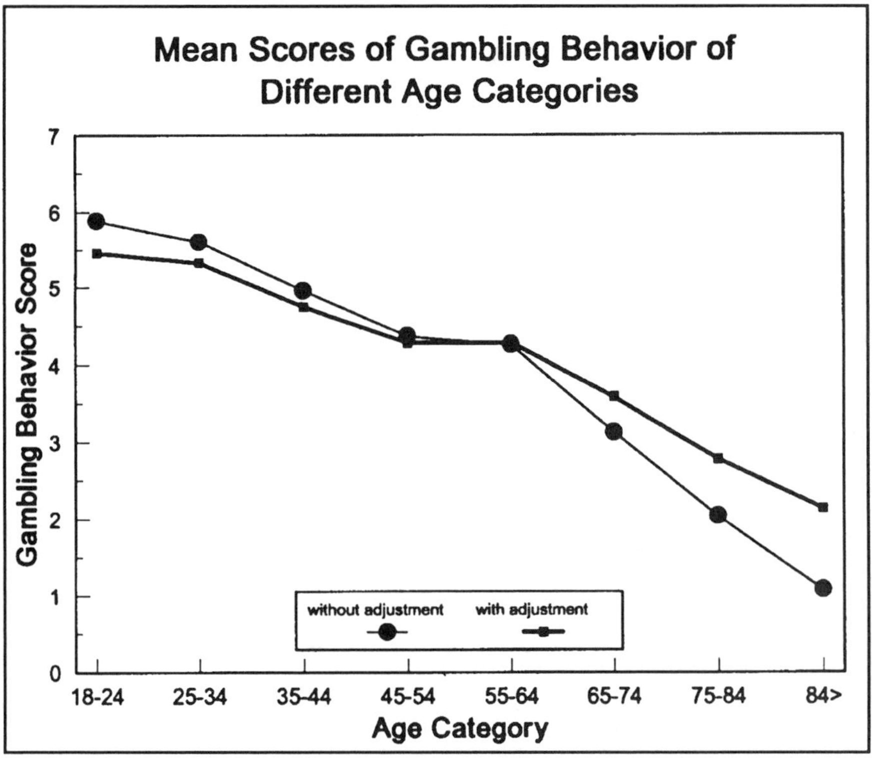

In general, younger people have higher scores on gambling behavior than do older people. The youngest age category has the highest gambling behavior mean score even when the effects of types of gambling are controlled. Nevertheless, gambling behavior scores decrease for those between 18 and 44 years old, but increase for those 55 years old or over after controlling for forms of gambling. The differences in gambling behavior between age categories are much less noticeable than they were before the control, and those aged between 45 and 64 deviate slightly from the previously observed trend. After adjustments are made for gambling types, age does not account for any detectable variance in gambling behavior. Instead of a general decline in gambling behavior with age, gambling behavior by age varies for different types of gambling.

TABLE 3

Mean Scores of Gambling Behavior by Different Age Categories when Controlling for Types of Gambling (N=967, Mean=4.31, R^2=0.707*, p(age)=0.213)

Age Category	Unadjusted Mean	ETA^2	Adjusted Mean	$BETA^2$
18-24	5.89		4.74	
25-34	5.63		4.48	
35-44	4.83		4.19	
45-54	4.39		4.38	
55-64	4.16		4.43	
65-74	3.01		4.13	
75-84	1.78		4.03	
≥85	0.95		3.67	
		0.12		0.004

*Significant at 0.001 level

Table 4 and Figure 2 present the percentages of respondents in different age categories by different types of gambling. In all age categories, lotteries have the highest percentage of participation, whereas dog or cock fights have the lowest. Types of gambling that showed declining participation with age are lotteries, betting money on games played at home, betting money on games played with others, betting on sports the individual played with others, and betting on spectator sporting events. Games that did not follow this pattern were betting on horse or dog races, casinos, investment speculations, dog or cock fights, and bingo. Some increased initially with age but decreased with older-age categories (horse and dog races, casinos, and investment speculations); and some decreased initially with age but increased with older-age categories (bingo). Among the two younger age categories (18-34 years old), betting on lotteries, games played at home, games in public places, spectator sports,

TABLE 4

Percentage of Respondents in Different Age Categories Participating in Different Types of Gambling

Age Categories	Types of Gambling									
	Lottery	Games in Public	Games at Home	Sport They Play	Sport Event	Horse or Dog Race	Casino	Stock or Commodity	Bingo	Dog or Cock Fight
18-24	71	42	33	20	38	29	16	9	36	7
25-34	75	33	30	18	36	36	18	20	25	4
35-44	62	24	18	15	32	36	24	23	22	5
45-54	57	13	11	10	18	32	24	25	19	9
55-64	49	19	12	9	19	25	23	19	19	7
65-74	33	8	10	7	7	17	19	16	27	4
≥75	19	9	5	9	4	7	7	10	14	0
N	998	996	997	999	999	996	998	995	996	998

FIGURE 2

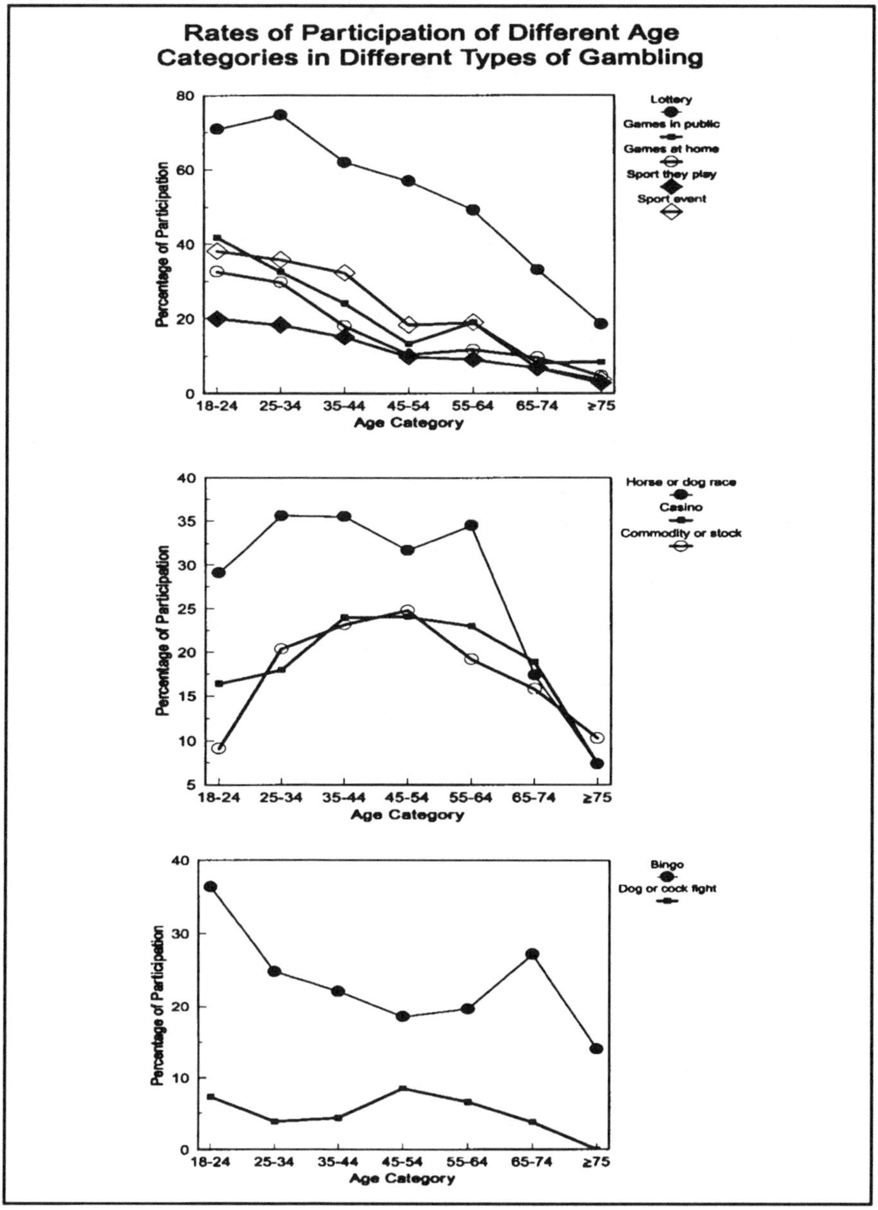
Rates of Participation of Different Age Categories in Different Types of Gambling
Percentage of Participation
Age Category
18-24
25-34
35-44
45-54
55-64
65-74
≥75
Lottery
Games in public
Games at home
Sport they play
Sport event
Horse or dog race
Casino
Commodity or stock
Bingo
Dog or cock fight

horse and dog races, and bingo were the most popular games. The middle-aged (35-64 years old) participated the most in betting on lotteries, horse or dog races, betting in casinos, and speculating on stocks and commodities. Elderly respondents were attracted to lotteries and bingo.

DISCUSSION

The results show a negative relationship between age categories and gambling behavior at both the zero-order level and when controlling for other correlates of gambling. The hypotheses of the age stratification, anomie, and Veblenian theories on gambling were not supported. These hypotheses predicted a parabolic relationship between age and gambling behavior. The data reveal a clear linear decline in gambling behavior with age category, however, before and after controlling for social class.

The results of the full model, which controlled for the effects of social class, gender, marital status, employment status, community size, and religion, did not negate the negative relationship between age and gambling behavior. However, the explanatory power of age weakened significantly, implying the presence of interaction effects among these control variables, which have not been explored in this study. The 65 or older (the 1916-25 and previous cohorts) were found to gamble less than those under 65 (the 1926-35 and younger cohorts). That is, while following the trend of the general age decline in gambling, age categories 65 or above seemed to have a much lower tendency to gamble than did the rest of the population.

Results suggest both aging and cohort effects on gambling behavior. The general decline in gambling with age can be interpreted to result from less experimentation for self-identity with age, a decline in the need for self-presentation with age, an historical increase in the social acceptance of gambling, and the need to maintain previous life styles. In the process of aging, as people accumulate life experiences, and as their self-concepts become more stable, they would become less likely to experiment and turn to gambling for self-presentation. From the cohort-effect perspective and continuity theory, individuals tend to maintain previous life styles, the historical increase in social acceptance of gambling since the turn of the century would translate into a general decline in gambling with chronological age. This is due to each consecutive cohort being socialized into a less conservative attitude toward gambling than the previous one, and their desire to keep the same gambling life style acquired earlier in their lives.

The sharp decline in gambling behavior for those 65 years or older suggests both aging and cohort effects. With aging, gambling decreases as the elderly perceive a loss of intellectual functions, which are required in most forms of gambling. They exit from casinos, horse racing, and financial speculation of the middle-age to concentrate on bingo and lotteries. The harsh economic situations of the Great Depression in the 1930s might have socialized the older cohorts to be more frugal, and to gamble less than the later-born cohorts (persons 64 years of age or younger). Bingo and lotteries are less financially risky than horse betting, casinos and financial speculations.

The effect of age became less significant when controlling for participation in different types of gambling. People of different ages have differential participation rates in different types of gambling. This is the moderating effect of the social-worlds-of-gambling hypothesis on the age-gambling relationship. Generally, those aged between 18 and 24 had the highest participation rate in five of the ten forms of gambling studied. They also had the highest score on the scope component of the gambling behavior scale, indicating they engaged in the largest number of types of gambling (Table 4). This may reflect the need to experiment with different roles in search of self-identity during the adolescent years (18-24 years of age). Adolescents experiment with types of gambling that are immediately available or related to their interests, like games played at home, sports they play, sporting events observed, lotteries, and bingo. The greater financial requirements (such as larger bets and long-distance travel), which most adolescents lack, keep games like casinos and horse racing out of reach for most adolescents.

With more financial resources, the young adults and the middle-aged (25-64 years old) shift from sports, home games, and bingo to games which are more risky and financially more rewarding, like casinos, investment speculations, and horse racing. Elderly (65 years or older) participated the least in all types of gambling, with the exception of bingo. The elderly are attracted to bingo, which provides a friendly setting for social relationships.

Although gambling behavior declines with age, people do not necessarily stop gambling as they age. Rather, it appears that they withdraw from multiple types of gambling and concentrate on more limited gambling activity. Thus, the shift into casinos, horse betting and financial speculation with middle age, and then into bingo for the elderly. As the American population ages, gambling in general should decrease, but the decrease will not be uniform across all forms of gambling. The popularity of games attractive to the elderly may actually increase in the future, as games that attract the young may decline.

REFERENCES

Abt, V., Smith, J.F. and Christiansen, E.M. (1985). *The Business of Risk: Commercial Gambling in Mainstream America.* Lawrence, KS: University of Kansas Press.

Andrews, F.M., Morgan, J.M. and Sonquist, J.A. (1967). *Multiple Classification Analysis.* Ann Arbor, MI: Institute of Social Research, University of Michigan.

Boyd, J.W. and Dowd, J.J. (1988). The diffuseness of age. *Social Behavior*, 3, 85-103.

Campbell, A. (1971). Politics through the life cycle. *The Gerontologist*, 11, 112-118.

Clarke, J. (1987). The paradoxical effects of aging and health. *Journal of Gerontological Social Work*, 10(3/4), 3-20.

Cumming, E. and Henry, W.E. (1961). *Growing Old: The Process of Disengagement.* New York, NY: Basic Books.

Dixey, R. (1987). It's a great feeling when you win: Women and bingo. *Leisure Studies*, 6, 199-214.

Cutler, S.J. and Kaufman, R.L. (1975). Cohort changes in political attitudes: Tolerance of ideological nonconformity. *Public Opinion Quarterly*, 39, 69-81.

Downes, D.M., Davies, B.P., David, M.E. and Stone, P. (1976). *Gambling, Work, and Leisure.* London, England: Routledge and Kegan Paul.

Erikson, E. (1963). *Childhood and Society.* New York, NY: Norton.

Erikson, E. (1968). Generativity and ego integrity. In Bernice Neugarten (ed.), *Middle Age and Aging.* Chicago, IL: University of Chicago Press.

Erikson, E. (1982). *The Life Cycle Completed.* New York, NY: Norton.

Fact Research Inc. (1976). Gambling in Perspective. In Fact Research Inc. (ed.), *Gambling in America: Appendix 1*. Washington, D.C.: Commission on the Review of the National Policy Toward Gambling.

Felton, B.J. (1987). Cohort variation in happiness: Some hypotheses and exploratory analyses. *International Journal of Aging and Human Development*, 25(1), 27-42.

Finn, P. and Braff, B.W.E. (1986). Perception of the risk of an accident by young and older drivers. *Accident Analysis and Prevention*, 18(4), 289-298.

Fletcher, C.N. and Lorenz, F.O. (1985). Structural influences on the relationship between objective and subjective indicators. *Social Indicators Research*, 16, 333-345.

Foner, A. (1988). Age inequalities: Are they epiphenomena of the class system? In M.W. Riley (ed.), *Social Change and the Life Course*, vol. 1. Newbury Park, CA: Sage Publications.

Frey, J.H. (1984). Gambling: A sociological review. *The Annals of the American Academy of Political and Social Science*, 474, 107-121.

Goffman, E. (1967). *Interaction Ritual: Essays on Face-to-Face Behavior*. New York: Anchor Books.

Gove, W.R., Ortega, S.T. and Style, C.B. (1989). The maturational and role perspectives on aging and self through the adult years: An empirical evaluation. *American Journal of Sociology*, 94, 1117-1145.

Herman, R.K. (1967). Gambling as work: A sociological study of the racetrack. In R.K. Herman (ed.), *Gambling*. New York, NY: Harper and Row.

Herzog, R., Rodgers, W. and Woodworth, J. (1982). *Subjective Well-being Among Different Age Groups*. Ann Arbor, MI: Institute of Social Research, University of Michigan.

Hogan, R. (1986). The working class gamble: Frontier class structure and social control. *Research in law, deviance and social control*, 8, 131-148.

Holtgraves, T.M. (1988). Gambling as self-presentation. *Journal of Gambling Behavior*, 4, 78-91.

Hraba, J., Mok, W. and Huff, D. (1991). Lottery play and problem gambling. *Journal of Gambling Studies*, 6, 355-378.

Hugick, L. (1989). Gallup's mirror of America: Gambling on the rise as lotteries lead the way. *The Gallup Report, Report No. 285*. Princeton, NJ: Gallup Organization, Inc.

Kallick, M., Suits, D., Dielman, T. and Hybels, J. (1979). Gambling participation. In M. Kallick, D. Suits, T. Dielman and J. Hybels (eds.), *A Survey of American Gambling Attitudes and Behavior*. Ann Arbor, MI: Survey Research Center, Institute for Social Research, University of Michigan.

Khullar, G.S. and Wyatt, B. (1989). Criminal victimization of the elderly. *Free Inquiry in Creative Sociology*, 17(1), 101-105.

Kiecolt, K.J. (1987). Age and political sophistication: A cohort analysis. *Journal of Political and Military Sociology*, 15(1), 47-59.

Lachman, M.E. (1989). Personality and aging at the crossroads: Beyond stability versus changes. In K.W. Schaie and C. Schooler (eds.), *Social Structure and Aging: Psychological Process*. Hillsdale, NJ: Lawrence Erlbaum Association.

Lavrakas, P.J. (1987). *Telephone Survey Methods: Sampling, Selection, and Supervision*. Newbury Park, CA: Sage Publications.

Li, W.L. and Smith, M.H. (1976). The propensity to gamble: Some structural determinants. In W.R. Eadington (ed.), *Gambling and Society*. Springfield, IL: Charles C. Thomas Publishers.

Lieberman, L. (1988). *A Social Typology of Gambling Behavior: Suggestions for a Short Screening Device*. New York, NY: National Council on Compulsive Gambling.

Lindesmith, A., Strauss, A. and Denzin, N. (1975). *Social Psychology*. Hillsdale, IL: Dryden Press.

Lindgren, H.E., Youngs, G.A. Jr., McDonald, T.D., Klenon, D.J. and Schriner, E.C. (1987). The impact of gender on gambling attitudes and behavior. *Journal of Gambling Behavior*, 3, 155-167.

Lorence, J. (1987). Age differences in work involvement. *Work and Occupations,* 14(4), 533-557.

Lorence, J. and Mortimer, J.T. (1985). Job involvement through the life course: A panel study of three age groups. *American Sociological Review*, 50, 618-638.

Loscocco, K.A. and Kalleberg, A.L. (1988). Age and the meaning of work in the United States and Japan. *Social Forces*, 67(2), 337-356.

Maguire, J.A. (1987). Against the odds: The survival of English working class gambling since 1800. *ARENA Review*, 11, 37-42.

Matthews, M.L. and Moran, A.R. (1986). Age differences in male drivers' perception of accident risk: The role of perceived driving ability. *Accident Analysis and Prevention*, 18(4), 299-313.

McPherson, B.D. (1983). *Aging as a Social Process: An Introduction to Individual and Population Aging*. Toronto, Canada: Butterworth.

Mohai, P. and Twight, B.W. (1987). Age and environmentalism: An elaboration of the Buttel model using national survey evidence. *Social Science Quarterly*, 68(4), 798-815.

Newman, O. (1968). The sociology of the betting shop. *British Journal of Sociology*, 19, 17-33.

Osgood, N. and Sontz, A. (1989). *The Science and Practice of Gerontology: A Multi-disciplinary Guide*. Westport, CT: Greenwood Press.

Penk, W.E. 1969. Age changes and correlates of internal-external locus of control scale. *Psychological Reports*, 25:856.

Riley, M.W. (1988). On the significance of age in sociology. In M.W. Riley (ed.), *Social Change and the Life Course*, vol. 1. Newbury Park, CA: Sage Publications.

Rosecrance, J.D. (1988). *Gambling Without Guilt: The Legitimation of American Past Time*. Pacific Grove, CA: Brooks/Cole Publishers.

Schneider, N. (1988). Locus of control as it relates to powerlessness, gender, age and victimization. *Free Inquiry in Creative Sociology*, 16(1), 99-102.

Schulz, R. (1986). Successful aging: Balancing primary and secondary control. *American Psychological Association Newsletter*, 3, 2-3.

Shavit, Y. and Rattner, A. (1988). Age, crime, and the early life course. *American Journal of Sociology*, 93(6), 1457-1470.

Shehan, C., Burg, M. and Rexroat, C. (1986). Depression and the social dimensions of the full-time housewife role. *The Sociological Quarterly*, 27(3), 403-421.

Sheley, J.F. and Smith, M.D. (1988). Age composition and alternative explanations of crime: Directions of theory and research. *Sociological Spectrum*, 8, 237-255.

Smith, M.D. (1986). The era of increased violence in the United States: Age, period, or cohort effect? *The Sociological Quarterly*, 27(2), 239-251.

Sommers, S. and Kosmitzki, C. (1988). Emotion and social context: An American-German comparison. *British Journal of Social Psychology*, 27, 35-49.

Stark, R. and Bainbridge, W.S. (1985). The religious economy. In R. Stark and W.S. Bainbridge (eds.), *The Future of Religion: Secularization, Revival and Cult Formation.* Berkeley, CA: University of California Press.

Steffensmeier, D., Allan, E., Harer, M. and Streifel, C. (1989). Age and the distribution of crime. *American Journal of Sociology*, 94(4), 803-831.

Strauss, A. (1978). A social world perspective. In N.K. Denzin (ed.), *Studies in Symbolic Interaction*, vol. 1. Greenwich, CT: JAI Press.

Turner, B.F. and Adams, C.G. (1988). Reported change in preferred sexual activity over the adult years. *The Journal of Sex Research*, 25(2), 289-303.

Veblen, T. (1899). *The Theory of the Leisure Class.* New York, NY: The Viking Press.

Williams, R. and Wirths, G. (1965). *Lives Through the Years.* New York, NY: Atherton.

Zola, I.K. (1963). Observations on gambling in lower class setting. *Social Problems*, 10, 353-361.

Scales of Risk-Taking — Structure and Interaction of Risk Activities and Dispositions

Johannes C. Brengelmann

This study reports on the construction of questionnaire scales of risk-taking and examines the interaction of risk activities and dispositions. Pleasure is an important aspect of risk-taking.

With factor analysis, daily activities can be reduced to:

- moderation, a composite of all low-risk activities;
- risk-taking/consumption, which combines risk-taking in recreation and sports with luxury-style eating and drinking; and
- gaming, a conglomerate of games played with and without money.

Dispositions form two major dimensions: risk-taking pleasure and risk-taking ambivalence. Dispositions are independently acting principles of order in that they responsibly organize activities, either in a positive, pleasureful manner, or in an ambivalent, aversive manner.

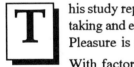

Dispositions for risk-taking are known to operate universally. They control personal economy and entrepreneurial enterprises as much as leadership and kindred social interactions. Finally, they may also control disorders such as stress disorder and pathological gambling, which are reducible to dispositions instead of activities.

All results discussed in this study are reported in detail, but in German, in Brengelmann (1989) and Brengelmann (1991).

THE UNIVERSE OF RISK-TAKING ACTIVITIES: A BRIEF LOOK

At the beginning of our current series of experiments on risk-taking activities and dispositions, we employed a short questionnaire, the essential content of which is shown in Table 1. This questionnaire is characterized by three important features.

TABLE 1

The six activity areas consisting of 14 high- and low- risk activities, each of which is scored for 6 attributes		
Cultural activities • serious • popular • continuing education	Recreation/sports • high-risk • low-risk	Games of skill • requiring concentration • relaxing
Eating/drinking • luxury style • middle-class style • simple	Investment • speculative • cautious	Money games • casino gambling • low-risk slot machines
Attributes Scored: Frequency Initiative	Stimulating Boring Valuable Valueless	Scoring: 14 activities 6 categories = 84 scores

Firstly, the fourteen activities listed vary greatly as to the presumed degree of risk-taking involved. Secondly, some activities are obviously concerned with pleasure rather than risk such as, for example, the cultural activities and the enjoyment of eating and drinking. Thirdly, the activities are scored with regard to the frequency of occurrence, elicitation of initiative (conation), positive and negative emotions (affect), and value (valuable versus valueless), i.e., cognition. The triad of conation, affect, and cognition dates back to Plato.

As a result, the administration of this questionnaire yielded the differentiated factorial structure shown in Figure 1. It divides the universe of daily activities into three basic dimensions.

FIGURE 1

Three dimensions of risk-taking: moderation, risk-taking/consumption and gaming

(Figures represent factor loadings)

Moderation		*Risk-taking/consumption*		*Gaming*	
Moderation	0.72	Luxury consumption	0.79	Money games	0.87
Culture	0.72	Risk-taking in recreation/sports	0.74	Games of skill	0.64
Saving	0.55				

Primary factors: 5 for frequency, 5 for initiative, 12 for evaluations
Major dispositional terms: saving, moderation, pleasure, gaming, speculating, risk-taking

The first dimension, termed *moderation*, comprises items and factors of low-risk value, including cultural activities of any kind, cautious use of money, and normal forms of food consumption and recreation. The second dimension, termed *risk-taking/consumption,* combines high-risk recreation and sports with luxury consumption.

The third dimension, simply called *gaming*, is concerned with games requiring money and/or skill. These dimensions reflect broad areas of activities, as well as pleasures. Therefore, they can be expected to possess many other correlates of risk-taking and/or pleasure, such as those discussed in the following.

Some of the correlates of risk-taking and pleasure are listed in Table 2. It is clear from this list that the three risk/pleasure types maintain their differential effects in a variety of ways. A German version of Zuckerman's Sensation-Seeking Scales correlates highly with risk-taking and gaming, with the exception of inner stimulus-seeking. The inner world does not seem pertinent. The same is true for cautious and speculative investment.

TABLE 2

Typicial correlates of risk-taking/pleasure dimensions in dealing with money and goods

Behavioral correlates	Dimensions of risk-taking/pleasure		
	Moderation	Risk-taking	Gaming
Risk-/sensation-seeking			
• daredevilry	0	+++	+++
• thrill-seeking	0	++	+++
• stimulation-seeking	0	+	0
Cautious investment	0	+++	+++
Speculative investment	0	+++	++
Purchasing behavior			
• insistence on quality goods	+++	0	0
• preference for luxury goods	0	+++	0
• careful use of money	++	--	0
Dealings with money			
• pleasure in saving	+++	+	+
• stinginess	+++	---	0
• frequent borrower	0	++	0
Attitude toward money			
• riches are dirty	-	0	0
• money solves problems	+++	0	0
• prosperity is a life goal	+	---	--
Old age security	++	0	0

Rough degrees of significance:

0	not significant	++/--	1%
+/-	5%	+++/---	0.1%

Moderation does not participate in these activities either positively or negatively. This confirms other results to the effect that moderation is not aversive to risk-taking and pleasure. Also, in our experience, risk-taking is not the opposite of aversion to risk and hedonia is not the opposite of anhedonia. Consequently, these two dimensions should be treated independently.

The remaining sections of Table 2 confirm the conservative nature of moderation, as indicated by the stinginess in dealing with money, the insistence on quality, and the preoccupation with old age security. At the same time, people in the moderation category accept money as a tool in solving their problems and consider prosperity to be a life goal.

The gaming people, on the other hand, are practically devoid of such conservative characteristics, although they frequently deal with money. Their goal may be gambling *per se* rather than accumulation of assets. Risk-takers occupy a middle position and are characterized by their strong rejection of stinginess and prosperity.

It can be concluded that the three dimensions of risk-taking are clearly identifiable and possess many correlates in daily activities, the scope of which has yet to be ascertained.

THE STRUCTURE AND FUNCTION OF DISPOSITIONS

Moderation, risk-taking, and gaming are dispositional terms. As a rule, activities do not "group themselves" on the basis of their content. Moderation, for example, combines various cultural activities, moderate forms of consumption, and thriftiness, as well as low-risk levels in recreation and sports. No activity concept could justifiably represent all of these things, but functional concepts such as moderation can do this very well.

This led us to develop a questionnaire about dispositions. Table 3 lists the twenty-four dispositions towards risk-taking, or to be more specific, regarding behavior in three situations: high-risk, gain, and loss. They represent primary factors obtained by principal component analysis followed by varimax rotation. Via a second-order analysis (see, for example, Figure 2) two third-order dimensions of risk-taking pleasure and risk-taking ambivalence were obtained.

As Table 3 shows, the positive risk-taker retains his composure during risks, displays positive emotions after a gain, and remains ready for risks after a loss, whereas the ambivalent risk-taker feels "fed-up" while taking a risk, has coping problems even after a gain, and feels stress in the face of a loss. Another look at Table 3 reveals that none of the pleasureful risk-taking dispositions correlates negatively with any of the three activities shown — games of skill, money games, or high-risk recreation/sports — and none of the ambivalent risk-taking dispositions correlates positively with any of these activities.

FIGURE 2

Dispositions towards Risk-taking as a function of high risk, gain, and loss. Behavioral dispositions remain stable, emotional dispositons fluctuate.

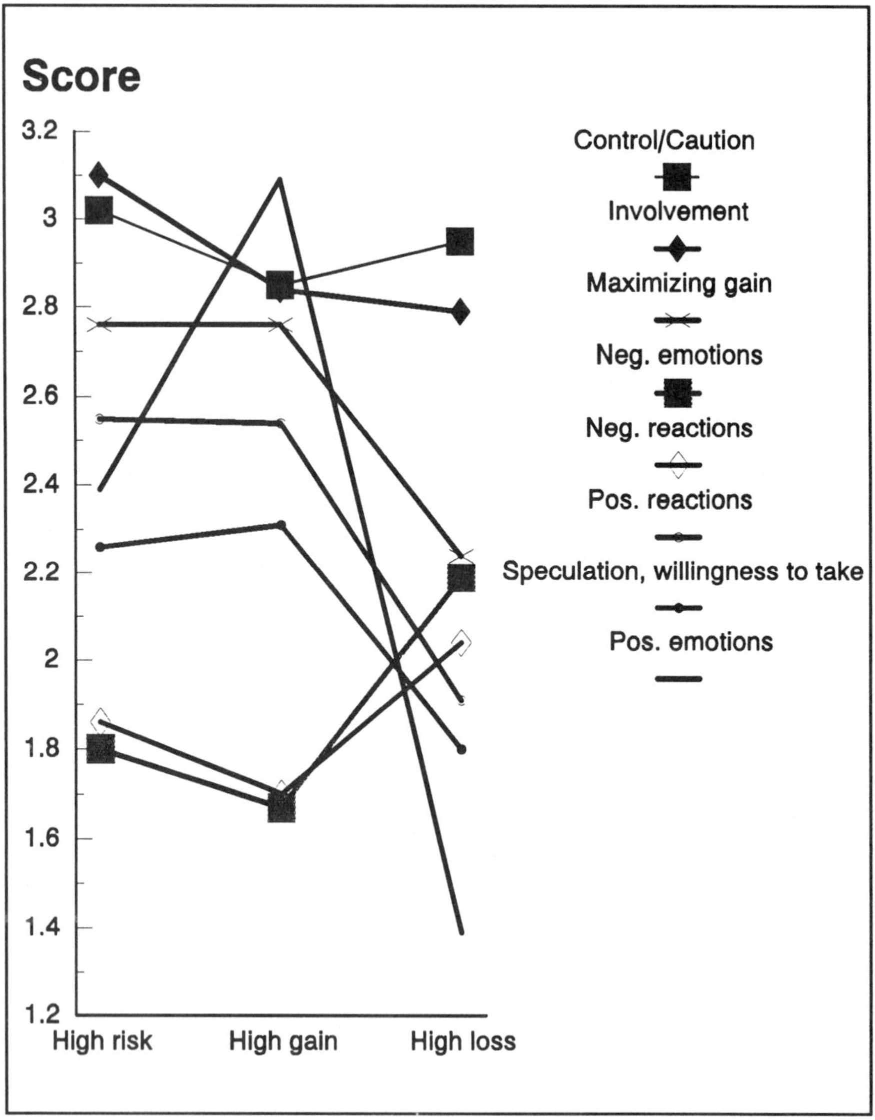

TABLE 3

Correlates of two basic dimensions of Risk-taking dispositions, pleasure and ambivalence, with Risk-taking activities

Disposition rank	24 Dispositions towards risk-taking (primary factors)	Situation	Risk-taking activities		
			Games of skill	Money games	High-risk recreation/sports
	Risk-taking pleasure (tertiary factors)				
1	remain ready for risks	L	++	+++	+++
2	positive emotions	G	+	+++	++
7	composure	R	++	0	+++
9	pleasure in speculation	G	0	+++	+
10	excitement	R	+	+++	0
11	add new risks	L	+	0	++
14	involvement	R	0	+++	0
18	friendly risk attitude	G	0	0	+
19	composure	L	+	0	+
21	compensate for loss	L	0	+	+
22	maximizing gains	R	0	+++	0
23	positive emotions	R	0	++	0
	Risk-taking ambivalence (tertiary factors)				
3	fed-up	R	-	0	---
4	negative emotions	R	-	0	---
5	ill-humored	R	--	0	---
6	coping problems	G	0	-	---
8	stressed motivation	L	--	0	---
12	negative emotions	L	0	0	---
13	cutting expenses	L	0	0	---
15	fear of problems	R	0	0	---
16	lack of influence	R	0	0	---
17	relying on providence	G	0	0	---
20	feeling exploited	L	0	0	---
24	reacting furiously	L	0	0	--

R = high risk
G = high gain
L = high loss

Significance level:	
0	not significant
+/-	5.0%
++/--	1.0%
+++/---	0.1%

Furthermore, the three activities themselves are separated by type of disposition. The high-risk sportsman scores well as regards risk-taking (dispositions 1, 7 and 11) and excels in rejecting any kind of negative or ambivalent disposition towards risks. This is apparently the hardy type of explorer or leatherneck. The person who likes money games scores higher with regard to emotions and pleasures (dispositions 2, 9, 10, 14 and 23) as well as with regard to maximizing gains (disposition 22). This is the excitable pleasure type. The profile for skill games is relatively flat and uneventful.

Figure 2 completes the picture by showing eight second-order dispositions and how they affect one's response to imagined high-risk, gain, and loss situations. The following two points should be emphasized. Firstly, the scores are highest for the factors *control/caution* and *risk involvement*, followed by *maximizing gains* and *speculation*. They control the game, so to speak. The emotional elements score much lower. And secondly, the behavioral dispositions are much more stable in all of these three conditions of risk, gain, and loss than the emotional reactions, which vary widely. This observation is important regarding success in coping with risky situations. It will become clear in the later discussion of how persons with stress disorders react.

LEADERSHIP CORRELATES OF RISK-TAKING DISPOSITIONS

Dispositions operate with about equal force in different risk situations. But they also vary greatly as to their efficacy in coping with these situations. Therefore it can be assumed that their effects can also be demonstrated in demanding social situations as, for example, in the conduct of leadership behavior, where risky decisions must be made under uncertain conditions. Evidence for this is found in Table 4.

Here, the significance of the relationship between risk-taking dispositions and the four leadership scales is seen to vary considerably. It is greater for person- than for problem-oriented leadership. There is also a considerable variation in significance levels between the dispositions. The emotional dispositions have been omitted because of a lack of significance. The three factors of most importance for both assertion and power appear to be speculation, willingness to take risks, and maximizing gains, in that order. Involvement, control/caution and positive reactions trail behind. This order is the reverse of that obtained for the "entrepreneurial" risks (shown in Figure 2). Our conclusion is that the sphere of activity of risk-taking dispositions covers a universe of situations with no boundaries. A final example of risk-taking follows.

TABLE 4

Positive Risk-taking dispositions correlate positively with leadership. The leadership questionnaire consists of 4 secondary and 15 primary scales.

	Leadership			
	Person-oriented		Problem-oriented	
Risk-taking dispositions (second-order factors)	*Assertion*	*Power*	*Problem-solving*	*Theory-orented*
Involvement	++		+	
Control/caution	+	++	+	
Positive reactions (Winner's pose)	+	+++		+
Maximizing gains	+++	+++	+	+
Speculation	++++	++++	++	++
Willingness to take risks	++++	+++	+	+

Significance level: 5% + 0.1% +++
1% ++ 0.01% ++++

RISK-TAKING DISPOSITIONS IN HEALTHY AND ILL PEOPLE

Dispositions affect the preparation, implementation, and utilization of activities. It is known that stress reactions contribute to behavioral inefficacy, as is the case in the famous Type A. It is further known that the balance between effective and ineffective behaviors is of paramount importance in illness, whether of the medical or psychiatric kind. The question to be answered, however, is exactly what kind of strategies are employed by healthy and ill people. One answer to this question is provided in Table 5. This table shows the differences in the risk-taking strategies of a group of 224 healthy persons and a group of 29 psychosomatic stress patients with similar socioeconomic characteristics.

The table can be read as follows. Healthy persons retain their composure in high-risk situations, they like to speculate after gains, and they are ready to

TABLE 5

Dispositional differences between healthy and ill people. Healthy persons use positive risk-taking strategies. Patients with stress disorders prefer negative strategies.

Disposition rank	24 Dispositions towards risk-taking (primary factors)	Situation	Level of significance
	Risk-taking pleasure: Effective reactions of healthy persons		
7	composure	R	+++
21	compensate for loss	L	+++
1	ready for new risks	L	+++
19	composure	L	++
11	add new risks	L	++
9	pleasure in speculation	G	++
2	positive emotions	G	+
23	positive emotions	R	+
Dispositions excitement (R10), involvement (R14), friendly risk attitude (G18) and maximizing gains (R22): correlation positive but not significant			
	Risk-taking ambivalence: Ineffective reactions of stress patients		
3	feeling fed-up	R	---
5	ill-humored	R	---
24	reacting furiously	L	---
6	coping problems	G	---
12	negative emotions	L	---
17	relying on providence	G	---
8	stressed motivation	L	--
20	feeling exploited	L	-
15	fear of problems	R	-
13	cutting expenses	L	-
16	lack of influence	R	-
Disposition negative emotions (4R): correlation negative but not significant			

R = high risk
G = high gain
L = high loss

Significance level:
+/- 5.0%
++/-- 1.0%
+++/--- 0.1%

compensate for their losses. They are successful risk-takers. Stress patients are fed-up in high-risk situations, have coping problems even after gains, and cut their expenses after a loss instead of boosting their efforts. This is ineffective behavior, leading to economic and psychological breakdown.

Similar investigations could be carried out to advantage with pathological gamblers in order to identify their risk-taking strategies. If similar differences were obtained, the pathology of gambling could be explained in terms of distinct behavioral strategies instead of vague concepts such as over-indulgence in gambling or seduction by the illusory expectation of gains. It is this author's conclusion that pathological gambling is a matter of personality, not of a gambling career.

REFERENCES

Brengelmann, J.C. (1989). *Unternehmerverhalten und Unternehmensqualität.* Zurich, Munich: Varia Press.

Brengelmann, J.C. (1991). *Spiellust und Risikolust.* Zurich, Munich: Varia Press.

A Study of the Cognitive Activity of Fruit Machine Players

Mark Griffiths

A number of studies have shown that there may be a strong cognitive bias involved in gambling behavior, especially in relation to continued gambling despite persistent losses. It has been reported by Griffiths (1988a, 1988b) that regular players of fruit machines believe their actions to be, in part, skillful. Furthermore, the recent introduction of specialist play features (e.g., "nudge" and "hold" buttons) may stimulate the illusion of control (Langer, 1975) through personal involvement and familiarity of a particular machine, in addition to these being perceived as elements of skill.

This study examined the cognitive activities of 60 individuals (30 regular players and 30 non-regular players) while playing fruit machines in a real amusement arcade. This was performed using the "thinking aloud method" (Ericsson and Simon, 1980) in which subjects are asked to verbalize all thoughts they have during the specified activity without censoring their content. The study also examined whether the "skill" involved in the playing of fruit machines is "actual" or "perceived" by recording how long regular players could stay on the machines (in both time and number of plays) than novice players. Subjective measures were also collected using a post-experimental semi-structured interview questionnaire.

THEORIES OF COGNITIVE ACTIVITY OF FRUIT MACHINE PLAYERS

It seems unlikely that any one theory can fully explain persistent gambling, and, as a consequence, the best conceptual models of gambling are those which take an eclectic approach (e.g., Brown, 1986). Although gambling behavior can be viewed from psychoanalytic, behavioral and biological frameworks, it can also be viewed from a cognitive standpoint.

A single theory of the cognitive psychology of gambling is as unlikely as other theoretical approaches in explaining persistent gambling. However, a number of recent studies show there may be a strong cognitive bias involved in gambling behavior (e.g., Gilovich, 1983) and that gamblers may suffer from illusion of control (Langer, 1975) and other erroneous perceptions, i.e., reference to factors other than chance (Ladouceur and Gaboury, 1988). Psychological variables such as belief in luck and skill are also considered important (Furnham and Lewis, 1983).

A. The Illusion of Control

Probably the most influential contribution to the cognitive psychology of gambling was Langer's (1975) experiments on the illusion of control. Langer's hypotheses were based on the observations that some people treat chance events as controllable. For instance, Goffman (1967) reported that Las Vegas dealers who experienced runs of bad luck could easily lose their job. Henslin (1967) studied dice players and noticed they behaved as if they were controlling the outcome of the toss. This was confirmed when players threw the dice softly for low numbers and hard for high numbers. A year earlier, Strickland, Lewicki and Katz (1966) had shown experimentally that when playing with dice, people bet less money and were less confident if asked to bet after someone else had thrown the dice rather than throwing it themselves, even though probability of success was the same in both situations. Langer argued that these behaviors were rational if the player believed their game was a game of skill.

The illusion of control was defined by Langer (1975) as being "an expectancy of a personal success inappropriately higher than the objective probability would warrant." This was tested for experimentally in a series of studies which supported her original hypothesis, i.e., under some circumstances people will produce skill orientations towards chance events.

Langer reported that subjects bet more when cutting cards against a "nervous" competitor than against a "confident" one, and that subjects would sell previously bought lottery tickets for a higher price if they had picked it themselves as opposed to having the ticket "assigned" by someone else. Other experiments showed that certain factors — such as the nature of the competition, the familiarity of the task and the degree of personal involvement — influence the belief that skill is a controlling force. In essence, Langer's basic assumption was that in some chance settings, those conditions which involve factors of choice, familiarity, involvement and/or competitions may stimulate the illusion of control to produce skill orientations.

In a later study involving the prediction of "heads" or "tails" after a coin was tossed, Langer and Roth (1975) reported that early wins during chance games induced a skill orientation. Similar findings have also been reported by Frank and Smith (1989) in a study of the illusion of control in coin toss predictions of children and by Reid (1986) using a rigged slot machine.

B. Biased Evaluations and Erroneous Perceptions

Oldman (1974) reported that roulette players see their game as skillful and offer explanations of why they failed. This observation was later tested experimentally by Gilovich (1983) in a study of the biased evaluations in gambling behavior. In three studies using people who bet on football games, Gilovich demonstrated that subjects transformed their losses into "near wins." Subjects pinpointed random or "fluke" events that contributed to a loss but were unaffected by identical events that contributed to a win. It was also reported that subjects spent more time discussing their losses and discounting them in addition to "bolstering" their wins. The same effects were also found in gambling activities (e.g., computerized bingo) in which losses could not easily be explained away (Gilovich and Douglas, 1986).

More recently, Gaboury and Ladouceur (1989) reported on the erroneous perceptions people produce while gambling. In two studies, they evaluated the cognitive activities of subjects while they played either slot machines or roulette using the "thinking aloud" method. Analysis of the verbalizations revealed that erroneous perceptions of the games (80%) far outnumbered the adequate perceptions. For instance, people attributed their success to personal factors such as skill whereas external factors (like bad luck) accounted for losses. Similar findings have been reproduced in other experiments by Ladouceur and associates (Ladouceur and Gaboury, 1988; Ladouceur, Gaboury, Dumont and Rouchette, 1988).

C. Cognitive Regret and the Psychology of the Near Miss

Reid (1986) noted that near misses, i.e., failures that are close to being successful, are believed to encourage future play, and that some commercial gambling activities (e.g., coin-in-the-slot fruit machines and instant lotteries) are formulated to ensure a higher than chance frequency of near misses.

Reid argued that at a behavioristic level, a near miss may have the same kind of conditioning effect on behavior as a success. For example, a fruit machine pays out money (and thus reinforces play) when three winning symbols are displayed. However, a near miss, e.g., two winning symbols and a third losing one, is still strongly reinforcing at no extra expense to the machine"s owner. Thus, at a lower cognitive level, a near miss could produce some of the excitement of a win (i.e., cognitive conditioning through secondary reinforcement). Reid pointed out that the near miss can also be explained in terms of Amsel's (1958) frustration theory. Basically, failing to fulfill a goal produces frustration which (according to the theory) strengthens ongoing behavior.

According to Kahneman and Tversky (1982), the frustration produced by "nearly winning" induces a form of cognitive regret. Loftus and Loftus (1983) elaborated on this idea and suggested that the elimination of regret may be achieved by playing again — encouraging persistent play (see Reid, 1986).

THE COGNITIVE PSYCHOLOGY OF FRUIT MACHINE GAMBLING

Traditionally, fruit machines have been viewed as games of pure chance. Most machines have the same basic design consisting of three reels with differing numbers of "fruit" symbols which spin on a random ratio schedule after money has been inserted. The pay out rates of between 70% and 90% are decided by the machine's owner and/or manufacturer, and money is won when the reels show a winning line, e.g., a row of three cherries.

However, it has been reported by Griffiths in *field* studies of *actual* gamblers (1990a, 1990b, 1990c) that regular players of fruit machines believe their actions to be, in part, skillful and that the recent introduction of specialist play features (e.g., "nudge" and "hold" buttons) may stimulate the illusion of control through personal involvement and familiarity of a particular machine, in addition to them being perceived as elements of skill. It was reported in one study (Griffiths, 1990b) that addicted fruit machine players were fully aware that they would lose every penny they possessed in the long run (playing "with" money rather than "for" it) but their expressed philosophy behind playing was "to stay on the machine as long as possible using the least amount of money" in much the same way as a video game player would do so. This statement implies that fruit machine playing has an element of skill in that the time taken to lose all your money can be lengthened by skillful playing.

In another study (Griffiths, 1990c) it was reported that those fruit machine players defined as pathological gamblers had a greater skill orientation than other less regular players. This strengthens the argument that cognitive factors may be crucial in understanding persistent gambling. The observation that gamblers give biased evaluations (Gilovich, 1983) and make erroneous perceptions (Gaboury and Ladouceur, 1989) towards their gambling behavior was also supported by Griffiths. This was particularly apparent in the explaining away of big losses or in reasons for "bad playing," although the explanations tended to come from the non-pathological gamblers.

In the study to be reported here, a number of factors and variables in the cognitive psychology of fruit machine gambling were examined including:

(a) whether the skill involved in fruit machine playing is "actual" or "perceived" by comparing behavioral monitoring data of regular and non-regular players,

(b) the cognitive activities of regular and non-regular players while gambling using the "thinking aloud method," and

(c) subjective measures of skill and skill perception in regular and non-regular fruit machine players using a post-experimental semi-structured interview.

METHOD

Sixty subjects (44 males and 16 females, average age 23.4 years old), all of whom had played a fruit machine at least once in their lives, were recruited via a small poster advertisement circulated around the local university and college campuses. Additionally, a number of regular players were recruited via a regular player known to the author.

Regular players (29 males and 1 female, average age 21.6 years old) were defined as those who played fruit machines at least once a week. Non-regular players (15 males and 15 females, average age 25.3 years old) were defined as those who played fruit machines once a month or less.

The study was performed on an individual basis at a local amusement arcade as opposed to a laboratory simulation, as the ecological validity of experimental studies in the laboratory study of gambling behavior has been seriously questioned (Anderson and Brown, 1984). Each subject was given £3 to play a fruit machine, which gave them 30 plays. All participants in the experiment were asked to try to stay on the machine for a minimum of 60 plays (i.e., their aim was to conserve — as best they could — the money they had been given). If a player managed to achieve 60 plays with the initial £3 stake they were then given the choice of either keeping any winnings or carrying on playing. Unless there was a prior objection, all subjects were asked to play on a particular fruit machine ("Fruitskill") selected by the author in the interests of controlling the experiment.

Regular and non-regular fruit machine players were randomly assigned to one of two groups, "thinking aloud" and "non-thinking aloud," yielding a 2 by 2 matrix of 15 subjects in each cell, as detailed in Table 1.

TABLE 1

BREAKDOWN OF SUBJECTS INTO CATEGORIES

	Regular players	*Non-regular players*	*Total*
Thinking Aloud	15	15	30
Non-Thinking Aloud	15	15	30
Total	30	30	60

At all stages and in all conditions of the experiment, the author was nearby, recording total time in minutes each subject was on the fruit machine, the total number of plays, the total number of wins, the amount of winnings, and the result of every play. The subjects assigned to the "thinking aloud" condition had their verbalizations recorded using a lapel microphone via a portable tape recorder. All verbalizations made during the playing session of each subject were then transcribed. Since this study used what could be described as a controversial method for studying the cognitive processes of fruit machine players, a brief overview of the issues will be considered.

A. The thinking aloud method

Throughout the history of psychology there has been considerable controversy over the validity of introspection and it's surrounding methodology. In a much cited paper, Nisbett and Wilson (1977) argued that the introspective method was "practically worthless" and at best "unreliable." They reported that, on the whole, participants seem entirely oblivious of the mental processes involved in determining behavior and argued "to be unaware of the processes affecting behavior is the rule."

Most cognitive psychologists were reluctant to agree with Nisbett and Wilson, and, as a consequence, they were attacked vehemently by a number of authors (Smith and Miller, 1978; Payne, Braunstein and Carroll, 1978; Ericsson and Simon, 1980, 1984). Accepting the criticisms of the introspective method, there are three points to bear in mind which relate to all introspective methodology:

(1) The real question is not whether people have access to cognitive processes but, more productively, "What are the *conditions* of access?" (Smith and Miller, 1978).

(2) There *are* limitations in the introspective method for identifying cognitive processes, but it can be extremely valid in *some* circumstances (Ericsson and Simon, 1980).

(3) The limitation of introspection is closely related to the limitations of the memory system (M. Eysenck, 1984).

As a consequence, Ericsson and Simon (1980) devised criteria with the intention of distinguishing between valid and invalid uses of introspection. These preliminary criteria were as follows:

(1) It is preferable to obtain introspective reports *during* performance of a task rather than retrospectively. In view of the fallibility of human

memory, retrospective reports may be incomplete due to failure of retrieval from long term memory.

(2) Subjects are more likely to produce accurate introspections when asked to *describe* what they are attending to, or thinking about, than when required to interpret a situation or to speculate their thought processes.

(3) It is clear that people cannot usefully introspect about several kinds of processes (e.g., neuronal events). The degree of involvement in attention is of much importance and it is assumed that only the information in focal attention can be verbalized. However, it must be noted that with an increase of experience a task may take the process from a cognitively controlled one to an automatic one. Hence, what is available for verbalization to the novice may be unavailable to the expert.

One common criticism of the introspective method is that some researchers argue that, by asking people to introspect while they are performing a task, the nature of the cognitive processes may change under study. Common sense suggests that the extent of any disruption of ongoing cognitive processes depends on what kind of information the subjects are asked to provide in their introspective reports (Ericsson and Simon, 1980). According to Ericsson and Simon (1980), verbalizing information is shown to affect cognitive processes only if the instructions require verbalization of information that would not otherwise have been attended to.

Therefore, the best probable method for a precise evaluation of the cognitive activities of an individual during some specified activity is the "thinking aloud method" (Ericsson and Simon, 1980). Basically, this method asks people to verbalize all thoughts they have during a specified activity without censoring their content. Payne, Braunstein and Carroll (1978) noted that in the studies by Nisbett and Wilson (1977), verbal reports were given *after* their experiments. This gives little comparison or insight into those results obtained by "thinking aloud" *during* a task.

Ericsson and Simon (1980) point out that when subjects verbalize concurrently, they must do two things: perform the task that is being studied, and produce the verbalizations. Due to the limited capacity of short term memory, time-lag, and level of accuracy, only the most recently needed information is accessible directly. In "concurrent verbalization" (i.e., the "thinking aloud method"), the additional cognitive load imposed by the instructions to verbalize may be negligible as thinking aloud is different from *explanation*. The "thinking aloud method," according to Ericsson and Simon (1980), should not change the course or structure of the task processes, although it may slightly decrease the speed of the task performance.

There have been many cases in which "thinking aloud" has been found to have no systematic effect on the structure and course of the process involved in performing the task (e.g., Newell and Simon, 1972). In addition, a number of studies involving problem solving under "think aloud" and "silence" conditions have shown that verbalization does not affect behavioral manifestations of thought processes; only speed of performance (Roth, 1966; Karpf, 1973; Kazdin, 1976; Carroll and Payne, 1977; Perkins, 1979).

The "thinking aloud method" was used in this study to examine the cognitive processes of regular and non-regular fruit machine players. The thirty subjects who underwent the "thinking aloud" condition were given the following additional instructions:

> The thinking aloud method consists of verbalizing every thought that passes through your mind while you are playing. It is important to remember the following points: (1) Say everything that goes through your mind. Do not censor any of your thoughts even if they seem irrelevant to you; (2) Keep talking as continuously as possible, even if your ideas are not clearly constructed; (3) Speak clearly; (4) Do not hesitate to use fragmented sentences if necessary. Do not worry about speaking in complete sentences; (5) Do not try to justify your thoughts (Ladouceur et al., 1988).

From the work of Ladouceur and his associates, it was hypothesized that regular gamblers would produce more irrational verbalizations than non-regular gamblers. It was also hypothesized that there would be no difference between regular and non-regular fruit machine players on objective measures of skill, (i.e., the eight monitoring data variables listed in Table 2), although it was hypothesized that "thinking aloud" subjects would take, on average, longer to complete the task. It was further hypothesized that on subjective measures of self report, regular gamblers would be more skill-oriented than non-regular gamblers.

TABLE 2

Key to the Eight Behavioral Monitoring Data Variables Used in the Study	
(1) TOTAL PLAYS	Total number of plays during the playing session
(2) TOTAL TIME	Total time in minutes of play during one playing session
(3) PLAY RATE	Total number of plays per minute during the playing session
(4) ENDSTAKE	Total winnings in number of 10 pences after the playing session
(5) HYPOTHETICAL PLAYS	Total minimum number of plays if "endstakes" had been used for further play
(6) WINS	Total number of wins during playing session
(7) WIN RATE (Time)	Total number of minutes between each win during the playing session
(8) WIN RATE (Plays)	Total number of plays between each win during the playing session

RESULTS

A. Analysis of Behavioral Data

The mean scores for the sixty fruit machine players show that on average they played approximately 56 times in just over 9½ minutes with an initial £3 stake (see Table 3). On average, they won at least 10 pence seven times during the playing session, i.e., a win occurred about every 11 plays with just over a minute and a half gap between each.

Of the 24 possible differences on the eight monitoring data variables, there were six significant differences, along with two results just failing to reach significance at the 0.05 level.

TABLE 3

MEANS, MEDIANS, AND STANDARD DEVIATIONS OF FRUIT MACHINE BEHAVIORAL MONITORING VARIABLES IN PLAYERS (n = 60)			
DEPENDENT VARIABLE	*Mean*	*Median*	*Standard Deviation*
Total Play	56.3	54.0	18.0
Total Time	9.6	8.8	4.7
Play Rate	6.9	5.9	2.9
End Stake	6.3	0	16.9
Hyp. Plays	62.7	54.0	29.1
Wins	7.1	7.0	3.7
Win Rate (time)	1.7	1.3	1.3
Win Rate (plays)	10.7	8.0	8.3

The ANOVAs showed that regular players in this study stayed on the fruit machine longer than non-regular players using the same initial stake in terms of number of plays (F (1,56) = 4.27, p = 0.044), although there was no significant difference between the time as measured in minutes. Regular players were also found to have a significantly higher playing rate of approximately eight plays a minute compared to six plays a minute of the non-regular players (F (1,56) = 7.96, p = 0.007).

Those players who were in the "thinking aloud" conditions (which consisted of both regular and non-regular players) managed to have significantly more total winnings after their playing session had ceased than those who did not think aloud (F (1,56) = 4, p = 0.05). As a consequence of this result, the thinking aloud group had significantly more hypothetical plays (F (1,56) = 5.73, p = 0.02), i.e., a significant increase in the total minimum number of plays if their total winnings had been used for further play after their playing session was over.

Regular players who were in the "thinking aloud" condition were found to have significantly more wins than the other groups (F (1,56) = 5.09, p = 0.028) and a significantly higher win rate in number of plays (F (1,56) = 7.85, p = 0.007), but not as measured by the time, i.e., the number of plays (but not the time elapsed) between each win was significantly lower than other groups.

TABLE 4

MEANS OF FRUIT MACHINE BEHAVIORAL MONITORING VARIABLES OF PLAYERS

(regular vs. non regular, n=30; thinking aloud vs. non-thinking aloud, n=30)

DEPENDENT VARIABLE	*Regular*	*Non-Regular*	*Thinking Aloud*	*Non-Thinking Aloud*
Total Play	60.9	51.7	60.6	52.0
Total Time	9.2	9.9	10.7	8.5
Play Rate	7.9	5.9	6.8	7.0
End Stake	6.9	5.6	10.6	2.0
Hyp. Plays	67.9	57.4	71.2	54.0
Wins	7.0	7.2	7.1	7.0
Win Rate (Time)	1.4	1.8	1.8	1.5
Win Rate (Plays)	11.1	10.2	11.3	10.0

Two results nearly reached significance at the 0.05 level. Those who were thinking aloud had a higher number of total plays on the machine with the same initial £3 stake than the group not thinking aloud (F (1,56) = 3.73, p = 0.059), and they also stayed on the fruit machine longer in terms of time in minutes (F (1,56) = 3.47, p = 0.068). A complete list of means and ANOVAs of the results can be found in Tables 4, 5 and 6.

B. Analysis of Verbalizations

In analyzing the verbalizations of the 30 players (15 regular, 15 non-regular) who were in the "thinking aloud" condition, a content analysis was performed on the transcriptions. The coding scheme was intuitively constructed by the author after all the transcripts had been collected and yielded 30 utterance categorizations and a further miscellaneous category. A full list of the coding scheme with appropriate examples is shown in Table 7.

Each type of utterance was tallied and subsequently given a weight as a percentage of total utterances by each subject. Regular and non-regular players were then compared on each utterance categorization using t-tests.

TABLE 5

MEANS OF FRUIT MACHINE BEHAVIORAL MONITORING VARIABLES OF PLAYERS

(regular; thinking aloud, n=15; non-regular, thinking aloud and non-thinking aloud, n=15)

DEPENDENT	*Non-Regular Non-Thinking Aloud*	*Regular/ Non-Thinking Aloud*	*Non-Regular Thinking Aloud*	*Regular/ Thinking Aloud*
Total Play	47.8	56.3	55.7	65.6
Total Time	8.4	8.5	11.5	9.9
Play Rate	6.5	7.5	5.3	8.4
End Stake	4.0	0	7.3	13.9
Hyp. Plays	51.8	56.3	62.9	79.5
Wins	6.1	8.0	8.3	6.0
Win Rate (Time)	2.0	1.0	1.7	1.8
Win Rate (Plays)	12.5	7.5	8.0	14.6

TABLE 6

ANOVAs OF FRUIT MACHINE BEHAVIORAL MONITORING DATA OF PLAYERS

(Regular/Non-Regular, Think Aloud/Non-Think Aloud, and their interaction)

DEPENDENT VARIABLE	*F-ratios for effect #*		
	REGULAR	*THINK ALOUD*	*REGULAR/THINK ALOUD*
Total Plays	4.27**	3.73*	0.03
Total Time	0.35	3.47*	0.50
Play Rate	7.96***	0.05	2.33
End Stake	0.09	4.00**	1.53
Hyp. Plays	2.14	5.73**	0.71
Wins	0.03	0.01	5.09**
Win Rate (Time)	1.67	0.66	5.61
Win Rate (Plays)	0.16	0.40	7.85***

degrees of freedom (1,56) in all cases
* = p<0.1
** = p<0.05
*** = p<0.01

TABLE 7

UTTERANCE CATEGORIZATION IN CONTENT ANALYSIS CODING SCHEME	
1.	Personification of the fruit machine
2.	Swearing/cursing
3.	Swearing at the fruit machine
4.	Talking to the fruit machine
5.	Reference to losing
6.	Reference to winning
7.	Sarcastic reference to winning
8.	Saying "no" (and its derivatives) in response to the machine's reels
9.	Saying "yes" (and its derivatives) in response to the machine's reels
10.	Reference to the gamble button
11.	Reference to gambling in general
12.	Reference to a near win
13.	Questions of confusion/non-understanding
14.	Statements of confusion/non-understanding
15.	Reference to skill
16.	Humor reference/joke
17.	Reference to chance
18.	Reference to blank mind
19.	Reference to holds or holds/nudges features
20.	Reference to the "number system"
21.	Saying "It's not worth it" in reference to holding
22.	Reference to sudden understanding
23.	Reference to machine being a waste of money, a rip-off, etc.
24.	Hoping/needing a certain feature on the machine
25.	Explaining away losses
26.	Reference to frustration
27.	Saying "see what happens/comes up"
28.	Reference to luck, being lucky, etc.
29.	Saying "I can't do anything" or "Nothing I can do"
30.	Questions in general
31.	Miscellaneous utterances

The results (see Table 8) showed that regular players made significantly more percentage verbalizations in personifying the fruit machine ($p<0.001$), in swearing at the fruit machine ($p<0.05$), referring to winning ($p<0.05$), referring to skill ($p<0.05$), explaining away losses ($p<0.05$), hoping or needing a certain feature on the machine (p<0.05), referring to the "number system" (p<0.01), and saying "it's not worth it" (in relation to "holding" a particular feature on the fruit machine) (p<0.05). Non-regular players made significantly more percentage verbalizations in questions of confusion/non-understanding (p<0.001),

TABLE 8

SIGNIFICANT DIFFERENCES IN VERBALIZATIONS BETWEEN REGULAR (n=15) AND NON-REGULAR (n=15) FRUIT MACHINE PLAYERS

UTTERANCE CATEGORY	% Utterance		t	d.f.	Significance
	Non-Regular	Regular			
Personification of the machine	1.1	7.5	-4.51	16	p=0.0004***
Swearing at the machine	0.08	0.6	-2.21	16	p=0.042*
Reference to winning	6.7	9.8	-2.15	27	p=0.041*
Reference to skill	1.5	5.3	-2.46	19	p=0.024*
Explaining away losses	0.4	3.1	-2.47	15	p=0.026*
Hoping/needing a certain feature	0.8	3.3	-2.75	16	p=0.014*
Reference to the "number system"	1.5	9.5	-3.53	15	p=0.003**
Saying "It's not worth it".	0.5	3.0	-2.48	18	p=0.023*
Questions of confusion/non-understanding	13.2	1.6	6.65	19	p=0.000***
Statements of confusion/ non-understanding	4.8	1.7	2.87	24	p=0.009**
Questions in general	4.7	2.4	2.19	19	p=0.041*
Reference to sudden understanding	2.3	0.4	2.88	16	p=0.011*
Sarcastic reference to winning	1.7	0.3	2.07	15	p=0.05*
Miscellaneous utterances	25.5	11.7	4.58	26	p=0.001***
Reference to blank mind	2.2	0	—	—	—
Reference to frustration	0.3	0	—	—	—

in statements of confusion/non-understanding ($p<0.01$), in questions in general ($p<0.05$), referring to sudden understanding of some aspect of the machine ($p<0.05$), sarcastically referring to winning ($p<0.05$), and miscellaneous utterances ($p<0.001$). There were also two utterance categories in which non-regular players made verbalizations (referring to mind going blank and referring to frustration) in which there was no verbalization equivalent in regular players.

No significant differences were found in the remaining 15 utterance categories outlined in Table 7. Although the majority of verbalizations of both regular and non-regular players were rational, regular gamblers did produce more total irrational verbalizations (14%) than non-regular gamblers (2.5%), a finding which was highly significant ($p<0.001$).

C. Analysis of Skill Variables

In a post-experimental semi-structured interview, a number of questions relating to skill variables were asked. In comparing the responses to the question, "Is there any skill involved in playing a fruit machine?" most non-regular players said "mostly chance" ($p<0.05$) and most regular players said "equal chance and skill" ($p<0.01$). The full results using the Fisher Exact test are given in Table 9.

In response to the question, "How skillful do you think you are compared with the average person?" there was a marked significant difference between regular and non-regular players. Regular players claimed they were at least of average skill, but more usually "above average skill" or "totally skilled" (see Table 10).

Non-regular players, on the whole, viewed themselves as "below average skill" or "totally unskilled" except for seven players who said that because fruit machines were "all" or "mostly" chance, they were as good or as bad (i.e., as average) as anyone else.

When asked, "What skill (if any) is involved in playing fruit machines?" the players put forward 21 skills, many of which were "knowledge" of some particular aspect of the fruit machine. Although there was a lot of similarity between skills listed between regular and non-regular players (see Table 11), there were a number of significant differences were obtained using the Fisher-Exact Test. Knowledge of the "gamble" button was viewed by regular

TABLE 9

RESPONSES TO THE QUESTION "IS THERE ANY SKILL INVOLVED IN PLAYING A FRUIT MACHINE?" BY FRUIT MACHINE PLAYERS (n=60)				
	Regular	*Non-Regular*	*Total*	*Significance*
All Chance	0	3	3	ns
Mostly Chance	10	19	29	p<0.05
Equal Chance/Skill	18	7	25	p<0.01
Mostly Skill	1	1	2	ns
All Skill	1	0	1	ns
Total	30	30	60	

TABLE 10

RESPONSES TO THE QUESTION "HOW SKILLFUL DO YOU THINK YOU ARE COMPARED TO THE AVERAGE PERSON?" BY FRUIT MACHINE PLAYERS (n=60)				
	Regular	Non-Regular	Total	Significance
Totally Unskilled	0	12	12	p<0.001
Below Average Skill	0	7	7	p<0.001
Average Skill	7	10	17	ns
Above Average Skill	18	1	19	p<0.001
Totally Skilled	5	0	5	p<0.005
Total	30	30	60	

players as more skillful than non-regular players (p<0.01) as was knowledge of "feature skills" (p<0.001), knowledge of when the machine will (or will not) pay out (p<0.001), light oscillation (p<0.05) and not playing if the fruit machine has just paid out (p<0.01).

There were also a number of other "indirect" skill factors. Three players — all regulars — objected to playing the chosen fruit machine because they were either not familiar with it or preferred playing another machine. Seven players — again, all regulars — began the experiment on the chosen machine but then changed to different fruit machines, changing at least three times. It was also noted that of the 14 regular players who managed to break even on their initial stake (i.e., staying on the machine for at least 60 plays), ten of them carried on playing until they had lost everything. Of the seven non-regular players who managed to break even, only two of them carried on playing until they had lost everything.

DISCUSSION

The results of the behavioral monitoring data showed that the null hypothesis — that there would be no difference between regular and non-regular fruit machine players — was rejected. Results of this study demonstrated that regular players can and do stay on fruit machines longer than non-regular players in terms of number of plays. This suggests that there are skillful aspects to fruit machine playing; however, the skill appears to be little more than taking a few more plays to lose the same amount of money in approximately the same time as non-regular players. Since there was no difference in win rates between regular and non-regular players, the skill in playing seems to stem from the ability of a regular player being able to "boost" or "gamble up" smaller wins into larger ones. It is very probable (although it cannot be confirmed from this study) that regular players believe their activity to be far more skillful than it actually is.

The results from players who thought aloud were very interesting. Those players who thought aloud had significantly more total winnings (both regular and non-regular players), and regular players who thought aloud had more wins. It could be argued that "thinking aloud" changed the fruit machine playing behavior in some way. However, a more likely explanation is that players who thought aloud concentrated more, thus making fewer mistakes. As expected, the players who thought aloud did take longer (in terms of time) to play the fruit machine, although the result just failed to reach significance.

The hypothesis that regular players would make more irrational verbalizations than non-regular players during fruit machine playing was supported. The results were markedly different from the previous work of Ladouceur and his associates (1988) who reported that their subjects produced 80% irrational verbalizations. In this study, irrational verbalizations constituted only 14% of regular players' speech and 2.5% of non-regular players' speech. This may have been because the coding scheme in this study was more stringent or may have been due to the fact that Ladouceur's experiments were laboratory simulations, and this study was done in the field. Accepting that the total amount of irrational verbalizations were significantly lower than previously

TABLE 11

SKILLFUL ASPECTS OF FRUIT MACHINE PLAYING AS REPORTED BY REGULAR AND NON-REGULAR FRUIT MACHINE PLAYERS (n=60)

Skill	*Regular*	*Non-Regular*	*All*	*Significance*
Knowledge of the fruit machine	15	10	25	ns
Knowledge of "hold" buttons	8	13	21	ns
Knowledge of "gamble" button	2	11	13	$p < 0.01$
Knowledge of "feature skills" (skill, chances etc.)	0	12	12	$p < 0.001$
Knowledge of reels	4	8	12	ns
Knowledge of buttons/features (non-specific)	5	5	10	ns
Knowledge of "number system"/ "lighting up"	5	5	10	ns
Knowledge of "nudges"	4	5	9	ns
Knowledge of when the machine will (or will not) pay out	0	8	8	$p < 0.001$
Light oscillation	1	6	7	$p < 0.05$
Reaction times to certain features	4	3	7	ns
Knowing when to quit	2	4	6	ns
Not playing if the machine has just paid out	0	5	5	$p < 0.01$
Prediction/intuition of what's coming next	1	4	5	ns
Hand-eye coordination	2	1	3	ns
Knowledge of probabilities and odds	2	1	3	ns
Concentration/patience	2	1	3	ns
Knowing when to take winnings	2	0	0	ns
Memory	1	0	1	ns
Recognizing high pay out symbols	1	0	1	ns
Avoiding playing (!)	1	0	1	ns
(N.B. Most players gave more than one response)				

reported studies, the study still supported the general postulation of Ladouceur et al. (1988) and the work on biased evaluations of Gilovich (1983).

It was not surprising that non-regular players asked more questions than regular players and produced significantly more questions and statements of confusion and/or non-understanding as this would have been expected. However, these utterance categories are still important as "manipulation checks" and demonstrate that the criteria used in this study for distinguishing between regular and non-regular players were valid.

There were a number of references to near misses/near wins. However, there was no difference between groups, and the verbalizations in this utterance category accounted for less than 1% of the total verbalizations. Despite the fact that a few non-regular players verbalized that their minds had gone blank, it was the regular players who did more so in actuality but never voiced it. This was probably because a lot of regular players seemed to be on "automatic pilot" in that they could play fruit machines without attending to what they were thinking about. It also echoes the point noted previously that increased experience of a task may take it from a cognitively controlled one to an automatic one, and that what is available for the novice may be unavailable for the expert.

The hypothesis that regular players would be more skill oriented than non-regular players was supported in both self-comparison ratings and in questions relating to skill factors in machine play. It seems likely that those skills reported by regular players which were significantly different to non-regular players' are the ones which enhance number of plays. However, this needs to be confirmed in further studies. The skillful aspects of fruit machine play were similar, although in this study far more detailed, to the earlier work of Griffiths (1990c).

It has yet to be ascertained fully which features of fruit machine play are genuinely skillful and which are only perceived as being skillful. For instance, Griffiths (1988), in communications with members of the gaming industry, has reported that the "gamble" button — a feature regarded by regular players in this study as very skillful — operates purely by chance.

The fact that a few players objected to playing the study's chosen fruit machine supports Langer's (1975) illusion of control through familiarity of particular machines; and the finding that most regular players gamble until they have lost all their money supports the findings of Griffiths (1990b) who reported that regular players know they will lose every penny they possess in the long run and that they play "with" money rather than for it, staying on the machine as long as possible using the least amount of money.

The study as a whole raises questions about the validity of the "thinking aloud method." In actuality, the behavior of those players who thought aloud did not differ substantially from those who did not, but the real question is not whether the cognitive behavior was affected, but whether the data gained actually explains persistent (losing) gambling behavior. In examining the verbalizations more closely, it would appear that although regular gamblers do produce irrational biases, the data gained were descriptive rather than explanatory.

Although it is interesting that there should be a descriptive difference between the two groups of players, it seems likely that the verbalizations produced are the "symptoms" of a deeper underlying cause which may be manifestations of a particular developmental phase, or may be concerned with the gambler's personality. As a consequence, these are the areas where more research needs to be carried out to ascertain the underlying causes of irrational gambling behavior.

As has previously been reported by a few authors (e.g., Stumphauzer, 1980; Griffiths, 1989, 1990a), knowledge of an irrational gambling bias may help in rehabilitating gamblers through cognitive-behavior modification. Using the design of this study, it might be possible in the future to inhibit irrational bias in gambling by playing back tape recordings of a pathological gambler's verbalizations to highlight their irrationalities.

REFERENCES

Amsel, A. (1958). The role of frustrative non-reward in non-continuous reward situations. *Psychological Bulletin*, 55, 102-119.

Anderson, G. and Brown, R.I.F. (1984). Real and gambling, sensation seeking and arousal: Towards a Pavlovian component in general theories of gambling addictions. *British Journal of Psychology*, 75, 401-411.

Brown, R.I.F. (1986). Arousal and sensation seeking components in the general explanation of gambling and gambling addictions. *International Journal of the Addictions*, 21, 1001-1016.

Carroll, J.S. and Payne, J.W. (1977). Judgements about crime and the criminal: A model and a method for investigating parole decisions. In B.D. Sales (ed.), *Perspectives in Law and Psychology: The Criminal Justice System*, vol. 1. New York: Plenum.

Ericsson, K.A. and Simon, H.A. (1980). Verbal reports as data. *Psychological Review*, 3, 215-251.

Ericsson, K.A. and Simon, H.A. (1984). *Protocol Analysis — Verbal Reports as Data*. Cambridge, MA: MIT Press.

Eysenck, M. (1984). *A Handbook of Cognitive Psychology*. London: LEA.

Frank, M.L. and Smith, C. (1989). Illusion of control and gambling in children. *Journal of Gambling Behavior*, 5, 127-136.

Furnham, A. and Lewis, A. (1983). *The Economic Mind: The Social Psychology of Economic Behaviour*. London: Harvester Press.

Gaboury, A. and Ladouceur, R. (1989). Erroneous perceptions and gambling. *Journal of Social Behavior and Personality*, 4, 411-420.

Gilovich, T. (1983). Biased evaluations and persistence in gambling. *Journal of Personality and Social Psychology*, 44, 1100-1126.

Goffman, E. (1967). *Interaction Ritual*. New York: Anchor.

Griffiths, M.D. (1988). The gaming industry: A summary of personal communications. *Economic Psychology Research Group Internal Report*, 88/13.

Griffiths, M.D. (1989). Gambling in children and adolescents. *Journal of Gambling Behavior*, 5, 66-83.

Griffiths, M.D. (1990a). The cognitive psychology of gambling. *Journal of Gambling Studies*, 6, 31-42.

Griffiths, M.D. (1990b). Addiction to fruit machines: A preliminary study among males. *Journal of Gambling Studies*, 6, 113-126.

Griffiths, M.D. (1990c). The acquisition, development and maintenance of fruit machine gambling in adolescence. *Journal of Gambling Studies*, 6(3), 193-204.

Henslin, J.M. (1967). Craps and magic. *American Journal of Sociology*, 73, 316-330.

Kahneman, D. and Tversky, A. (1982). The psychology of preferences. *Scientific American*, January, 136-142.

Karpf, D.A. (1973). Thinking aloud in human discrimination learning. Doctoral dissertation, State University of New York, 1972. *Dissertation Abstracts International*, 33, 6111B.

Kazdin, A.E. (1976). Assessment of imagery during covert modelling of assertive behaviour. *Journal of Behaviour Therapy and Experimental Psychiatry*, 7, 213-219.

Ladouceur, R. and Gaboury, A. (1988). Effects of limited and unlimited stakes on gambling behavior. *Journal of Gambling Behavior*, 4, 119-126.

Ladouceur, R., Gaboury, A., Dumont, M. and Rochette, P. (1988). Gambling: Relationship between the frequency of wins and irrational thinking. *Journal of Psychology*, 122, 409-414.

Langer, E.J. (1975). The illusion of control as a function of the sequence of outcomes in a purely chance task. *Journal of Personality and Social Psychology*, 32, 951-955.

Langer, E.J. and Roth, J. (1975). The illusion of control as a function of the sequenced outcomes in a purely chance task. *Journal of Personality and Social Psychology*, 32, 951-955.

Loftus, G.R. and Loftus, E.K. (1983). *Mind at Play*. New York: Basic Books.

Nisbett, R.E. and Wilson, T.D. (1977). Telling more than we can know: Verbal reports on mental processes. *Psychological Review*, 84, 231-259.

Oldham, D. (1974). Chance and skill: A study of roulette. *Sociology*, 8, 407-426.

Payne, J.W., Braunstein, M.L. and Carroll, J.S. (1978). Exploring predecisional behavior: An alternative approach to decision research. *Organizational Behavior and Human Performance*, 22, 17-44.

Perkins, D.N. (1979). *A primer on introspection.* Paper presented at the American Theatre Association Convention, New York.

Reid, R.L. (1986). The psychology of the near miss. *Journal of Gambling Behavior*, 2, 32-39.

Roth, B. (1966). The effect of overt verbalization on problem solving. Doctoral Dissertation, New York University, 1965. *Dissertation Abstracts*, 27, 957B.

Smith, D.N. and Miller, F.D. (1978). Limits on perception of cognitive processes: A reply to Nisbett and Wilson. *Psychological Review*, 85, 355-362.

Strickland, L.H., Lewicki, R.J. and Katz, A.M. (1966). Temporal orientation and perceived control as determinants of risk-taking. *Journal of Experimental and Social Psychology*, 2, 143-151.

Stumphauzer, J.S. (1980). Learning to drink: Adolescents and alcohol. *Addictive Behaviors*, 5, 277-283.

The Role of Fixed Interval Conditioning in Promoting Involvement in Off-Course Betting

David Shewan and R. Iain F. Brown

Although recent general trends in gambling in the United Kingdom are well documented (Downes et al., 1976; National Council on Gambling, 1983; Royal Commission on Gambling, 1978), patterns of involvement and expenditure of individual gamblers have received insufficient attention, and overall figures fail to highlight the behavior of those individuals whose gambling may be causing them economic, personal and social problems. Despite the increase in gambling research in the last few years, there is still a lack of information regarding patterns of participation of gamblers in ecologically valid settings. There are great difficulties in generalizing from controlled laboratory set-ups to real-life gambling situations (Anderson and Brown, 1984; Dickerson, 1984).

There are a number of sociological studies of real-life gambling situations, usually by participant observation (Newman, 1972; Lesieur, 1978; Oldman 1974, 1978; Rosecrance, 1985, 1986). Where the researcher is knowledgeable of the situation — of the participants and of the gambling process — this type of study can be valuable in relation to the examination of gambling and its social function and providing insight into the gambler's own view of the situation. There is, however, a scarcity of empirical data from real-life gambling situations.

The work of Dickerson is one of the few exceptions. He had been primarily concerned with collecting data from populations of gamblers in real life situations. The theoretical basis of his work has shifted somewhat form its early Skinnerian perspective (Dickerson, 1977, 1979) to now encompass cognitive, social and affective factors (Dickerson, 1987; Corless and Dickerson, 1989). This study takes issue with the early Skinnerian position rather than with the later eclectic one, but the concept of impaired control is common to both.

THE CONCEPT OF IMPAIRED CONTROL

Dickerson's early position (1977, 1979) represents a strict operant learning theory account of how the situation in an off-course betting office may control gambling behavior through reinforcement contingencies and, furthermore, that this may lead to progressively higher levels of involvement until the gambler is "trained" to bet later (for maximum reinforcement), more frequently, and with higher stakes. Within this model, the learning history of the heavy gambler is assumed to dictate his behavior while in the betting office. Adopting the position of a true Skinnerian, Dickerson left no role for cognition or social factors as intervening variables.

Dickerson has now moved away from suggesting a simple conditioning model for regular or problem gambling and is currently looking at a model which involves affective (depression and frustration) and cognitive (perceived control) variables (Corless and Dickerson, 1989). However, the issue of impaired control amongst heavy gamblers is still present in his work.

The concept of impaired control amongst heavy gamblers is still central to much of gambling research, where loss of control has been seen as central to compulsive or pathological gambling and as marking the difference between it and other gambling (e.g., Custer, 1982). But Dickerson (1974) found that loss of control was reported, ". . .by regular gamblers who do not express a need to stop or reduce their gambling, who do not consider they have a problem" (pp. 80-81). Reporting on comparisons between Gamblers Anonymous (GA) compulsive gamblers and high-frequency (regular) off-course gamblers

Dickerson (1974) concluded that, ". . .once again compulsive gamblers may be a slightly more extreme group, reporting more frequent loss of control than comparable high-frequency off-course bettors" (p. 56). He goes on to conclude that, ". . .similarities rather than differences between high-frequency and compulsive gamblers are the order of the day" (p. 66). Thus Dickerson takes the view that impaired control operates as a continuum (Dickerson, 1974, 1985; Corless and Dickerson, 1989).

But, whether it is all or nothing or a question of degree, the argument is still essentially deterministic — problem gamblers gamble because they cannot help it. Furthermore, there is still almost universal support for the view that there is a point at which the individual gambler becomes "compelled" to carry out a particular behavior, or in some way becomes unable to resist. This is part of a more general view of compulsive gambling as an addiction-like phenomenon. Evidence of the possible existence of withdrawal symptoms reported by some heavy gamblers after a sudden cessation of gambling (Wray and Dickerson, 1981) lends some support to this view.

The early, essentially deterministic explanation of compulsive gambling offered by Dickerson arises from his application of learning theory principles to gambling behavior in an off-course betting shop. The application of learning theory principles to gambling behavior has largely been on the proposed operation of variable ratio money-reinforced schedules in the gambling environment (Skinner, 1953).

However, Dickerson (1979) reported that within the betting shop situation, ". . .there exists little of the true randomness that is the important feature of variable interval scheduling." He suggested that variable reinforcement (VR) schedules may operate out with the gambling situation, with the distinct reinforcer being "cash won" and, as such, may be implicated in causing the gambler to return to the betting shop and stay longer once he is there. The VR schedules may, Dickerson suggested, also be implicated in leading an occasional gambler into gambling more regularly, with "beginner's luck" an important function of this. It has been suggested that the novice gambler requires an early win to reinforce the VR schedule (Cornish, 1978; Custer, 1982). Many other factors have been proposed as influences on the novice gambler entering the betting shop environment: economic factors, early learning within the family (Bergler, 1957), life stress (Boyd, 1976), and a variety of possible social pressures (Cornish, 1978). Dickerson (1977, 1979) suggested that once the gambler has begun to bet in the betting office, the environment there may be involved in increasing his level of participation.

Both Dickerson (1979) and Newman (1972) commented on the importance of the role of the "blower race commentary," and Dickerson (1977, 1979) noted a "strong and definite time-based component running through the sequence of events in the betting shop," creating a regular pattern of auditory stimuli prior to the start of each race. This, Dickerson proposes, acts as a stimulus chain, (Table 1) for a Fixed Interval (FI) reinforcement schedule which operates distinct from the "cash" reinforcer of the VR schedule discussed earlier, the FI reinforcer being, ". . .the interval of time immediately following the start of a race whether defined in terms of a race commentary, the subjective experience of the gambler, or his physiological reactions" (Dickerson, 1979, p. 321). Dickerson gives the general term "excitement" for this reinforcer. He reported that those gamblers who bet heaviest described tachycardia, sweating, muscle tension and general excitement when betting close to the start of the race.

Dickerson (1977) proposes that the FI schedule operates as a training schedule, its influence causing the gambler to bet later and later to obtain maximum reinforcement. The FI schedule has been demonstrated to be one of the most powerful controlling schedules in animal learning experiments (Ferster and Skinner, 1957), and Dickerson proposes that it plays a crucial role in the gambler's loss of control and persistence when losing while in the betting shop.

It is suggested by Dickerson that an increase in stake-size will also occur. As the gambler becomes more heavily involved in the betting shop training program and their betting responses become closer to the OFF, then so they will come into contact with the existing group of heavy gamblers in the shop and social pressures may encourage the novice to increase his stake-size to match those of the experienced gambler. Eventually, an increased tolerance factor may also operate. The gambler may require to raise the level of his stake-size in order to maintain an acceptably high level of excitement when betting.

Dickerson rejects the possibility that late betting by heavy gamblers is not the result of conditioning but rather that it reflects their superior skills and knowledge of the process over mere novice gamblers on four counts: that the frenetic conditions under which bet selection is carried out in the last few

TABLE 1

Blower Stimulus Chain for Dog and Horse Races (Dickerson , 1979)						
	STIMULUS Dogs	REPs Dogs	TIME BEFORE OFF (min)	STIMULUS Horses	REPs Horses	TIME BEFORE OFF (min)
1	They're parading	1	9-13	They're parading They all go at The runners at	1	15-20
2	They bet at — 6/4 trap 2, etc.	3	0-4	They bet at	8-15	0-16
3	They're going in	1	0-2	They're going down	1	5-8
4	The hare's running	1	3-5 sec	They're at the start	1	1-5
5	—	1	—	They're going behind They're in the stalls	1	1-2
6	—	—	—	They're under orders	1	0-1
7	They're off	—	0	They're off	—	0

minutes makes the exercise of skill more difficult; that there is a general shortening of odds over the board as the OFF gets closer which skilled gamblers should wish to avoid that heavy gamblers tend to place their bets in the very last minute prior to the OFF and that heavy gamblers place their bets latest of all on the shortest races. Many gamblers themselves believe there is an element of skill involved in betting on horse and dog races (Custer, 1982 Lesieur, 1984) but Dickerson saw this as an illusion largely irrelevant to the conditioning process which takes place within the betting shop. Johnson and Bruce (1990), however, found a significant superior performance for later as compared to earlier betting, suggesting that there is some substance in the gambler's belief.

This study involves a near replication of Dickerson (1977, 1979) work on the possible role of an FI schedule in late betting. The more recent introduction of live televised racing in the betting shop offered the additional opportunity to study gambling behavior governed by a visually dominated FI schedule.

METHODS

The betting behavior of customers in a Glasgow betting office placing bets on horse and dog races was observed directly. The observer was seated behind the betting shop counter in a deliberate move to convey the impression to customers that he was actually a member of staff in order to make his presence less intrusive. The betting response was recorded when the customer passed his slip to the clerk at the place-take counter. In addition informal interviews were carried with gamblers out with the betting shop used in this study. The betting office in which the study took place was situated on a busy main road, in an area which appeared to be of mixed social class. All customers who placed a bet during the study period were included in the data. Customers were mostly male, and there was a wide range as regards age. Following Dickerson, two sub-groups of customers were subsequently identified with the help of the betting office staff — regular gamblers and occasional gamblers. Regular gamblers were defined as those who bet on eight or more races per day, at least 3 days each week. Six such customers were eventually chosen. Occasional gamblers were defined as those gamblers who bet on three or fewer races per day. For each day that data was collected on any one high frequency gambler, data was also collected on three low frequency gamblers in order to facilitate statistical comparison.

The study coincided with the introduction of televised racing within betting shops in the UK and data were collected for a small number of televised traces for comparison with "blower only" commentaries. Televising of a race involved silent pictures of the sequence of events from parading to the winning horse entering the winner's enclosure while Dickerson's proposed prerace stimulus chain is broadcast over the blower. The volume on the TV was only turned up for the actual race commentary. The TV commentary was then still in competition with the different blower commentary.

Data was collected for over a month at the end of the flat racing season and the beginning of the National Hunt season. Data was also collected for greyhound races. The pre-race stimulus chain described by Dickerson did seem to occur. It was very rare for the start of a dog race to be delayed, and although the start of horse races was delayed occasionally, generally they ran close to advertised time, but never before.

It was apparent that regular gamblers spent more time studying form and generally paid more attention to what was going on. Occasional gamblers, in contrast, tended to enter the shop, place a bet and leave soon after, sometimes before the next result was broadcast. These customers seemed to be out with what was going on in the betting office, rarely studied the form sheets and seemed to place their bets without much deliberation.

Following Dickerson (1979), the frequency and stake-size of betting responses were recorded in relation to its occurrence prior to the OFF. A period of 8 minutes (6 before and 2 after the OFF) was studied. If the study period for one race interfered with another race then this data was not included in the results.

The OFF rarely coincided with the observer's minute time interval. To account for this, the same practice as Dickerson (1979) was observed. When the OFF was called over the blower, the observer noted the position of the second hand on his watch. If the next minute interval occurred within 30 seconds, all the bets that were recorded within that period were placed in category 0 minutes before the OFF. If the next minute interval occurred more than 30 seconds after the OFF was called, the row was categorized as -1 minutes (1 minute after the OFF). During the first two weeks, data was collected on all gamblers during study periods. For the second part of the study, separate data was collected on high-frequency and low-frequency gamblers.

Due to circumstance, there was no opportunity for inter-observer reliability studies. As such, the existence of observer bias or error cannot be ignored. However, the recording method was simple and unambiguous, the observer was given all the help required as regards position and information and data was discarded if the observer felt he had lost control due to the number of customers at the counter. In addition, written descriptions were made each day and if necessary referred to, of the high-frequency gamblers present and of the low-frequency gamblers as they arrived. However, as in Dickerson's study, this may have reduced but not eliminated observer bias or error.

RESULTS

Data was collected for all gamblers during the first part of the study from 42 races with starts sufficiently spaced for there to be no overlap for the six minutes prior to the OFF and the two minutes after. The total number of bets recorded for these races was 1235. The frequency of bets at specific times is set out in Figure 1. This distribution confirmed Dickerson's (1979) report which showed there was a marked increase in the frequency of bets placed just before the OFF and a decrease there after (df = 4, Chi-square = 213.02, $p < 0.001$).

Figure 1

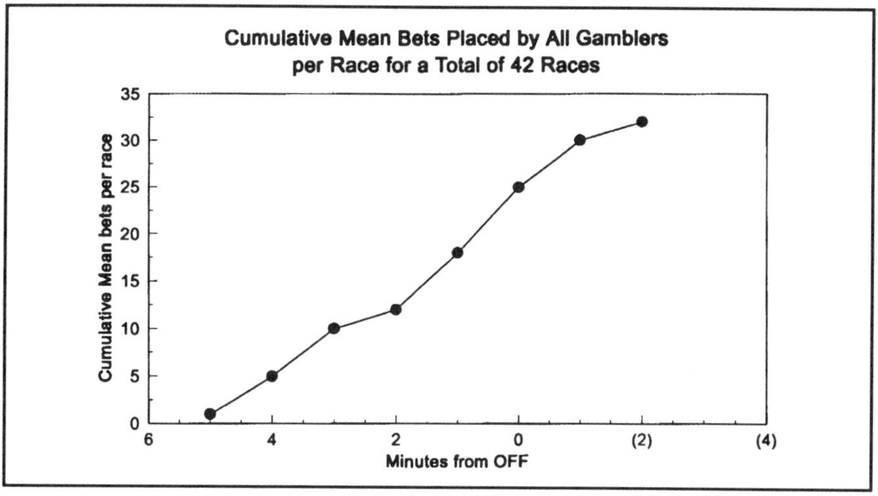

During the second part of the study data was collected for high and low-frequency gamblers. The comparison between these two groups for time of bet placement and size of bet within the eight minute period is summarized in Figure 2. Both figures summarize only data obtained for the two groups within the eight minute study period.

Following Dickerson, a chi-squared analysis was made comparing high and low-frequency gamblers on time of bet placement for the six one-minute time intervals before the OFF. This was not significant at the 0.05 level (df = 5, Chi-squared = 9.32) However when the two one-minute intervals after the "OFF" were included in an analysis the difference between the two distributions was significant (df = 7, Chi-squared = 21.06, $p < 0.01$), suggesting that high-frequency gamblers were much more likely to wait until the last possible moment before placing their bets. In addition, it was found that high-frequency gamblers placed a significantly higher proportion of their bets within the eight minute study period compared to low-frequency gamblers (df = 1, Chi-squared = 38.954, $p < 0.001$).

Figure 2

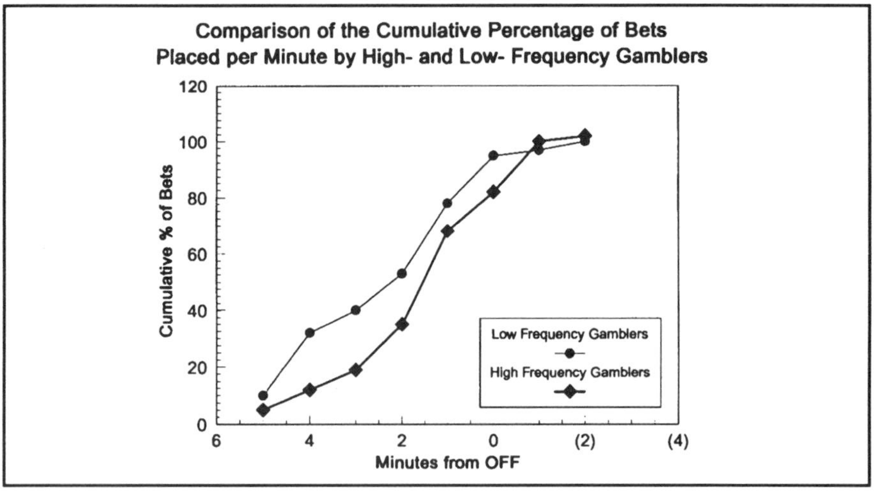

Figure 3

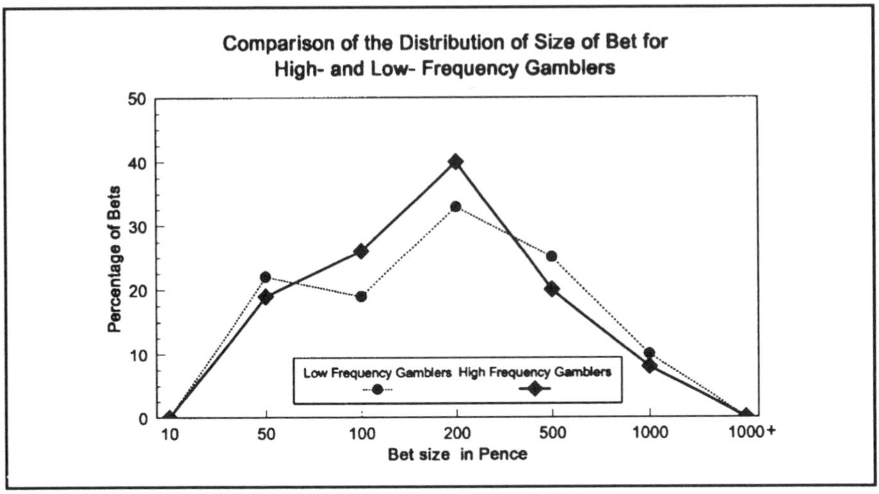

The distribution of bet sizes in the high- and low-frequency groups of bettors is set out in Figure 3. Chi-squared analysis showed no significant difference between bet sizes for high and low-frequency gamblers (df = 6, Chi-squared = 5.22). No data was available concerning the gambler's levels of income.

Data for televised races had been collected for all gamblers from seven races (total number of bets = 240). Distributions of cumulative mean bets for each group are summarized in Figure 4.

It was deemed inadvisable to compare high and low-frequency gamblers on such a small number of races. Comparison with data from blower-only races for all gamblers showed a highly significant difference (df = 7, Chi-squared = 45.29, $p < 0.001$), there being a general tendency for gamblers to place their bets longer before the OFF when the race was being televised.

DISCUSSION

Operant learning theory explanations of the heavy gambler's persistence under conditions of tangible loss have to take into account the fact that the gambler is punished repeatedly in this activity. Rosecrance (1986a, 1986b) described the persistence of "hard core" gamblers as ". . . remarkable since gambling researchers estimate that 95 percent of horse race gamblers lose money from

Figure 4

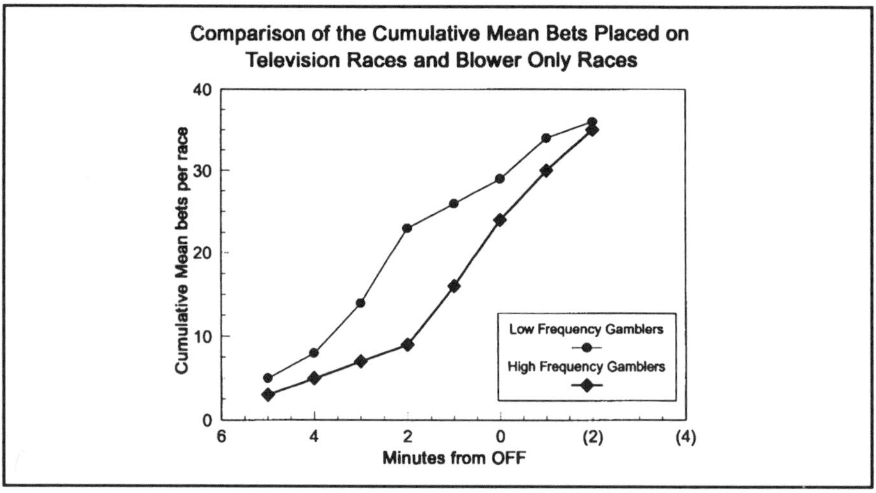

that endeavor." Oldman (1974, 1978) gave a similar scenario for casino gamblers. Punishment may not only take the form of financial loss. Social and personal problems may also occur along with sustained participation (Dickerson, 1984; Lesieur, 1979, 1982; Kusyszyn, 1978).

If an explanation of gambling solely in terms of operant conditioning were to be sufficient, the operation of the schedules of reinforcement must be sufficiently powerful to offset the tendency of the punishments to inhibit the activity altogether. If the rewards were overridingly powerful, it could be expected that everyone who gambled for a significant period of time would become compulsive. Yet the majority of gamblers bet only occasionally and, of those who gamble regularly, only a minority ever seek clinical help (Downes, Davies, David and Stone, 1976).

Even if the reinforcement schedule is not so powerful as to make every bettor a compulsive gambler, Dickerson proposes that an FI schedule of reinforcement operates within the betting shop environment to progressively "train" regular higher frequency bettors to bet later and more often with increasingly higher stakes. If this is so, a clear difference should be demonstrable between those regular gamblers who have been "trained" and the novice gamblers who have not been so "trained." This difference should occur so that high frequency gamblers bet not only more often than low frequency gamblers, but also bet later to obtain maximum reinforcement and with consistently higher stake sizes. From Dickerson's approach the focus on the proposed operation of an FI "scalloped" schedule of reinforcement as the highly dominant, even exclusive influence there suggests that anyone who is exposed to these influences will, in time, become a "trained" regular gambler and demonstrate a style of betting behavior distinctive from that of the low frequency gambler who has not been "trained."

Accordingly it would be predicted that the high-frequency group should place virtually all their bets within the last few minute intervals before a race and certainly within the eight minute period. It would also be predicted that there should be marked differences between low and high-frequency gamblers in this respect.

Late betting has been reported as a general phenomenon by Saunders (1981). Unlike in Dickerson's study and the present study, Saunders did not attempt to discriminate between high and low frequency gamblers. In the present study the results show no significant differences between the high and low-frequency groups in terms of timing of bet for the six one-minute time intervals before the OFF. Although there does seem to be a significant tendency for high-frequency gamblers to wait until the last possible moment to place their bet, this does not occur consistently enough to support Dickerson's theory. The distinction made in terms of frequency of betting does not discriminate between the two groups as regards timing of the bet.

High frequency gamblers did, as predicted, place a significantly higher proportion of their bets within the eightminute study period compared with low-frequency gamblers. Of all the bets recorded for the high-frequency group, 89% were placed within the study period, leaving 11% of bets which were placed out with the eight minute study period for any race, although these could have been multiple bets made out on ordinary betting slips (slips designed for multiple bets were excluded).

In addition to this lack of marked difference between the two groups, several gamblers were observed who, while staying frequently in the betting office all afternoon, and appearing to be very much involved in what was going on around them, bet only occasionally. Betting shop staff described these customers as "regulars who don t bet much." Continued exposure to the blower stimulus chain and both active and passive experience of the excitement reinforcer should have led them to increased frequency of betting but there were no signs of this being so.

No significant differences in bet size were found between high and low-frequency gamblers, suggesting that regular gamblers are not "trained" to bet consistently with larger sums of money than low frequency gamblers. The absence of information in the present study about relative income levels would only qualify the conclusions if it were the case that there were systematic differences in income between high and low frequency gamblers and these have never been reported.

It appears that the FI schedule proposed by Dickerson is not so powerful as to discriminate between regular high frequency gamblers and the occasional low frequency gamblers. The results obtained from televised races may also offer an indication that the proposed conditioning schedule is not the powerful controlling force suggested.

TELEVISED RACES

The results obtained from TV races must be interpreted with caution as data are limited both in terms of number of races and in the respect that no data is available to comparing high and low frequency gamblers. However, there does seem to be a general trend for bets to be placed earlier before the OFF when the race is being televised.

It is possible that the FI schedule is reduced in effect by having TV pictures compete with the blower commentary and it could be speculated that the general level of excitement and the rewards in terms of raised arousal levels at the end of the race may be lower when the race is televised. When the race is being described by the blower commentary, the gambler can use his imagination to an extent, as regards the shape of the race. The commentary can have the effect of maintaining a high level of excitement for the majority of gamblers in a way that does not occur when the race is televised. Unless the horse backed by the gambler falls or is pulled up, the nature of the blower commentary will encourage him to believe that all is not lost. Occasionally a horse which has been in contention throughout the race may not be mentioned until the final stages, giving the impression that the horse has come from nowhere. It was a commonly expressed belief among gamblers interviewed in this study that the race only starts 2 or 3 furlongs from home, and if the gambler's attention and involvement can be kept up until that stage, some excitement pay-off should occur.

If the switch of attention from the blower proves to have these effects with high frequency gamblers then again the conditioning effect does not seem to be sufficiently powerful in itself to account for their persistence.

COGNITIVE AND SOCIAL FACTORS AS MODIFIERS OF CONDITIONING EFFECTS

A general drawback with strict learning theory explanations of gambling, and in particular heavy gambling, is that they tend to deny the importance of cognitive and social factors. The view of the heavy gambler as simply a victim of conditioning falls into a very similar trap as describing problem gamblers as "compulsive" or sick in that both approaches see the heavy gambler as predominantly a responder to factors out with his control, be they internal or external.

Although Dickerson has now moved away from suggesting a simple conditioning model for regular or problem gambling, and is currently looking at a model which involves affective (depression and frustration) and cognitive (perceived control) variables (Corless and Dickerson, 1989), the inclusion of these are in addition to his earlier theory and his position is still one which allows heavy gambling to be seen as reactive and the notion of impaired control is still a feature. This suggests that there is still a point at which the individual becomes unable to resist carrying out a particular behavior. If there is a distinction between this position and the view that the gambler is "compelled" to carry out a particular behavior, then it is a very fine one.

COGNITIVE FACTORS AS MODIFIERS OF CONDITIONING EFFECTS

Regular gamblers are more likely to see their gambling as skilful. Dickerson (1974) reported that 60% of high-frequency gamblers rated their bet selection as more than 50% skill. In contrast, he reported that the majority of less frequent gamblers rated their selection as "all luck" or less than 25% skill. High-frequency gamblers, in addition, were reported as being more confident of winning with the betting slip they had in their hand. Although Dickerson rejects the idea that late betting is skillful betting, it may be seen as skillful by the gambler because of its association with betting from the board prices, and with attempting to use information from the odds being shortened or lengthened right up until the "OFF" before deciding on the size of the stake. The gambler may be on the look-out for a "job horse" (a horse heavily backed at the last moment but not before) in order to get a more favorable starting price or may decide that a late tumble in the odds for a horse is an indication that "something is going on." While this type of belief may be misplaced, the information it is based on might not be expected to be available to the novice gambler.

Wagenaar (1970; 1988) has demonstrated how the expectation that small samples of chance events will be representative of larger populations of chance events is commonly not met in runs of real events. People expect many short runs and no long runs, so that, when the long runs occur, they are interpreted as "caused" by the operation of a different factor from pure chance, commonly called luck. Keren and Wagenaar (1985) demonstrated that in the minds of gamblers, the outcome of gambles was dependent on at least three causal factors: chance - 18%; skill - 37%; and luck - 45%. Further, factor analyses (Wagenaar, 1988; Wagenaar and Keren, 1988) appear to confirm that in the minds of gamblers chance and luck are separate, both determining the outcomes in their own way, and that luck is seen as the more important.

Wagenaar who applied (1988) the cognitive heuristics and biases listed by Hogarth (1981) and studied by Kanneman, Slovic and Tversy (1982) to the explanation of the cognitive processes of gamblers even goes so far as to claim that such explanations are sufficient alone to account for the behavior of gamblers, regardless of their level of participation.

Quite apart from falling victims to the representativeness bias demonstrated by Wagenaar (1970) as mentioned above (which is the basis of the well known "Gambler's Fallacy"), the thinking of most gamblers appears to be affected by a closely related group of cognitive biases studied by Gilovich (1983). These are confirmation biases (which seek information consistent with a theory or prediction and discount disconfirming information); inconsistency of processing (where two contradictory prediction models are used as alternatives for each other, creating the illusion that outcomes are predictable, whatever occurs); flexible attribution (a tendency to attribute successes to one's own skill and failures to other influences); hindsight bias (belief, after the event, that outcomes were predicted and can be again) and biased learning structures (in which only one of several possible strategies is ever pursued leading to a failure to explore the others and compare their effectiveness). There is also evidence from Langer (1975) that they are affected by illusions of control (where activity concerning an uncertain outcome can by itself induce in a person feelings of control over the uncertain outcome). Finally, in addition to the turgid effects of the gamblers attributions of cause to chance, luck and skill, the bias of illusory correlation (the detection of variables that seen to covary when in fact they do not) produces a wealth of often exotic superstitious beliefs among gamblers which notoriously affect their gambling behavior in quite irrational and idiosyncratic ways.

SELF PRESENTATION, SELF IMAGE AND SELF ESTEEM AS A MODIFIERS OF CONDITIONING EFFECTS

For the gambler, by these processes, his skill at gambling may become attributed as being internal and stable, an identifiable and perhaps salient feature of himself. This self image can become combined with the perceived opinions of fellow gamblers so that the self-image and self-presentation of the person, at least within the gambling environment, becomes that of "a skilled gambler." He comes to see himself and imagines others as seeing him as such. Rosecrance describes this as the gambler's "situated identity." Status among gamblers can be shown to be more closely related to demonstrations of skill than to actually winning money (Zola, 1964) and Rosecrance (1986) suggested that "the illusion of control helps to sustain the serious horse player's credibility." It is likely that once the self-image and presentation become that of "a skilled gambler," much of the gambler's self esteem will be riding on his own and other's perception of him as skilled. A failure to maintain his situated identity would deal a considerable blow to his self esteem. Such a commitment of self identity and self esteem can only increase the arousal levels associated with gambling in high frequency gamblers because much more is at stake than just money.

AFFECTIVE FACTORS AS MODIFIERS IN HIGH FREQUENCY GAMBLING

The affective element described by Corless and Dickerson (1989) seems to belong within the wider tradition in addiction research as a whole which sees illegal drug use (the dominant view still being that any use of illegal drugs is problematic), problem drinking and, any extension, problem gambling as a response to stressful life events. This assumption was shown to be somewhat simplistic in a study by O'Doherty and Davies (1988), which indicated that while, compared to appropriate control groups, life events may be interpreted differently by drug users and problem drinkers, the actual incidence of stressful life events does not distinguish the addicted groups from controls. It is possible, however, that Corless and Dickerson may be referring to strategies used to cope with more temporary mood states rather than to more permanent internal traits or to external situational variables.

ATTRIBUTION EFFECTS IN THE EXPLANATION OF GAMBLING ADDICTIONS

Within the literature on gambling the concept of the "compulsive gambler" and the medical model in general is still influential (e.g., Lesieur and Custer, 1984). While neither the original DSM III (1980) nor the revised version (Lesieur, 1988) suggest that the "pathological" gambler's loss of control is irreversible, loss of control is still a central concept, matching the picture of subjection of the gambler to the more mechanistic and powerful response schedules advanced as the central features of explanation by behavioristic learning theorists.

Lesieur's adoption of the medical model within a sociological framework (Lesieur, 1988) contrasts with the views of other sociologists, particularly Oldman (1974, 1978). Oldman has suggested that the term "compulsive gambler" is a functional explanation adopted by a gambler in crises to explain his behavior and associated problems in non-volitional terms, and suggests that this label would prove acceptable to family, friends and treatment agencies. In other words the gambler cannot be blamed for the trouble he is in, because it is not his fault; he cannot help gambling.

While Oldman's suggestion has not received much support within the gambling literature, some empirical evidence consistent with his argument has come from recent studies involving drug users. Essentially these studies have demonstrated the operation of a systematic bias in the explanations given by the drug users for their behaviors. Davies and Baker (1988), for example, conducted a series of parallel interviews with heroin users, one set conducted by a "straight" interviewer, the other by a locally known heroin user. The results showed that with the straight interviewer the users presented themselves as being more "addicted" than they did with the user-interviewer. This difference was systematic, i.e., the ordinal characteristics of the data did not change. Similar findings arose from a study by Coggans and Davies (1988) where results indicated that the pattern of drug use constrains the available explanations. A heavy "chronic" user, for example, is expected by others to provide an "addicted" explanation for his drug use and, in turn, providing this explanation is beneficial to the user's self presentation and self esteem.

Results such as these do not show drug users as being more devious or duplicitous than other people. Rather they demonstrate a principle fundamental to attribution research, namely that the answers people give are functional and should be understood in the context in which they are offered. In the case of the gambler with massive financial problems, it will very likely be functional for him to explain these problems as a result of a behavior he could not control, rather than in volitional terms. The notion the "the explanation is the addiction," or that a drug user (and probably also a heavy drinker and heavy gambler) learns the appropriate explanation as they learn their behavior (Eiser, 1986), should be given serious consideration.

The concept of addiction itself, while not tied classical medical model with irreversible loss of control or to a mechanistic behavioral model with imperial schedules of reinforcement which, until re-learned have the same short term effects in loss of control, nevertheless appears to involve a complex balancing of perspectives of subjective perceptions of free choice and unavoidable behavior. It is a concept with widespread acceptance in the general population and, while it is likely to be an accurate model of real phenomena, it also likely to generate behavior to fit that model. This is not an unknown phenomenon in psychiatric disorders, the best example being the suspicions that the more widely publicized are the real cases of multiple personality the cases appear of predominantly iatrogenic origin and the more likely that the condition will be feigned to escape responsibility for criminal acts (Aldridge-Morris, 1989).

THE INTERACTION OF CONDITIONING AND AROUSAL AS MEDIATED BY COGNITION AND SELF-ESTEEM

The importance of schedules of reinforcement are not denied but they are assigned a different and less central role to that proposed by Dickerson. Cognitive factors are given a major role, although not the monopolistic role given to them by Wagenaar (1988). Attributional effects on the interpretation of addictive and "compulsive" behavior are acknowledged and the high-frequency gambler can be seen as betting with his self esteem.

It is likely then, that the arousal level when betting will be experienced as more pronounced than for the low-frequency gambler. This will be particularly so when betting close to the "OFF." Dickerson's (1977) reports of the extreme increase in arousal experienced by high frequency gamblers would seem to support this and the tendency of gamblers to increase bet size when winning has been reported by Anderson and Brown (1984).

The role and importance of arousal as a component of gambling has long been noted (Boyd, 1976) and is a central feature of the work of Brown (Anderson and Brown 1984; Brown, 1986; Brown, 1988a, 1988b), Dickerson (1984, Leary and Dickerson, 1985; Dickerson and Adcock, 1986; Corless and Dickerson, 1989) and Jacobs (1986, 1988).

Taking into account the gambler's thought processes and the operation of social factors, the gambler can be seen in the context of his betting environment without being a mere respondent to it and learning, cognitive, social and arousal components can be gradually integrated in a multifactorial model of gambling and gambling addictions.

REFERENCES

Aldridge-Morris, R. (1989). *Multiple Personality: An Exercise in Deception.* London: Hove Lawrence Erlbaum Associates.

Anderson, G., and R.I.F. Brown (1984). Real and laboratory gambling, sensation-seeking and arousal. *British Journal of Psychology*, 75, 401-410.

Bergler, E. (1957). *The Psychology of Gambling.* New York: Hill and Wang Inc.

Boyd, W.H. (1976). Excitement: The gambler's drug. In W.R. Eadington (ed.), *Gambling and Society.* Springfield, IL: Charles C. Thomas.

Brown, R.I.F. (1986). Arousal and sensation-seeking components in the general explanation of gambling and gambling addictions. *International Journal of Addictions*, 21, 1001-1016.

Brown, R.I.F. (1988a). Reversal theory and subjective experience in the explanation of addiction and relapse. In Japter, M.J., Kerr, J.H., and Cowal, M. (eds.), *Progress in Reversal Theory.* Amsterdam: North-Holland.

Brown, R.I.F. (1988b). Relapses from a gambling perspective. In M. Gossop. (ed.), *Relapses and Addictive Behavior*. London: Croom-Helm.

Coggans, N., and Davies, J.B. (1988). Explanations of heroin use. *Journal of Drug Issues*, 18, 457-465.

Corless, T., and Dickerson, M. (1989). Gambler's self perceptions of the determinants of impaired control. *British Journal of Addiction*, 84, 1527-1537.

Cornish, D.B. (1978). *Gambling: A Review of the Literature and Its Implications for Policy and Research*. London: Home Office Research Study No. 42.

Custer, R.L. (1982). Pathological gambling. In A. Whitfield (ed.), *Patients with Alcoholism and Other Drug Problems*. New York: Year Book Publishers.

Davies, J.B., and Baker, R. (1987). The impact of self presentation and interview bias effects on self reported heroin use. *British Journal of Addiction*, 82, 907-912.

Dickerson, M.G. (1974). *The Effect of Betting Shop Experience on Gambling Behavior*. Unpublished Ph.D. thesis. University of Birmingham.

Dickerson, M.G. (1977). The role of the betting shop environment in the training of compulsive gamblers. *Behavioral Psychotherapy*, 1, 24-29.

Dickerson, M.G. (1979). FI schedules and persistence at gambling in the U.K. betting office. *Journal of Applied Behavior Analysis*, 12, 315-323.

Dickerson, M. (1984). *Compulsive Gamblers*. Sydney: Longman.

Dickerson, M.G. (1985). The characteristics of the compulsive: A rejection of a typology. In Caldwell, G., Dickerson, M.G., Haig, B., and Sylvan, L. (eds), *Gambling in Sydney, Australia*. Australia: Croom Helm.

Dickerson, M., and Adcock, M. (1987). Mood, arousal and cognitions in persistent gambling: Preliminary investigation of a theoretical model. *Journal of Gambling Behavior*, 3, 3-15.

Downes, D.M., Davies, B.P., David, M.E., and Stone, P. (1976). *Gambling, Work and Leisure: A Study Across Three Areas*. London: Routledge & Kegan Paul.

Eiser, J.R. (1986). *Social Psychology.* Cambridge: Cambridge University Press.

Ferster, C.B., and Skinner, B.F. (1957). *Schedules of Reinforcement.* New York: Appleton.

Gilovitch, J. (1983). Biased evaluation and persistence in gambling. *Journal of Personality & Social Psychology*, 44, 110-126.

Hogarth, R. (1981). *Judgement and Choice.* New York: Wiley.

Jacobs, D.F. (1986). A general theory of addictions: A new theoretical model. *Journal of Gambling Behavior*, 1, 15-31.

Jacobs, D.F. (1988). Evidence for a common dissociative reaction among addicts. *Journal of Gambling Behavior*, 4, 27-37.

Johnson, J.E.V., and Bruce, A.C. (1992). Successful betting strategies: Evidence from the U.K. off-course betting market. In W.R. Eadington and J.A. Cornelius (eds.), *Gambling and Commercial Gaming: Essays in Business, Economics, Philosophy and Science.* Reno, NV: Institute for the Study of Gambling and Commercial Gaming, University of Nevada.

Kanneman, D., Slovic, P., and Tversky, A. (1982). *Judgement Under Uncertainty: Heuristics and Biases.* Cambridge, MA: Cambridge University Press.

Keren, G., and Wagenaar, W.A. (1985). On the psychology of playing blackjack: Normative and descriptive considerations with implications for decision theory. *Journal of Experimental Psychology: General*, 114, 133-158.

Kusyszin, J. (1978). "Compulsive" gambling: The problem of definition. *International Journal of Addictions*, 13, 1095-1101.

Langer, E.J. (1975). The illusion of control. *Journal of Personality and Social Psychology*, 32, 311-328.

Leary, K., and Dickerson, M.G. (1985). Levels of arousal in high and low-frequency gamblers. *Behavior Research and Therapy*, 23, 635-640.

Lesieur, H.R. (1979). The compulsive gambler's spiral of options and involvement. *Psychiatry*, 42, 79-78.

Lesieur, H.R. (1984). *The Chase: The Career of the Compulsive Gambler.* Cambridge, MA: Schenkman.

Lesieur, H.R. (1988). Altering the DSM III criteria for pathological gambling. *Journal of Gambling Behavior*, 4, 38-47.

Lesieur, H.R., and Custer, R.L. (1984). Pathological gambling: Roots, phases and treatment. *Annals of American Academy of Political Science*, 474, 146-156.

National Council on Gambling (1983). *Gambling: Some Key Statistics.* National Council on Gambling, 26 Bedford Square, London, WClB 3HU.

Newman, O. (1972). *Gambling Hazard and Reward.* London: Athlone Press.

O'Doherty, F. and Davies, J.B. (1988). Life event stress and addiction. In F. Fisher and J.D. Reason (eds.), *Handbook of Cognition and Health.* Hove: Wiley.

Oldman, D.J. (1974). Chance and skill: A study of roulette. *Sociology*, 8, 407-26.

Oldman, D.J. (1978). Compulsive gamblers. *Sociological Review*, 26, 349-71.

Rosecrance, J. (1985). *Degenerates of Lake Tahoe.* New York: Peter Lang Publishing.

Rosecrance, J. (1986a). Adapting to failure: The case of horse race gamblers. *Journal of Gambling Behavior*, 2, 81-94.

Rosecrance, J. (1986b). The next best thing: A study of problem gambling. *International Journal of Addictions*, 20, 1727-1739.

Rosecrance, J. (1986c). Why regular gamblers don't quit: A sociological perspective. *Sociological Perspectives*, 29, 357378.

Royal Commission on Gambling (1978). *Final Report.* London: Her Majesty's Stationary Office.

Saunders, D.M. (1981). The late betting phenomenon in relation type of bet and type of race. *Behavioral Psychotherapy*, 9, 330-37.

Skinner, B.F. (1953). *Science and Human Behavior.* New York: Free Press.

Wagenaar, W.A. (1970). Subjective randomness and the capacity to generate information. In A.F. Sanders (ed.), *Attention and Performance III, Acta Psychologica*, 33, 233-242.

Wagenaar, W.A. (1988). *Paradoxes of Gambling Behavior.* London: Hove Lawrence Erlbaum Associates.

Wagenaar, W.A. and Keren, G. (1988). Chance and luck are the same. *Journal of Behavioral Decision Making*, 1, 65-75.

Wray, I. and Dickerson, M.G. (1981). Cessation of high frequency gambling and withdrawal symptoms. *British Journal of Addiction*, 76, 401-405.

Zola, J.K. (1964). Observations on gambling in a lower-class setting. In Becker, H.S. (ed.), *The Other Side Perspectives on Deviance*. Illinois: Free Press.

II

Studies in Compulsive and Pathological Gambling Behavior

The Growing Presence of Pathological Gambling in Society: What We Know Now

Emanuel Moran

In the light of the explosion of research on the issue of problem gambling in the past few years, it is a tall order for me to summarize in a few pages, what we know now about pathological gambling. However, I am happy to do so, in terms of some personal comments.

What **do** we know about pathological gambling? In practice, we still know remarkably little about this condition. We know that it is a clinical entity which is defined in the *Diagnostic and Statistical Manual* of the American Psychiatric Association (DSM III and III-R) as well as the *10th Edition of the International Classification of Disease of the World Health Organization* (*ICD10*). By virtue of this, it is now truly on the medical map. We may argue whether the medical model is relevant or not. The facts are that, when it comes to providing facilities for those in difficulty as a result of excessive gambling, governments and their agencies appear only to be willing to consider putting their money where their mouth is, if the medical model is applied to the condition.

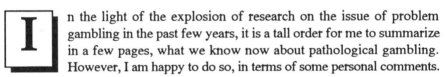

One is reminded of the statement made four hundred years ago by Cardano, in his book, *Liber de ludo alae* (*The Book on Games of Chance*):

> "Even if gambling were altogether an evil, still, on account of the very large number of people who play, it would seem to be a natural evil. For that very reason it ought to be discussed by a medical doctor like one of the incurable diseases" (Ore, 1953).

However, it has been observed that if a clinical entity is only recognizable by certain behavior, the individuals showing it will vary greatly in many other respects. Rather than one condition, we are therefore dealing with a heterogeneous group of states characterized by excessive gambling with problems. When faced by a rather complex condition such as pathological gambling, there is a tendency to concentrate on certain aspects of it to the exclusion of others. This is particularly so if it is being studied by a number of different disciplines which all have their own approach. Both in understanding causation and assessing response to intervention and treatment, there will inevitably be great diversity.

Over twenty years ago, when I first became interested in this condition, it was always referred to as compulsive gambling. Apart from the semantic inaccuracy of this, this latter term wrongly implied a condition which could be explained in terms of a single cause. Furthermore, it was assumed that this cause resided in the unconscious and always did so, and could only be dealt with adequately by psychoanalytic techniques (Moran, 1970a, 1970b).

The papers presented in this volume demonstrate that we have come a long way from that position. However, in pursuing the matter, we need to remind ourselves continually that the repertoire of human behavior is restricted. Consequently, since the forces acting on the human organism are almost limitless, a particular behavioral response, such as excessive gambling, is the possible outcome of a variety of processes (Moran, 1970c). The search for one explanation which will account for all this is a chimera. Ultimately, many of the explanations for pathological gambling will elude us until we have much more knowledge about the activity of gambling. We need to know more about normal gambling — using the word normal in a statistical sense.

We can learn a great deal from our experience in relation to other types of behavior, such as alcohol misuse. Much time and effort were wasted in alcohol research because early studies were solely preoccupied with people in trouble.

Once researchers concentrated on the use of alcohol within the whole population rather than limiting their view to those in difficulty as a result of its use, two things were recognized. Firstly, those whose difficulty was overt were only "the tip of the iceberg." Secondly, many of the original explanations were not specific to the particular behavior but more relevant to the fact that those previously studied were often very disturbed individuals, who as part of their general disorder, were also misusing alcohol.

We need to recognize that gambling, like any other activity, can be misused even by normal individuals. Indeed, by its very nature, it is more likely to be misused than many other activities. While the preoccupation with the pathological gambler has had many benefits, particularly in encouraging interest in this matter, we now need to concentrate on pathological gambling. When we look at the patterns of gambling in the general population, we find that every society has its own ethic in relation to gambling. This varies from total abstinence as in some Moslem groups, for example, to qualified endorsement as in American and European societies, to a relatively high level of participation as occurs among the Chinese.

What is the present Western attitude towards gambling? Basically, it tends to be rather hypocritical. Most people gamble and in the materialistic society in which we live that encourages dreams of sudden affluence, the myth that gambling is an easy way of becoming rich is encouraged. Gambling is often referred to as an investment. Yet the fact that empirical evidence strongly indicates that the best way of finishing up with a small fortune as a result of gambling is to start with a large fortune, is played down. In contrast, there are still very negative attitudes towards gambling and even the very term has pejorative overtones. The approach is basically one in which it is considered that, "I have a flutter. You have a bet. He gambles." Many punters deny that they "gamble," and they would see gambling as an activity characterized by excess and misuse, having overtones associated with the undesirable and even the frankly criminal. These conflicting attitudes towards gambling lead to double standards. Depending on what aspect of the situation we are preoccupied with at a particular time, we applaud it or condemn it.

The person who gets into difficulties because of gambling points out a truth about gambling: For the punter, gambling is not primarily an activity to make money. As far as the majority of people are concerned, the reality is that fortunes gained as a result of gambling are illusory. It is basically a form of entertainment for which most people pay. The person who gets into difficulties demonstrates that winning money at gambling is, especially in the long term, a rarity. Yet, psychologists attempt to explain this behavior by formulations such as "playing to lose," as though the rest of those who gamble were all winners.

How can psychologists and other professionals make sense of this situation in a more rational manner? It seems to me that the only way that we can do this is to recognize that gambling behavior is a continuum from total abstinence to occasional gambling and from there to moderate gambling and finally to heavy gambling which ultimately leads to problems.

Within this situation a number of factors operate. They fall into three broad categories: social, psychological and physiological. In the consideration of these factors, it is important to recognize that gambling is an activity which has an important social dimension, not only in terms of the effects on others as a result of the activity, but others are essential for gambling to take place at all (Moran, 1970a). As far as most people who gamble are concerned, the gambling industry provides the facilities, and the availability of these and the incitements that are incorporated, encouraging excess by the punter, play a very important role. The adequacy of legislative and administrative controls on gambling are therefore important determinants of the incidence of pathological gambling.

Individuals vary in their personality and psychological make-up, and therefore in their response to situations that offer gambling. However, more important than this is the fact that the activity of gambling becomes subject to the laws of learning which apply to a great many other repeated acts which individuals perform. All the factors which behavioral psychology teaches as important in learning — such as imitation, practice, setting, mental set, and reward — affect this aspect of behavior as well. Thus, the act of gambling becomes a piece of learned behavior — in short, a habit. Habits are very powerful components of mental organization so that the continuation of gambling, begun under social pressures, may later continue for quite different psychological reasons. Once the habit is established — and this may happen quite rapidly or it may take some years to do so — the person concerned often discovers that, on withdrawal from gambling, there is a feeling of not quite being oneself. This is the condition which is usually referred to as psychological dependence.

This reaction closely parallels the feeling of the habitual smoker that he needs another cigarette. Having become conditioned to associating a removal of psychic discomfort with more gambling, an individual may respond to a variety of events which cause such discomfort by increased gambling. The person who has become dependent is especially vulnerable to responding to everyday pressures by more gambling than the person not so dependent. Such escalation would carry in its train the risk of economic and social damage. Ultimately, it results in financial pressures which perpetuate the problem, as does the social disorganization which accompanies it.

Therefore, as is usually the case in human behavior, one can see an intimate interaction between social and psychological factors. As far as physiological factors are concerned, it is important to emphasize that there must always be a physiological substratum to all psychological states. While recent research in this area provides interesting contributions, accounting for individual differences among those who gamble, it is difficult to see physiological factors as doing anything more than providing a predisposition. Further studies may well clarify these issues.

It would seem therefore, that while all these factors play some part in the causation of pathological gambling, there are strong indications that psychological factors, in the setting of social pressures, are the most important. Central to this formulation is the view that gambling behavior is a continuum. The implications of adopting this view are as follows. First, it encourages a new approach to personal history taking, in which the amount of money staked and the frequency of gambling is noted at key points in relation to the person's life events. It also enables a judgement to be made of the differing strengths of various factors — cultural, occupational and psychological — at different times and at the onset of a change in gambling behavior. In short, this view gives a dynamic aspect to formulation.

Second, the view of gambling as a continuum opens up a preventative approach to pathological gambling by providing a role for education, in the broadest sense, by enabling the individual to monitor his own gambling (Moran, 1979). It also provides for environmental measures of a legislative and administrative kind to play a part in relation to the control of participation. It suggests that if treatment is failing to halt the growth of the problem, as it appears to, then a shift to prevention in greater degree than hitherto is worth a trial. This approach also has a lot to say about further preparing for a preventative role the helping agencies, which at present are almost entirely involved in treatment and after-care. Most important, it specifies quite different gambling goals for prevention, goals which have nothing to do with abstinence, and so might be acceptable in the way prohibition is not.

Third, in relation to treatment, this view provides a rational basis for an educative or cognitive approach, using some knowledge of the true facts of gambling and behavior therapy. The suggested use of behavior therapy is by no means synonymous with formal measures to that end. It is usually enough simply to explain these mechanisms and counsel appropriate changes in lifestyle in accord with the principles which govern the learning and unlearning of habits. Fourth, in after-care, this view recognizes the contribution of lifestyle to the earlier established gambling pattern, and points to the importance of a changed lifestyle, if that pattern is not to be repeated. Above all, it emphasizes the need to deal with the "here and now" of everyday life.

Within the above formulation, it is obviously important to give special consideration to the impact of gambling on children and young people. In general, gambling is seen to be an adult activity. It is unsuitable for the young who, because of immaturity, are more likely to take it to excess. Yet, there is presently a situation in Great Britain where certain types of gaming machines, euphemistically referred to as amusements with prizes (AWPs), are legally available to children and young people in public places such as cafes, restaurants and amusement arcades. This situation has been associated with alarming reports of serious gambling problems among children and young people under the age of eighteen years as a result of their gambling on these machines (Moran, 1987).

The last Royal Commission on Gambling, which reviewed public policy on gambling in Great Britain and reported in 1978, emphasized the importance of the following:

> "Gamblers should invariably be made aware of what they are letting themselves in for when they gamble — in other words what they may lose" (Para. 1.8, Final Report, Royal Commission on Gambling, HMSO, 1978).

As is well documented elsewhere, the modern gaming machine is a major growth area of the present-day commercial gaming industry. Furthermore, as some research has shown, it is also a major growth area for pathological gambling among adults. Children and young people tend to be extreme optimists. Modern gaming machines with flashing lights conveying messages of great bonanzas are not set up, in the words of the Royal Commission, to let them know "... what they are letting themselves in for when they gamble." In view of the fact that children are at the peak of their learning potential, the learning mechanisms referred to earlier, which can lead to pathological gambling, will be particularly effective. There is, therefore, growing concern about the long-term effects of a situation in which children have such ready access to gambling on modern gaming machines. This anomaly in the law must be rectified by restricting all gaming machines to licensed premises where only adults can have access to them. It is most regrettable that, so far, the British government has not been persuaded that legislative action should be taken to this end.

Finally, what do we really now know about pathological gambling? Perhaps this can best be summarized by quoting the British Royal College of Psychiatrists. In commenting on the help that needs to be provided for those in difficulty as a result of pathological gambling, the College recently stated:

> ". . . the contribution that treatment can be expected to make is definitely limited. The success of prevention and treatment of gambling problems is in large measure dependent upon appropriate public policies in relation to the availability of gambling facilities and the social pressures encouraging participation . . .
>
> Experience . . . leads to the conclusion that costly treatment programmes are far less effective in dealing with excess than preventative measures in terms of a public policy encouraging moderation. An essential part of this is the adequate control of commercial availability . . ." (Royal College of Psychiatrists, 1988).

In essence, the more gambling that is taking place, the more are some people going to misuse it. In the ancient temple at Delphi, there was an aphorism on the wall which read: "Nothing in excess." We would do well if this could be applied at both personal and national levels.

REFERENCES

HMSO (1978). *Final Report of the Royal Commission on Gambling, 1976-1978*, Cmnd. 7200. London: HMSO.

Moran, E. (1970a). *British Journal of Psychiatry*, 116, 593.

Moran, E. (1970b). *British Journal of Addiction*, 64, 419.

Moran, E. (1970c). Proc. Roy. Soc. Med., 63, 1273.

Moran, E. (1987). *Report on fruit machine gambling among schoolchildren.* London: The National Council on Gambling.

Moran, J. (1979). *Mind Out: Six Topics For Social Education.* London: Edward Arnold.

Ore, O. (1953). *Cardano the Gambling Scholar.* Princeton: Princeton University Press.

Royal College of Psychiatrists (1988). *Consultation on Amusement Arcades: Submission to the Home Office.*

Some Causes of Pathological Gambling

Richard J. Rosenthal

Why does anyone gamble? Predicting the outcome of some future event, even if it is only the turn of a card or the winner of a football game, gives us an illusion that we possess greater power and control than we really have. *People gamble to control the uncontrollable.* At a time when they are feeling helpless or overwhelmed, they turn to just such solutions.

There is a big increase in gambling today. Some of the reasons might include the break-up of the nuclear family, and the loss of familiar and established values, the threats of destruction to society and to our planet, uncertainty about our economic futures and, at least for those of us in the United States, uncertainty about our role as a nation. Of course, we cannot ignore the impact of new technologies, and the acceleration of change. We now have a generation raised entirely upon television. Gambling caters to a need for immediate relief and gratification, a preoccupation with material success, and a kind of action without involvement — very much the mind-set inculcated by television.

Thus, the increase in legalized gambling may be not so much a cause as a consequence of the problems. The validity of this opinion is supported by supply and demand patterns in the drug trade. As Norman E. Zinberg observed:

> . . .availability is always intertwined with the social and psychological factors that create demand. . .. For example, when the morale of U.S. troops in Germany declined in 1972, large quantities of various drugs, including heroin, became readily available, even though Germany is far from opium-growing areas (1984, p. 13).

A more recent example is the use of cocaine in the 1980s.

There is no doubt that, when it comes to gambling, greater legalization brings about greater accessibility. Particularly when coupled with aggressive marketing, this produces an increase in the number of gamblers, as well as the number of compulsive gamblers. However, rather than blame the lotteries or the other forms of commercial gaming which have proliferated, we might consider them as a reflection of the deeper changes which are taking place in society.

II.

What about compulsive or pathological gambling? I have gradually come to believe that pathological gambling is indeed an addiction. There is a great deal that we do not know about addiction, but I am convinced that whatever we will learn about neurotransmitters — about endorphins, and noradrenalin, and serotonin and dopamine — that addiction is not just a chemical reaction in the brain, and that we will still need to talk about the experience produced by the drug. Some drugs create feelings of exhilaration or euphoria. Gambling produces a sense of power.

This is an oversimplification. Gambling is more complex than that. In fact, its complexity adds to its attraction. Usually thought of as a stimulant, it is just as capable of functioning as a relaxant or tranquilizer — for many it is the numbing effect that is important — while for others it is disinhibiting. These occur in various combinations.

Gambling can be used to regulate affect, arousal, or self-esteem. But in every case, it is the feeling, or more accurately, the state of mind, to which the person becomes addicted.

I have said that I consider *omnipotence* the central concept for an understanding of pathological gambling (Rosenthal, 1986; 1986, November). I defined omnipotence as an illusion of power and control which defends against intolerable feelings of helplessness, depression, or guilt. To feel omni-potent (literally meaning all-powerful) is the most basic of the self-deceptions, since it is experienced precisely at the moment one is most helpless and out of control. Omnipotence is borne out of desperation. There is *omnipotence of thought*, in which one's thoughts are regarded as all-powerful (wishing will make it so); *omnipotent action*, in which doing something, anything, even if it is something destructive, is felt to be better than doing nothing; and *omnipotent provocation*, in which one flirts with danger, and the risk of great loss, in order to prove oneself powerful and in control. *Pathological gambling is basically an addiction to a false state of mind.*

So what causes pathological gambling? There appear to be at lease three components:

1. *An intolerable feeling state* — helplessness, depression, or guilt.

   Specifically, the individual may feel pulled equally in two directions at once, so that there is a sense of futility about doing anything. They may feel they can never do enough, or that they can never be good enough. Or they may feel unlovable. For some, there is a sense of irreparable guilt. I have never seen a pathological gambler who did not have significant problems in self-esteem prior to the onset of his or her gambling.

2. *A highly developed capacity for self-deception.*

   In addition to the omnipotence, there are other types of magical and primitive superstitious thinking, a belief that problems can be avoided, and frequently, an early pattern of lying. Again, these precede the gambling.

3. *Exposure to gambling under circumstances in which it is valued.*

   Compulsive gambling seems to run in families. Many gamblers are initiated into gambling by a parent, the experience providing the only closeness between them, or perhaps that and sports. For some, there was a family poker game, where to be allowed a seat was a sign of acceptance, either as a family member or adult. Others gambled away from home where, through luck or skill — and many were initially skillful gamblers — their early winnings brought recognition and status.

III.

It is not the length of time spent gambling, or the amount of money lost, nor is it bad luck, or poor money management, that makes a pathological gambler. In fact, it may surprise some people to learn that there are pathological gamblers who come for treatment while they are still winning! Not many certainly, but a few. Some recognize their over-involvement with gambling; their preoccupation with it while at work, or when they should be concentrating on other things. They notice that they are escalating their bets, or taking greater risks than they should. Or perhaps they are concerned about the sweaty palms, rapid heart beat, or that feeling in the pit of their stomach. Maybe winning, or just not losing, has become too important.

Just as some people can recognize an early gambling problem, researchers are beginning to identify those who are at risk of becoming pathological gamblers. Possible predisposing factors include:

1. *A family history of compulsive gambling.*

   As many as one third of compulsive gamblers have a biological relative with the disorder. It is not unusual to find such a history extending through two and three generations.

2. *Growing up in a family with an extremely critical, or rejecting, or emotionally unavailable parent.*

   For men, this is usually the father, and there is a lifelong campaign to please that parent and win their approval. This is generalized on to others as a need to impress, and an over-concern with being appreciated. There may be a rebellion against this — a kind of pseudo-independence — as well as a great deal of destructive anger.

   Many pathological gamblers grow up believing they can never be good enough, or they can never do enough. They develop compensatory fantasies of some spectacular success, like a "big win," which will show others just how good they are. Such a win, they believe, will also bring them financial (i.e., emotional) independence.

3. *An emphasis in the family on status — or an overvaluing of money.*

   Many pathological gamblers were taught at an early age to equate money with self-worth — or with power, control, or security. For example, I have seen a number of pathological gamblers among the children of holocaust survivors, who grew up with fathers who were not only angry, depressed, or emotionally unavailable, but who believed that the only way to achieve security was to have enough money. This was their only way to counter a profound sense of helplessness, and to assure themselves that what happened to them could not happen again. It is what they transmitted to their children, who then became pathological gamblers.

4. *Men, in particular, brought up to be extremely competitive.*

Pathological gamblers are, typically, extremely competitive. Many were deliberately raised that way, usually by their fathers. Winning became everything. Initially essential for parental approval, it was soon the basis of their self-esteem. For many, there is a kind of "all-or-nothing" thinking, in which one is good or bad, perfect or worthless, a super-hero or piece of garbage. In other words, a winner or a loser.

5. *The existence of an early physical or developmental problem.*

Also at risk seem to be those who are compensating for some physical or developmental problem which caused them great shame and humiliation early in life. This might include some congenital abnormality, speech defect, a problem with bed-wetting, obesity, short stature, or delayed puberty. This seems to be a factor for addictions in general.

6. *Hyperactivity.*

For many with Attention Deficit Hyperactivity Disorder, gambling initially serves as a rather specific way to medicate oneself. Just as they discover with video games, or with certain drugs such as cocaine or the amphetamines, gambling has a paradoxical effect on them — it slows them down, calms them, allows them to concentrate. However, when there are other factors present, it gets out of hand. This is a subtype of pathological gambler we are only just beginning to recognize.

In conclusion, it is very exciting to participate in international forums and meetings which explore causes of pathological gambling. It is my hope that the kind of interchange of ideas, theories, and observations which are presented in volumes such as this will be at the vanguard of many more such explorations.

REFERENCES

Rosenthal, Richard J. (1986). The pathological gambler's system of self-deception. *Journal of Gambling Behavior*, 2, pp. 108-120.

Rosenthal, Richard J. (1986, November). *Chance, Luck, Fate and Destiny: Toward a Developmental Model of Pathological Gambling.* Keynote address of the Second Annual Conference on Gambling Behavior, sponsored by the National Council on Compulsive Gambling.

Zinberg, Norman E. (1984). *Drugs, Set, and Setting: The Basis for Controlled Intoxicant Use.* New Haven, CT: Yale University Press.

The Catalonia Survey: Personality and Intelligence Structure in a Sample of Compulsive Gamblers©

Angel Martínez Pina, José Luis Guirao, Rafael Fusté i Vallverdú, Xavier Serrat Planas, Miguel Martín Mateo, and Víctor Moreno Augado

Since gambling was legalized in Spain in 1977, the only message that has prevailed has been the advertising by the various institutions involved, including the State. This advertising has bombarded the population, encouraging them to gamble. However, in the last three years, gambling has become a subject of public controversy (Guirao, 1985; Rosecrance, 1988). Both government agencies and a number of other bodies have been studying its personal and social implications and there has been considerable debate on the subject in the media. Concurrently, investigators have started to study gambling and gamblers (Martinez Pina, 1989; Serrat and Fuste, 1990; Guirao, 1988; Line Staff, 1989; González, 1988) and a number

© A version of this article has been published in the *Journal of Gambling Studies* (1991), 7(4), 275-300. New York: Human Sciences Press, Inc. Permission to reprint granted by the authors and publisher.

of prevention and treatment mechanisms have been developed including organizations such as "Gamblers Anonymous," self-exclusion systems (National Gambling Commission list — or its equivalent in the "Generalitat" of Catalonia — giving the names of gamblers who voluntarily — or at the request of members of their families or of gambling institutions — decide to have their access to places of gambling prohibited in order to help them overcome their addiction. In Catalonia, there are more than 6,500 people on this list) and treatment in public centers (Instituto Español para la atención a los problemas del Juego de Azar, 1989).

Insofar as pathological gambling is included as a separate nosological entity in psychiatric classifications, there is a need for research aimed at increasing knowledge on addiction's etiology and psychopathology. "Pathological gambling" describes a condition, whereas the "compulsive" and "addictive" flavor suggest a particular and homogeneous etiology which in fact may not accompany all instances of gambling pathology (Moran, 1970a; Moran, 1970b). Moran (1970c) distinguishes between five varieties of pathological gambling: subcultural, neurotic, impulsive, psychopathic and symptomatic.

Three main psycho-sociogenetic theories have been formulated to account for pathological gambling: that of the "moral escape valve" (Kruijt, 1973), a kind of release through gambling from the tension created in the individual by social inequalities ; the "domino theory": a social or recreational activity becomes pathological and may end in addiction; finally, the "specific personality theory" (Jacobs, 1989). Addiction is the transition from use to abuse, and has three characteristic features: loss of control, obstruction in normal functioning and tolerance.

It is possible to distinguish between three different attitudes to gambling: *Recreative or social participation, dangerous custom* and *addiction or pathological gambling* (Becker and Hermkens, 1987).

The *general theory of addiction* (Jacobs, 1989) proposes that the factors that enhance an maintain an addictive behavior pattern are:

1. A physiological level of mood excitation (unipolar resting state) which is perceived constantly as hypertensive or excited, or as hypotensive or depressed. A chronically high state of activation leads the subject to feel tense, while a low state of activation makes the subject feel bored. Both states are aversive and lead

to a compulsion to take part in activities that provide some release. According to Jacobs, the gambler usually comes under the group of hypoexcited subjects.

2. Childhood and adolescence marked by deep feelings of maladjustment, inferiority and rejection. The author considers that people in a chronically abnormal mood state, and who tend to respond to feelings of inferiority and rejection by fleeing towards negation and compensatory fantasy, are at a greater risk of acquiring an addictive behavior pattern. Given these predisposing conditions in a favorable environment, addictive behavior may appear if a substance or activity has the following attributes:
   - It clouds critical judgement of reality, even if this is through focusing attention, as in the case of gambling.
   - It diminishes self-criticism and self-awareness.
   - It enables pleasurable fantasies about oneself (narcissism).

As the number and intensity of these three attributes increases, the more likely it is that the subject will enter a dissociative state (Jacobs, 1988).

The theory of the Addictive Response Syndrome (Taber, Collachi, and Lynn, 1986), considers that underlying all addictive or pathologically excessive behaviors there is a generalized addictive response syndrome and it argues that all addicts have had their development stunted in one way or another. The process may be triggered by a significant life event or by any other type of risk factor. If this risk or vulnerability factor actually cause a dysphoric mood and cognitive state the subject will be exposed to a high risk of suffering an addictive loss of control. Any practice or substance that immediately reduces the dysphoria is liable to pathological use.

Studies on the specific psychopathology of the pathological gambler led to the development an evaluation of the concepts of "chasing" — an impulse to want to recover the lost money — and "action seeking" — a search for action that produces extreme sensations (Lesieur, 1979; Lesieur, 1984; Lesieur and Klein, 1987; Volberg and Steadman, 1988; Nadler, 1982).

Also in the field of psychopathology, current studies describe the pathological gambler as a subject who suffers from a moderate level of depression and a degree of anxiety—state and trait—above that of the control population (Blaszczynski and McConaghy, 1989). Other authors insist on the importance of studying depression (Moravec and Munley, 1983) and anxiety (Linden, Pope and Jonas, 1986; Taber, McCormick and Ramírez, 1987) in the pathological gambler. This shows a relationship between pathological gambling and major affective disorders (Linden, Pope and Jonas, 1986). The personality categories postulated by Eysenck and Eysenck are currently under study: the pathological gambler scores high in psychoticism and neuroticism (Roy et al., 1989). Also, there are highly significant correlations between scores on the EPQ extraversion scale and indexes of noradrenergic function in pathological gamblers (Roy, De Jong and Linnoila, 1989). Other authors find that sensation seeking correlates positively with the traits of extraversion and psychoticism as measured by the EPQ (Eysenck and Zuckerman,1978) and with changes of the noradrenergic system (Roy et al., 1988). It is also found that pathological gamblers are more extroverted and intuitive than recreative gamblers (Malkin and Syme, 1986). Hostility (Roy et al., 1989) and the degree of psychopathy (Moravec and Munley, 1983; Blaszczynski, McConaghy and Frankova, 1989) have also been put forward as discriminative variables.

The study of Zuckerman's SSS scale has been the subject of significant controversy. While some authors (Dickerson, Hinchy and Fabre, 1987) find a significant correlation between the results obtained in the various subscales of the SSS and the degree of addiction in a population of pathological gamblers, others (Allcock and Grace, 1988) argue that there are no significant differences in SSS scores between pathological gamblers and controls. These differences between the study performed by Dickerson, Hinchy and Fabre and that performed by Allcock and Grace, may be due to the fact that the former looked at the subscales whereas the latter did not. Other studies (Taber, McCormick and Ramirez, 1987; Roy et al., 1988) refer to the importance of life events in the development and maintenance of pathological gambling. Another aspect to be considered is the existence of polyaddiction in pathological gamblers (Lesieur, Blume and Zoppa, 1986; Meyer, 1986; Kagan, 1987), with inconsistent results.

To date, little work has been done on studying the pathological gambler's intelligence. Some Australian teams, however, have suggested that the intelligence quotient (IQ) is a factor that should be taken into account in the variable "length to addiction" in the specific case of horse-race betting. After administering the WAIS to a population of expert and non-expert men, who were avid racetrack patrons, Ceci and Liker (1986; 1987; Liker and Ceci, 1987) reached the conclusion that the IQ is unrelated to skilled performance at the racetrack as well as unrelated to real-world forms of cognitive complexity that would appear to conform to some of those that scientists regard as the hallmarks of intelligence behavior. These results were challenged by other authors (Reagan, 1987; Detterman and Spry, 1987), who found a negative correlation between IQ and years of horse-racing experience among horse-racing experts. According to these observations, the IQ is related to the degree of skill in gambling that the subject acquires. Finally, another author (Moravec, 1983) who studied the intelligence of a group of pathological gamblers, obtained results that he defined as normal.

In our study, on the basis of the reports contained in the literature and conversations with experts on the subject of pathological gambling, we formulated the following hypotheses:

1. Pathological gamblers' intelligence may have a specific profile, both because it is conditioned by their addiction and because of the skills developed in the course of their practice of gambling. We assumed that the tests that explored the WAIS' third factor (follow-up, memory and resistance to distraction) would score higher and those that explored ability to abstract oneself and understanding would score lower for pathological gamblers.
2. We expected to find a certain relationship between the degree of addiction and the presence of psychopathology (trait and state) in the sample of pathological gamblers.
3. Verify the existence of polyaddiction among pathological gamblers.
4. It was our intention to verify the existence of specific psychological and behavioral features in addiction to gambling and which have been described in the international literature: chasing, sensation seeking, focusing, dissociative state, aversive unipolar resting state, narcissism, experiences of rejection, and presence of painful life events.

SUBJECTS AND METHODS

A. Pathological Gamblers (PG)

Fifty-seven casino gamblers were studied (Table 1) (forty-seven males and ten females aged between 21 and 68; the most common age group was 40-50 years, followed by the 30-40 age group). All the subjects were recruited in a casino by a psychologist professionally involved in gambling atmospheres, and who had been instructed to carry out the research protocol , after first verifying with the South Oaks Gambling Screen (SOGS) (Lesieur and Blume 1987) that they were in fact pathological gamblers. Henceforth, when we refer to gamblers (G) , we mean pathological gamblers (PG) as indicated by the results of this test, which we used as a screen. All the PGs were collected in a "standard" Catalonian town representative of a large urban center and characterized by its heavy industrialization and high expenditure on gambling (2,500 million pesetas/year, out of the 500,000 million pesetas spent in the entire region of Catalonia, 15 % of the Spanish total) (Line Staff, 1989). A "standard" population sample means, in restricted territory terms, a representative market of a much more extensive area in which market behavior (purchasing) or opinion (elections, referendums) reproduces the same reactions that can be observed in territories with larger populations. The general behavior of a "standard" population — which could be a province, region, city or even district — provides a miniature replica of the regional or national market. They are therefore suitable population areas for the implementation of test markets for launching new products or for trying out new advertising or communication codes. This type of population is also used to select samples for case studies having a basically qualitative methodology.

City A is located in inland Catalonia and has a population of 66,000 inhabitants. The active population is 36% of the total and per capita income (active population) is 834,000 pesetas (98 pesetas = $1 U.S.). It is an industrial-commercial town, with 6 different types of industry and 481 retail sale establishments. The data, dating from 1989, were supplied by the Official Chamber of Commerce and Industry. The PGs in this town are middle-class and left school at age 14. There are no casino gamblers belonging to other socioeconomic classes or other educational levels. All gamblers were paid (20,000 pesetas — approximately $204) to take part in the study.

B. Controls (C)

There were two features to the collection of this sample which we do not consider to detract from the validity of the results but which must be mentioned:

1. The one hundred and fifteen subjects did not come from the same town but from another equivalent "standard" **Town B**.
2. Being a clinical study, the control sample was not strictly speaking representative of the population, as this would have required a much larger sample. This is a customary procedure in case-control studies.

TABLE 1

AGE GROUPS OF PATHOLOGICAL GAMBLERS AND CONTROLS

Pathological Gamblers

	men		*women*			
Age Decade	*N*	*%*	*N*	*%*	*Row Total*	
20-30	8	17.0	2	20.0		10
31-40	18	38.3	2	20.0		20
41-50	14	29.8	5	50.0		19
51-60	4	8.5	1	10.0		5
61-70	3	6.4				3
Column total	47	82.5%	10	17.5%	57	100.0%

Controls

	men		*women*			
Age Decade	*N*	*%*	*N*	*%*	*Row Total*	
20-30	16	18.2	4	14.8		20
31-40	26	29.5	8	29.6		34
41-50	28	31.8	13	48.1		41
51-60	11	12.5	2	7.4		13
61-70	7	8.0				7
Column Total	88	76.5%	27	23.5%	115	100.0%

A control population consisting of one hundred and fifteen people (eighty-eight males and twenty-seven females), two for each gambler, of the same age and sex, was collected. All the controls came from another "standard" Catalonian town B at the same distance (35 kilometers) as the former town from the reference casino, also located in inland Catalonia, with a population of 62,000 inhabitants, an active population of 38 % of the total and a per capita income (active population) of 843,000 pesetas. It is another industrial-commercial town with 9 types of industry and 470 retail sales establishments. For logistic reasons, it was not possible to recruit controls in the same town as the pathological gamblers. In order to avoid possible differences, another town having very similar sociocultural and demographic features was chosen. In any case, the factors that could lead to differences between the two populations (age pyramids, educational level, social class, professions, industrial versus commercial level, etc.) were studied and no noticeable differences were found. Recruitment was through the "star system" used in market studies (each control was invited to recruit another subject who could fulfill the age, sex, social class and educational level characteristics required by the investigators. They were all given a financial reward (10,000 pesetas) for taking part in the study.

With regard to the gamblers' and the controls' education level, it was found that the controls had a higher education level (X^2 = 12.9, df = 6, p = .040). Subsequently, in order to prevent the results from being attributed to age, sex, educational level or overall intelligence, an adjusted analysis was performed taking these factors into account. In any case, 57.9% of the PGs and 41% of the controls left school at 14 years of age.

Both the PGs and the controls carried out the protocol through the same member of our team, a psychiatrist, who interviewed and administered the tests to all the subjects over the course of the one-year study duration.

C. Statistical Methods

The data were analyzed using the statistical packages SPSS-x and BMDP on a VAX computer in the Autonomous University of Barcelona. Two types of analysis were performed:

1. Univariated analysis, in which the association between pathological gambling and quantitative variables was studied using Student's t-test or through analysis of variance, and the association between qualitative variables was studied with chi-square test.

2. Multivariated analysis:
   a. A factor analysis was conducted using principal components analysis, with the aim of evaluating the dimensions in which the variables studied can be grouped.
   b. Using a logistic regression analysis, the relationship between test's subscales and whether or not a subject was a PG was studied, adjusting for age, sex, eduction level and global IQ on the WAIS. Odds ratios (OR) of significant variables have been calculated using controls as the reference group. OR greater than 1 are interpreted as being in favor of PG, and OR lower than 1 are interpreted as being in favor of controls.

D. Psychometric Tests

The psychometric tests used — all were self-administered, except for the WAIS, which was hetero-administered — are :

1. FH/RDC criteria (Spitzer, Endicott and Robins, 1989) for the diagnosis of "antisocial personality disorder" and "drug dependence."
2. Cage's test (Borrell, 1988) for the diagnosis of "alcoholism."
3. SCID-P (Spitzer and Williams 1985), administered in part DSM-III-R criteria (APA, 1988) for the diagnosis of: "kleptomania," "pyromania," "impulse control disorder," "trichotillomania" and "transvestism."
4. Criteria established by the authors for diagnosing "work rejection," "dependence on people (bereavement)," "illness prone behavior," "living alone," "human groups membership," "risk-taking" and "risk working."
5. Goldberg-Lobo's GHQ-28 (Lobo, 1987) for general psychopathological screening. A cutoff has been applied (probable case/probable normal = 6/7 in Spain. Sensitivity: 76.9%. Specificity: 90.2%. Incorrectly classified: 15%).
6. Lynfield scale (Allen and Tune, 1975; Allen, 1977) for evaluating obsession-compulsion.
7. Derogatis' SCL-90-R (Derogatis, 1983) for obtaining psycho-pathological state components.

8. Eysenck's EPQ-A (Eysenck and Eysenck, 1984) for studying personality factors. Subscale "A" (Gossop and Eysenck, 1980) has been used to evaluate the "addiction" factor.
9. Lesieur and Blume's SOGS (Lesieur and Blume, 1987; Volberg and Steadman, 1988) for diagnosing pathological gambling. The cutoff (4/5) suggested by the authors has been applied.
10. Eysenck and Zuckerman's SSS (Zuckerman, 1989, Gossop and Eysenck, 1980) for studying sensation seeking.
11. Weschler's WAIS (Weschler, 1988; Zimmerman and Woo-Sam, 1989) for measuring intelligence.

RESULTS

When questioned as to their degree of inclination towards gambling using a questionnaire devised by the authors, all the controls were grouped under the categories of "non-gambler" or "recreative gambler." Twelve PGs defined themselves as "recreative gamblers," nineteen as "dangerous habit" and twenty-six admitted to being "addicts." The PGs who denied being addicts but, in fact, were (SOGS), obtained the same scores on the EPQ-A (L) subscale (sincerity) as the PGs who admitted they were addicts, consequently, they were not excluded from the study. Fifty-two PGs (91.2%) had a SOGS above the cutoff (5 or more), while none of the controls reached this figure. The three PGs who did not fulfill the criteria of the SOGS to be considered as such were also included as their pathological addiction was known by the recruiting psychologist.

A. Social and Clinical Conditions of the Study Population

FAMILY STABILITY: Family instability was significantly greater in pathological gamblers — 59.6% versus 33.9% of the controls — (X^2 = 10.33, df = 1, p = .001).

With regards to the parameter *lives alone* versus *lives with another person*, a significantly higher number of pathological gamblers live alone — 19.3% of the pathological gamblers live alone versus 8.8% of the controls — (X^2 = 3.90, df = 1, p = .048). Also, the average number of people who live with the pathological gambler (2.1 subjects) is lower than the average number of people who live with the controls (2.9 subjects; t = -2.87, df = 169, p = .005).

WORK STABILITY: Forty percent of the pathological gamblers were unstable in this area versus 24.6% of the controls (X^2 = 4.24, df = 1, p = .039) [Domingo and Marcos, 1989; Registrar General, 1970].

PSYCHIATRIC AND SOMATIC ANAMNESIS:

Psychiatric disorders: Of the pathological gamblers, 45.6% admitted to having suffered some kind of nervous disorder such as anxiety, sadness, behavioral problems, doubts, etc., versus only 10% of the controls; the difference was significant (X^2 = 12.27, df = 1, p = .000). The pathological gamblers surveyed denied any alcoholism, although when Cage's test was performed subsequently, a significantly positive result was shown indicating addiction to alcohol (t = 4.25, df = 170, p = .000).

Somatic disorders: This is highly significant in pathological gamblers (X^2 = 21.79, df = 1, p = .000) with a greater presence of anorexia, restless legs, asthenia and weight problems, among other complaints.

The control group is significantly (X^2 = 7.75, df = 1, p = .005) more healthy (19.1% no diagnoses) as regards both mental and physical disorders than the pathological gambler group (3.5% no diagnoses).

The results are consistent with those obtained by the GHQ which are given later on as a subjective measure of psychophysical health.

B. Polyaddiction

Upon examining an extensive series of substances and situations that a person can come to depend upon, a list significantly linked with the pathological gambler population has been found (See Figure 1 and Table 2).

ALCOHOL DEPENDENCE:

Alcohol dependence was examined using Cage's test; a significant difference in favor of the pathological gambler is found (t = 4.25, df = 170, p = .000).

PRONENESS TO PSYCHOPHYSICAL DISEASE AND REJECTION OF WORK:

This area was examined by three means significant in pathological gamblers:

- Subjective estimation of poor state of physical health (X^2 = 10.76, df = 1, p = .001);
- Greater number of physical complaints from a list of 40 drawn up for the research protocol (X^2 = 21.79, df = 1, p = .000); and

- Marked rejection of work which was examined using six questions written for protocol — time off work, job changes, dismissals, etc. — ($X^2 = 8.19$, df = 1, p = .004).

FIGURE 1

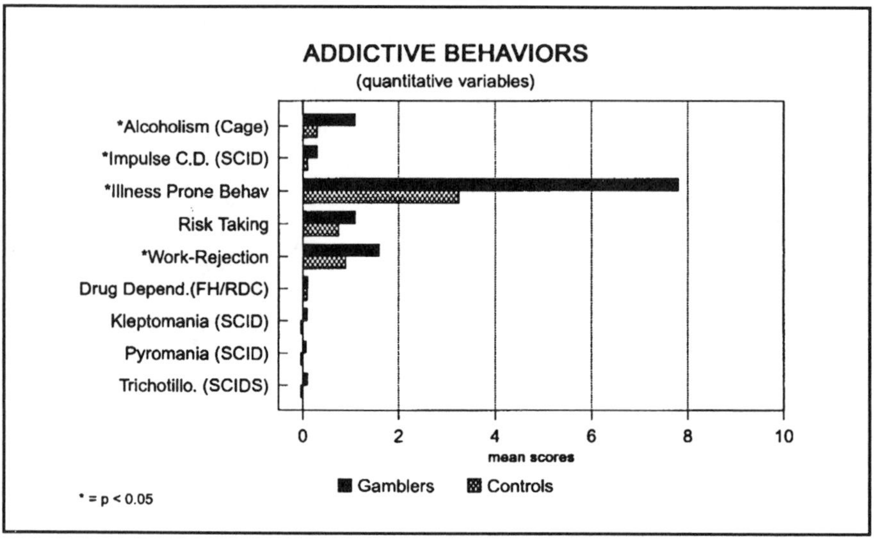

RISK WORKING:

Upon applying Eysenck and Zuckerman's SSS to the pathological gamblers, we have not found any significant differences in this test (t = 0.15, df = 169, p = ns) nor in nine items written by us to examine risk taking (t = 1.37, df = 170, p = ns.).

We devised three items whose results were highly significant (t = 6.72, df = 168, p = .000) for the pathological gambler group:

- Do you like taking risks when you are carrying out a task, financial operation or personal project?
- At some time or other have you lost what you had earned at work or have you bankrupted your company because you took too many risks?
- Have you earned a lot of money or power at work because you took a risk?

The risk at work may suggest selective sensation seeking which may be why some studies have failed previously, as this one does, to show any difference on the general SSS scale.

TABLE 2

Significant Qualitative Variables in Addictive Behaviors*

Variables (in a decreasing order)	*Number of PG cases*	*Number of control cases*
Significant		
Living alone	24	13
Illness prone behavior	28	18
Bereavement	18	12
Risk working	8	2
Alcoholism (Cage)	23	22
Work rejection	4	0
Nonsignificant		
Drug dependence (FH/RDC)		
Kleptomania (SCID-P)		
Pyromania (SCID-P)		
Impulse control disorder (SCID-P)		
Transvestism (SCID-P)		
Human groups		

*$p < .05$

UNCONTROLLED IMPULSES:

The gambling addicts did not fulfill the DSM-III-R (SCID) diagnostic criteria for impulse control disorders. However, a greater number of positive answers to the various items of the test has been verified for pathological gamblers (SCID) ($t = 2.44$, $df = 167$, $p = .016$).

HUMAN RELATIONSHIPS:

Membership in human groups (i.e., political, sports, religious, cultural, etc.) was not significant in the pathological gamblers ($X^2 = 0.38$, $df = 1$, $p = ns$).

GRIEF AND MOURNING:

The association of pathological grief as an expression of personal sorrow disproportionate to the severity of the loss (bereavement) was significant (X^2 = 12.07, df = 1, p = .000).

The preference for solitude was also significant (X^2 = 21.81, df = 1, p = .000).

The association between pathological gambling and *drug dependence* was not significant (X^2 = 1.54, df = 1, p = ns). It was only verified that, when gambling, the pathological gambler spends long periods without feeling any need to eat; this is part of their dissociative state (X^2 = 17.88, df = 1, p = .000).

In order to avoid the influence of factors such as age, sex, educational level and intelligence (Global IQ on the WAIS), a logistic regression analysis has been performed. It was observed that the tests that significantly differentiate pathological gamblers from controls are those that examine "risk working" (OR = 3.6), alcoholism (Cage) (OR = 1.9) and "illness prone behavior" (OR = 1.27) in favor of pathological gamblers in all cases.

C. Psychopathology

PSYCHOPATHOLOGICAL STATE:

The psychopathological state screening, carried out using *GHQ-28* (Figure 2) gives the following results in favor of the gambler group: all the subtests and the GHQ-Total were significantly in favor of the pathological gamblers (t = 6.40, df = 170, p = .000). Twenty-one pathological gamblers (36.8%) had a GHQ above the cutoff (6 or more) while there were only seven controls above the cutoff (X^2 = 26, df = 1, p = .000).

PSYCHOPATHY:

This was examined using FH/RDC criteria. The pathological gamblers fulfilled the diagnostic criteria to a significantly greater proportion in comparison with the controls (X^2 = 6.75, df = 1, p = .009), and the number of items answered in the test was significantly higher (t = 3.93, df = 170, p = .000), even though they did not fulfill the criteria for diagnosis.

OBSESSIVENESS:

When obsessiveness was examined using Lynfield's test, the results were not significant (t = 1.36, df = 170, p = ns). However, they became significant (OR = 0.94) for controls when an analysis adjusted for age, sex, educational level and overall intelligence (Global IQ of the WAIS) was performed.

FIGURE 2

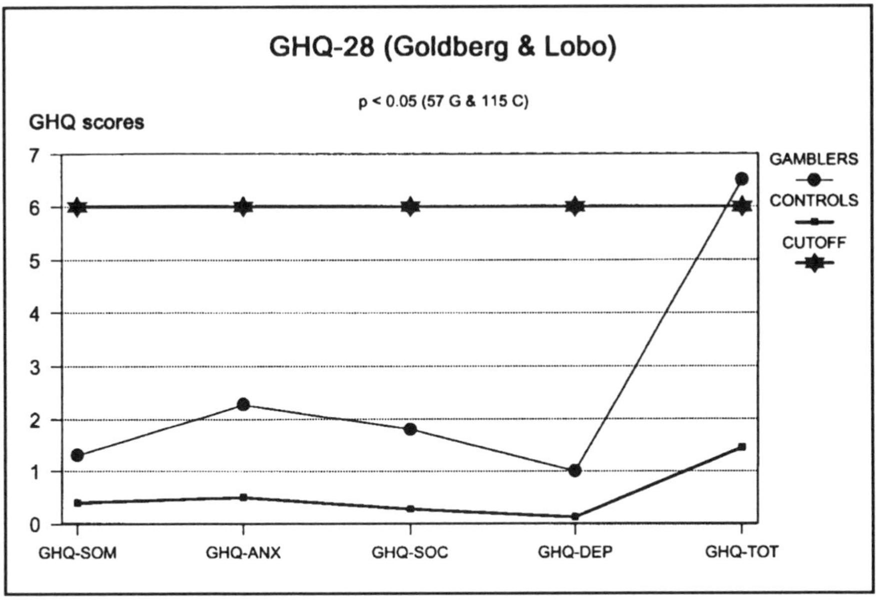

When examined with the O-C subtest of Derogatis' SCL-90-R, the results are significant for this condition (t = 5.77, df = 170, p = .000) in PG.

GENERAL STATE PSYCHOPATHOLOGY:

General state psychopathology was examined using SCL-90-R (Figure 3). All the subtests and the GSI-Global Severity Index — (t = 6.35, df = 170, p = .000), PSDI — Positive Symptoms Distress Index — (t = 4.34, df = 170, p = .000), and PST — Positive Symptoms Total — (t = 6.28, df = 170, p = .000) are highly significant for the gambler group.

In order to avoid the influence of age, sex, educational level and intelligence (Global IQ of the WAIS) on the results of the SCL-90-R, a logistic regression analysis was performed. The only subtest that continues to significantly differentiate between pathological gamblers and controls is that for depression (OR = 1.14), with pathological gamblers scoring higher than controls.

FIGURE 3

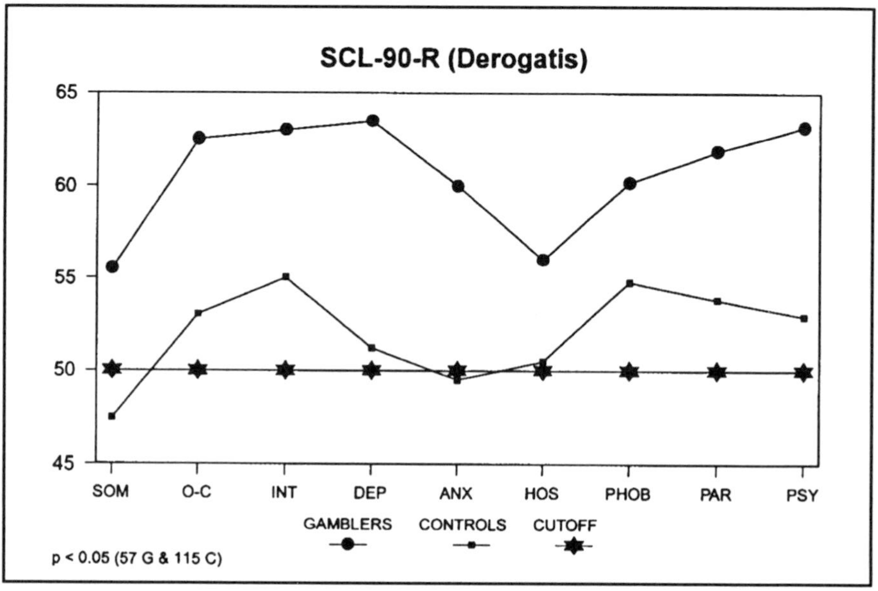

PERSONALITY:

Examination of the personality was done using Eysenck's EPQ-A (Figure 4), with subscale A for addiction. The pathological gamblers showed significant differences in subscales N, P, L, and A ($p < .000$ in all of them). Subscale E had a higher proportion in the control group, without becoming significant ($t = -1.78$, $df = 170$, $p =$ ns). In order to verify the reliability of the answers given by the study subjects (pathological gamblers and controls), the variables neuroticism (N) and lie (L) of the EPQ-A were related, verifying as Eysenck suggests (Eysenck and Eysenck, 1984), that the quotient between both variables was less than + 0.50 for both pathological gamblers and controls. This means that the conditions motivating deception (insincerity) are low and comparable in both study groups. This result confirms the validity of the answers to the protocol.

ADDICTION TO GAMBLING:

Examination of *addiction to gambling* was made using Lesieur and Blume's SOGS (1987), EPQ-A (A) and list of items written for the research protocol.

As was to be expected, all instruments were significantly in favor of the pathological gamblers ($p < .000$ in all of them).

FIGURE 4

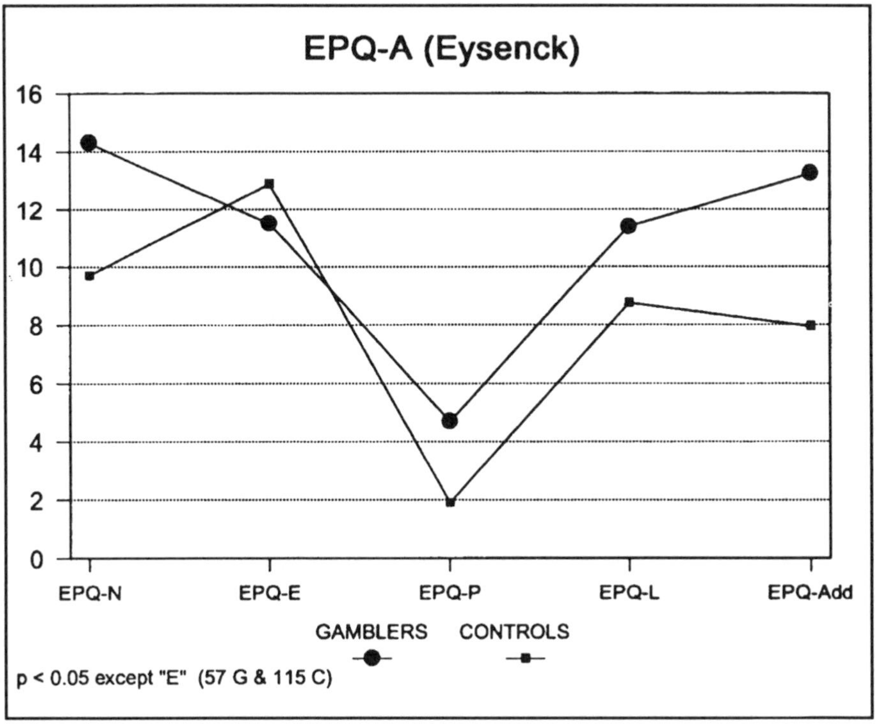

PSYCHOGENETIC PARAMETERS OF GAMBLING:

Eight items, devised by the authors, which synthesize the hypothesis currently accepted concerning the genesis of addiction were studied in the population of pathological gamblers and controls. The following significant differences were found, in decreasing order, using Pearson's X^2 test:

1. Irresistible tendency that forces the subject to recover the money lost in pathological gambling (chasing) (PG = 78.9%, C = 0.0%; $X^2 = 118.87$, df = 1, $p = .000$).
2. When gambling, the subjects feel so involved that they lose all notion of time and space, entering into a state of confusion and flight from

reality that provides them relief (dissociative state) (PG = 71.9%, C = 0.0%, X^2 = 106.36, df = 1, p = .000).

3. Gambling takes subjects out of a problem-filled real world, enabling them to concentrate their attention on something concrete (focusing) (PG = 71.9%, C = 1.7%, X^2 = 97.97, df = 1, p = .000).
4. The subject's lifestyle is so stressful (or boring) that they only manage to feel good when they gamble (aversive unipolar resting state) (PG = 61.4%, C = 0.0%, X^2 = 86.73, df = 1, p = .000).
5. During their life, the subjects have experienced painful events (trauma, disease, personal crisis, etc.) that gambling has relieved (life events) (PG = 40.4%, C = 0.0%, X^2 = 51.89, df = 1, p = .000).
6. Gambling enables the subject to daydream, hallucinating ideal abilities and situations (narcissism) (PG = 45.61%, C = 4.3%, X^2 = 42.70, df = 1, p = .000).
7. Desire to experience extreme situations that cause extreme sensations (sensation seeking) (PG = 43.9%, C = 7.0% , X^2 = 32.76, df = 1, p = .000).
8. During their life, subjects have experienced situations of inferiority and rejection, particularly during childhood (rejection) (PG = 42.1%, C = 20.9%, X^2 = 8.34, df = 1, p = .003).

D. Intelligence

This was tested by administering the WAIS. The Global I.Q., Verbal I.Q., and Performance I.Q. were significantly higher ($p < .001$) in the control group (Figure 5).

The subtests of Information (I), Comprehension (C), Similarities (s), Arithmetic (A), Vocabulary (V), Picture Completion (PC), Block Design (BD), and Picture Arrangement (PA) were also significantly higher ($p < .003$) in controls than in pathological gamblers. The difference in the "third factor" of WAIS (A + DS + DSy + PC) (t = -3.41, df = 161, p = .001) and the "analytic index" (BD + PC + OA) (t = -2.25, df = 161, p = .026) was also significantly higher in controls than in PG. The controls were also higher, although the difference was not significant, in the Digit Span (DS) (t = -0.64, df = 161, p = ns) and Digit Symbol (DSy) (t = -1.67, df = 161, p = ns). The pathological gamblers were only higher, without attaining significance, in Object Assembly (OA) (t = 1.49, df = 161, p = ns).

In order to avoid the influence that the controls' higher education level could have on these results, and in order to evaluate the possible differences between the various subtests of the WAIS, the values have been reported relative to the Verbal I.Q. and Performance I.Q., depending on which each subtest belongs to (Figure 6).

The result, in relative terms, was that the PG were significantly above the controls in *Object Assembly* (t = 3.38, df = 161, p = .001) and *Digit Span* (t = 2.34, df = 161, p = .020) adjusted for the IQ-V or IQ-P level and they were very close to the controls in *Arithmetic* (t = 0.01, df = 161, p = ns).

From all of this information, it can be deduced that the lower results obtained for Intelligence Quotient by the pathological gamblers may be due to three reason: a problem in choosing the sample; that pathological gamblers, as a result of psychopathology, have done less well in the WAIS test; or that the pathological gamblers have a below-average intelligence quotient.

FIGURE 5

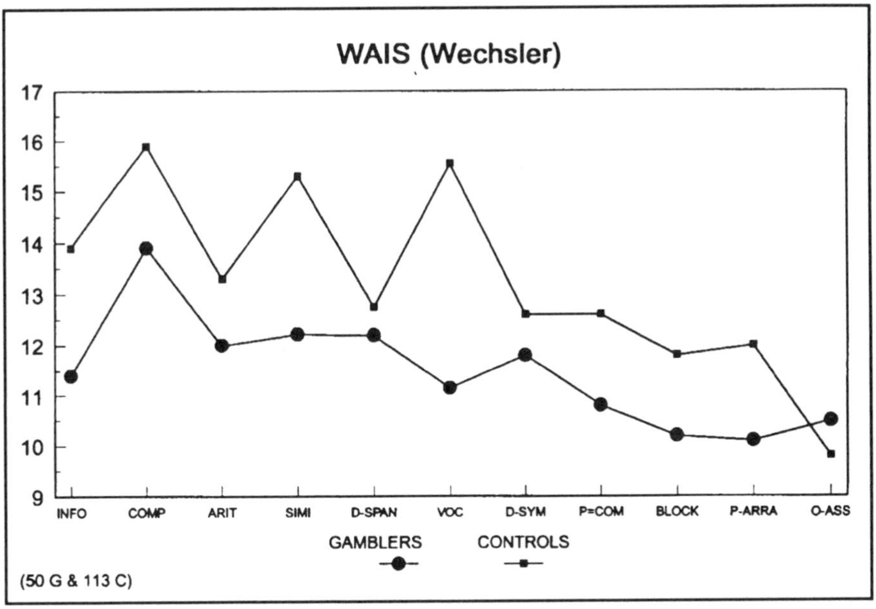

FIGURE 6

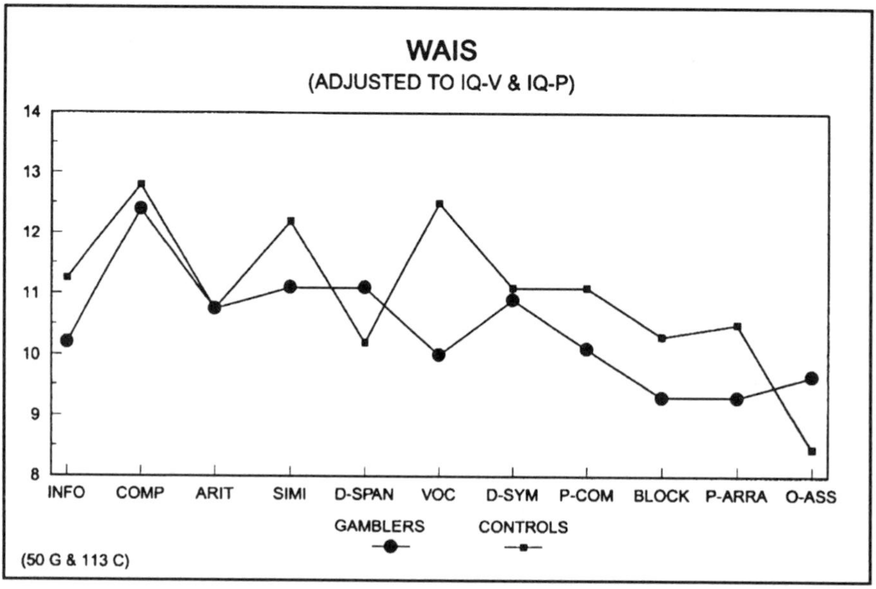

In any case, the most noteworthy aspect in the sample of pathological gamblers studied is a factor composed of Object Assembly-Digit Span, and to a lesser degree Arithmetic. In order to give strength to this argument, a logistic regression analysis was performed adjusting for age, sex and educational level. (In this analysis, the correlation matrix indicates that most of the WAIS subscales are unrelated to each other.) This avoided the influence that such factors could have on the results of the various subtests. After performing this analysis, the WAIS subtests that best differentiate pathological gamblers and controls are the following, in decreasing order: Vocabulary in favor of controls (OR = 0.29); Object Assembly in favor of pathological gamblers (OR = 2.25); Block Design in favor of controls (OR = 0.65) and Digit Span in favor of pathological gamblers (OR = 1.51). This means that the significant differences observed in each of the variables are probably due to sex, age and educational level.

E. Relationship Between the Tests Studied

A principal components factor analysis with a Varimax rotation has been performed with the aim of studying how the subscales of the various quantitative tests are associated with each other in category or factor terms. Four dimensions were considered, which accounted for 51.7% of variance. Table 3 gives the salient factor loadings (>0.50). It will be seen how the first factor correlates mainly with the SCL-90-R subscales, the second with those of the WAIS, the third with items of action and sensation seeking and psychopathy, and the fourth with work rejection and illness prone behavior.

The SOGS has also been related with scale A of the EPQ-A. The result of the analysis shows that both tests study different areas of addiction, both in pathological gamblers and in controls.

Finally, an analysis of the GHQ-Total, SCL-90-R (GSI), SOGS, and the various subscales of the EPQ-A has been performed on the group of pathological gamblers, dividing them into three groups of similar size, according to the results of the IQ-overall of the WAIS. A one-way analysis of variance was performed in order to assess to what extent the results obtained in the quantitative tests are due to an intellectual factor. The analysis indicates that the GHQ-Total is significantly greater ($p = .015$) in the pathological gamblers with a lower IQ. Although differences are observed in the results of the SCL-90-R (GSI) and the EQP-A (N), they are not statistically significant ($p = .109$ and $p = .221$, respectively). No differences were found in the other results of the EPQ-A or of the SOGS.

We can conclude that in pathological gamblers, the lower degree of overall intelligence concurs with a greater degree of psychopathology (GHQ) but not with a greater degree of addiction (SOGS and EPQ-A(A)).

CONCLUSIONS

The *study sample* was composed of fifty-seven casino pathological gamblers (forty-seven men and ten women) and one hundred and fourteen controls of the same age and sex.

FAMILY STABILITY:

There were more single/separated/divorced people among the pathological gamblers than married/widows/widowers. More pathological gamblers than controls lived alone. The average number of people living with pathological gamblers is significantly lower than the average number of people living with controls.

TABLE 3

Rotated Factor Loadings
(Only Loadings > .50 are Shown)

	Factor 1	*Factor 2*	*Factor 3*	*Factor 4*
SCL-90 Par	.79606			
SCL-90 Hos	.75774			
EPQ-A N	.73373			
SCL-90 PSDI	.72828			
SCL-90 Som	.71122			
SCL-90 Fob	.65878			
GHQ-28 Total	.65526			.50797
GHQ-28 Anx	.62226			
GHQ-28 Social	.61606			
Illness prone	.59834			
Lynfield	.58616			
GHQ-28 Dep	.58218			
EPQ-A Add	.56569		.54583	
Global IQ		.95752		
Verbal IQ		.89001		
Performance IQ		.83290		
WAIS V		.76920		
WAIS S		.73654		
WAIS I		.72346		
WAIS BD		.69461		
WAIS PA		.69246		
WAIS C		.64743		
WAIS A		.62614		
WAIS PC		.61692		
WAIS OA		.51141		
EPQ-A L			.71457	
Risk working			.59585	
FH/RDC psychopathy			.58884	
EPQ-A P			.53277	
SSS			.51876	
Workaholic				-.73549
Work rejection				.65912
GHQ-28 Som				.56054

WORK STABILITY:

With regard to work, pathological gamblers were more unstable than the controls.

PSYCHIATRIC AND SOMATIC ANAMNESIS:

More than twice as many pathological gamblers admitted to having suffered some kind of nervous disorder compared with the controls (i.e., 45.6% versus 20%). Also, the pathological gamblers admitted to having a generally poorer state of physical health.

POLYADDICTION:

The following is observed with respect to this point: A significant addiction to alcohol and pathological gambling, a correlation between pathological gambling and the feeling of being ill, and the presence of physical illness and time off work. There was no correlation between addiction to gambling and Eysenck and Zuckerman's SSS. There was significant correlation between pathological gambling and presence of physical and mental illnesses, work rejection and feeling of being a sick person. There was significant correlation between a liking for risk at work and pathological gambling. The PG did not fulfill the diagnostic criteria for impulse control disorders. The correlation between pathological gambling and group membership was not significant. There was a significant correlation between proneness to pathological grief and solitude, and pathological gambling. The correlation between pathological gambling and drug dependence and eating disorders was not significant.

PSYCHOPATHOLOGY:

The following observation was made with regard to psychopathology: All the general and specific psychopathology vectors were significant in the pathological gamblers (GHQ, SCL-90-R, EPQ-A, Cage, FH/RDC-psychopathy, and the SOGS). The following were not significant: EPQ (E), FH/RDC (drug dependence), Lynfield and SSS.

INTELLIGENCE:

In the study of intelligence, the following was observed:

- The results for intelligence are lower in PG than in controls;
- The pathological gambler obtains higher scores in OA and DS when adjusted in relation to IQ-V and IQ-P level;

- Although the intellectual level affects the results of the tests, the following are still significant in pathological gamblers when this factor is eliminated: SCL-90-R depression, "illness prone behavior," "risk working," and alcoholism (Cage); and
- A lower degree of intelligence in pathological gamblers is associated with a greater GHQ but not with a greater degree of addiction.

REFERENCES

Allcock, C.C. and Grace, D.M. (1988). Pathological gamblers are neither impulsive nor sensation-seekers. *Australian New Zealand Journal of Psychiatry*, 22(3), 307-311.

Allen, J. (1977). The measuement of obessionality: First validation studies of the Lynfield obsessional-compulsive questionaires. *Journal of International Medical Resource (supplement 5)*, 5, 12-15.

Allen, J.J. and Tune, G.S. (1975). The Lynfield obsessional compulsive questionnaire. *Scott Medical Journal (supplement 1)*, 20, 21-24.

American Psychiatric Association (1988). *DSM-III-R. Manual diagnóstico y estadístico de los trastornos mentales.* Barcelona: Masson Ed.

Becker, H.A., Hermkens, P.L.J. and Mutsaers, H.P.M. (1987). *Proyecto "LARGO": Juegos de azar en su aspecto de costumbres peligrosas en fase de desarrollo.* Utrecht: Facultad de Ciencias Sociales, Universidad del Estado.

Blaszczynski, A. and McConaghy, N. (1989). Anxiety and/or depression in the pathogenesis of addictive gambling. *International Journal of Addictions*, 24(4), 337-350.

Blaszczynski, A, McConaghy, N. and Frankova, A. (1989). Crime, antisocial personality and pathological gambling. *Journal of Gambling Behavior*, 5(2), 137-152.

Borrell, F. (1988). *Manual de Entrevista Clínica.* Barcelona: Ed. DOYMA, S.A.

Ceci, S.J. and Liker, J.K. (1986). A day at the races: A study of IQ expertise, and cognitive complexity. *Journal of Experimental Psychology: General*, 115(3), 255-266.

Ceci, S.J. and Liker, J.K. (1987). A day at the races: A study of IQ expertise, and cognitive complexity. *Journal of Experimental Psychology: General*, 116(2), 90.

Derogatis, L.R. (1983). *SCL-90 Administration, Scoring and Procedures. Manual-II for the R(evised) version* (2nd edition). Towson: Clinical Psychometric Research.

Detterman, D.K. and Spry, K.M. (1988). Is it smart to play the houses? Comment on "A day at the races: A study of IQ expertise, and cognitive complexity" (Ceci and Liker, 1986). *Journal of Experimental Psychology: General*, 117(1), 91-95.

Dickerson, M., Hinchy, J. and Fabre, J. (1987). Chasing, arousal and sensation seeking in off-course gamblers. *British Journal of Addiction*, 82(6), 673-680.

Domingo, A. and Marcos, J. (1989). Propuesta se un indicador se la "clase social" basado en la ocupación. *Gaceta Sanitaria*, 3(10), 320-326.

Eysenck, H.J. and Eysenck, S.B.G. (1984). *Cuestionario de Personalidad para Niños y Adultos. Adaptación española* (3rd edition). Madrid: TEA Ed.

Eysenck, S. and Zuckerman, M. (1978). The relationship between sensation seeking and Eysenck's dimentions of personality. *British Journal of Psychology*, 69, 483-487.

Ganzález, A. (1988). *Joc Patològic: Una Nova Adicción*. Barcelona: Tibidabo Ed., S.A.

Gossop, M.R. and Eysenck, S.B.G. (1980). A further investigation into the personality of drug addicts in treatment. *British Journal of Addiction*, 75, 305-311.

Guirao, J.L. (1985). Gambling in Spain: The unplanned revolution. In W.R. Eadington (ed.), *The Gambling Studies: Proceedings of the Sixth National Conference on Gambling and Risk Taking*, vol. 1, pp. 394-413. Reno, NV: University of Nevada.

Guirao, J.L. (1988). The casino gaming industry in Spain. In W.R. Eadington (ed.), *Gambling Research: Proceedings of the Seventh International Conference on Gambling and Risk Taking*. Reno, NV: University of Nevada.

Instituto Español para la atención a los problemas del Juego de Azar (1989). *Memoria*. Madrid.

Jacobs, D.F. (1989). A general theory of addictions: Rationale for and evidence supporting a new approach for understanding and treating addictive behaviors. In H.J. Shafer, S.A. Stein B. Gamino and T. Cummings (eds.), *Compulsive Gambling: Theory, Research, and Practice*, pp. 35-62. Lexington, MA: Lexington Books.

Jacobs, D.F. (1988). Evidence for a common dissocative-like reaction among addicts. *Journal of Gambling Behavior*, 4, 27-37.

Kagan, D.M. (1987). Addictive personality factors. *Journal of Psychology*, 121(6), 533-538.

Kruijt, J.P. (1973). *The Escape Valve Function*. Utrecht: Werkboek Sociologie.

Lesieur, H.R. (1973). The compulsive gambler's spiral of options and involvement. *Psychiatry*, 42, 79-87.

Lesieur H.R. (1984). *The Chase: Career of the Compulsive Gambler*. Cambridge: M.A. Schenkman Publishing Co.

Lesieur, H.R. and Blume, S.B. (1987). The South Oaks Gambling Screen (the SOGS): A new instrument for identification of pathological gamblers. *American Journal of Psychiatry*, 144, 1184-1188.

Lesieur, H.R., Blume, S.B. and Zoppa, R.M. (1986). Alcoholism, drug abuse and gambling. *Alcoholism* (NY), 10(1), 33-38.

Lesieur, H.R. and Klein, R. (1987). Pathological gambling among high school students. *Addictive Behaviors*, 12, 129-135.

Liker, J.K. and Ceci, S.J. (1987). IQ and reasoning complexity: The roles of experience. *Journal of Experimental Psychology: General*, 116(3), 304-306.

Linden, R.D., Pope, H.G. Jr. and Jonas, J.M. (1986). Pathological gambling and major affective disorder: Preliminary findings. *Journal of Clinical Psychiatry*, 134(4), 558-559.

Line Staff (1989). *Resultados Estudio Sobre el Jeugo en Cataluña. Hábitos y Actitudes*, vol. 1-2. Barcelona: Line Staff.

Lobo, A. (1987). *"Screening" de trastornos psíquicos en la práctica médica. GHQ/"Mini-Examnen."* Zaragoza: Universidad de Zaragoza.

Malkin, D. and Syme, G.J. (1986). Personality and problem gambling. *International Journal of Addictions*, 21(2), 267-272.

Martínez Pina, A. (1989). Juego patológico. Una vieja psicopatología. *IMP-Psiquiatría*, 3, 123-127.

Meyer, G. (1986). Dependence on gambling. *Klin Psychol Psychopatol Psychoter*, 34(2), 140-156.

Moran, E. (1970a). Pathological gambling. *British Journal of Psychiatry*, 4, 59-70.

Moran, E. (1970b). Clinical and social aspects of risk taking. *Proceedings of the Royal Society of Medicine*, 63, 1273-1277.

Moran, E. (1970c). Varieties of pathological gambling. *British Journal of Psychiatry*, 116, 593-597.

Moravec, J.D. and Munley, P.H. (1983). Psychological test findings on pathological gamblers in treatment. *International Journal of Addictions*, 18(7), 1003-1009.

Nadler, L. (1982). The conduct of the pathological gambling research: Covering all bets. In W.R. Eadington (ed.), *The Gambling Papers: Proceedings of the Fifth National Conference on Gambling and Risk Taking*, vol. 2. Reno, NV: University of Nevada.

Reagan, R.T. (1987). Complexity of IQ: Comment on Ceci and Liker (1986). *Journal of Experimental Psychology: General*, 116 (3), 302-303.

Registrar General (1970). *Classification of Occupations*. London: HMSO.

Rosecrance, J. (1988). *Gambling without Guilt: The Legitimation of an American Pastime*. New York: Brooks/Cole Publishing Co.

Roy, A., Adinoff, B., Roehrich, L. et al. (1988). Pathological gambling: A psychobiological study. *Arch Gen Psychiatry*, 45(4), 369-373.

Roy, A., Custer, R., Lorenz, V. & Linnoila, M. (1988). Depressed pathological gamblers. *Acta Pyschiatr Scand*, 77(2), 163-165.

Roy, A., Custer, R., Lorenz, V. and Linnoilo, M. (1989). Personality factors and pathological gambling. *Acta Psychiatr Scand*, 80(1), 37-39.

Roy, A., De Jong, J. and Linnoila, M. (1989). Extraversion in pathological gamblers: Correlates with indexes of noradrenergic function. *Arch Gen Psychiatry*, 46(8), 679-681.

Serrat, X. and Fusté, R. (1990). Teoría general de la adicción según Jacobs. *IMP-Pisiquiatría*, 2, 99-101.

Spitzer, R.L., Endicott, J. and Robins, E. (1989). *Sistema RDC. Criterios Diagnósticos de Investigación. Versión Española Revisada.* Madrid: Ed. Médicos S.A.

Spitzer, R.L. and Williams, J.B.W. (1985). *Structured Clinical Interview for DMS-III-R-Patient Version.* New York: New York State Psychiatric Institute.

Taber, J.L., Collachi, J.L. and Lynn, E.J. (1986). Pathological gambling: Possibilities for treatment in Northern Nevada. *Nevada Public Affairs Review*, 2, 39-42.

Taber, J.L., McCormick, R.A. and Ramirez, L.F. (1987). The prevalence and impact of major life stressors among pathological gamblers. *International Journal of Addictions*, 22(1), 71-79.

Volberg, R.A. and Steadman, H.J. (1988). Refining prevalence estimates of pathological gambling. *American Journal of Psychiatry*, 145, 502-505.

Weschler, D. (1988). *WAIS — Esala de Inteligencia de Weschler para Adultos: Manual. Adaptacion Española.* Madrid: Sección de Estudio de Tests de TEA Ed., S.A.

Zimmerman, I.L. and Woo-Sam, J.M. (1989). *WAIS: Interpretación Clínica de la Escala de Inteligencia de Weschler para Adultos.* Madrid: TEA Ed., S.A.

Zuckerman, M. (1989). *Abbreviated Manual with Scoring Keys and Forms for Form V of the Sensation Seeking Scale.* Delaware: University of Delaware.

ACKNOWLEDGEMENT

We thank Ricardo Cayuela (Line Staff, Barcelona) for his help in collecting the sample; Jordi Daura for data processing work; Mercedes Lemonier, psychologist, for her help in administering and correcting the tests; Consol Marina and Teresa Ruiz for their secretarial assistance and contact with the 172 study subjects.

Tonight's Numbers Are. . .Lottery Play and Problem Gambling©

Joseph Hraba, Waiman P. Mok and David Huff

The present era of state lotteries began in 1963 with the New Hampshire lottery. Lotteries had been popular in the past, however, in both England and the American colonies (Kaplan, 1984; Rosecrance, 1988). About 2,000 authorized lotteries were operating in the United States in 1795, and lotteries were routinely held by states and municipalities early in the 1800s (Rosecrance, 1988). Opposition toward lotteries then developed, and no authorized lotteries remained by 1865. There was a subsequent revival of lotteries, but they were again banned by 1878 in all states except Louisiana, which itself was banned in 1894. For the next seventy years there were no state lotteries, until the New Hampshire lottery

---

© A version of this article has been published in the *Journal of Gambling Studies* (1991), 6, 355-378. New York: Human Sciences Press, Inc. Permission to reprint has been granted by the authors and publisher.

in 1963 began the present era of state lotteries. Now, state-sponsored lotteries are back and bigger than ever, serving states once again in the raising of additional revenues. The wagering on lotteries increased between 1983 and 1988 by nearly 230 percent, an increase which led any other form of gambling.

State sponsorship of gambling raises several social issues. The main issue is that it might bring increased gambling and thus a rise in the number of problem gamblers throughout the country. Problem gambling is defined in the psychiatric literature as pathological or compulsive gambling, a disorder of impulse control. This disorder is "a chronic and progressive failure to resist impulses to gamble, and gambling behavior that compromises, and disrupts, or damages personal, family, or vocational pursuits" (American Psychiatric Association, 1980:291).

Problem gambling is thought to be a progression into more gambling and heavier wagering, resulting in a loss of control over gambling and the eventual disruption of one's life due to gambling (Bergler, 1958; Custer, 1979; Kallick et al., 1979; Lesieur, 1977; Moran, 1975; Orford, 1985; Winston and Harris, 1984). Compulsive gamblers chase old betting losses with new wagers, trying to get even (Lesieur, 1979). Estimates of compulsive gamblers in the United States range from two to ten percent of the population, with another ten to fifteen percent betting more than they can afford (Wells, 1989).

PROBLEM GAMBLING

There are various theories on the reasons people gamble. Gambling represents "action," according to Goffman (1967), a risky and fateful activity in which something of value can be lost as well as won. Routine life presents little opportunity for such action, and thus some turn to gambling. Playing the lottery represents little in the way of action, however, and this theory is hardly helpful in explaining attraction to the lottery and any subsequent connection between lottery play and problem gambling.

Big winnings can trigger later problem gambling (Berry, 1968; Custer and Milt, 1985; Dunne, 1983; Greene, 1982; Lesieur and Custer, 1984; Wagner, 1972; Waller, 1974). Unrealistic expectations due to a big win can lead to unbridled optimism, particularly for younger gamblers, but the reality of the odds means that a gambler's losses mount until a desperation stage is reached. This progression can unfold over many years, and has been identified by clinicians treating compulsive gamblers who wish to stop.

Of course, not all problem gamblers begin as big winners, and thus people can become problem gamblers for other reasons (Lesieur and Custer, 1984). This is particularly true with lottery play. Big winnings apply only to lottery winners, a minuscule percentage of all lottery players, and thus the theory cannot explain any connection between lottery play and subsequent problem gambling for the vast majority of its players.

Other researchers have found neither a role for a big win in problem gambling nor an inevitable progression into problem gambling (Hayano, 1982; Herman, 1967 and 1976; Oldman, 1974 and 1978; Rosecrance, 1985-86 and 1986; Scott, 1968; Tec, 1964). These researchers have studied gamblers in natural settings, e.g., poker parlors, casinos and horse tracks, not those seeking treatment for problem gambling. Many gamblers control their gambling behavior, for example, by stopping or limiting gambling for a time when their losses grow.

If problem gambling does result, causes other than a big win can lead to it. Rosecrance (1986) found that because of a "bad beat" — a huge betting loss for inexplicable reasons (e.g., a horse jumping the rail) — a gambler can become disoriented, change his or her gambling behavior, and the result can be even greater losses and other problems. This observation is consistent with Langer's (1983) psychology of control. Gamblers can have an illusion of control over the chance events on which they bet, and this illusion is heightened by obtaining pertinent information, planning gambling strategies, as well as assessing one's gambling ability against other players. The illusion can dissipate, however, when the reality of wins and losses shifts the focus back to chance. Unfortunately, this theory is no more helpful than the others in explaining a connection between lottery play and problem gambling. It is hard to imagine a bad beat in a lottery drawing or instant game leading to problem gambling.

Nevertheless, speculation abounds about state lotteries contributing to problem gambling in the country. It is an alarming picture. The nation has 97 million lottery players, who can be seen mobbing ticket outlets to have a chance at big winnings, such as an April 1989, $115 million jackpot in Pennsylvania (Wells, 1989). Are these 97 million people at risk of becoming compulsive gamblers? Culleton and Lang (1985) observed an increase in pathological gambling in New Jersey, which they judged to be associated with the inception of a lottery and casinos in that state.

The fear is that through their sponsorship and media advertising of gambling, states are legitimizing gambling and motivating the American public into it. Gambling could become more acceptable, actual gambling could grow, and for two to ten percent of the population, this could lead to problem gambling.

Past research has found a connection between many variables and problem gambling. The correlates of problem gambling include numerous economic and social characteristics, such as gender, race and ethnicity, age, occupation, education, income, religion, and armed forces service (Frey, 1984; Kallick et al., 1979). From the perspective of anomie theory (Merton, 1938), the lower classes gravitate to gambling because their opportunities to the good life are blocked elsewhere. Early and current exposure to gambling; leisure pursuits, including spending styles; residence; marital status; and personality traits are also suspected correlates of gambling (Bergler, 1958; Culleton and Lang, 1985; Lieberman, 1988; Lesieur, 1979; Kallick et al., 1979; Moran, 1975; Orford, 1985; Rosecrance, 1986; Transitional Planning Associates, 1985; Winston and Harris, 1984). Measures of virtually all of these variables have been brought into this research, and the objective is to determine the extent to which lottery play along with other possible causes engenders problem gambling.

METHODS

A. The sample

The sample utilized in this study was a stratified random sampling of working household telephone numbers in the state of Iowa. The list of telephone numbers (N=2,000) was obtained from Survey Sampling, Inc., and is a computer-based listing of all residential telephone numbers in the state. This listing was stratified by counties, and the telephone numbers provided for each county are proportional to its population size relative to that of the entire state. This procedure assured a statewide distribution of respondents and protected the anonymity of respondents, for no names were known to the interviewers. A target of 1,000 interviews was established, and the interviews were conducted from April to June, 1989.

When a household was contacted by telephone, interviewers determined the number of adult female and male household members, selected a respondent in accord with random selection tables, and no substitutions were allowed. This procedure circumvents any bias arising from who would typically answer the phone at home. If the selected respondent was not at home, a call-back was arranged. In cases where respondents were difficult to catch at home, the design included a minimum of seven potential call-back attempts.

Interviews were completed with 1,011 of the eligible respondents contacted, representing an overall response rate of 80.2 percent. Among those who were not interviewed, 215 refused and 49 could not be reached within the time frame of the study. Over seventy percent (72.8%) of the 736 respondents reported gambling of some sort, including lottery play, whereas 27.2 percent (275) reported that they did not play the lottery or gamble in any way. The gambling subsample is the focus of this research.

B. The Interview Guide

The interview guide was put into a CATI (computer-assisted telephone interview). After an introduction and screening of household members, interviewers asked a series of questions about lottery play. These were measurements of lottery play and a device to screen respondents as either lottery players or non-players. The questions were about lottery play in the past seven days, lottery play since the inception of the Iowa lottery, wagering on the lottery in a typical week, how the lottery is played, when lottery play is most likely, the attribution of chance and/or skill to lottery play, and reasons for lottery play. Respondents who indicated no lottery play were routed to questions on other gambling behavior, and those who also indicated no gambling are excluded from this analysis.

Respondents who indicated any lottery play and/or other forms of gambling in the past six months were asked a larger series of questions about their gambling. These questions included those on types of gambling and frequency of play, chronicity of gambling, frequency and wagering on gambling in recent weeks, loss of control over their gambling behavior, and whether or not they experienced consequences due to their gambling behavior. Many of these questions have been previously used in gambling research and constitute standard items in surveys about gambling (APA, 1980 and 1987; Lesieur and Blume, 1987).

The next section of the interview guide was a series of questions on personality characteristics of respondents and their socio-economic background. Respondents were asked to attribute 21 personality traits to themselves on a scale of 1 to 8, from very little to very much. Background questions included those on passive sports participation, spending styles, alcohol consumption, exposure to gambling, residence, marital status, age, gender, ethnicity, income, financial status, military service, employment, education and religion. Many of these items are correlates of gambling behavior found in past research.

C. Gambling Scales

Problem gambling is considered to be a progression into more frequent and heavier gambling, a loss of control over gambling, and a consequent disruption of routine and normal life. Fourteen questions about gambling, control over it and its consequences were first subjected to a factor analysis, varimax rotation, and three principal factors were extracted from the items (Table 1). The factors were *gambling behavior, loss of control over gambling,* and *consequences due to gambling.*

Three scales were constructed from these factors. An item was selected for a scale when its factor loading on that factor was greater than .45 and that item did not have a larger loading on any other factor. A scale score for each respondent was computed by summing his/her scores on the individual items selected for that scale. The component items of the first scale, *gambling behavior*, were leisure time spent at gambling, frequency of gambling since the New Year, money spent on gambling in the past seven days, money bet at one time since the New Year, and types of gambling in the past year. The question on money spent in the past seven days was not used in the scale, since it is possibly redundant with questions asked about the number of lotto tickets and instant games purchased in the past seven days and money spent on the lottery in a typical week. Nevertheless, there could be a spurious association between lottery play and this scale of gambling behavior, and this is checked below.

The component items of the second scale, *loss of control*, were gamble more money for longer periods than intended, return to gambling as soon as possible, unable to resist gambling, and hide gambling from loved ones. The component items of the third scale, *gambling consequences*, were borrowed money to gamble or pay gambling debts since the New Year, lost time from work or school due to gambling since the New Year, recently criticized for gambling, recently tried to stop gambling, considered an illegal action to pay for gambling since the New Year.

TABLE 1

FACTOR LOADINGS FOR GAMBLING AND PERSONALITY SCALES

Gambling Factors

Item	Factor 1 Behavior	Factor 2 Control	Factor 3 Consequences	Communality
Gambling frequency	.741	.090	-.015	.558
Money in past 7 days	.674	.226	.356	.632
Money bet at one time	.521	.109	.193	.321
Types of gambling	.497	.226	.138	.317
Leisure time gambling	.457	.376	.309	.446
Hide gambling	.138	.651	.556	.752
Unable to resist	.125	.573	.247	.405
Gamble more than intended	.219	.519	.122	.332
Return to gambling	.166	.511	.170	.318
Lost time from work/school	.211	.229	.942	.985
Consider illegal behavior	.222	.224	.894	.899
Borrow money	.211	.470	.736	.807
Criticism for gambling	.198	.490	.518	.548
Tried to stop gambling	.206	.340	.486	.395

Table 1 continued. . .

CONTINUATION OF TABLE 1. . .

Personality Factors					
ITEM	FACTOR 1 CIVIC	FACTOR 2 SELF-CENTERED	FACTOR 3 COMPETITIVE	FACTOR 4 BIG SPENDER IMPULSIVE	COMMUN-ALITY
Hard-working	.688	-.186	-.016	-.171	.537
Energetic	.703	-.136	.247	-.186	.609
Generous	.603	-.271	-.028	-.287	.520
Intelligent	.609	-.160	.043	.026	.399
Optimistic	.553	-.154	.282	-.076	.414
Conventional	.436	-.235	.023	-.019	.246
Responsible	.653	-.328	-.337	.191	.684
In-control	.556	-.280	-.131	.293	.491
Mature	.471	-.285	-.263	.118	.386
Loner	.134	.326	-.062	.038	.130
Self-centered	.237	.558	.096	.275	.452
Materialistic	.335	.331	-.093	.131	.248
Demanding	.376	.484	.016	.139	.396
Anxious	.331	.440	-.298	-.182	.426
Irritable	.267	.560	-.190	-.056	.424
Restless	.329	.572	-.285	-.242	.575
Competitive	.543	.239	.276	.185	.462
Risk-taker	.385	.336	.328	.157	.394
Athletic	.452	.047	.414	-.048	.380
Big-spender	.315	.386	.075	.020	.255
Impulsive	.281	.415	-.022	-.037	.253

A reliability check on each scale was done. A reliability coefficient, alpha, was computed for each scale, and it should be .60 or higher if the scale items are reliable. The alpha for the scale on *gambling behavior* was .65, the one for *loss of control* was .67, and the alpha for the scale on *gambling consequences* was .85. The scales were judged to be reliable. That is, the progression into problem gambling was broken down into three parts, and these parts are internally consistent and each is distinct from the other two parts.

D. Personality Types

Responses to 21 self-attributed personality traits were subjected to the same factor analysis procedures and criteria as those used for the gambling items listed in Table 1. Four factors were extracted, and reliability checks were done on the four resulting scales. The first personality type was the *civic personality*, composed of hard working, energetic, generous, intelligent, optimistic, conventional, responsible, in-control, and mature. The alpha for this scale was .80. The second was the *self-centered personality*, composed of being a loner, self-centered, materialistic, demanding, anxious, irritable, and restless. The alpha was .74. The third is the *competitive personality*, that is, being competitive, a risk-taker, and athletic. Although these items were not truly distinguishable from the civic personality, we wanted to isolate a competitive personality type, anticipating that it might be closely correlated with gambling. The alpha was .64, due to so few items in the scale. The fourth was composed of being a big-spender and impulsive. This alpha was only .53, however, and too low for scale use. These variables were used only as single items in the analysis. The means and standard deviations for the three scales were 6.08, SD=1.09; 3.79, SD=1.21; 4.32, SD=1.62, respectively.

E. Economic and Social Characteristics

The background data collected on respondents were basic demographic data and/or known correlates of problem gambling. The items included gender, ethnicity, religion, residence, marital status, education, employment, income, financial status, home ownership, residential mobility, age, birthplace, armed forces service, household composition, exposure to gambling, leisure activities, and money spent on leisure. In a separate analysis, lottery players could not be distinguished from non-players by these background characteristics (Hraba, 1989).

F. Data Analysis

Data analysis proceeded through the following steps. First, the frequency distributions on all variables were checked, and all open-ended questions were coded. Secondly, the scales of *gambling behavior, loss of control over gambling* and *gambling consequences* were constructed. The same was done for the self-attributed personality traits. Next, the effects of lottery play and other possible causes on gambling behavior, loss of control over gambling and gambling consequences were assessed with correlation and multiple regression analyses.

RESULTS

A. Correlation Analysis

Problem gambling in this research was measured by three scales: *gambling behavior, loss of control over gambling,* and *gambling consequences.* Lottery play was measured by four items: the purchase of instant games in the past seven days, the purchase of lotto tickets in the past seven days, money spent on the lottery in a typical week, and ever playing the Iowa lottery if there were no purchases in the past seven days. Personality types and background variables, along with measures of respondents' economic and social characteristics were subjected to a correlation analysis.

First, respondents reported more gambling behavior (mean=2.3) than loss of control over gambling (mean=1.15) and disruptive consequences due to gambling (mean=1.02). These sum scores were standardized across scales by dividing unadjusted means by the number of items in each scale. T-tests comparing means on the gambling scales were done, and all were significant at $p<.001$. The T value for gambling behavior and loss of control was 44.45, df=696; gambling behavior and gambling consequences was 48.74, df=697; and loss of control and gambling consequences was 11.47, df=725. All respondents in the gambling sub-sample have a score of one or greater on the gambling behavior scale; 26 percent have such a score on loss of control, and 6 percent have a similar score on gambling consequences. Moreover, on virtually all items constituting these three scales, more respondents reported gambling behavior than loss of control and disruptive consequences due to gambling. This suggests that gambling behavior is not always associated with loss of control and undesirable consequences.

This point was also illustrated in the correlations between these respondents' scores on gambling behavior, loss of control and gambling consequences. While gambling behavior was correlated with loss of control ($r=.36$, $p<.001$) and consequences ($r=.35$, $p<.001$), loss of control was strongly correlated with gambling consequences ($r=.55$, $p<.001$). It appears that once respondents report a loss of control over gambling, their chances increase significantly of also experiencing its undesirable consequences.

The next step was to compare the effects of lottery play on problem gambling with those of other possible causes. First, respondents were dichotomized into lottery players and non-players who gamble in other ways (Table 2). This measure of lottery play combined those who have made recent purchases with those who have played the lottery only in the more distant past. The second measure of lottery play was respondents' scores on money spent on lottery play in a typical week. The measures of recent lottery play were dropped from further analysis because they correlated with money spent on lottery play in a typical week, and this would have introduced a problem of multicolinearity in the regression analysis. The other independent variables were the three personality scales; their self-report of being a big-spender and impulsive; leisure pursuits; exposure to gambling; residence; marital status; and background characteristics.

The two measures of lottery play were correlated with gambling behavior (Table 2). Of course, respondents could be including recollection of lottery play in reporting their general gambling behavior, and this possibly inflates the correlations between lottery play and gambling behavior. To check for this possibility, the four items of the gambling behavior scale were decomposed into single items and correlated with the two measures of lottery play. The only modest correlations (greater than .30) were between gambling frequency and the measures of lottery play (.34 and .41).

Nearly 31 percent of the respondents indicated gambling either twice per week or weekly, which might reflect the periodicity of lottery play. However, to preserve the face validity of the gambling behavior scale, it was deemed necessary to include this item on gambling frequency in the scale. A measure of gambling behavior must include at the minimum items on the frequency of gambling as well as types of gambling. Individual items in the scales on loss of control and gambling consequences were not correlated ($r>.15$) with the two measures of lottery play.

To reduce the possible redundancy between measures of lottery play and the scale of gambling behavior, items on the number of lottery purchases in the past week were deleted from the following analysis, as was the item on money spent on gambling in the past seven days deleted from the gambling behavior scale. What remains, however, is the item on gambling frequency since the New Year among the other items in the gambling behavior scale, and money spent on the lottery in a typical week as well as lottery play as measures of lottery play. Thus, it is possible that not all the redundancy has been eliminated, and lottery play and general gambling behavior overlap somewhat in this analysis.

Certain personality types and traits were correlates of gambling behavior, namely, being competitive, a big-spender and impulsive. Drinking alcohol and a leisure interest in sports were also correlates of gambling behavior, as were childhood and current exposure to gambling. These findings are consistent with those of past research.

Residential mobility was correlated with gambling behavior, but marital status appeared to have no association with gambling behavior. Among the respondent characteristics, age, gender, full employment, education, religion, church attendance and armed forces service were correlated with gambling behavior. Being Protestant was negatively correlated, but being Catholic and Jewish were positively correlated with gambling behavior. Age, education and church attendance were negatively correlated with gambling behavior, while being male and having experience in the armed forces were both positively correlated with gambling behavior.

The correlation between lottery play and loss of control was not as strong as that between lottery play and gambling behavior. The personality traits of competitiveness, impulsiveness and big-spender were more strongly associated with loss of control than with gambling behavior. Drinking and watching sports were not as strongly correlated with loss of control as with gambling behavior. Childhood exposure to gambling was correlated with loss of control. Residential mobility and being a renter seemed to improve as correlates of problem gambling as we moved to loss of control, as did being Jewish and never married. Some correlates of gambling behavior were not correlated with loss of control, such as gender and armed forces service. Other respondent characteristics were correlated to roughly the same degree with loss of control as with gambling behavior.

Lottery play was less of a correlate of undesirable consequences due to gambling than it was for gambling behavior and loss of control over gambling (Table 2). However, money spent on lottery play in a typical week remained a correlate of problem gambling across all three scales. Exposure to gambling, alcohol consumption and some of the personality traits declined as correlates of problem gambling as we moved to gambling consequences. The variables that were becoming better correlates of problem gambling, as we moved to measures of increasing seriousness, were residential mobility, being widowed, having multiple marriages, being non-white, Jewish, and having armed forces service, although the correlations were quite modest.

B. Prediction of Problem Gambling By Regression Analysis

Stepwise multiple regression analysis was used to explore the relationship between independent variables (correlates shown in Table 2) and the three gambling scales. In the cases of loss of control and gambling consequences, regression equations were computed including and then excluding the previous stages of problem gambling as predictor variables. The reason for their inclusion was to test for the progression of problem gambling, from gambling behavior to loss of control and gambling consequences. Since this represents a possible confusion of using gambling behavior and loss of control as both dependent and independent variables, these previous states were excluded in separate regressions.

In Table 3, eight variables explained 37 percent of the variance in the scale of gambling behavior. Given the variables used, this was the best possible prediction of gambling behavior. The best predictor of gambling behavior was money spent on lottery play in a typical week, followed by lottery play both in the past and present. These two variables explained 21 percent of the respondents' gambling behavior. Being Jewish was the next predictor, but there were only four Jews in this sample.

Current and childhood exposure to others who gamble were also predictors of gambling behavior. The other predictors were alcohol consumption, being Catholic, and education (lower). Because F-level and tolerance levels were insufficient for further computation, other correlates of gambling behavior in Table 2 were not brought into the regression equation.

Twenty-six percent of the respondents' *loss of control over gambling* was explained by five independent variables. Lottery play was not a predictor of loss of control over gambling, at least not for these respondents. The best predictor was being Jewish and this was followed by respondents' gambling behavior, which was the dependent variable in the previous equation. Being

TABLE 3

STEPWISE REGRESSION FOR INDEPENDENT VARIABLES ON GAMBLING BEHAVIOR, LOSS OF CONTROL AND GAMBLING CONSEQUENCES

Variables	*B*	Standard Error of *B*	Multiple Correlation Coefficient Squared *R*
GAMBLING BEHAVIOR			
Money Spent on Lottery Typical Week	.782	.089	.11
Lottery Play	2.000	.254	.21
Religion (Jewish)	10.302	1.328	.28
Exposure To Gambling (Current)	.778	.141	.32
Alcohol Consumption	.309	.070	.35
Religion (Catholic)	.624	.223	.36
Education	-.178	.069	.36
Exposure To Gambling (Childhood)	.346	.136	.37
F= 41.59, df=8,565, p<.0001			
LOSS OF CONTROL			
Religion (Jewish)	5.440	.683	.16
Gambling Behavior	.128	.020	.21
Income	-.169	.040	.23
Impulsive	.108	.029	.26
F= 46.97, df=4,540, p<.0001			
GAMBLING CONSEQUENCE			
Religion (Jewish)	6.958	.263	.63
Loss of Control	.167	.015	.71
Gambling Behavior	.023	.007	.72
Widowed	.159	.067	.72
F= 361.333, df=4,562, p< .00001			

TABLE 2

CORRELATIONS BETWEEN GAMBLING BEHAVIOR (GB), LOSS OF CONTROL (LC), GAMBLING CONSEQUENCE (GC) AND SELECTED INDEPENDENT VARIABLES

	GB	LC	GC
LOTTERY PLAYERS	.32*	.12*	.07
MONEY SPENT ON LOTTERY TYPICAL WEEK	.33*	.13*	.11*
PERSONALITY			
Civic personality scale	-.03	-.08	-.04
Self-centered personality scale	.03	.10*	.05
Competitive personality scale	.12*	.10*	.01
Big-spender	.11*	.14*	.09*
Impulsive	.11*	.18*	.06
LEISURE			
Alcohol consumption	.22*	.14*	.04
Watch sports	.14*	.05	-.03
Money spent on leisure past week	.06	.001	-.02
Recreational pursuits			
Sports	.04	.09	-.0006
Hunting, fishing, etc.	.05	.02	-.02
Dining, dancing	.004	.03	-.02
Hobbies	.08	.008	.07
Television and music	-.08	.01	-.04
EXPOSURE TO GAMBLING			
Childhood	.15*	.12*	.07
Current	.25*	.06	.02
RESIDENCE			
City over 100,000	.03	-.019	-.02
Suburb of city over 100,000	-.007	.03	.03
Rural area or farm	-.04	-.06	.06
Home ownership (owners=1, renters=2)	.04	.10*	.06
Residential mobility	.16*	.21*	.24*
MARITAL STATUS			
Divorced or separated	.07	-.03	.002
Widowed	-.06	.03	.11*
Married	-.03	-.08	-.09*
Never married	.04	.11*	.02
Years married	-.05	-.10	-.04
Number of marriages	.04	-.02	.15*
Number of adults at home	.03	.04	.08
RESPONDENT CHARACTERISTICS			
Iowa-born	.02	.02	.004
Age	-.11*	-.12*	-.10*
Ethnicity (non-white=1, white=2)	-.002	.07	-.19*
Gender (female=1, male=2)	.12*	.015	-.05
Employed	.08	.002	-.08
Full employment	.12*	-.04	-.0002
Education	-.12*	-.03	-.06
Occupation (farmer, blue-collar, service, and white-collar)	-.06	.009	-.07
Income	.07	-.11*	-.06
Financial status (stocks, bonds, or property)	.009	-.10*	-.02
Religion (Protestant)	-.12*	-.11*	-.08
Religion (Fundamentalist)	-.03	-.01	-.03
Religion (Catholic)	.09*	.05	-.05
Religion (Jewish)	.28*	.38*	.79*
Church attendance	-.10*	-.06	-.02
Armed forces service	.15*	.04	.12*

* *Correlation is statistically significant at p<.01*

Jewish and gambling behavior accounted for 21 percent of the respondents' scores on loss of control. The other predictors were income (lower), and respondents being impulsive.

Lottery play as measured above helped predict *loss of control* over gambling once gambling behavior as a previous stage in the progression was removed from the equation. The predictors in order of importance were: being Jewish, impulsive, income (lower), childhood exposure to gambling, money spent on the lottery in a typical week, and alcohol consumption. This equation predicted 23 percent of the variance in loss of control.

In another equation, being Jewish was excluded as an independent variable. Recall that there were only four Jews in the sample. This is simply a biased estimate of the influence of being Jewish on problem gambling. With being Jewish excluded, 19 percent of the respondents' loss of control over gambling was explained. The predictors in order of importance were: gambling behavior, income (lower), changes in residence in the past five years, and impulsiveness.

Seventy-two percent of the variance in the *gambling-consequences* scale was explained by four independent variables. The best predictor of gambling consequences was being Jewish, followed by loss of control, gambling behavior, and being widowed. For reasons stated above, being Jewish was excluded, and the resulting equation explained 43 percent of the respondents' scores on gambling consequences. The predictors in order of importance were loss of control and gambling behavior, which together accounted for 36 percent of gambling consequences. These were followed by number of marriages, changes in residence in the past five years, being widowed, armed forces service and age. Gambling, losing control over it, having had more than one marriage, changing residence frequently, being widowed, and having served in the armed forces were a composite characterization of those who experienced gambling consequences.

In the last equation, gambling behavior and loss of control were removed as predictors of gambling consequences. This equation explained 64 percent of the variance in gambling consequences. The predictors were being Jewish, money spent on lottery in a typical week, being unmarried, and a big-spender. Again, lottery play helped predict problem gambling once its previous stages of the progression into problem gambling were removed from a prediction equation. All regression equations reported were significant at $p<.0001$.

DISCUSSION

The results showed that problem gambling is a progression. This progression can be decomposed into three distinct phases: gambling behavior, loss of control and gambling consequences. The factor analysis of problem-gambling items and composition of the three gambling scales provide support that the stages are distinct from one another. Moreover, the T-tests of the adjusted means of the three scales indicate that respondents reported far more gambling behavior than either loss of control and gambling consequences, and more loss of control than gambling consequences. That is, the progression into problem gambling narrowed to fewer and fewer respondents in the deeper stages. Nearly 73 percent of the entire sample reported some gambling behavior, including lottery play, but of those who gambled, no more than 26 percent indicated any loss of control, and only six percent reported any gambling consequences on their lives. This suggests that gambling behavior preceded loss of control and gambling consequences, and loss of control was prior to consequences.

By the same token, the three stages of problem gambling were connected. Both the correlation and regression analyses showed an association among the three scales. For example, previous stages were always important predictors of latter ones in the regression analysis, further evidence of a progression. Of course, this was hardly surprising, for one must first gamble before losing control over it and experiencing its consequences. We must keep in mind, however, that most who gambled in this sample reported no loss of control and gambling consequences, meaning that gambling does not always result in problem gambling.

What was not obvious is the exact connection between losing control and consequences. An in-depth analysis could find that people use consequences as signs of their losing control over gambling, and thus would raise the question of which comes first, loss of control or consequences.

The primary objective of the research was to determine the role of lottery play along with other variables in problem gambling. In the regression analysis, both measures of lottery play were predictors of gambling behavior. This, too, was hardly surprising. However, further analyses showed that at least one measure of lottery play, money spent on the lottery in a typical week, was a predictor of the two other stages of problem gambling once the preceding stages of the progression were removed from the equations.

This is a very interesting issue, one that would be best answered through longitudinal research. The issue is: Can lottery play alone propel people into the deeper stages of problem gambling, or must it expand into more general gambling behavior and loss of control before the deeper stage of problem gambling results? Longitudinal research is needed to date these events, lottery play, other gambling, loss of control and consequences, and thereby ascertain the temporal progression of cause and effect. Of course, those who proceed along any such progression into problem gambling must be compared with a control group who do not.

The other predictors of problem gambling were its earlier stages, two personality traits, and a number of background characteristics of respondents. Religion, education, alcohol consumption and exposure to gambling, along with lottery play, predicted gambling behavior. Religion, exposure to gambling, income, residential mobility and alcohol consumption predicted loss of control, combining the results of three separate equations. One personality trait — impulsiveness — was also a predictor of loss of control. Gambling consequences were predicted by religion; residential mobility; three different measures of marital status — multiple marriages, unmarried at this time, and widowed; armed forces service; and one personality trait — being a big-spender. Whereas lottery players were not truly distinguishable from the general population, gamblers who progress into later stages of problem gambling were (Hraba, 1989).

It seems that a background composed by the following dimensions — religion, exposure to gambling, lower educational attainment, and alcohol consumption — combines with lottery play at some point and evolves into gambling behavior. Some of these dimensions carry over as predictors of loss of control, namely, religion, exposure to gambling and alcohol consumption. At this stage, residential mobility, a lower income and impulsiveness also help predict problem gambling. Religion and residential mobility remain as predictors of gambling consequences, but at this stage marital status, armed forces service and being a self-attributed big-spender also help predict problem gambling. Of course, caution on the role of being Jewish as a religious variable must be exercised for reasons given above.

While these results are generally consistent with past survey research on gambling, they bear little on theory about problem gambling. The "big win" theory is not tested, but the results do imply that most gamblers control their gambling, showing no loss of control nor gambling consequences.

If measures of education, income, and residential mobility are construed as indicative of those who face blocked opportunity in the mainstream, then these results lend some support to anomie theory. However, it is impossible to unravel cause and effect in this regard. For instance, are income and residential mobility causes or effects of problem gambling? Other findings hint at a socialization theory. Exposure to gambling and armed forces service, as indicators of a bigger set of variables on differential socialization, when combined with alcohol consumption and certain personality traits, namely, impulsiveness and being a big-spender, might unfold into problem gambling.

Lastly, a social control theory of gambling is suggested. Deeper stages of problem gambling are predicted by marital statuses which might translate into reduced family control over a respondent's gambling. However, being currently unmarried and/or having multiple marriages could be either a cause or effect of problem gambling.

REFERENCES

American Psychiatric Association (1980). *Diagnostic and Statistical: Manual III*. Washington, D.C.: American Psychiatric Association.

American Psychiatric Association (1987). *Diagnostic and Statistical Manual of Mental Disorders*, 3rd edition. Washington, D.C.: American Psychiatric Association.

Bergler, E. (1958). *The Psychology of Gambling*. London: Harrison.

Berry, J.R. (1968). What makes a gambling addict. *Today's Health*, October, 21-23.

Culleton, R.P. and Lang, M.H. (1985). *The Prevalence Rate of Pathological Gambling in the Delaware Valley in 1984*. Camden, NJ: Rutgers University.

Custer, R.L. (1979). *An overview of compulsive gambling*. Paper presented at the Ninth Annual Conference on Problems of Industrial Psychiatric Medicine.

Custer, R.L. and Milt, H. (1985). *When Luck Runs Out*. New York: Facts on File Publications.

Dunne, J.A. (1983). The president's message. *National Council on Compulsive Gambling Newsletter*, 1, 2.

Frey, J.H. (1984). Gambling: A sociological review. *Annals*, 474, 107-120.

Goffman, E. (1967). *Interaction Ritual: Essays On Face-to-Face Behavior*. New York: Anchor Books.

Greene, J. (1982). The gambling trap. *Psychology Today*, 16, 50-55.

Hayano, D.M. (1982). *Poker Faces*. Berkeley: University of California Press.

Herman, R. (1967). Gambling as work: A sociological study of the race track. In R. Herman (ed.), *Gambling*, pp. 87-106. New York: Harper and Row.

Herman, R. (1976). *Gamblers and Gambling*. Lexington, MA: Lexington Books.

Hraba, J. (1989). *Report to Iowa Department of Human Services: Research on Iowa Lottery and Gambling*. Ames: Department of Sociology, Iowa State University.

Kallick, M., Suits, D., Dielman, T. and Hybels, J. (1979). *A Survey of American Gambling Attitudes and Behavior*. Ann Arbor, MI: Institute for Social Research.

Kaplan, H.R. (1984). The social and economic impact of state lotteries. *Annals*, 474, 91-106.

Langer, E.J. (1983). *The Psychology of Control*. Beverly Hills: Sage Publications.

Lesieur, H.R. (1977). *The Chase*. Garden City, NY: Anchor.

Lesieur, H.R. (1979). The compulsive gambler's spiral of options and involvement. *Psychiatry*, 42, 79-87.

Lesieur, H.R. and Blume, S. (1987). The South Oaks Gambling Screen (SOGS): A new instrument for the identification of pathological gamblers. *American Journal of Psychiatry*, 114, 1184-1188.

Lesieur, H.R. and Custer, R.L. (1984). Pathological gambling: Roots, phases, and treatment. *Annals*, 474, 146-156.

Lieberman, L. (1988). *A Social Typology of Gambling Behavior*. New York: National Council on Compulsive Gambling.

Merton, R.K. (1938). Social structure and anomie. *American Sociological Review*, 3, 672-682.

Moran, E. (1975). Pathological gambling. *Contemporary Psychiatry, British Journal of Psychiatry*, Special Publication No. 9. London: Royal College of Psychiatrists.

Oldman, D. (1974). Chance and skill: A study of roulette. *Sociology*, 8, 407-426.

Orford, J. (1985). *Excessive Appetites: A Psychological View of Addictions*. New York: John Wiley and Sons.

Rosecrance, J. (1985-86). The next best thing: A study of problem gambling. *The International Journal of the Addictions*, 20, 1727-1739.

Rosecrance, J. (1986). Attributions and the origins of problem gambling. *The Sociological Quarterly*, 27, 463-477.

Scott, M.B. (1968). *The Racing Game*. Chicago: Aldine.

Tec, N. (1964). *Gambling in Sweden*. Totowa, NJ: Bedminister Press.

Transitional Planning Associates (1985). *A Survey of Pathological Gamblers in the State of Ohio*. Philadelphia: Transitional Planning Associates.

Volberg, R.A. and Steadman, H.J. (1988). Refining prevalence estimates of pathological gambling. *American Journal of Psychiatry*, 145, 502-505.

Wagner, W. (1972). *To Gamble or Not To Gamble*. New York: World Publishing.

Waller, A. (1974). *The Gamblers*. Toronto: Clarke, Irwin Ltd.

Waller, A. (1978). Compulsive gamblers. *Sociological Review*, 26, 349-371.

Wells, C. (1989). America's gambling fever: Everybody wants a piece of the action — but is it good for us? *Business Week*, April, 112-120.

Winston, S. and Harris, H. (1984). *Nation of Gamblers*. Englewood Cliffs, NJ: Prentice-Hall.

Pathological Gambling and Couple Relationship Issues©

Marvin A. Steinberg

Discussion in this paper of the assessment and treatment of couples is based primarily upon the author's clinical experience with approximately fifty couples over the las decade in a public mental health outpatient and inpatient compulsive gambling treatment program. While there are wide variations among the couples on a number of dimensions, the typical couple was in its early thirties, married with children, and Italian Catholic or Jewish. The gambler's occupations were most often salesmen, proprietors of a small business or skilled blue collar workers. Most gamblers at the time of treatment were attending Gamblers Anonymous (GA) and their partners attending Gam-Anon (G-A).

© A version of this article has been published in the *Journal of Gambling Studies* (1993), 9(2). New York: Human Sciences Press, Inc. Permission to reprint has been granted by the author and publisher.

Since the author's experience is predominantly with couples in which the gambler is a white male, all discussion in this paper will assume a white male gambler. Lesieur's (1988) research with female compulsive gamblers has pointed to a number of significant differences between male and female gamblers, including family issues. Therefore, caution is warranted in generalizing from the author's clinical experience to couples in which the woman is the compulsive gambler.

Generalizations, conclusions, interpretations and estimates presented in this article derive from the author's cumulative clinical practice rather than statistical analysis of case material. The author's primary intention is to share an approach and conceptualization to couples treatment which will stimulate discussion and encourage systematic research.

SYSTEMS PERSPECTIVE

The mental health approach to assessment and treatment of compulsive (pathological) gamblers in the United States has paralleled the approach of Gamblers Anonymous (GA) as it has focused on changing the addictive pattern within the gambler. Professional work with spouses has similarly paralleled the emphasis in Gam-Anon (G-A) where the spouse is assisted in learning to focus on change within herself rather than feeling responsible for carrying the gambler's problem or trying to change him. Increased attention to the co-addictive (co-dependent) process in the general addictions literature has expanded awareness of the need for change within the spouse (and/or other co-dependents) independent of change within the addict (Beattie, 1987). Until very recently, couple and family interventions have generally been perceived as only ancillary or supportive of individual and group treatment. As clinicians trained in family therapy increasingly enter the gambling field, a family systems perspective of assessment and treatment is beginning to come to the forefront (Lorenz, 1987; Steinberg, 1985). Wildman (1989) has recently reviewed couples treatment in the gambling literature.

FAMILY ASSESSMENT ISSUES

It is important to include the partner and key significant others as early as possible in the assessment of a gambling problem for the following reasons:

a) it orients family members to the treatment setting and prepares them for potential involvement in the process;

b) by gaining the perspective of significant others, a more accurate picture of the nature and extent of the gambler's problem may be developed;

c) by observing family interaction, family dynamics may be better understood and interpersonal deficits and strengths become clearer;

d) by opening an avenue of communication with someone within the home, the probability of honesty, accountability and early detection of signs of relapse are increased; and

e) it increases the likelihood that a significant other will enter into or remain in treatment even if the gambler drops out.

As is typical of other addictions, it is the partner of the compulsive gambler who most often initiates therapeutic contact. Whether she arrives to treatment alone or with the gambler, it is helpful to interview her alone as she is typically depressed, lacking in confidence and easily intimidated by her husband. Interviewing each partner alone facilitates the process of forming a therapeutic bond with the individuals.

Children in pathological gambling families have not yet received adequate therapeutic attention. Research over the last decade has pointed to an over-representation of addictions and other problems among children of pathological gamblers (Jacobs, 1989; Lesieur and Klein, 1987; Steinberg, 1989). Professional treatment programs for pathological gamblers typically do not focus on the children in these families. Similarly, Gam-A-Teen tends to be limited in availability as compared to its counterpart, Al-A-Teen, for children of alcoholics.

Depending upon the extent of crisis in the home and the age of the children, children should be considered for inclusion during the assessment phase. Generally, treatment does not include children until the couple relationship is stabilized. However, children may be treated earlier if separation or divorce is imminent, if they request to be included, or if they are highly symptomatic. There is frequently resistance on the part of the gambler to include the children in treatment, much as there is typically initial resistance to the inclusion of the partner, parents and any other extended family member.

The assessment process within each family determines the most favorable composition of family members in future sessions. Change in therapy usually occurs more rapidly, more broadly and is longer lasting when the assessment and treatment include other family members.

COUPLES FOCUS

For some time, there have been reports in the gambling literature of significant marital problems among gamblers and their spouses (Boyd and Bolen, 1970; Custer, 1985). When the couple first enters treatment, everything is chaotic. The partners are arguing constantly or not talking at all, stemming from a variety of problems such as finances, lies and serious legal problems. Both may be depressed or even suicidal. Despite the enormous stress both partners are experiencing, they are typically still in their separate forms of denial. Often comments reflecting denial are as follows:

> The gambler: "Maybe I gamble a little too much, but it's not a big issue." "Yeah, I made a mistake, but it won't happen again, and I don't need Gamblers Anonymous or counseling."
>
> The spouse: "He has the problem, so you cure him." "Why should I be in therapy? I'm only suffering the consequences of his problem."

It is assumed in twelve step work and in most psychotherapeutic approaches that couples treatment should be postponed until there has been significant individual change through individual and group therapy. While this sequence makes logical sense, couples therapy may be necessary from the beginning of recovery work in order to manage and negotiate crises and to halt further unnecessary deterioration in the relationship. Appropriate confrontation of issues in couples work can also break through the denial more rapidly.

Frequently, the partner is co-dependently enmeshed in the gambler's addiction and, therefore, viewing the partners as having interconnecting dynamics is a useful working assumption (Darvas, 1981). It follows that in order for significant change to occur, it is necessary to intervene directly in the dysfunctional couples system.

Based upon the needs of each couple, different combinations of couple and individual interventions may be required. Couples sessions may be primarily conjoint focused or individual sessions with the gambler or partner and conjoint sessions with the couple may be alternated or sessions may be divided in time between either partner alone and the couple together. During conjoint sessions, goals for change are arrived at for the relationship and targets for change within each partner are identified which are needed to facilitate growth in the relationship. Where sufficient numbers of appropriate couples are available, a couples' group may be a useful intervention (Tepperman, 1985).

CAUTIONS TO THE CLINICIAN

When couples therapy is indicated, there may be an underlying collusion between the therapist and the gambler to postpone couples work indefinitely. Gamblers are typically resistant to treatment due to their denial and projection of problems. It is difficult to form a therapeutic bond with them because they have limited interpersonal trust, they lack insight and are impatient with extended discussion. Therefore, the therapist may decide to begin individual treatment with the gambler in order to help develop a therapeutic alliance. This decision is reinforced by the fact that most traditionally trained therapists tend to feel more comfortable with individual than couple treatment. The gambler also prefers individual sessions as these offer less threat to his secretiveness and allows him to maintain limited openness with his family. In individual sessions, the gambler may provide the therapist with only that information he wishes to disclose and thereby be able to manipulate the therapy into nonproductive directions. The therapist may wish to agree to a time limited contract for individual therapy with the gambler during which time any barriers to conjoint sessions may be worked through. Individual therapy for the spouse may occur during the same time period with the same or another member of the treatment team.

The clinician working alone with the couple must be aware of the tendency to join with one partner at the expense of the other as well as the therapy. For example, it is easier to fall into the trap of feeling sorry for the female partner while feeling anger toward the gambler, especially since the partner is the one who typically seeks the help and the gambler is typically skeptical and resistant. In order to be able to adopt a neutral stance, the therapist must achieve an understanding of the factors which created and maintain the gambler's behavior, especially his underlying fear and low self-esteem. Also, viewing the couple relationship from a systems perspective, which recognizes that individual behavior is reinforced within the system the partners have created together, helps the therapist avoid forming a nonproductive alliance with one client.

It is important for the couples therapist to recognize the potential influence of his or her gender on the therapy. A male therapist may subtly or overtly support familial and cultural expectations which give the male more power in the relationship. A female therapist, who is not liberated herself, may reinforce gender stereotypes which keep the female partner in a subordinate position. On the other hand, a male therapist may find himself rescuing the "damsel in distress" and victimizing the victimizer, while a female therapist who is herself immersed in a struggle for liberation as a woman may join with the female partner against the gambler. Co-therapy is a helpful resolution in some of these cases by providing gender balance. Individual sessions for either spouse may be conducted as needed by the therapist of the same sex.

The clinician who treats the recovering gambler and his partner often finds themself confronted with couple's issues related to the membership of the partners in GA and G-A. Frequently, gamblers who are reluctantly attending GA express their grievances about GA and/or G-A in the conjoint therapy sessions. The partner typically responds by defending these programs. Many professionals harbor strong reservations about twelve step programs and are all too eager to use an opportunity to offer suggestions for improving the way these programs operate. In the context of therapy, there are two reasons for the clinician refraining from comments critical of the process or structure of either program. First, the couple's confidence in the efficacy of GA and G-A may be compromised and, secondly, the partners may utilize critical comments by the clinician to triangle him or her into their own issues with the self help groups. The clinician may be helpful to the partners by identifying when they are projecting their relationship problems into the arenas of GA and G-A and by redirecting the focus to these relationship issues. However, there are specific couple's issues which are elicited or exacerbated by virtue of the partners' membership in GA and G-A. In these cases, the therapist who has a strong working knowledge of GA and G-A will be able to assist couples to work through the inevitable conflicts which result from their attempts to follow their separate programs. An example is the demand by the partner that the gambler turn over his paycheck which is discussed later in this paper.

MAJOR COUPLES TREATMENT ISSUES

The challenge to the couples therapist is to move beyond the goal of helping the couple become a functional unit to the goal of creating an intimate relationship through resolution of long term emotional issues and changing dysfunctional interactions which prevent relationship growth.

A. Commitment

Is there enough commitment and love left? Having remained in the relationship through the chaos of the gambling, the partner may consider leaving when the gambling stops as she reflects on past disappointments and hurts and considers the potential for relapse into gambling. This is a healthier response than that of the spouse whose self esteem is so low she is not able to consider leaving the relationship. Many partners think about leaving and even threaten it for years but lack the strength and resources to follow through. At the beginning of therapy, in most cases, precipitous decisions about the relationship should be discouraged. A number of months of therapeutic exploration and recovery are typically needed in order to provide a clearer and healthier base from which to make a decision regarding the future of the relationship. However, the crises created by the gambling may require urgent interventions, e.g., negotiation of a temporary conditional separation.

B. Addictive/Co-Addictive Behavior

Healthy intimacy is possible only when there is an ending to both the addiction to gambling and the enmeshment of the co-addicted spouse. Other addictions (e.g., alcohol, sex, food, etc.) may co-exist in either partner during the gambling period or new addictions may emerge for one or the other after the gambling has stopped (Taber, 1983). These also will serve as barriers to intimacy, and general recovery, unless dealt with directly. Approximately forty percent of pathological gamblers have significant substance abuse problems, with some abusing several substances (Ramirez, McCormick and Taber, 1987). For example, cocaine may be used when gambling (or as a substitute for gambling); alcohol may then be used to slow down, numb or block out the consequences of gambling losses and cocaine use; nicotine, caffeine or food addictions may also complete the picture. The interactions of addictions within and between each partner points to the need for multiple interventions and especially involvement in self help groups.

It is important for professionals who treat couples with gambling issues to perceive GA and G-A as significant and even essential recovery programs in many cases. Each of these programs helps the respective partners become aware of their individual problems, especially the denial of the problem and the loss of ability to deal with it without help. Gam-Anon is especially helpful to the partner with respect to facilitating the development of confidence and assertiveness. As the typical gambler is relatively isolated, secretive, manipulative and not deeply emotionally connected with family and friends, GA provides the context for the development of the bond of empathy and connection with other recovering gamblers. The work of the therapist is greatly facilitated in instances where the gambler has progressed in GA to an acceptance of his problem and has begun to relate honestly to his peers.

While GA and G-A are helpful in facilitating change in individual "personality defects," the partners frequently need couples focused therapy to work through past hurts, deal with current issues and create a more intimate bond. The couple must adjust from the individual focus of GA and G-A to viewing the relationship as the client.

C. Preventing Relapse

Relapse prevention work is essential for all addictions. The goal is to prevent lapses (slips) and, when they do occur, prevent a lapse from developing into a full scale relapse. The recovering pathological gambler is helped to identify and avoid triggers that could result in lapses. Stress reduction techniques, assertiveness training and other skill development play important roles in maintaining abstinence from gambling. There is also the need to develop a detailed plan of constructive action to be implemented when urges get stronger or a lapse occurs (Marlatt and Gordon, 1985).

Family response during recovery may be pivotal regarding whether gambling lapses and relapses occur. As issues of codependence are addressed by the spouse and significant others, enabling (e.g., bailout) behavior is minimized. The partner becomes clearer regarding her boundaries within the relationship. She learns to focus primarily on her own growth and goals and not to assume inappropriate responsibility regarding her partner's maintaining his abstinence. She is assisted in developing contingency plans for the possibility of relapse on the part of the gambler.

D. Finances

If the couple is involved in GA and Gam-Anon, budgeting and debt management are typically dealt with through the use of the pressure group. In the best circumstances, little may be required of the therapist in this area. However, if one or both partners is unwilling to participate in the self help programs, the therapist will need to provide some direction regarding realistic budgeting and financial restitution. In addressing gambling related debts the therapist also needs to be knowledgeable about the impact of loan consolidation, bankruptcy, and gifts (bailouts) from relatives or others. When locally available, a referral to a Consumer Credit Counseling Service is often helpful. Finances often become a major focal point in the partners' struggle for power and control in the relationship.

E. Control and Power Issues

Both partners have control and power issues. Frequently, the gambler and his partner grew up in homes in which gambling or substance abuse prevailed. In such an atmosphere, they both felt overwhelmed and unsafe. The residual for the gambler is resentment and resistance to rules and requirements imposed by authority figures. As a female, the partner of the gambler was typically socialized to have a more passive response to similar family of origin issues, while taking responsibility for causing and/or resolving such problems. This theme is represented in the spouse's relationship with the gambler as she helplessly struggles to restrain the gambling and the acting out behavior associated with it.

During the years of the gambling, the gambler usually has little involvement in parenting and other responsibilities in the home. The partner assumes responsibility for management of the household by virtue of the gambler's unavailability. Often the spouse comes to view the gambler as immature and irresponsible, almost as another child in the family. In recovery, the helping systems foster the expectation that the gambler should now assume his share of the responsibilities in the home. However, both partners typically have significant difficulty negotiating a change in roles.

If the partner is a member of G-A, she typically receives advice and feedback aimed at her gaining financial and emotional security. Control issues are heightened as the partner is encouraged to make "demands" of the gambler, which he typically resists. The therapist can be helpful in defusing the power struggle through restatement and interpretation. For example, when the partner makes the "demand" that the gambler turn over his entire paycheck, the therapist can reframe the statement as an expression of her desire to be sufficiently financially secure so that she would be able to remain in the relationship. The therapist also offers the suggestion to the gambler that if he "chooses" to give his paycheck to his family, it would be an expression of caring toward his family and himself. That is, they would be protected against serious financial loss should he relapse into gambling.

Once the power struggle has subsided, the couple is helped to accept and value their different points of view. With the expression of their differences no longer creating a major confrontation, they are helped to utilize negotiation skills in blending their differences to make joint decisions. In the example of the gambler who resists turning over his paycheck to his partner, the therapist assists him to recognize that by agreeing to this he has not given up participation in decision making. In fact, it is an opportunity to participate, perhaps for the first time, in making joint decisions regarding the family's use of its income.

F. Anger

Both parents tend to express anger in unhealthy ways. When the gambler is angry at his spouse, it may quickly become destructive rage and is used as an excuse to leave the conflict situation to create an opportunity for gambling. The partner may deal with her anger in a variety of nonconstructive ways — brief intense tearful outbursts; retreat into cold silence and passive aggressiveness; covering the anger with compulsive eating or other addictions; and/or displacing anger toward the children. Both partners need assistance in defusing rage and expressing anger in direct constructive ways and recognizing the need to be present to each other's constructive expression of anger. The couple is assisted in identifying the internal and external triggers for anger and identifying and responding positively to the vulnerable emotions (e.g., hurt and disappointment) often behind the anger.

G. Deficit in Emotional Intimacy

A major relatively neglected area of recovery for the couple relationship shattered by pathological gambling is that of intimacy consisting of trust, mutual vulnerability and the sharing of feelings. Unfortunately, in many cases, even after years of abstinence from gambling, the couple relationship is still unhappy on the emotional and sexual levels. One explanation for this outcome is found in the history of the relationship, where long periods of hurt, anger and alienation may have taken an irreparable toll on the emotional bond. Deeper roots of this prolonged marital problem are found in the social and emotional development of each of the partners in their families of origin. The genogram may be utilized to pictorially represent three or more generations of the families of both partners. Highlighted are such inter-generational issues as addictive patterns and ways in which each partner symbolically assumes a role played by a member of the other partner's family of origin. For example, consider the case of both partners having fathers who were compulsive gamblers (or other types of addicts) and whose mothers were long suffering women who tried in vain to restrain their husbands' addictive behavior. Both partners can be helped to see how they have adopted the roles vis-a-vis each other that their same sexed parents had in each of their families of origin.

The gambler is typically raised in a home in which intimacy is quite limited. There are deficits in understanding, support and positive emotional sharing. "Love" isn't verbalized and affection is most frequently expressed through exchange of gifts and money. The dream of excitement, glamour and power in successful gambling eventually replaces the striving for connectedness with another person which the gambler has not been able to achieve. In other words, success in gambling is the symbolic substitute for the vulnerability, sharing and interdependence of emotional intimacy. However, since gambling cannot satisfy basic emotional and interpersonal needs, the gambler remains a loner, alienated from others.

When the gambler marries, intimate emotional sharing is not sought or possible. The gambler does not believe that his partner will be truly and dependably nurturing. Even if nurturance were available, he fears it would come with the price of total control over his autonomy, which he is still struggling to assert.

While the gambler's partner is usually more desirous of intimacy, she frequently has a history, stemming from her family of origin, of not having successfully achieved it. There is an over-representation of alcohol or gambling abuse among the parents of the partners of gamblers (Heineman, 1987). As an adult, she may crave intimacy without knowing how to create it or may not basically believe she deserves it. Despite her ambivalence she may express her need for emotional closeness. This heightens the gambler's fear of being smothered and endangers his pursuit of gambling as a substitute for love. As he moves further away, her ambivalence toward intimacy decreases and her desire for it increases. An ongoing pursuer/distancer relationship is created.

Considering the historical factors, there is little basis for assuming that intimacy will be spontaneously created when there is abstinence from gambling. The growth of each individual resulting from participation in the separate recovery programs of GA and G-A and/or professional individual and group treatment is often not sufficient to overcome the barriers to nurturance within the relationship. The early phase of couples recovery is not fertile soil for the development of intimacy, as the tasks focus on basic survival of the relationship. An enormous amount of the couple's energy is consumed in meeting current financial responsibilities and repaying debts. Rebuilding occurs primarily on the material and structural levels of the family unit and deep emotional connection and sharing must wait (Lorenz and Yaffee, 1989; Steinberg, 1987).

For a long time after the gambling has stopped, the partner does not emotionally trust the gambler because of the many ways his behavior has been hurtful. She fears becoming open and vulnerable to lies, to the loss of family finances if he returns to gambling, and to personal attacks. She is angry that he has been emotionally unavailable to her, frequently exacerbated by extra-marital sex.

The spouse must learn that there is a healthier alternative to being closed off emotionally and sexually to her partner. However, before she develops a new more realistic trust in place of her previous blind trust, the recovering gambler must evidence growth. He must learn to respect the importance of trust in a love relationship and to identify and value such components of trust as honesty and following through with commitments. As trust slowly develops in the relationship, the door opens to mutual vulnerability, empathy and the sharing of feelings. However, the recovering gambler typically needs substantial assistance in getting in touch with vulnerable feelings and taking the risk to express these. Having been extremely self focused, he also requires help in becoming emotionally sensitive to his partner's needs. Frequently, both partners need help in understanding that neither should be expected to mind read the other's needs. Both must take responsibility for identifying their own needs and for being as direct and clear in communicating them as possible. Because both partners typically have difficulty in assertiveness and in initiating and maintaining communication of positive feelings outside of therapy sessions, it is frequently necessary that the therapist focus on facilitating these processes within the sessions.

Another important aspect of the development of emotional intimacy is the necessity for the partners to commit themselves to creating sufficient time alone together. They must learn to feel comfortable in each other's presence even when not interacting. In the past, the gambler's invitations to his spouse for social activities were likely to have been gambling connected, e.g., at a race track or a vacation at a Caribbean resort which had a casino. As the gambling increased, the couple most likely spent very little time together. He used all his spare time to gamble while she engaged in activities with their children, her female friends or she spent a good deal of time alone and depressed. During recovery, the gambler substitutes work and GA for gambling, while his partner now adds G-A to her life. They may spend some more time together than before but it is mainly in the presence of other people. Both their multiple responsibilities and their discomfort about intimacy are barriers to overcome in order to have the time alone to build a sense of closeness and sharing.

H. Sexual Problems

The psychoanalytic literature has postulated a relationship between gambling and sex (Rosenthal, 1987). Gamblers report a similarity in excitement between the anticipation of gambling and the anticipation of having sex, with winning a big bet equivalent in intensity to having an orgasm. Since many gamblers report that gambling is more enjoyable than sex, it is not surprising that sexual interest may be replaced with an absorption in gambling.

While there has not been systematic research studying the extent of sexual dysfunctions among pathological gamblers, there are case reports indicating low sexual desire and erectile problems (Daghestani, 1987). Instead of decreased sexual interest and sexual dysfunction, some gamblers are preoccupied with sex and act out sexually in a compulsive way. One research report indicates evidence of a relationship between pathological gambling and sex addiction. Adkins, Rugle, and Taber (1985) found a 14 percent incidence of sex addiction within a sample of 100 inpatient male compulsive gamblers. These researchers reported a high incidence of "womanizing" (involvement with multiple female sexual partners) within this sample of sexually addicted pathological gamblers. The excitement associated with the pursuit of women closely resembled the excitement associated with pursuing the "big win" in gambling. Steinberg

(1990) reports that "... a similar positive and negative anticipatory excitement is associated with the risks involved in certain kinds of sexually addictive behaviors (exhibitionism, for example) and the risks associated with placing a sizeable wager."

There is an absence of systematic information regarding the frequency and types of sexual problems of the spouses of gamblers. However, it is reasonable to infer from other intimacy difficulties observed in this group that there is an over-representation of sexual problems, especially low sexual desire.

Where either or both partners are found to have a sexual dysfunction (e.g., difficulty with erection and low sexual desire) or a sexual addiction (e.g., compulsion regarding massage parlors/prostitution), more detailed sexual histories should be obtained followed by referral to a sex therapist for a course of treatment appropriate to the problem(s). [See Kaplan (1983) and Carnes (1989) for examples of approaches to sexual dysfunction and sexual addiction, respectively.]

Once the gambler stops gambling, one of the areas in which his energy is often redirected is the couple's sexual relationship. However, his partner is frequently not sexually responsive at this point in time. This creates a problem as the recovering gambler believes his efforts toward recovery should be rewarded by resumption of regular sexual contact. There are several possible reasons for the partner's lack of sexual openness or interest. When the gambler was sexual toward her during his gambling periods, she typically experienced him as sexually self centered, focusing only on satisfying his own biological needs. He may also have attempted to use sex as a pacifier in anticipation of his spouse learning about gambling losses or afterwards to try to smooth over the loss of money and trust. The partner may have also felt sexually rejected because he appeared preoccupied during sex or seemed to just want to get it over with. Or, he may have expressed no sexual interest in her during times of intense gambling. Since the gambling is often done secretly, she may have assumed he was involved with another woman.

Some partners consciously or unconsciously withhold sex in retaliation for past hurts or as a means of current control in the relationship. However, even in situations where the spouse is not motivated by revenge or control, it may be difficult for her to be sexually responsive again if she had been protecting herself by withholding sexually over a long period of time. Under these circumstances, some partners refuse to engage in sexual contact because they lack sexual drive; others lack the assertiveness to say no and continue to have sexual intercourse even when they have no desire. The absence of sexual desire helps protect the partner from feeling emotionally vulnerable during sex. Even when the partner is interested in resuming sex with the recovering gambler, her need for emotional nurturance is still not met in their sexual relationship as he is not readily able to share his feelings. In a survey of 151 couples in which the husband was a member of GA and the wife a member of G-A, Lorenz and Yaffee (1989) concluded that with respect to reported level of sexual satisfaction of the partners ". . . 38 percent of the couples do not appear to communicate to one another about their sexual feelings" (p. 119).

Each partner can be helped to be more assertive about their needs in and out of bed. Both often find it difficult to ask directly for what they want and to say no without feeling guilty or acting in a rejecting manner. Because of the recovering gambler's need to be liked and his avoidance of conflict, he frequently says yes when he wishes to say no and then does not follow through on what he has agreed to do. The spouse, in particular, must learn to verbalize any discomfort which arises during sexual contact and to interrupt contact until subsequent communication creates the necessary comfort. It becomes easier for her to be assertive in this way as her self-esteem increases.

Many gamblers view sex with their partners as primarily a genital experience and even something to be bartered. One gambler stated that he assumed there was an implicit understanding between he and his wife when they got married that he would give her luxuries and she would give him sex. His wife sensed he believed this and was angry but never discussed it with him; instead, she withheld sexually. In therapy, the expectation that sex is to be implicitly or explicitly bartered to gain something else was changed. Couples in treatment learn to view sexual expression as part of a loving context, where genital sex is not disconnected from verbal and nongenital physical affection.

Some gamblers report a lack of need for and appreciation of nongenital sensuousness. They may not even receive comfort from cuddling and other forms of nongenital physical contact. This typically reflects a deficit in early life experience and is difficult to overcome, e.g., "How can I know what I'm missing, since I never had it?" Sensate focus, the technique utilized in sex therapy, may be helpful in increasing nongenital pleasure. However, if this approach is not successful, the therapist may need to primarily focus on helping the gambler empathize with and respond to his partner's need for physical closeness because he loves her even though he is not experiencing physical pleasure on this level. This strategy will not be successful if the gambler's lack of interest masks an underlying extreme fear of intimacy or unconscious rage toward his partner.

SUMMARY

Until recently, the couple relationship has been relatively neglected in both clinical reports and systematic research in the compulsive gambling literature. This article suggests the need for family and intergenerational assessment as well as early interventions within the couple system. The following treatment issues are discussed: commitment; addiction/co-addiction; relapse; finances; control and power; anger; emotional intimacy; and sexuality. Overcoming deficits in intimacy is viewed as central to couples recovery.

REFERENCES

Adkins, B.J., Rugle, L.J. and Taber, J.I. (1985, November). *A note on sexual addiction among compulsive gamblers.* Paper presented at the First National Conference on Gambling Behavior, National Council on Compulsive Gambling, Inc., New York.

Beattie, M. (1987). *Codependent No More.* New York: Harper and Row.

Carnes, P. (1989). *Contrary to Love: Helping the Sexual Addict.* Minneapolis: CompCare Publishers.

Custer, R.L. and Milt, H. (1985). *When Luck Runs Out.* New York: Facts on File Publications.

Daghestani, A.N. (1987). Impotence associated with compulsive gambling. *Journal of Clinical Psychiatry*, 48, 115-116.

Darvas, S.F. (1982). The spouse in treatment: There is a woman (or women) behind every pathological gambler. In W.R. Eadington (ed.), *The Gambling Papers: Proceedings of the Fifth National Conference on Gambling and Risk Taking*, 3, 92-108. Reno: University of Nevada.

Heineman, M. (1987). A comparison: The treatment of wives of alcoholics with the treatment of wives of pathological gamblers. *Journal of Gambling Behavior*, 3, 27-40.

Jacobs, D.F. (1989). Children of problem gamblers. *Journal of Gambling Behavior*, 5, 261-268.

Kaplan, H.S. (1983). *The Evaluation of Sexual Disorders.* New York: Brunner/Mazel.

Lesieur, H.R. and Klein, R. (1987). Pathological gambling among high school students. *Addictive Behaviors*, 12, 129-135.

Lesieur, H.R. (1988). The female pathological gambler. In W.R. Eadington (ed.), *The Gambling Studies: Proceedings of the Sixth National Conference on Gambling and Risk Taking*, 5, 230-258. Reno: University of Nevada.

Lorenz, V.C. (1987). Family dynamics of pathological gamblers. In T. Galski (ed.), *The Handbook of Pathological Gambling*, pp. 71-88. Springfield, IL: Charles C. Thomas.

Lorenz, V.C. and Yaffee, R.A. (1989). Pathological gamblers and their spouses: Problems in interaction. *Journal of Gambling Behavior*, 5, 113-125.

Marlatt, G.A. and Gordon, J.R. (eds.), (1985). *Relapse Prevention: Maintenance Strategies in the Treatment of Addictive Behaviors.* New York: Guilford Press.

Ramirez, L.F., McCormick, R.A. and Taber, J.I. (1987). Patterns of substance abuse in pathological gamblers undergoing treatment. *Addictive Behaviors*, 8, 425-428.

Rosenthal, R.J. (1987). The psychodynamics of pathological gambling: A review of the literature. In T. Galski (ed.), *The Handbook of Pathological Gambling*, pp. 41-70. Springfield, IL: Charles C. Thomas.

Steinberg, M.A. (1985). Pathological gambling: Developing intimacy in the couple relationship. In W.R. Eadington (ed.), *The Gambling Studies: Proceedings of the Sixth National Conference on Gambling and Risk Taking*, 5, 176-184.

Steinberg, M.A. (1987). *Developing emotional and sexual intimacy in couples in which the husband is a recovering compulsive gambler.* Paper presented at the Twentieth Annual Meeting of the American Association of Sex Educators, Counselors and Therapists, New York City.

Steinberg, M.A. (1989). *Gambling behavior among high school students in Connecticut.* Paper presented at the Fourth National Conference on Compulsive Gambling, Des Moines, Iowa.

Steinberg, M.A. (1990). Sexual addiction and compulsive gambling. *American Journal of Preventive Psychiatry and Neurology*, 2, 39-41.

Taber, J.I. (1983). *Compulsive gambling and 'substitution therapy.'* Paper presented at the Fifth Annual Northwestern Conclave of Gamblers Anonymous, Portland, Oregon.

Tepperman, J.H. (1985). The effectiveness of short-term group therapy upon the pathological gambler and wife. *Journal of Gambling Behavior*, 1, 119-130.

Wildman, R.W. (1989). Pathological gambling: Marital-familial factors, implications, and treatments. *Journal of Gambling Behavior*, 5, 293-301.

A Two to Nine Year Treatment Follow-up Study of Pathological Gambling©

Alex Blaszczynski and Neil McConaghy

Programs offered for the treatment of addictive behaviors have traditionally emphasized abstinence as the specific outcome objective. This emphasis, reflecting the medical disease concept of illness, is based on the premise that a single act of indulgence will automatically and invariably lead to a relapse and subsequent prolonged excessive consumption (Fredrickson, Peterson and Murphy, 1976).

However, since the apparent success of controlled drinking and smoking reduction treatment strategies, the assumption that abstinence is a fundamental and necessary goal of treatment has been challenged (Sobell and Sobell, 1978; Heather and Robertson, 1981). While acknowledging that results remain

© This article is based substantially on papers which have appeared in the *British Journal of Addiction*. We gratefully acknowledge permission to reprint this article from the publishers, the ©Society for the Study of Addiction. *Complete citations are at the end of this article.

inconclusive and controversial, the potential benefits of controlled use in preference to abstinence has been argued for for a number of reasons. For example, Bacuum (1984) and others (Glascow, Moray and Lichtenstein, 1989) have suggested that the requirement for abstinence may discourage gamblers from initially seeking treatment, either because they are unconvinced of their ability to achieve complete abstinence or because they are reluctant to cease participation in a socially approved of and promoted activity. The tendency to procrastinate or avoid seeking treatment may ultimately increase the risk for the development of severe problems and affect prognostic outcome.

The offer of controlled use may entice ambivalent addicts to enter treatment earlier in their career, with successful outcome potentially leading to enhanced self-efficacy and an increased probability of their accepting later abstinence (Heather and Robertson, 1981). Further, intervention strategies aimed at control are less likely to produce abstinence violation effects (Marlatt and Gordon, 1988) in which minor breaches of abstinence are interpreted as indicative of total treatment failure and thus act as the initial step in the process leading toward continued relapse.

Reynolds and his colleagues (Reynolds, Tobin, Creer, Wigal and Wagner, 1987) have suggested that research, at least in the area of addictive smoking, has demonstrated that long term controlled use is possible, that outcome rates between abstinence and controlled treatment strategies are comparable, and importantly, that controlled smoking was not associated with higher relapse rates.

Despite its classification as a disorder of impulse control (A.P.A., 1987), pathological gambling has become conceptualized as an addictive behavior sharing many commonalities with alcoholism and drug dependence (Jacobs, 1986; Brown, 1987). As a consequence, the addictive disease model of illness as applied to alcoholism has similarly been extended to include pathological gambling. This view is perhaps best exemplified by the Gamblers Anonymous assertion that pathological gambling is an "an illness, progressive in its nature which cannot be cured but can be arrested" (Gamblers Anonymous, 1977) through the practice of total abstinence.

Similarly, apart from two single case studies (Dickerson and Weeks, 1979; Rankin, 1982), the majority of psychoanalytic (Bergler, 1943; Greenson, 1947; Matussek, 1955; Harris, 1964), behavioral (Barker and Miller, 1968; Goorney,

1968; Seager, 1970; Cotler, 1971; Koller, 1972; Bannister, 1977) and multi-modal (Russo, Taber, McCormick and Ramirez, 1984; Taber, McCormick, Russo, Adkins and Ramirez, 1987) approaches have also emphasized abstinence as the objective or criterion of success.

However, careful evaluation of the empirical evidence presented in three recent treatment outcome studies has suggested that significant benefit can be achieved in response to treatment even though total abstinence has not been attained.

In a twelve month follow-up study, McConaghy and his colleagues (McConaghy, Armstrong, Blaszczynski and Allcock, 1983) classified responses to aversive therapy or imaginal desensitization as either abstinent or markedly reduced. Marked reduction was defined as less than $10 per week gambled with no concomitant financial hardship resulting.

As shown in Table 1 below, abstinence was achieved by 20% of subjects treated by imaginal desensitization, but the proportion showing a relatively good outcome was increased to 70% if the response criteria was liberalized to include markedly reduced gambling.

Russo and his colleagues (Russo, Taber, McCormick and Ramirez, 1984), in their twelve month post-treatment follow-up survey of 124 gamblers, reported that 55% of the 60 successfully followed-up had maintained complete abstinence since being discharge, while a further 21% observed abstinent during the month immediately preceding follow-up assessment. Altogether, a total of 91.5% of patients showed a reduction in gambling behavior with associated improvements observed across a range of sociodemographic parameters.

Similar results were obtained by Taber and his colleagues in a subsequent prospective six month follow-up study of 66 gamblers who completed the same highly structured treatment program (Taber, McCormick, Russo, Adkins and Ramirez, 1987). Of the 57 subjects completing a telephone interview, 56% claimed complete abstinence, while 67% reported periods of abstinence, during the six month post-treatment period. The average number of days spent gambling for the total sample reduced from 15.7 per month to 4.75 per month.

The purpose of the present study was to compare subjects' self-reports of abstinence and control following behavioral treatment of pathological gambling in respect to a number of psychological test scores and sociodemographic indices of improvement, and patterns of any relapse episodes.

TABLE 1

GAMBLING TREATMENT OUTCOME RATES calculated as % of sample actually followed-up				
			CRITERIA FOR SUCCESS	
Study	*F/U period*	*N*	*Abstinence*	*Abstinence &/or Control*
			%	%
McConaghy et al., 1983	1 yr	10 (AT)*	0	20
		10 (ID)*	20	70
Russo et al., 1984	1 yr	60	55	
Taber et al., 1987	6 mo	57	56	

* AT = Aversive Therapy, ID = Imaginal Desensitization

METHOD

Between 1977 and 1981, 120 pathological gamblers were treated at the Prince of Wales Pathological Gambling Treatment Clinic. This clinic offered a one week inpatient program within the confines of a psychiatric unit of a large university teaching hospital. The number of subjects followed-up receiving each particular treatment is shown in Table 2.

TABLE 2

Number of Subjects Allocated to Each Behavioral Treatment		
Treatment Type	*N: Treated*	*N: Followed-up*
	N =	N =
Imaginal Desensitization	60	33
Aversive Therapy	30	33
Relazation	20	14
Brief Exposure	10	6
Prolonged Exposure	10	4

At pre-treatment assessment, subjects were informed that as part of an outcome evaluative research program, they would be randomly allocated to receive either imaginal desensitization or an alternative behavioral treatment, either aversive therapy, relaxation or brief or prolonged in-vivo exposure. All treatments were administered during a five day hospital admission, each patient receiving fourteen twenty minute sessions of each treatment.

However, the comparative effectiveness of each type of treatment will not be described here given that the focus of this paper is restricted to reporting long term outcome independent of the type of behavioral treatment received.

Prior to treatment and at follow-up, subjects completed a battery of psychological tests which included the Eysenck Personality Questionnaire (Eysenck and Eysenck, 1975), Zuckerman's Sensation Seeking Scale (Zuckerman, 1979), Symptom Checklist-90 (Derogatis, 1977) and Spielberger's State-Trait Anxiety Inventory (Spielberger, Gorsuch and Luschene, 1970), and at follow-up only, the Beck Depression Inventory (Beck, Ward, Mendelson, Mock and Erlbaugh, 1961). In addition, at follow-up, each patient was interviewed using a structured interview schedule to obtain data on gambling, health, marital and financial states.

SUBJECTS

All subjects met *DSM-III* (A.P.A., 1980) criteria for diagnosis of pathological gambling. As shown in Figure 1, of the 120 subjects initially treated, 57 were lost to follow-up. Of these, 41 were not able to be contacted, 13 refused cooperation and three were deceased as a result of myocardial infarct or carcinomas.

Sixty-three subjects, 55 males and eight females, were successfully followed-up, giving a response rate of 52 percent.

Results suggested that the followed-up and non followed-up groups were intrinsically similar to each other in that statistical analyses revealed no significant between group differences on such relevant variables as age, marital or socioeconomic status or on any of the pretreatment psychological test scale scores.

RESULTS

The mean post-treatment follow-up period was 5.5 years with a standard deviation of 1.6 years, the range being between 2 years and nine years, and a median of six years.

FIGURE 1

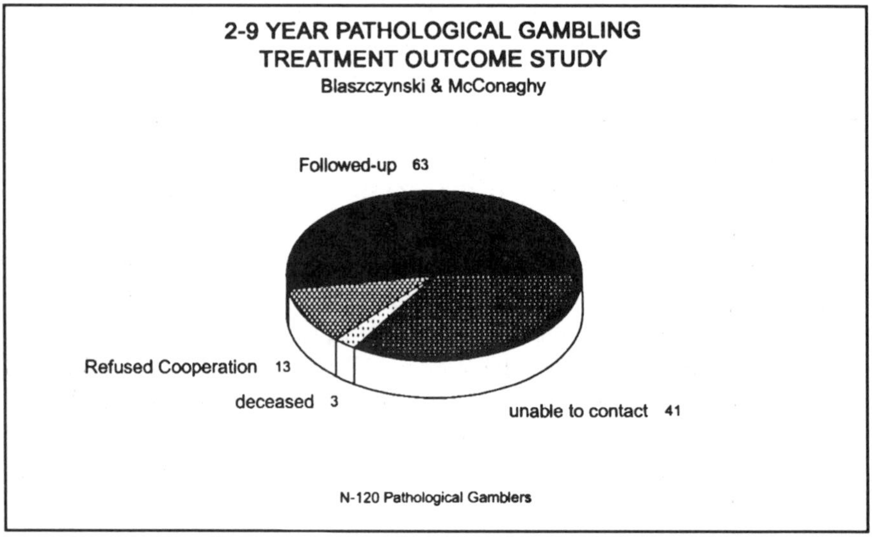

At interview, subjects were asked to classify themselves as abstinent, controlled or uncontrolled in respect of their post-treatment gambling behavior.

Abstinence was defined as no episodes of gambling in the month immediately preceding follow-up and for the predominant portion of the post treatment period; and controlled gambling as gambling in the absence of both a subjective sense of impaired control and adverse financial consequences (Table 3).

TABLE 3

Criteria Used to Define Self-Reported Abstinence and Controlled Gambling Behavior	
ABSTINENCE:	• No gambling in preceding month, and
	• Predominantly no gambling during post-treatment period
CONTROLLED:	• Absence of a subjective sense of impaired control, and
	• No adverse financial consequenses associated with the current level of gambling.

This broad definition was designed to include subjects who may have experienced brief and/or infrequent episodes over periods of up to nine years but otherwise regarded themselves as remaining essentially abstinent.

Eighteen subjects classified themselves as abstinent, 25 as controlled and 20 as uncontrolled gamblers (Figure 2).

Confirmation from spouses or significant other was obtained for 14 of the 18 abstinent, and 14 of the 25 controlled subjects. One controlled subject had his statements disconfirmed and was subsequently reclassified as uncontrolled.

As shown in Table 4, the mean age of the abstinent, controlled and uncontrolled subgroups was 43.38 years, 42.12 years and 44.86 years respectively.

There were no significant age differences between the three groups ($F = 0.299$, $df = 2,60$, NS).

Statistical comparisons were made using SPSSPC+ based one way analysis of variance multiple comparison tests with Least Significant Difference levels set at $p = 0.05$.

As seen from Figure 3, pretreatment State Anxiety subscale scores of the Spielberger's State-Trait Anxiety Inventory did not differ significantly between groups although there was a tendency for controlled subjects to have slightly lower scores.

FIGURE 2

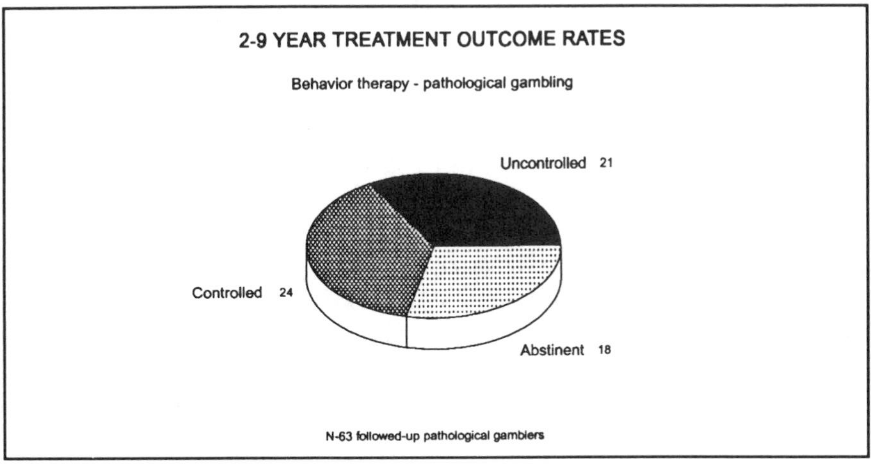

FIGURE 3

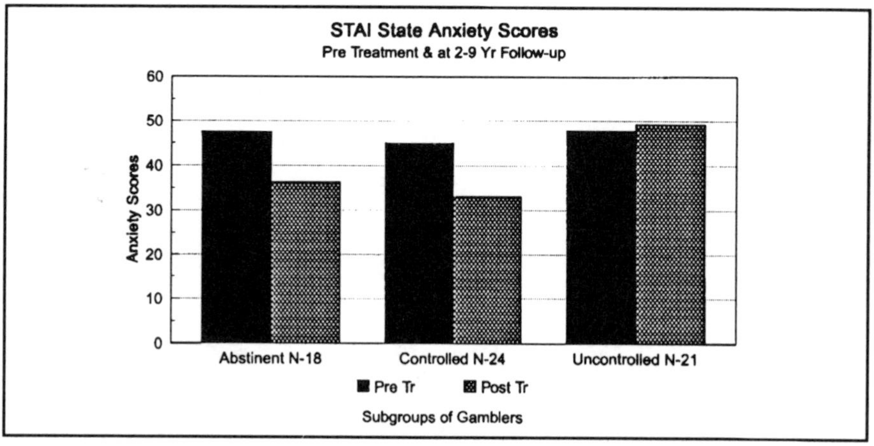

At follow-up, the scores for abstinent and controlled subjects were not different from each other, but both were significantly lower in relation to the uncontrolled group who remained essentially unchanged. This pattern of between group differences and trends was similar for the trait anxiety scores on the same measure (Figure 4).

Again, the same pattern was repeated on the Neuroticism scale of the Eysenck Personality Questionnaire (Figure 5) and on the depression subscale of the Symptom Checklist-90 (Figure 6).

Beck Depression Inventory scores of the uncontrolled group were found to be in the mildly depressed category but significantly higher than both the abstinent and controlled groups who fell in the depressed range (Figure 7).

The urge to gamble was found to persist despite positive treatment response. Of the abstinent subjects, nine (50%) experienced no urge to gamble, four (22.2%) felt the urge at least once weekly or more, and 5 (27.7%) at least once per fortnight. However, as expected, the strength of this urge correlated negatively with outcome. On a seven-point visual-analogue scale the mean strength of the gambling urge was rated as significantly lower for the abstinent (mean = 1.83; S.D. = 1.95) as compared to controlled subjects (mean = 2.83; S.D. = 1.49) who, in turn, were significantly lower than uncontrolled subjects (mean = 4.90; S.D. = 1.14) subjects ($F = 20.711$, $df = 2, 60$, $p<0.0001$).

FIGURE 4

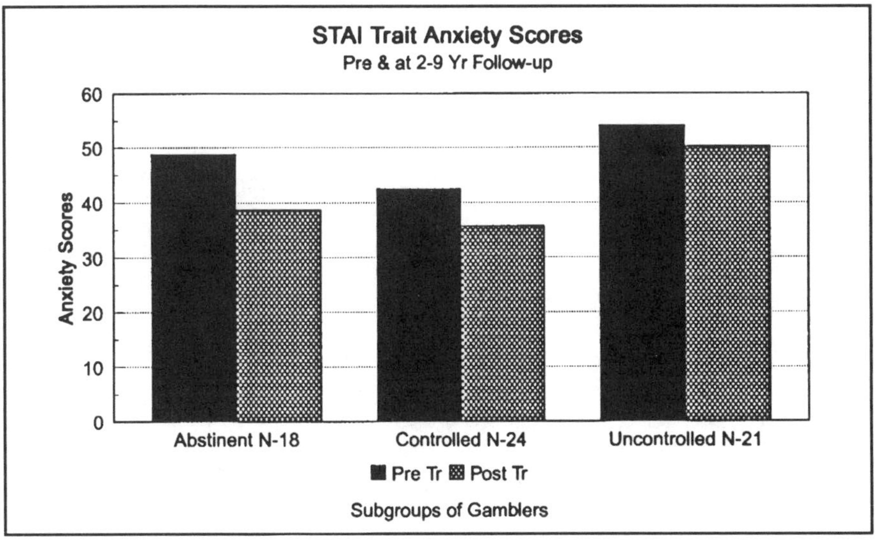

FIGURE 5

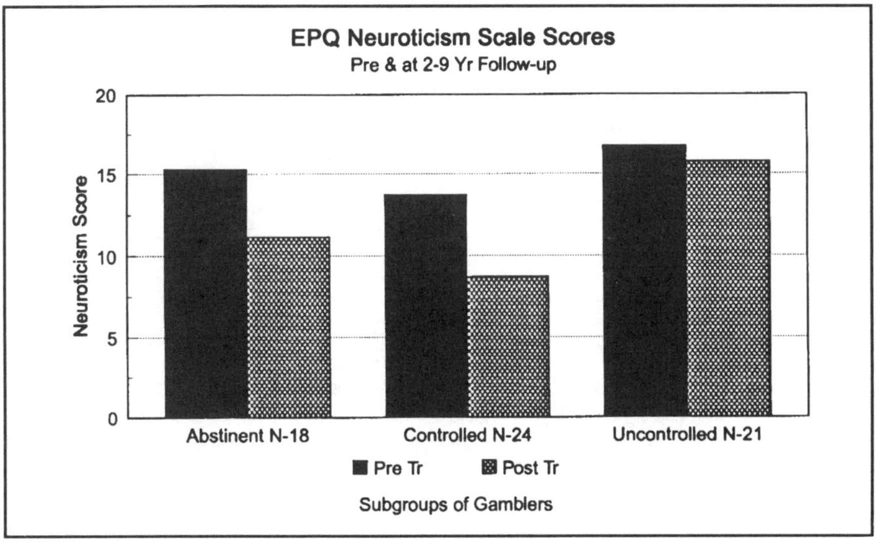

FIGURE 6

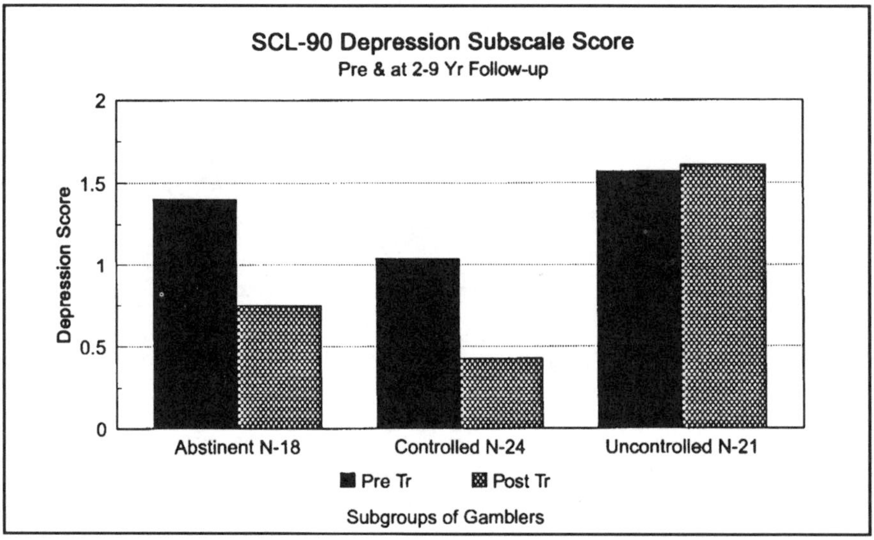

FIGURE 7

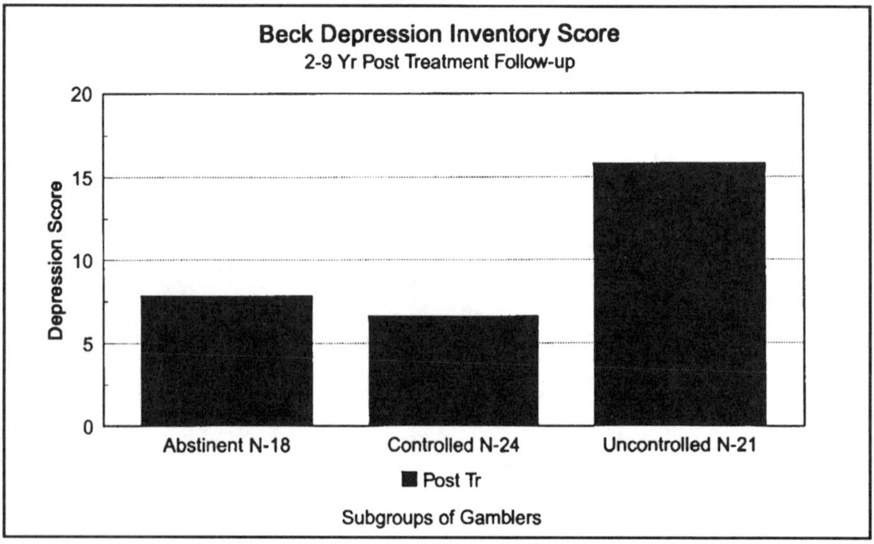

Reported emotional and arousal states associated with winning, losing and waiting for betting results were found to differ between subjects continuing controlled gambling and those reporting uncontrolled gambling at follow-up. On a visual analogue scale, uncontrolled subjects rated themselves as being significantly less relaxed, more tense and more guilty than controlled subjects in the period just prior to their commencing gambling (Figure 8).

FIGURE 8

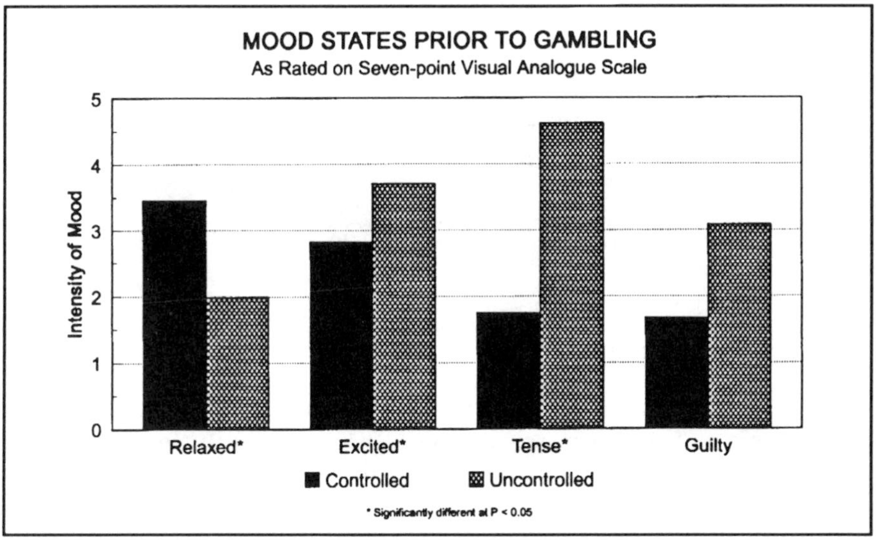

They also reported higher levels of anticipatory excitement than controlled subjects in the period intervening between having placed a bet and waiting for results (Figure 9).

Although there were no differences in their degree of excitement, relief or confidence after winning, the uncontrolled subjects experienced a greater sense of urgency to keep gambling (Figure 10).

They also experienced greater levels of anger, depression and tension following losses (Figure 11).

In respect of receiving additional treatment following discharge, five of the abstinent and all nine uncontrolled subjects subsequently attended Gamblers

Anonymous, while of the controlled group, one sought hypnotherapy, and one, psychotherapy from a psychiatrist.

FIGURE 9

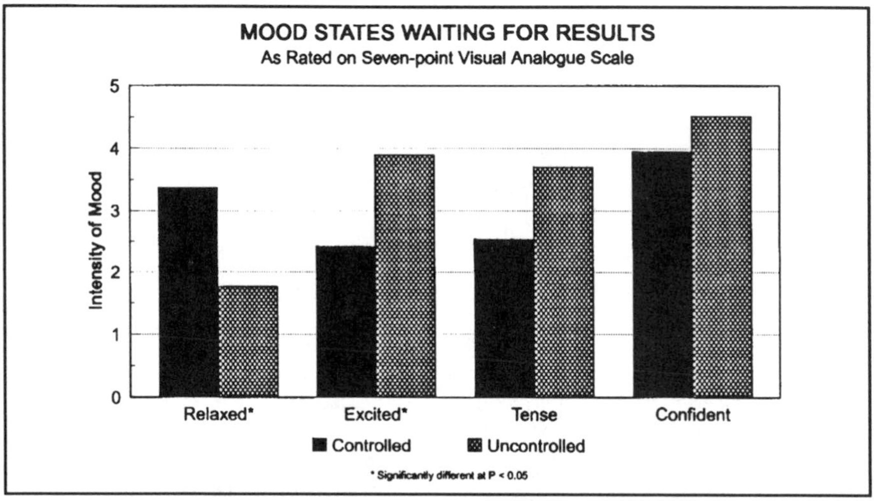

The average amount lost per week was significantly greater for uncontrolled gamblers (F= 13.918, df = 1, 42, $p < 0.001$). Controlled gamblers lost a mean of $AUS 29.39 (S.D. = $AUS 36.12) and uncontrolled gamblers lost a mean of $AUS 176.02 (S.D. = $AUS 186.02) per week.

As compared to uncontrolled subjects, controlled subjects showed a nonsignificant tendency to place smaller bets, but there was no difference in terms of the reported frequency with which they gambled.

Changes along sociodemographic parameters paralleled improved psychological functioning. Eighty-three percent (n=15) of abstinent subjects, 58% (n=14) of controlled subjects, but only 33% (n=7) of the uncontrolled subjects stated that their family's standard of living improved since treatment. Thirty-three percent of abstinent (n=6) and controlled (n=8) compared to 4% (n=l) of uncontrolled subjects reported that since treatment there had been an improvement in their relationship with their spouse. Fifty percent (n=9) of

FIGURE 10

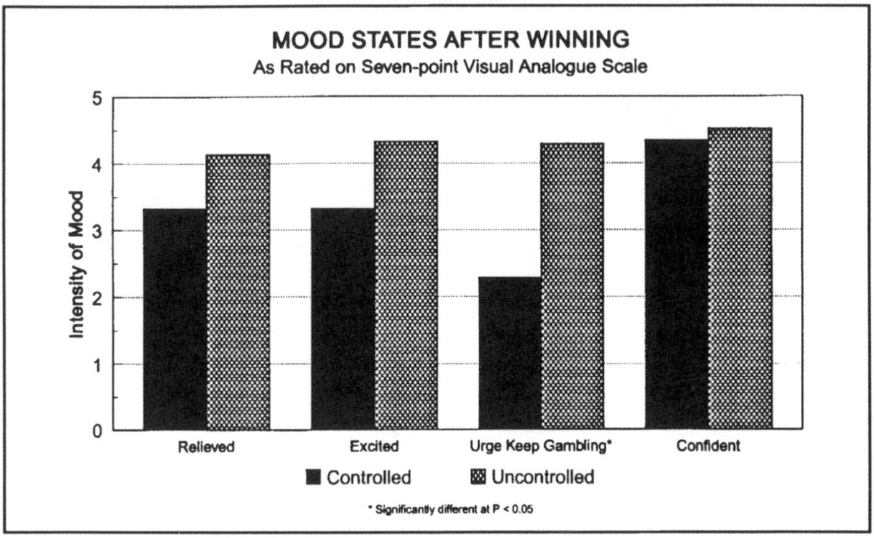

FIGURE 11

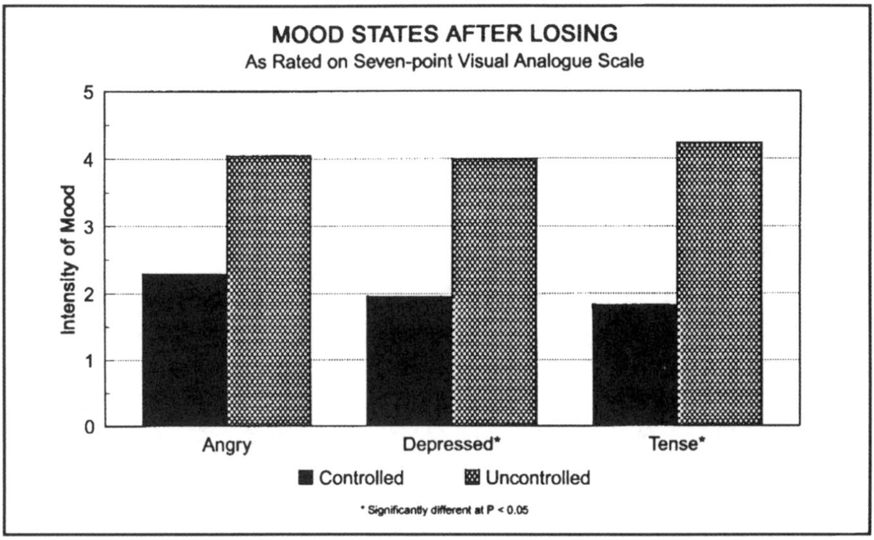

the abstinent group and 37% (n=9) of the controlled gamblers reported a general improvement in physical health compared with only 9% (n=2) of the uncontrolled subjects.

Subjects reporting abstinence were asked if in the post-treatment period they gambled any amount of money, no matter how insignificant, on any form of gambling, and to estimate the frequency and duration of gambling periods which they considered constituted a relapse. Relapse was defined as an episode or period of excessive gambling accompanied by a subjective sense of loss of control.

Fifteen (83.3%) of the abstinent subjects admitted gambling on at least one occasion post-treatment. Nine reported that the extent of their gambling constituted a relapse while the remainder described minor instances of *soft* gambling, that is, one or two dollars on instant scratch lotteries, lotto or raffles. The mean number of relapses was 1.89 (S.D. = 4.76). Of this group, six reported having one relapse and the other three reported experiencing between six and twenty episodes each. The mean length of the longest relapse was 5.6 months (S.D. = 17.5 months).

There were no significant differences between relapsed and non-relapsed subjects on any of the psychological test measures at either pre- or posttreatment assessment.

There did not appear to be any differences in the form of gambling participated in with both non-relapsed and relapsed subjects showing a preference for horse racing (7 subjects), slot-machines (7 subjects) and lotto/lotteries (6 subjects).

All relapsed and eight non-relapsed subjects reported significant improvements in lifestyle. Three relapsed subject and five non-relapsed subjects reported a marked improvement in their relationships with their spouse.

DISCUSSION

The most stringent criteria for outcome is to stipulate complete abstinence over the total post-treatment period with the rate calculated as a percentage of the total population of subjects treated. This approach considers that all non followed-up subjects and those showing marked improvement in their condition, are in fact treatment failures. Under these conditions, 7.5% or 9 of the original 120 subjects responded to treatment. This figure compares to the two year rate of 7.3% reported by Brown (1988) for Gamblers Anonymous.

Maintaining abstinence as the criteria but calculating the rate as a percentage of those subjects actually followed-up, doubles the figure to 14.2 percent.

Utilizing a more liberal criteria of abstinence, that is no episodes of gambling in the immediate month preceding follow-up interview, and for the majority of the post treatment period, increases this figure to 28.6%. Abstinence in this sense includes patients who reported episodes of relapse within the specified follow-up period. With the exception of three (16.6%) patients who admitted to three or more relapses of longer than three months duration, relapses appeared limited and were not associated with a resumption of continued uncontrolled gambling.

Criteria of success based solely on abstinence could be considered excessively stringent in that they ignore important indices of improvement such as reduced frequency, intensity and urge to gamble, enhanced self control in limiting gambling once commenced, and improved social, financial and interpersonal functioning. Of the follow-up patients, 38% reported that they were able to maintain controlled gambling. The most liberal success rate therefore can be calculated on the basis of combining abstinent, partially abstinent and controlled gambling as a percentage of the followed-up subjects. This provides a figure of 66.6 percent.

Consistent with Taber, McCormick, Russo, Adkins and Ramirez' (1987) observations, reduced expenditure on gambling was associated with increased quality of life. Patients reporting abstinence and controlled gambling showed comparable improvements in social and financial functioning and decreased ratings of psychopathology compared to those admitting to continued uncontrolled gambling.

Possibly the most impressive evidence that abstinence and control are comparable in outcome was the finding that subjects reporting these responses obtained scores within the normal range on psychopathology scales of established validity, namely, neuroticism, psychoticism, state and trait anxiety and depression. Prior to treatment they had shown pathological levels of such psychopathology. Controlled gamblers showed a greater reduction in post-treatment state and trait anxiety scores than did the abstinent gamblers. In contrast, uncontrolled gamblers were characterized by continued significantly higher levels of psychopathology on these scales.

Findings of marked and equivalent improvement on measures of social and psychological functioning following treatment suggest that some gamblers have the ability to return to and maintain controlled gambling over substantial periods with minimal risk for relapse.

It is apparent that despite one or more relapses gamblers may continue to regard themselves as abstinent over a longer time frame. To suggest that one or more relapses constitutes treatment failure because it violates the criteria of abstinence could be excessively rigid and result in leading patients to regard such relapses as a total failure so they lose motivation to attempt further control. Relapse immediately post treatment appears at times to be a testing out of the treatment response and can be followed by no subsequent episodes over several years. This would seem a successful outcome.

It has been suggested that a subgroup of gamblers exist who in response to environmental stresses increase their gambling as a maladaptive coping strategy. Adverse consequences produced by excessive gambling acts to produce high arousal, anxiety, depression and generalized psychopathology. These emotional states negatively feedback to increase the drive to continued gambling (Blaszczynski, Winter and McConaghy, 1986) and entry into the process of decreasing spiral of options (Lesieur, 1979).

Prior to treatment, controlled gamblers showed a trend to have lower levels of assessed psychopathology and following treatment they exhibited a greater degree of reduction of these levels. It is possible that controlled gambling is attained by more psychologically adjusted gamblers, who, following treatment, show a greater sense of self-efficacy and are able to regain selfconfidence to the extent of maintaining control over their behavior.

Abstinent gamblers, on the other hand, lack sufficient control over their behavior so that if they recommence gambling, they readily lose control. This would explain their increased need for additional treatment as compared to controlled gamblers. For such gamblers, abstinence and long term attendance at Gamblers Anonymous may be required.

Although the findings of this study suggested controlled gambling is an acceptable outcome, it seems prudent to encourage abstinence as the preferred treatment goal until predictor variables are available which could identify the subjects who are able to maintain controlled gambling following treatment. However, it would seem equally prudent to emphasize that relapse does not mean that abstinence could not be regained, and that to accept that patients who are reporting control are showing a worthwhile response to treatment, so they are not alienated.

REFERENCES

American Psychiatric Association (1987). *Diagnostic and Statistical Manual of Mental Disorders, Revised* (Third Edition). Washington D.C.: American Psychiatric Association.

Bannister, G. (1977). Cognitive behavior therapy in a case of compulsive gambling. *Cognitive Therapy and Research*, 1, 223-227.

Barker, J. and Miller, M. (1968). Aversion therapy for compulsive gambling. *Journal of Nervous and Mental Disorders*, 146, 285-302.

Bacuum, D. (1984). Arguments for self-controlled gambling as an alternative to abstention. In W.R. Eadington (ed.), *Proceedings of the Sixth National Conference on Gambling and Risk Taking*, vol. 5, 199-204. Reno, NV: University of Nevada, Reno.

Beck, A.T., Ward, C.M., Mendleson, M., Mock, J.E. and Erbaugh, J.K. (1961). An inventory for measuring depression. *Archives of General Psychiatry*, 4, 561-571.

Bergler, E. (1943). The gambler: A misunderstood neurotic. *Journal of Criminal Psychopathology*, 4, 379-393.

Blaszczynski, A., Winter, S. and McConaghy, N. (1986). Plasma endorphin levels in pathological gambling. *Journal of Gambling Behavior*, 2, 3-14.

Brown, R.I.F. (1987). Classical and operant paradigms in the management of gambling addictions. *Behavioral Psychotherapy*, 15, 111-122.

Cotler, S.B. (1971). The use of different behavioral techniques in treating a case of compulsive gambling. *Behavior Therapy*, 2, 579-584.

Davies, D.L. (1962). Normal drinking in recovered alcohol addicts. *Quarterly Journal of Studies on Alcohol*, 23, 94-104.

Derogatis, L.R. (1977). *SCL-90 Administration, Scoring and Procedures Manual for the Revised Version.* Baltimore, MD: John Hopkins School of Medicine.

Dickerson, M.G. and Weeks, D. (1979). Controlled gambling as a therapeutic technique for compulsive gamblers. *Journal of Behavior Therapy and Experimental Psychiatry*, 10, 139-141.

Eysenck, H.J. and Eysenck, S.B. (1975). *Manual of the Eysenck Personality Questionnaire.* London: Hodder and Stoughton.

Frederiksen, L.W., Peterson, G.L. and Murphy, W.D. (1976). Controlled smoking: Development and maintenance. *Addictive Behaviors*, 1, 193-196.

Gamblers Anonymous (1977). *Gamblers Anonymous Leaflet.* Los Angeles: Gamblers Anonymous Publishing.

Glascow, R.E., Morray, K. and Lichtenstein, E. (1989). Controlled smoking versus abstinence as a treatment goal: The hopes and fears may be unfounded. *Behavior Therapy*, 20, 77-91.

Goorney, A.B. (1968). Treatment of compulsive horse race gambling by aversion therapy. *British Journal of Psychiatry*, 114, 329-383.

Greenson, R. (1947). On gambling. *American Imago*, 4, 61-77.

Harris, H. (1964). Gambling addiction in an adolescent male. *Psychoanalytic Quarterly*, 34, 513-525.

Heather, N. and Robertson, I. (1981). *Controlled Drinking.* New York: Methuen.

Jacobs, D.F. (1986). A general theory of addictions: A new theoretical model. *Journal of Gambling Behavior*, 2, 15-32.

Koller, K. (1972). Treatment of poker machine addicts by aversion therapy. *Medical Journal of Australia*, 1, 742-745.

Lesieur, H. (1979). The compulsive gambler's spiral of options and involvement. *Psychiatry*, 42, 79-87.

Marlatt, G.A. and Gordon, J. (1988). *Relapse Prevention.* London: Guilford Press.

Matussek, P. (1955). On the psychodynamics of the gambler. *Journal of Psychology and Psychotherapy*, 1, 232-252.

McConaghy, N., Armstrong, M., Blaszczynski, A. and Allcock, C. (1983). Controlled comparison of aversion therapy and imaginal desensitization in compulsive gambling. *British Journal of Psychiatry*, 142, 366-372.

Norusis, M.J. (1986). *SPSS/PC+ for IBM PC/XT/AT*. Illinois: SPSS Inc.

Rankin, H. (1982). Control rather than abstinence as a goal in the treatment of excessive gambling. *Behavior Research and Therapy*, 20, 185-187.

Reynolds, V.C., Tobin, D.L., Creer, T.L., Wigal, J.W. and Wagner, M.D. (1987). A method for studying controlled substance use: A preliminary investigation. *Addictive Behaviors*, 12, 53-62.

Russo, A.M., Taber, J.I., McCormick, R.A. and Ramirez, L. (1984). An outcome study of an inpatient treatment program for pathological gamblers. *Hospital and Community Psychiatry*, 35, 828-827.

Seager, C. (1970). Treatment of compulsive gamblers using electrical aversion. *British Journal of Psychiatry*, 117, 545-553.

Sobell, V. and Sobell, L.C. (1978). *Behavioral Treatment of Alcohol Problems*. New York: Plenum Press.

Spielberger, C.D., Gorsuch, R.L. and Lushene, R.E. (1970). *Manual for the State-Trait Anxiety Inventory (Self Evaluation Ouestionnaire)*. Palo Alto, CA: Consulting Psychologist Press.

Taber, J.I., McCormick, R.A., Russo, A.M., Adkins, B.J. and Ramirez, L. (1987). Follow-up of pathological gamblers after treatment. *American Journal of Psychiatry*, 144, 757-761.

Zuckerman, M. (1979). *Sensation Seeking: Beyond the Optimal Level of Arousal*. New Jersey: Hillsdale.

***ACKNOWLEDGEMENT**

This article is based substantially on the following previously published articles:

Blaszczynski, A., McConaghy, N. and Frankova, A. (1991). Control versus abstinence in the treatment of pathological gambling: A two to nine year follow up. *British Journal of Addiction*, 86, 299-306.

Blaszczynski, A., McConaghy, N. and Frankova, A. (1991). A comparison of relapsed and non-relapsed abstinent pathological gamblers following behavioural treatment. *British Journal of Addiction*, 86, 1485-1489.

The *British Journal of Addiction* is published by the ©Society for the Study of Addiction, London, England.

Female Compulsive Gamblers in Las Vegas

Mary Lou Strachan and Robert L. Custer

A study of female compulsive gamblers is long overdue. This was the conclusion that the authors came to after attending the Third Annual Conference on Compulsive Gambling which was held at the Golden Nugget Hotel in Las Vegas, Nevada, in 1986. After all the speeches and studies had been presented, the authors realized that the subject of the female compulsive gambler had never been addressed.

There were two other reasons that the authors observed in Las Vegas that showed a real need for this study. First, in Las Vegas, women make up over fifty percent of those attending Gamblers Anonymous meetings; second, almost half of the patients treated for compulsive gambling at Charter Hospital in Las Vegas are women.

With these observations in mind, the following study was undertaken.

METHOD AND RESULTS

The method of collecting the data was a comprehensive questionnaire consisting of 106 questions. During a nineteen day period from March 3 to March 19, 1989, Strachan personally attended fourteen Gamblers Anonymous meetings in the Las Vegas area and distributed the questionnaires to the women in attendance. The questionnaires were filled out after the meetings and in her presence. Fifty-two completed questionnaires were returned to Strachan.

The results of this study will be presented by categories. There are four areas that will be covered:

A. Demographic Characteristics,

B. Family History,

C. Mental Health History, and

D. Gambling History and Characteristics.

Since this was a pilot study and there was nothing to compare the data to, the results will be presented in percentages.

A. Demographics

The majority of the women were Caucasian (83%) and in their thirties and forties (76%). Most of them were married (67%) and had children (75%). Thirty-nine percent were Catholic, 31% Protestant and 6% Jewish. Eighty-eight percent had at least a high school diploma and 14% were college graduates. The majority were employed (67%) with 48% being employed in or having been employed in the gaming industry at one time.

All 52 subjects lived in the Las Vegas area with 75% having resided in the city for over ten years. Four of the subjects were born in Las Vegas.

B. Family History

The vast majority of subjects — 96% — had siblings. Only two reported being an only child. Thirty-one percent of the subject's parents were divorced before they were fifteen years of age.

Thirty-one percent of the subjects had lost a spouse, parent, child, or close friend or relative from death in the two years prior to coming to Gamblers Anonymous. Forty-two percent of the subjects had an alcoholic parent. Forty-two percent had a parent or parents who gambled too much.

Thirty-three percent of the women were physically abused by their parents as a child. Twenty-nine percent reported being sexually abused by someone as a child.

C. Mental Health History

The suicide rate among compulsive gamblers has been cited in other studies as being one of the highest of any measured group. The authors felt that the findings in this study substantiate that claim. Sixty-nine percent of the subjects had contemplated suicide and 23% had actually attempted it.

Another area of interest was that of dual addictions. The women were asked if "they are presently or have been in the past" using or addicted to alcohol, illegal drugs or prescription medications. Ten percent answered "yes" to alcohol, 23% answered "yes" to illegal drug use and 15% answered "yes" to prescription medications.

Twenty-three percent of the subjects reported that they belonged to another twelve step program other than Gamblers Anonymous.

The authors were also interested to see how much recognition the problem of compulsive gambling was receiving in the mental health professions. To look into this, we asked three related questions. First we asked, "Did you ever consult a psychiatrist or psychologist?" Sixty-five percent had. Secondly, we asked, "Did you ever consult a marriage or family counselor?" Forty-six percent answered in the affirmative. Then we asked, "Did any of these professionals diagnose a gambling problem?" Of the thirty-six women who sought professional help, 72% answered "no" — gambling was never mentioned.

Also under this awareness area, we asked the women themselves, "During your gambling career, were you aware that compulsive gambling was a disease?" Sixty-two percent of these women reported that they were unaware that compulsive gambling was considered a disease.

D. Gambling History and Characteristics

Forty-seven of the 52 subjects — 90% — were addicted to video poker machines. Three subjects were slot machine players and one was a live poker player. Forty-four percent indicated they gambled in "local's" casinos — not in the primarily tourist casinos of the Las Vegas Strip or Downtown Las Vegas. Seventeen percent indicated their preferred gambling venue was in grocery or drug stores, while 17% played in Downtown casinos, 10% in bars or lounges, and 8% in Strip casinos. Another 4% indicated their gambling took place in laundromats.

For 90% of the subjects, the time spent playing the machines at any given session was between 7 and "25 or more" consecutive hours. Twenty-one percent of the subjects reported playing a poker machine in excess of twenty-four hours at a stretch.

In terms of methods of obtaining gambling money, at one time or another, 73% wrote bad checks, 87% spent their entire family savings, and 76% utilized their entire credit card credit line — they "maxed-out" their credit cards by using cash advances.

Sixty percent sold or pawned jewelry or other valuables, and 37% admitted embezzling money from their employers. A total of 27% indicated they considered prostitution, whereas 10% actually prostituted themselves. A total of three subjects — 6% — resorted to blackmail or extortion. Twenty-five percent of the subjects reported that they had to declare bankruptcy as a direct result of their gambling.

Using the *DSM III-R* criteria for compulsive gambling diagnosis, we asked six specific questions. The vast majority of the subjects reported that: 1) the amount they bet and the frequency of their gambling progressed steadily; 2) they became more preoccupied with gambling; 3) they had had big wins; 4) they had received a financial "bail-out"; 5) they had gone through extended losing streaks, and 6) they had become intensely angered or depressed when they lost. The figures for these questions ranged between 83% and 100%, with all 52 subjects — 100% — answering "yes" to the question about losses leading to anger or depression.

DISCUSSION

The authors feel that the findings from this survey show a very serious problem does exist involving the female compulsive gambler. Further, the findings reflect how destructive and demoralizing the disease can become. While this study was conducted in Las Vegas, the authors foresee this problem spreading throughout the United States and other countries as widespread legalization and availability of many forms of gambling occurs. It is the authors' hope that this study and similar studies that will follow will serve to raise the knowledge and awareness level of mental health professionals, government officials, the general public, and the gamblers themselves that a problem with female gambling exists, and it might indeed be an extremely serious one.

III

Theories on Addiction

Some Contributions of the Study of Gambling to the Study of Other Addictions

R. Iain F. Brown

There are at least four major areas in which the study of gambling addictions can make a contribution to the study of addictions in general. They are:

- in drawing attention to the role of arousal in the development and maintenance of addictions, and, through that, to the role of mood management;
- in drawing attention to the role of cognitive distortions;
- in emphasizing the commonalities of addictions and the need to redefine the boundaries of the concept; and
- in focussing on psychological processes as the core of the addiction phenomenon.

THE ROLE OF AROUSAL

A. The Concept of Arousal

There are several conceptions of arousal ranging from Duffy's model of a single general system (1972) through Routtenberg's two system hypothesis (1968) to Lacey's (1967) three interacting systems of cognitive/cortical, autonomic/affective, and somatic/effort stress. More recently, Thayer (1989) has put forward a two system model of arousal involving separate dimensions of "energetic" arousal and "tense" arousal, and a complex curvilinear relationship between the two varying with levels of stress. It would be manifestly premature to single out any one conception of arousal as the best fit for the explanation of addictions, but it seems safe to affirm that it is often useful to conceive of arousal as a single unitary dimension and that, in general, subjective feelings of arousal relate very closely to physiological measures of arousal such as, especially, heart rate (Thayer, 1989). Arousal will be used in this general sense throughout this analysis.

B. First Studies in Arousal in Normal Gambling

The importance of understanding the role of arousal in the development and maintenance of gambling addictions is now well established. In a nationwide survey conducted for the U.S. federal government (Commission on the Review of National Policy Towards Gambling in America, 1976), the University of Michigan Survey Research Center asked why people gambled. The most frequent reasons for betting were "excitement" or "to have a good time". Anderson and Brown (1984) asked Scottish regular gamblers why they gambled and found 50% for excitement; 33% to be sociable; 8.5% to pass the time and only 8.5% to win money.

Anderson and Brown (1984) found that the heart rate of normal regular gamblers playing blackjack in the real casino was found to increase by a mean of 24 beats per minute throughout the cycle of blackjack; some individual increases of up to 54 beats per minute were recorded, which is as great as for fairly considerable physical exercise. They concluded that gambling is very exciting and that some form of arousal or excitement is a major, and possibly *the* major, reinforcer of gambling behavior for regular gamblers. In corroboration, Leary and Dickerson (1985) and Dickerson and Adcock (1986) reported supporting experimental data from poker machine players in Australia, showing more modest but still significant heart rate increases while gambling. More recently, the psychobiological underpinnings of a functional disturbance in the noradrenergic system have been traced in the brain chemistry of addicted gamblers (Roy, Adinoff, Roehrich, Lamparski, Custer, Lorenz, Barbaccia, Guidotti, Costa and Linnoila, 1988).

Anderson and Brown also advanced evidence of interactions between the role of arousal and a personality dimension of *sensation seeking*. Although considerable doubts have been raised about the importance of sensation seeking in the development of gambling addictions (Dickerson, Hinchy and Fabre, 1987; Blaszczynski, Wilson and McConaghy, 1986), it still may be an important variable (Coventry and Brown, 1993).

C. Implications for the Understanding of Gambling Addictions

The above empirical studies gave rise to new theoretical orientations in the explanation of gambling and gambling addictions (Brown, 1986) and to some treatment implications (Brown, 1987a).

In this new arousal and classical conditioning model, the central phenomenon of normal gambling is a personal experience and an objectively verifiable state of arousal, not sexual, but probably autonomic and/or cortical. This arousal component of normal gambling was open to explanation by an optimal level of stimulation model or a biological optimum-pessimism model (Brown, 1986). Alternatively, it could be explained by a more sophisticated model of the role of arousal derived from reversal theory; this leads to explanations of the development of addictions as attempts to manipulate hedonic tone and maintain continuous states of high positive hedonic tone as acquired secondary goals which are pursued just as other secondary goals such as money or social approval may be in other circumstances. These explanations can be applied to all addictions (Brown, 1988a).

A somewhat different and new explanation arising from the understanding of the role of arousal in gambling — which can be generalized to explain all addictions — was put forward by Jacobs (1986; Kuley and Jacobs, 1988). Jacobs' explanation relies on two major factors predisposing to addiction, both of which have to be present. A chronic pre-existing stress condition, presumably inherited, imprisons the vulnerable pre-victim in a continuous state of either very high or very low arousal, producing prolonged stress which is relieved by the addictive activity. Concurrently, a chronic state of low self-esteem and feelings of inadequacy, presumably mainly acquired, are coped with, not by positive assertion, achievement, or anger, but by a withdrawal into fantasy and, eventually, into a range of dissociated states, entry into which is facilitated by the addictive activity.

Support for the existence and validity of both these factors comes from a range of studies (Kuley and Jacobs, 1988), and also from studies in multiple personality which provide evidence that most multiple personality disorder (MPD) patients have at least one addicted personality; furthermore, MPD may be only an extreme instance of a range of dissociated states extending from mild feelings of depersonalization (Ross, 1989). Jacobs thus sees addictions as having a necessary self-medicating function to bring the victim back to levels at which they can function normally and allow a gateway to escape. These two factors can be found across the whole varied field of addictions and the theory easily generalizes to other addictions.

One of the most important contributions of the study of gambling to the study of other addictions, then, has been in the highlighting of the role of arousal in the development and maintenance of other addictions.

D. Arousal in Normal Drinking of Alcohol

It is generally accepted that alcohol is a depressant drug. But the situation is more complicated than that. There is good evidence that alcohol has a biphasic effect, beginning with a heightening of arousal and mood immediately after ingestion, and only developing its stronger depressant effects later and with higher dosages. Kelly, Myrsten, Nevi and Rydberg (1970) experimentally induced acute alcoholic intoxication in 16 moderate social drinkers. Subjective ratings by the subjects of their moods — along the dimensions of talkative, elated, tired, etc. — and of their working capacity, tended to peak one hour after alcohol consumption and then tended to fall rectilinearly, thus paralleling their blood alcohol curves.

In the light of such findings, Russel and Mehrabian (1975) suggest that the reinforcing properties of alcohol may be due to the emotional and physiological "high" corresponding to the ascending blood alcohol level. Morris and Reilly (1987), in their review of mood-management techniques, concluded that the use of alcohol to elevate mood provided the most convincing case for the existence of behaviors intended to manipulate mood. Hull and Bond (1986) reviewed fourteen studies which were quite consistent with their findings that alcohol increased positive mood and reduced negative mood states. Marlatt,

Kosturn and Lang (1975) showed that insults delivered by an experimental confederate at a staged wine tasting increased consumption among those who were the objects of the remarks without affecting consumption of the controls, suggesting that alcohol is used to combat unpleasant social conditions. In another staged wine tasting experiment, Hull and Young (1983) found increases in alcohol consumption among those failing in an intellectual task.

Donovan and Chaney (1985) made an extensive opponent process analysis of the effects of a series of drinks based on the assumption of the bi-phasic effects of alcohol. If the first (alpha) effect of alcohol is to raise arousal and elevate mood, and the second (beta) effect is the rebound which depresses arousal and mood below the initial starting point, then the well-trained and practiced drinker learns how to time the ingestion of another dose of alcohol to produce another alpha effect which counteracts or even overrides the beta effect of the previous dose or doses. By timing each fresh dose of alcohol to coincide with the onset of the beta effect, it is possible to stay aloft on a plateau of high arousal and elevated mood for an evening at least. Larger and larger doses counteract the accumulating beta effect until it is finally not possible to hold back the beta effect anymore and, like a surf rider on a high wave, the drinker comes crashing down in a deep dip in arousal and mood from which prolonged sleep frequently rescues him.

Similar bi-phasic effects have been observed over a longer time scale in drinking bouts of several days with a reduction in tension recorded in the beginning of the bout followed by a large build-up of tension toward the end. However, the relationship between alcohol ingestion and "tension reduction" is a controversial one (Cappell and Herman, 1972; Higgins, 1976; Stockwell, Hodgson and Rankin, 1982; Hodgson, Stockwell and Rankin, 1979), perhaps not surprisingly since the drug has a bi-phasic effect.

The special value of a drug with bi-phasic effects is that the users can learn, sometimes without being fully aware of what they are doing, to time doses and regulate intake to achieve whatever effects they want — arousal and elation in small measures, but anxiety reduction in increasing doses, or lethargy and even rapid oblivion in large overwhelming doses. A perfect example of such a drug is tobacco.

E. Arousal in the Explanation of Smoking Behavior

The intake of tobacco can also be titrated to achieve and maintain a preferred level of arousal. The role of arousal in the development and maintenance of tobacco addictions has been beautifully expounded by, among others, Ashton and Watson (1977), Ashton, Millman, Rawlings, Telford and Thompson (1978) and Stepney (1980) based on the bi-phasic effects of the drug.

Several studies have shown that nicotine results in autonomic arousal (e.g., heart rate increments from five to forty beats per minute), but that skeletal-muscular tension is reduced by it (Domino, 1973; Gilbert, 1979; Mangan and Golding, 1984). Ashton and Stepney (1982) have delineated a model of smoking behavior which centers around the regulation of arousal levels. Small amounts of nicotine raise arousal, particularly cortical arousal, and lead to improved mood and concentration; but large amounts lower arousal and promote lassitude, calm and tranquility.

Following studies by Frith (1971), Ashton and Stepney have shown how some smokers use nicotine predominantly in situations where they need to increase arousal — e.g., when fatigued, bored or apathetic — and others use it predominantly in situations of stress and anxiety when they need to decrease arousal to perform more efficiently in complex tasks. Most use nicotine for both kinds of situations and titrate their dose to give the desired mood management effect for the occasion.

F. Arousal in Eating Behavior and In Eating Problems

Excessive eating has long been viewed by many as an addictive problem (Miller, 1980: Warburton and Wesnes, 1983; Orford, 1985; Flood, 1989), but, more recently, excessive concentration on the rarer and more peculiar extremes of anorexia and bulimia has tended to obscure the addictive nature of the majority of less extreme eating problems. In Glasgow, Brown and Perry (1990) found that attenders at a Weightwatchers club scored significantly higher on an "Involvement in Eating" questionnaire than a sample of normal students, and the profile of their scores were more like those obtained by a sample of self-acknowledged alcohol addicts on a parallel scale measuring "Involvement in Drinking."

Ruderman (1986) concluded after a review of research that restrained eaters (e.g., dieters) significantly increase their consumption when in a dysphoric mood. Rosenthal et al. (1986) found that a carbohydrate lunch significantly reduced depression, and Lieberman, Wurtman and Chew (1986) found that carbohydrate cravers experienced reduced depression following a lunch with a high proportion of carbohydrates. Thayer (1987) found that among a sample who were instructed to eat a sugar snack on multiple occasions at fixed times of the day over a three week period, subjective awareness of energy increased and tiredness decreased at first within twenty minutes of ingestion and that the effects were reversed an hour later.

G. Arousal Effects of Major Illegal and Legal Prescribed Drugs

The arousal effects of the major illegal and legally prescribed psychomimetic drugs are much more obvious and more widely recognized than those of alcohol, tobacco and eating. There is no need to enlarge on these issues here. It is enough to note that the CNS stimulants, such as amphetamines, methamphetamines and cocaine — known as "uppers" because they elevate mood and arousal — notoriously increase arousal through action on nor-epinephrinine. The major "downers" to which people become addicted — such as the benzodiazepines, the opiates and the barbiturates — depress arousal and sedate. Both groups are used to manage mood states.

H. Addictive Activities as Manipulation of Arousal

In addition to the classic "uppers" and "downers" such as heroin , cocaine and tranquilizers, the regulation of arousal is recognized as playing an important part in drinking, smoking and eating to excess. Studies in normal and addictive gambling have highlighted this role of arousal and, through that, drawn fresh attention to the function of all addictive activity in managing emotional and mood states and in attaining and maintaining positive feeling states as goals in their own right.

This study began with an analysis of the tactical manipulations of arousal used by normal people to maintain short-term hedonic tone in normal day-to-day living. Such an analysis provides a valuable contrast which helps define and understand addictions by pointing out the normal coping strategies which addictions are designed to replace and improve upon.

The short term maintenance of happiness — or good hedonic tone — is a perilous and unpredictable business for normal people. Attempts to intervene and manipulate our moods and feeling states are often ineffective, have undesirable side effects, or even provoke the exact opposite to what was intended. If we were better at it, we would all be able to maintain high positive hedonic tone for extended periods. Even if we were successful in this, there would be no unpleasantness with which to compare and contrast the unbroken positive feeling state, and it would soon become meaningless in itself. No one manages to maintain good hedonic tone for much of the time. As Apter (1982) puts it:

> ". . .it is hardly to be wondered at that high levels of positive hedonic tone are not typically maintained for extended periods. To put this in everyday terms, it is not surprising that people have difficulty in remaining happy for very long."

The core of the addictive process can easily be seen, in contrast to this normal state of poorly managed uncertainty, as the discovery and continuous use by the individual of relatively reliable and effective methods which do enable him or her to manipulate hedonic tone in the directions wanted, at least in the short term.

Using their chosen method of maintaining high hedonic tone, the reliable attainment of prolonged periods of bliss becomes, for a period called *The Golden Age* (Brown, 1988a), so attainable compared to anything which has been possible in the past, that the addict begins to identify an altered state of consciousness and the desirable feeling state associated with it as a goal. A goal acquired in this way is accompanied by an acquired drive towards it with all the characteristics of flexible purposive behavior. Characteristic of the pursuit of this drive is the kind of frenzied salience of a single activity that was shown by the rats in the experiments of Olds and Milner (1954) which had discovered how to reward the pleasure centers of their brain directly by pressing bars, and continued to do so ignoring opportunities to eat or drink until they dropped with exhaustion.

But even the crudest, most brutal, and direct attempts to manipulate arousal using addictive activities or substances are not always successful, even in the short term. There are always "bad trips," times when the gambling arousal-jag rebounds in massive anxiety, when the alcohol-induced convivial elation turns unexpectedly to maudlin loneliness. The very unreliability of even the chosen method of mood management, superior though it is to the relatively amateur ineffectiveness and chaos of the normally conducted search for high positive hedonic tone, gives rise to an intermittent schedule of reinforcement. This makes for great resistance to extinction and a tendency to ready reinstatement, not just in gambling, as is well known, but in all addictions by their central nature.

THE ROLE OF COGNITIVE DISTORTIONS

The activity of gambling, unlike many addictions, has a strong cognitive and intellectual component, usually perceived by the participants as a skill. It should be no surprise then that the study of gambling and gambling addictions has long been concerned with cognitive elements in the development and maintenance of addictions, and will strengthen the already existing concerns with these themes in the field of addiction studies as a whole.

A. Irrational Thinking

The cognitive phenomena of biased evaluation investigated by Gilovich (1983), cognitive regret (Kanneman and Tversky, 1982), and the illusion of control investigated by Langer (1975) are already well known to those who work in the field of gambling. Ladouceur and Gaboury (1988; 1989) have reported extensive and systematic studies mostly using a technique which asks subjects to verbalize their thinking as they play roulette, blackjack and slot machines in a laboratory. Gamblers were shown to use strategies, attribute wins to their personal skills, and make causal links between their actions and the outcomes of their bets. Audio recordings of subjects' verbalized thinking were recorded and transcribed. Then, in a form of content analysis, they were categorized by independent raters as rational when the cognitions referred to chance and irrational when they referred to variables other than chance such as strategy, skill, and interdependence of events. Ladouceur and Gaboury (1988) and Gaboury and Ladouceur (1989) found that more than 75% of the thinking thus displayed was irrational. Griffiths (1990), in a study of adolescent fruit machine players, broadly replicated these results and found that 48% believed (wrongly) that there was some significant amount of skill involved in winning.

B. Chance, Skill and Luck

Recently, Wagenaar (1988) has enriched the field by demonstrating how small samples of chance events are usually quite unrepresentative of larger runs from the same population of events. People expect many short runs of a particular chance outcome and not any long ones. So when long runs occur, as inevitably they will, they are interpreted as "caused" by a different factor from pure chance and so a belief in "luck" is developed to account for them. Wagenaar showed that, in the minds of gamblers, "luck" and "chance" are separate factors, each determining the outcome of events in their own ways. He also demonstrated that in the minds of gamblers the outcomes of gambles were dependent on at least three causal factors: chance (8%); skill (37%); and luck (45%).

Wagenaar has thus imported into the study of addictions an extensive additional range of cognitive biases and distortions affecting the judgements of gamblers which might be expected to yield rich pickings for researchers in all addictions in the years to come.

C. Superstitious Thinking

By common self-report, the everyday life of heavy regular gamblers is riddled with superstitions. For example, a member of Gamblers Anonymous relates how he used to look at the billboards, bus destinations, and street names on the way to the betting shop. If he found a written word which made a credible association with the name of the selection of his choice, it would win. Another used to set walking races with unwitting others in the street on the way to the betting shop. If the rival reached a preset point such as a telephone box or a tree before the gambler, then the selected horse would lose. Scholarios and Brown (1988) made a collection of such superstitions and attempted to classify them.

The enforced attention paid to cognitive illusions and distortions in the play of normal and addicted gamblers should further encourage other researchers to direct their attention to the rich culture of cognitive distortions and misattributions employed by drinkers and drug takers, to mention only two groups, in explaining their behavior to others and to themselves. The study of the role of arousal and the study of cognitive distortions may combine in studies of the effects of high arousal states on attention (Easterbrook, 1959) and on the accuracy or rationality of cognitive processes. This may come to be an important area of study in the understanding of gambling addictions.

COMMONALITIES AND THE DEFINITION OF ADDICTIONS

The current refusal of the American Psychiatric Association to classify "Pathological Gambling" with the addictions, and their determination to retain it as a "Disorder of Impulse Control" in the forthcoming DSM IV, vividly illustrates that it is still controversial to assume that gambling is just another addiction. It is still equally controversial to assume that there is a unified field of study, namely "the study of addictions."

As a heuristic device, it may be useful to think of a "unionist" set of arguments which point to what is seen as common features in the phenomena of human problems with eating, alcohol, gambling, heroin, cocaine, medically prescribed tranquilizer drugs, tobacco, and many other substances. Common features in successful treatment are also pointed to. In contrast, there are, in the same way, "separatist" arguments which point to the peculiarities of physical and psychological phenomena surrounding the use of each substance to excess and to the unique problems that each presents in treatment. Recently, there has been a tendency for the "unionists" to expand the field of addictive study to include virtually all activities known to man — from television watching and coffee drinking through romantic love to sky-diving and repeated sexual offending. There is probably a "unionist" and a "separatist" within each of us, and it would be too simple to classify workers in the field as "unionists" and "separatists," but it may a useful heuristic device for this discussion.

Beginning in the late 1970s (Miller, 1980) and gathering force in the 1980s (Orford, 1985; Peele, 1985) against weak opposition (Levison, Gerstein and Maloff, 1984), the recognition of the commonalities between addictions has advanced now to the stage where, after reading the latest books published in the United States, one might be excused for thinking that all of life was involved with acquiring addictions, having addictions, or avoiding addictions. Milkman and Sunderworth's book, *Craving for Ecstacy: The Consciousness and Chemistry of Escape* (1987), takes in all the traditional addictions and adds sex, especially sado-masochism, along with dieting, binging, eating, caffeine, romantic love, etc. The boundaries of the concept of addiction are not well defined, and they are in danger of being drawn so widely and made so inclusive as to become almost meaningless.

The criteria for pathological gambling in DSM III-R and in the proposed DSM IV now parallel those of drug addictions. There are obvious and overwhelming commonalities with the other addictions in elements of both checklists. The study of gambling addictions not only enlarges the field of study of addictions in general by aligning a relatively "new" addiction with the ingestion of various mood-altering substances; it also opens up connections with a vast range of mood altering activities rather than just substances. The most obvious of these are the addictions to computer games (Brown, 1990) but there is a vast range of others (Wittman, Fuller and Taber, 1988) leading to an urgent need to redefine the boundaries of the concept of addiction.

Although there is currently fairly widespread agreement among "unionists" on the core phenomena of the concept of addiction, there are two major problems with it. First, the boundaries of the concept are not well defined and they are in danger of being drawn so widely and made so over-inclusive as to become almost meaningless (see Table 1). There is — almost literally — an explosion in the concept of addictions, and before all of psychological and physical experience becomes classified as currently or potentially addictive, it is essential to rediscover the boundaries of the concept. Secondly, it is far from being value free. It is loaded with heavy moral and emotional overtones of fear and rejection.

The four central psychological features of the old familiar clearly negative addictions can usefully be seen as salience (Edwards and Gross, 1977), conflict (Orford, 1985), loss of control (Heather and Robertson, 1989) and relief (Edwards and Gross, 1977).

By salience, we mean that the addictive activity, the drinking for example, comes to dominate all of the person's life, their thinking, their feeling and their behavior. For the addicted person, the central actions of their addiction become more important than anything else in their lives, more important than eating, sleeping or sexual satisfaction; more important than relationships. All of life revolves around the addiction. It is virtually the only source of satisfaction, of pleasure, or of relief from pain.

The second most important distinguishing feature of an old fashioned negative addiction is conflict, usually conflict with people immediately around the harm which the excessive activity may be doing to the addict and to them. Even where there is a positive addiction like jogging or transcendental meditation, (Glasser, 1976) there is almost always some dispute about the extent of the behavior and about the desirability of that extent. At the very minimum, there is criticism from friends and onlookers that the jogging fanatic is missing out on a lot of other pleasures in life. It may be that, for the addicted person himself, there is no dispute, no concern about the excesses or about the salience, but that for the friends and relatives, the behavior is clearly excessive, and they are continually in conflict with the addicted person about the extent of it. But most often in a powerful negative addiction, there is an internal dispute

TABLE 1

List of Potentially Addictive Activities	
1.	Cocaine*
2.	Heroin*
3.	Amphetamine or similar "pep" pills*
4.	Morphine or related opium-like drugs*
5.	Gambling for money
6.	Marijuana*
7.	Pipe, cigar, cigarette, snuff and/or chewing tobacco*
8.	Alcohol, including beer, wine, liquor, whiskey, etc.*
9.	Barbiturates and similar sedative drugs*
10.	Hallucinogenic drugs (LSD, PCP, mescaline, etc.)*
11.	Caffeine (tea, coffee, cola beverages, etc.)*
12.	Stealing, shoplifting, petty theft, etc.
13.	Sugar based foods (candy, baked goods, ice cream, etc)*
14.	Fatty, oily, or greasy foods*
15.	Salt from the shaker and/or salty foods*
16.	Highly seasoned foods*
17.	Spending just for the sake of spending
18.	Work for the sake of being busy
19.	Anger, fights and arguments
20.	Trying to manipulate and/or control other people
21.	Trying to get attention for attention's sake
22.	Reading for reading's sake
23.	Trying to get others to take care of me and do things for me
24.	Exercise, jogging, playing sports or working out
25.	Seeking and having sex with another person
26.	Seeking and using pornography (sexually oriented pictures, books etc.)
27.	Watching television
28.	Talking for talking's sake
29.	Searching for, buying, and collecting certain items
30.	Lying (for no good reason)
31.	Aspirin or other non-prescription pain medications*
32.	Controlled (prescription only) pain medications*
33.	Laxatives*
34.	Nasal decongestants, sprays and inhalants*
35.	Antihistamine pills or other decongestant pills *
36.	Antacids, stomach remedies*
37.	Fast and/or reckless driving (not to include driving under the influence)
38.	Valium, librium and related "minor tranquilizers"*
39.	Physical violence
40.	Cough and/or cold medications

Note: The 22 substance oriented activities such as alcohol and tobacco use are marked with an asterisk (*) and the remaining 18 items refer to nonsubstance addictive activities.
(From Wittman, G.W., N.P. Fuller, and J.I. Taber, 1988)

within the addicted person himself about the extent of his behavior. He knows he does it too much.

The third major feature of the "old fashioned" conventional substance based solely on the negative concept of addictions has, since the 1930s, been recognized as "loss of control." The history of the idea of loss of control in the disease concept of alcoholism demands study (Heather and Robertson, 1989). It has gained acceptance mainly through the ideology of Alcoholics Anonymous which contributed very substantially to the formulation of the disease concept of alcoholism by Jellineck (1960). In the late 1930s, when the ideology of AA was being formulated, drinking was almost universally seen in terms of a moral model in which the alcoholic was held responsible for all his drinking, and therefore for the misery it caused to all around him. He thus became a moral and social pariah. At that time, drinkers had been deserted by the medical profession which hitherto had had little or no success in the treatment of "dipsomania." The power of the old religious beliefs had declined and the spiritual conversion route to recovery no longer worked its old magic for so many. A new secular model which restored credibility and respectability to the potentially recovering drinker was essential.

The switch from the old moral model of religious belief and blame to a new ideological vehicle of hope was accomplished by bringing back a medical framework of explanation in a new form. The renewed belief in "loss of control" absolved the drinker from responsibility for the past, and the reclassification of the addiction as a disease brought the credible possibility of recovery and restoration of status and respect in the community. The inner experience of the drinker was reinterpreted as reduced and patchy control over overwhelming cravings and urges, and it was sometimes elevated into the myth of total loss of control. The "loss of control" apparently experienced by the addict was then used as an explanation for the drinker's behavior in an attribution of cause after the event.

Loss of control was never absolute. Otherwise, how would a recovering alcoholic arriving at AA perform the "miracle" of suddenly regaining total control of his drinking in abstinence, as many did? With a credible alternative goal, the "out of control" drinker always was able to change his behavior as a series of crucial laboratory experiments demonstrated (Mendelson and Mello, 1965; Mello, McNamee and Mendelson, 1968; Cohen, Liebson, Faillace and Speers, 1971). The apparent loss of control based on the reports of drinkers was then accepted by the medical profession and became a hallowed and central feature of the disease concept of alcoholism (Jellinek, 1960) which has so substantially shaped the thinking of the Western world on addictions and their treatment.

But the apparent loss of control is more parsimoniously explained as a reduced utility in doing anything else (where "utility" of a behavior is a dependent function of both desirability and credibility of the anticipated reward, as in normative decision theory). The reduced utility of any other behavior than the addictive activity can be seen as a direct result of the effects of salience and conflict in restricting the alternative plans for reward (see Table 2).

The fourth major feature of old fashioned substance-based negative addictions has traditionally been relief. Edwards and Gross (1977) latterly made relief drinking to avoid the onset of withdrawal symptoms the central feature of the *Alcohol Dependency Syndrome.* All such relief is concerned with the learned avoidance of rebound effects from the cessation of very strong stimulation which had major effects on hedonic tone. This points clearly to a general feature of addictions, that they tend to develop most strongly around an activity which has strong and immediate effects in altering hedonic tone, often through altering arousal, activities such as ingesting amphetamines or valium, or gambling.

Other important distinguishing features of addictions are tolerance and withdrawal, effects which have always been accepted as major physiological features of the concept of dependencies. Indeed, the existence of withdrawal effects has been identified as the single criterion of the existence of a dependency. Although tolerance and withdrawal are most clearly seen in connection with the abuse of substances, there has been increasing evidence that there is a potentially important psychological component in each of them. This evidence from studies such as Siegel's (1979) into conditioned tolerance to drugs is mainly about psychological factors in tolerance. But there is some evidence of psychological factors in the intensity of withdrawals (Peele, 1985). More recently, from the study of gambling addictions, comes a well researched study which documents the existence of withdrawal effects following cessation of excessive gambling (Wray and Dickerson, 1981), which could be purely psychological if no physiological basis in the ingestion of substances can be pointed to.

TABLE 2

Common Components of Addictions
SALIENCE: The addictive activity becomes the most important thing in the person's life and dominates thinking (preoccupations and cognitive distortions), feeling (cravings), and behavior (deterioration of socialized behavior).
CONFLICT: Disputes about the extent of the excessive behavior arise both between the addicted person and others around, and within the addicted person themselves. Continuing conflict increases salience and the need for relief.
"LOSS OF CONTROL": Apparent inability to limit time or resources given to, or amount of, excessive behavior, even when a decision appears to have previously been made to do so. Explainable in terms of salience and relief.
RELIEF: At a late stage, the effects of the addictive activity are so powerful that there is a rebound effect when it ceases (withdrawals) and the only way to avoid feeling more miserable than before (to find relief) is to do it again at the earliest opportunity. Continual choosing of short term pleasure and relief leads to disregard adverse consequences and long term damage, which in turn increases salience as the apparent need for the addictive activity as a coping strategy.
TOLERANCE: Increasing amounts of the addictive activity are required to achieve the former effects.
WITHDRAWALS: Unpleasant feeling states and/or physical effects when the addictive activity is discontinued or suddenly reduced
RELAPSE AND REINSTATEMENT: Tendency for repeated reversions to earlier patterns of addictive behavior to recur, and for even the most extreme patterns typical of the height of the addiction to be quickly restored even after many years of abstinence or control.
From Iain Brown, *Towards a Value Free and Psychologically Centered Concept of Addiction.* Paper presented to the Scottish Branch of the British Psychological Society, Glasgow, December 1988b (1990)

Relapses are another universally accepted feature of both addictions and dependencies with both psychological and physiological components. Edwards, in his description of the Alcohol Dependence Syndrome (1977), includes as a major feature of it the *reinstatement effect*, which is the name he gives to the rapid reinstatement, immediately following even a minor relapse, of the former maximum levels of addictive activity. Some extreme examples of this are frequently reported, such as the gambler who two weeks before he was about to receive recognition for ten years total abstinence from his local group of Gamblers Anonymous, gambled again, and within a few weeks was betting at the same levels as just before he sought help ten years earlier. I knew the man at the time, and accepted the account without questioning it.

Such stories are also frequent about drinkers and smokers as well. They require systematic investigation and verification because, in many of them, the time lapse is so great that there can clearly be no physiological component and it might be a better description to refer to them as examples of a reinstatement phenomenon. Pavlov found that, even long after the conditioned responses had been extinguished in his dogs, flashbacks could occur, and even the full conditioned reflex could be reliably and rapidly restored. Any pattern of behavior which has been overlearned to the extent that an addictive activity usually is would then be expected on purely theoretical grounds to produce the reinstatement phenomenon from time to time without any further physiological factors being necessary to the explanation.

THE BOUNDARIES OF THE CONCEPT OF ADDICTION

There is, sadly, often confusion, not just in the minds of educated lay persons, between addictions and habits, obsessions, compulsions, attachments, and dependencies. An important part of our task of the refinement and remodelling of the concept of addiction must consist in the satisfactory differentiation of addiction from each of these.

Like addictions, both obsessions and compulsions can come to dominate a person's life, if only because they dominate their thinking and behaving. Sometimes the feature of addictions which involves being preoccupied with aspects of the addictive action (e.g., with plans for gambling, with thoughts of drinking) can seem like an obsession and can lead to the confusion of an addiction with an obsession. But, unlike addictions, obsessions are often, if not usually, suffered internally or mentally without leading directly to extensive action, and particularly to goal-directed action. If they do lead to action, it tends to be quite limited, inflexible and repetitive, without the goal-directed quality found with addictions. They tend to result in repetitive and sterile acts of checking and rechecking of a kind which is no more harmless than being a waste of time and energy and, indeed, are more likely to inhibit other goal-directed activity just because they are so preoccupying.

If obsessions are thinking which is "out of control," then compulsions are behavior which is "out of control," and again, addictions have been confused with them in the past. A notable instance of this is so-called "compulsive" gambling. Like addictions, compulsions can come to dominate all of the unfortunate person's life. Furthermore, as with addictions, if the person is not allowed or able to do what they appear to want, considerable distress can be experienced (seeming like the equivalent of withdrawal symptoms and further confusing addictions and compulsions). But, unlike addictions, compulsions are experienced as an action which the person does not consciously want to do even as they are carrying it out, as something entirely involuntary, even as quite alien to the self, often regarded with powerful revulsion and disgust before, during, and afterwards, and frequently accompanied by fear and distress.

Obsessions and compulsions are mostly driven by fear, and issue in relatively short behavior sequences having the effect of reducing the fear. This is not the usual experience of addicts, who generally make a conscious and near wholehearted decision to engage in their addictive behavior, who usually expect pleasure — or at least relief from pain — to accompany the action, and who often plan it well in advance like other goal-directed activity.

Other disorders of impulse control — such as kleptomania and pyromania — have more complex bases and may be best managed using an addiction model, as recent advances in the application of behavioral relapse avoidance techniques to repeated sexual offending suggests (Laws, 1989; MaCulloch, Snowden, Wood and Mills, 1983; and Marques and Nelson, 1989).

With regard to attachments, for all of us, our first attachments are to our parent figures. Typically, the young child becomes unhappy and fearful if it is separated from its mother even for a few moments; it is quite different as long as she is around, much bolder, happier, more outgoing and communicative. Later in adulthood, most of us have particular important people to whom we are attached, so that their loss becomes a threat to our emotional well-being and their presence and accessibility is a guarantee of our background security and happiness. Attachments of the same kind, but perhaps less important, can be formed with animals, houses, places, cars, ideas, groups of people, beliefs, etc. Separation from and loss of these persons and objects leads to anxiety and grief.

TABLE 3

Some Problems to be Distinguished From Addictions
OBSESSIONS: Recurring patterns of thought that people cannot control and distress over.
COMPULSIONS: Repeated involuntary acts that the person tries to resist and feels revulsion over at the time.
DISORDERS OF IMPULSE CONTROL: Includes obsessions and compulsions and isolated actions like kleptomania, pyromania, etc.
ATTACHMENTS: Usually benign and constructive, they center on persons and objects, involve long term relationships with them, and do not involve increasing tolerance, relapses or withdrawal effects.
DEPENDENCIES: Refer narrowly to substance-based addictions, and particularly to physical aspects of them.
From Iain Brown, *Towards a Value Free and Psychologically Centered concept of Addiction*. Paper presented to the Scottish Branch of the British Psychological Society, Glasgow, December 1988b (revised 1990).

Confusingly, there are almost certainly elements of attachments in all addictions. For example, the alcohol addict feels safer if she has her bottle, and if she has to give up drinking altogether, she goes through a mourning process. (McAughtrie and Brown, 1988). Potentially even more confusing, some attachments may come to look like old fashioned negative addictions. Stanton Peele first pointed out the addictive components of romantic love (Peele, 1975) such as when an infatuation comes to dominate a person's whole life in a malignant and destructive way, and such persons persist with it even when it is obviously destroying them and possibly others. Robin Norwood is currently doing quite well on this theme with the book, *Women Who Love Too Much* (Norwood, 1985). But attachments are not the same thing as the addictions themselves.

Attachments are more commonly thought of — although not always — as benign and constructive in their effects. Addictions are more commonly thought of as — but not always are — malignant and destructive in their effects. Attachments center on particular persons and objects, and involve long-term relationships with them. Addictions are centered on particular activities — which may involve the consumption of some substance — and the repetition of some experiences associated with them, and are otherwise independent of people, material objects, places and ideas. They can be and are pursued anywhere with anyone, and often eventually alone. Attachments also have further distinguishing features, such as absolutely no tolerance effects, and a different pattern of withdrawal symptoms called grief and mourning.

Dependencies, on the other hand, are all included within the broader term "addictions." Dependency began as a narrower term for addiction. It was first used to describe only those addictions which involve the ingestion of some substance, for example drugs, tobacco and alcohol. The term "dependency" was launched by the World Health Organization which defined it as "an adaptive state of the body that is manifested by physical disturbances when substance use is discontinued." The concept of dependencies was promoted partly in a brave and commendable attempt to get away from the sensationalism and the value-laden "bogey-word" qualities of the term "addiction," and partly to narrow the concept of addiction down to something which was physically based and therefore — they imagined — more easily definable and quantifiable and maybe even value-free, especially because it excluded from consideration in any diagnosis all the addiction-related problems and the value-laden social damage associated with them.

Its use has, however, had the unfortunate effect of narrowing the field of phenomena by artificially excluding from it a range of activities which did not involve the ingestion of substances. It has thus distorted our perception of the central phenomena by insisting that the central processes and the crucially identifying phenomena of addictions are physical and physiological when it is now emerging that just the opposite is the case: that central processes of addictions and the crucial identifying features are psychological phenomena, and it is the physiological phenomena which are peripheral, though important. The introduction of the term "dependency" did have one useful function, however. It helped to distinguish between the core of the addiction/dependency itself (which turns out to be much more psychological than physical) and all the consequent problems — social, psychological, physical, legal and occupational — which it produced in the person's life and so in turn led to greater addiction/dependency. The distinction between the Alcohol Dependency Syndrome and alcohol related problems has proved usefully transferable to other addictions, but the term dependency may have tended to lead to a sterile narrowing of the area of study of addictions to ingestion of substances and the physical processes accompanying that.

THE PROBLEM OF VALUE IN THE CONCEPT OF ADDICTION

Glasser (1976) has described the concept of "Positive Addictions" as activities, such as jogging and transcendental meditation, deliberately cultivated to wean addicts away from their more harmful and sinister preoccupations. Marlatt and Gordon (1985) have demonstrated that the cultivation of such newfangled addictions does reduce the grip of the old fashioned ones on some of their patients.

Glasser defines positive addictions as new rewarding activities such as exercise and relaxation which produce increased feelings of self-efficacy. There are six criteria to be fulfilled in the identification of a positive addiction. They must be:

- chosen, non-competitive and needing about an hour a day;
- easy, so no mental effort is required;
- able to be done mostly alone, not dependent on others;
- believed in as having some value — physical, mental or spiritual;
- believed in to the extent that, if persisted in, some improvement will result; and
- involve no self criticism (Glasser, 1976).

While such addictions, when applied to games and gaming or to "workaholism," do not have quite the beneficial qualities required to meet Glasser's criteria for a positive addiction, it is noteworthy that several subjects in Brown's study of games and gaming took the trouble — unsolicited — to note on the questionnaire that games and gaming had improved their health (Brown, 1990). It is also clear that for some unknown proportion of those people more heavily involved, they have other potentially seriously harmful associations. Perhaps these activities could for many be called "Mixed Blessing Addictions." If this is so, it appears increasingly likely that similar investigations will show that other activities in which individual people are known to become excessively involved — such as golf or gardening — can be identified as similarly "Mixed Blessing Addictions." Indeed, it becomes possible to identify a moral continuum or dimension of value along which frequently indulged activities — including "addictions" — may be strung out. These may range from rare and noble passions such as oil painting or writing poetry through Glasser's lesser positive addictions like jogging and yoga. Continuing on through more neutral, cozy and commonplace preoccupations erosive on time and money such as golf, knitting and fishing to dangerous but still barely acceptable activities such as motor racing and hang gliding and eventually to the "old fashioned" spectacular stereotypes, the potential killers and wreckers conventionally recognized as addictions — heroin, gambling and drinking.

Even these potential wreckers are rarely wholly negative in moral or social values, wholly evil, wholly without benefit to the individual, or wholly to be deplored in their effects by any government (See Table 4). Especially in one's "Golden Age" when the individual to be addicted has learned all the skills of maximizing the control and effects of his or her chosen addictive instrument for sustaining eternal high hedonic tone (Brown, 1988a). Addictions have several clearly positive functions: They produce reliable changes of mood and subjective experience (escape from pain, boredom, etc.); they provide positive experiences of pleasure, excitement, relaxation, etc.; they provide the potential addict with the ability to do things he or she could not do before because of disinhibition of behavior, especially sex and aggression; they provide a coping strategy for all vulnerabilities to insults, injuries, frustrations, setbacks and dominators; and they provide a coping strategy for social anxiety, hostility, suspicion, fear and tension.

Even in the latter stages of deterioration, they still simplify all decisions because all decisions can be made according as to whether or not they allow the pursuit of one single (addictive) activity or not. They simplify and coarsen the potential addict's feelings as subtle feelings are increasingly eclipsed by only a few (addiction-activity-related) very strong ones. They maintain a safe emotional distance from any close relationships as the potential addict cannot find time or energy to invest in them. They provide a strategy for threatening those others around who are emotionally involved or dependent, or for rebelling against them, or for taking revenge on them by increasing the addictive activity or by relapsing. Finally, as hustling develops into a full-time activity, they become a source of meaning to life and even, later, whether recovered from or not, a source of personal identity (Brown, 1987b). Clearly not even the most destructive addiction at the furthest point of the good-bad value scale is always entirely an unmixed personal disaster.

It is time that the perception of addictions came out from under the dominance of moral and medical models which obscure our views of them and filter our perceptions of the wider context of phenomena within which they are embedded. Addictions are no more "evil" or "sick" as a particular case of the wider class of motivational monopolies and reward specialisms than tornados and hurricanes are "evil" and "sick" as particular case of the wider spectrum of global weather systems involving winds, or than maelstroms and whirlpools are "evil" and "sick" as examples of the class of phenomena known as ocean currents.

Probably most social scientists would doubt that a completely value-free concept of addiction (or indeed of anything) is either desirable or possible. Those who insisted on a completely value-free concept have tried to take refuge in the concept of dependence with the apparent safety of being tied to respectably measurable physical effects of the ingestion of measurable amounts of substances. But the ingestion of substances is only a small part of the total field of addictions, as most current lists of addictions implicitly acknowledge, and as anyone who has tried to treat addiction problems — and has found that the psychological effects and problems persist long after the effects of the withdrawal of the substances have disappeared — has discovered. Nevertheless, many would still strive to make the concept of addiction as value-free as possible, and so, I believe, should we.

Beyond the addiction-related problems of, for example, drinking or heroin or gaming, and simulations which may confuse us because of their value-laden content, are a set of enduring core characteristics of addictions. These are now almost value-free, always present to some degree in even the most "positive" of addictions, but still most clearly seen in the old fashioned negative addictions than in the others. These core characteristics remain salience, conflict and relief (and traditionally also "loss of control"), with secondary consequences such as tolerance, withdrawal and reinstatement.

PSYCHOLOGICAL PROCESSES AT THE CORE OF THE ADDICTION PHENOMENON

It has been argued extensively elsewhere (Brown 1988a; 1989b) that there is a single core process in the development and maintenance of addictions, the continual mismanagement of the quest for happiness. Although this has previously been presented in association with some reversal theory explanations of the function of the manipulation of arousal, the basic model is independent of the acceptance or rejection of reversal theory explanations.

According to this model, in the development of an addiction, the normal functions of planning for intermediate and long term goals that might bring satisfaction to the addicted person and might reach and maintain tolerable levels of hedonic tone are increasingly disrupted or become progressively deficient. This can be because the person's life situation is so confusing and unpredictable that the participant loses the conviction that long term strategies for securing high sustained hedonic tone will ever pay off and so fails to invest in them. Or in another individual it may be because the life situation is objectively inherently devoid of the possibility of reward. This situation may be partly contributed to by previously inherited or acquired skill deficiencies in the individual before the process of development of the addiction began a progressive further deterioration in them. Or, in yet another individual, the addictive process may develop because of the ready availability of easy short-term rewards making for a style of life that gradually brings the individual to rely almost solely on immediate and short-term satisfactions.

When the normal management functions of planning for intermediate and long-term goals are thus made deficient, a "crisis management" style of conducting day-to-day, hour-to-hour, and even minute-to-minute manipulations of arousal and subjective perceptions is developed in order to sustain high hedonic tone by lurching from one "crisis intervention" (more of the addictive activity) to another (yet more of the addictive activity). After some time of this, the participant gradually loses the management skills in any other way of living involving intermediate and long-term goals and so becomes locked into or enslaved in their particular addictive activity and life style (Brown, 1989b).

On this kind of model, the salience feature of addictions is seen as the prime independent variable which is affected in turn in several positive feedback loops. This primary salience is seen as a consequence of the progressive deterioration of the skills required to reach and maintain acceptable levels of hedonic tone by any other means than through the increasingly salient activity. The apparent loss of control and the disregard of adverse consequences which so often leads to conflict equally springs not from total lack of choice, but from the same basic mainly-acquired disability which makes alternative choices more difficult. Once salience and conflict are established, then, especially if the addictive activity has sufficient inherent power to alter hedonic tone, tolerance — both psychological and physical — and withdrawals — psychological and perhaps physical — usually develop. Relief indulgence in the addictive activity then becomes the only way in which the painful rebound effects from the last indulgence can be offset by pleasure strong enough to overcome them temporarily. So the last-stage characteristic identifying feature of the predicament of being addicted becomes established.

CONCLUSIONS

It is arguable that the concept of addiction has, especially in the popular press, one of the heaviest burdens of surplus value in the histories of both medicine and of morals. Even though it may be shown to be a concept which is ultimately value-free, it will always be dogged by its bad record. One of the avowed aims in the redefinition of "dependency" was an attempt to get away from the past in this way. If the concept of dependency — with its physiological centeredness and its implications of a narrow substance base — is not a satisfactory replacement for "addiction," perhaps some other term may allow scientists to study the real psychological, social and physiological phenomena of addiction but under a less distracting and less easily misunderstood name. Based on the present review, a label such as "monopolistic activities" has the merits that it includes phenomena beyond the ingestion of substances.

A more narrowly behaviorist description which would take in the whole range of beneficial, mixed blessing and harmful phenomena might be "reward specialisms." The classical Greek hedonists had a proverb — *maiden agan* — meaning, nothing too much. This seems, correctly, to recognize the potential of all rewarding or pleasurable activities to encroach on every other one. But since it is possible to point to criteria that help identify some activities as having a greater addictive potential than others, it may be useful to refer to a special class of "monopolistic" activities in that sense.

The concept of addiction has a recognizable common core distinguishable from other problem phenomena of human experience. It is also clear that not only the crude and powerful stimulants and depressants of the well known addictive activities and substances which produce massive alterations in hedonic tone can be the instruments and vehicles of such a debasement of the normal planning and management skills of the pleasure seeking individual. Many other leisure activities too, such as games and gaming, can be abused to gain short term satisfactions in the same way, although not, perhaps usually, with the same spectacular effects. And the concept of addictions, now relatively value-free, can be studied in a much wider range of situations and functions — such as gambling — than in just the "old fashioned" negative substance-based phenomena hitherto conventionally thought of as addictions.

REFERENCES

Anderson, G., and R.I.F. Brown (1984). Real and laboratory gambling, sensation seeking and arousal. *British Journal of Psychology*, vol. 75, pp. 401-410.

Apter, M.J. (1982). *The Experience of Motivation: The Theory of Psychological Reversals*. London: Academic Press.

Ashton, H., J.E. Millman, M.D. Rawlings, R. Telford, and J.W. Thompson (1978). The use of event-related slow potentials of the brain in the analysis of effects of cigarette smoking and nicotine in humans. In K. Batting (ed.), *Behavioral Effects of Nicotine*. Basel: S. Karger.

Ashton, H., and R. Stepney (1982). *Smoking, Psychology and Pharmacology*. London: Tavistock.

Ashton, H., and D.H. Watson (1977). Puffing frequency and nicotine intake in cigarette smokers. *British Medical Journal*, vol. 3, pp. 679-681.

Blaszczynski, A., S.W. Winter, and N. McConaghy (1986). Plasma endorphin levels in pathological gambling. *Journal of Gambling Behavior*, vol. 2, pp. 3-14.

Brown, R.I.F. (1986). Arousal and sensation seeking components in the general explanation of gambling and gambling addictions. *International Journal of Addictions*, vol. 21, pp. 1001-1016.

Brown, R.I.F. (1987a). Classical and operant paradigms in the management of compulsive gambling. *Behavioral Psychotherapy*, vol. 15, pp. 111-122.

Brown, R.I.F. (1987b). *Deviations Along the Road to Recovery*. London: Gamblers Anonymous General Service Board.

Brown, R.I.F. (1988a). Reversal theory and subjective experience in the explanation of addiction and relapse. In Apter, M.J., J.M. Kerr, and M. Cowal (eds.), *Progress in Reversal Theory*. Amsterdam: North-Holland.

Brown, R.I.F. (1988b). *Gambling addictions: commonalities, peculiarities and implications for a value-free and psychologically-centered concept of addiction.* Paper presented to the British Psychological Society, Scottish Branch, Glasgow, December.

Brown, R.I.F. (1989a). Relapses from a gambling perspective. In M. Gossop (ed.), *Relapse and Addictive Behavior.* London: Croom Helm.

Brown, R.I.F. (1989b). *Addictions as deficiencies in planning.* Paper presented at the Fifth International Conference on Reversal Theory, University of Athabaska, Northern Alberta, Canada, June.

Brown, R.I.F. (1990). Games and gaming as addictions. In Apter, M.J.and J.N. Kerr (eds.), *Adult Play.* London: Routledge.

Brown, R.I.F. and B. Perry (1990). *Arousal and addictive eating behavior among weight watchers.* Unpublished manuscript: Department of Psychology, University of Glasgow.

Capell, H. and C. Herman (1972). Alcohol and tension reduction: A review. *Quarterly Journal of Studies in Alcohol*, vol. 33, pp. 33-47.

Cohen, M., I.A. Liebson, L.A. Faillace and W. Speers (1971). Alcoholism: Controlled drinking and incentives for abstinence. *Psychological Reports*, vol. 28, pp. 575-580.

Commission on the Review of National Policy Towards Gambling in America (1976). *Gambling in America.* Washington, D.C.: United States Government Printing Office.

Coventry, K. and R.I.F. Brown (1993). Sensation seeking in gamblers and non-gamblers and its relation to preference for gambling activities, chasing, arousal and loss of control in regular gamblers. In W.R. Eadington and J.A. Cornelius (eds.), *Gambling Behavior and Problem Gambling.* Reno: Institute for the Study of Gambling and Commercial Gaming, University of Nevada.

Dickerson, M.G. and S.G. Adcock (1986). Mood, arousal and cognitions in persistent gambling: Preliminary investigations of a theoretical model. *Journal of Gambling Behavior*, vol. 1, pp. 3-15.

Dickerson, M., J. Hinchy and J. Fabre (1987). Chasing, arousal and sensation seeking in off-course gamblers. *British Journal of Addiction*, vol. 82, pp. 673-680.

Domino, E.F. (1973). Neuropsychopharmacology of nicotine and tobacco smoking. In W.L. Dunn (ed.), *Smoking Behavior: Motives and Incentives.* New York: Wiley.

Donovan, D.M. and E.F. Chaney (1985). Alcoholic relapse prevention and intervention: Models and methods. In G.A. Marlatt and J.R. Gordon, *Relapse Prevention: Maintenance Strategies in the Treatment of Addictive Behaviors.* New York, Guildford Press.

Duffy, E. (1972). Activation. In N.S. Greenfield and R.A. Sternbach (eds.), *Handbook of Psychophysiology.* New York: Holt Rinehart & Winston.

Easterbrook, J.A. (1959). The effects of emotion on cue utilization and the organization of behavior. *Psychological Review*, vol. 66, pp. 183-201.

Edwards, G. and M.M. Gross (1976). Alcohol dependence: Provisional description of a clinical syndrome. *British Medical Journal*, vol. 1, pp. 1058-1061.

Flood, M. (1989). Addictive eating disorders. *Nursing Clinics of North America*, vol. 24, pp. 45-53.

Frith, C.D. (1971). Smoking behavior and its relation to the smoker's immediate experience. *British Journal of Social and Clinical Psychology*, vol. 10, pp. 73-78.

Gaboury, A. and R. Ladouceur (1988). *Irrational thinking and gambling.* Unpublished manuscript.

Gilbert, D.G. (1979). Paradoxical tranquilizing and emotion-reducing effects of nicotine. *Psychological Bulletin*, vol. 86, pp. 643-661.

Gilovich, T. (1983). Biased Evaluation and Persistence in Gambling. *Journal of Personality and Social Psychology*, vol. 22, pp. 228-241.

Glasser, W. (1976). *Positive Addictions.* New York: Harper and Row.

Griffiths, M. (1990). The cognitive psychology of gambling. *Journal of Gambling Studies*, vol. 6, pp. 31-42.

Heather, N. and I. Robertson (1989). *Problem Drinking.* London: Oxford University Press.

Higgins, R.L. (1976). Experimental investigations of tension reduction models of alcoholism. In G. Goldstein and C. Neuringer (eds.), *Empirical Studies in Alcoholism*. Cambridge, MA: Ballinger Publishing Co.

Hodgson, R.J., T.R. Stockwell, and H.J. Rankin (1979). Can alcohol reduce tension? *Behavior Research and Therapy*, vol. 17, pp. 459-466.

Hull, J.G. and C.F. Bond (1986). Social and behavioral consequences of alcohol consumption and expectancy: A meta-analysis. *Psychological Bulletin*, vol. 99, pp. 347-360.

Hull, J.G. and R. D. Young (1983). Self-consciousness, self-esteem and success-failure as determinants of alcohol consumption in male social drinkers. *Journal of Personality and Social Psychology*, vol. 44, pp. 1097-1109.

Jacobs, D.F. (1986). A general theory of addictions: A new theoretical model. *Journal of Gambling Behavior*, vol. 2, pp. 15-31.

Jellinek, E.M. (1960). *The Disease Concept of Alcoholism*. New Haven: Hillhouse Press.

Kahneman, D. and A. Tversky (1982). The psychology of preferences. *Scientific American*, pp. 136-142, January.

Kelly, M., A.L. Myrsten, A. Nevi, and V. Rydberg (1970). Effects and after-effects of alcohol on physiological and psychological functions in man: A controlled study. *Blutalcohol*, vol. 7, pp. 422-436.

Kuley, N.B. and D.F. Jacobs (1988). The relationship between dissociative-like experiences and sensation seeking among social gamblers. *Journal of Gambling Behavior*, vol. 4, pp. 197-207.

Lacey, J.I. (1967). Somatic response patterning and stress: Some revisions of activation theory. In M.H. Apley and R. Trumbull (eds.), *Psychological Stress*. New York: Appleton Century Crofts.

Ladouceur, R. and A. Gaboury (1988). Effects of limited and unlimited stakes on gambling behavior. *Journal of Gambling Behavior*, vol. 4, pp. 119-126.

Langer, E.J. (1975). The illusion of control. *Journal of Personality and Social Psychology*, vol. 32, pp. 311-328.

Laws, R. (ed.), (1989). *Relapse Prevention with Sex Offenders*. New York: The Guildford Press.

Leary, K. and M.G. Dickerson (1985). Levels of arousal in high and low frequency gamblers. *Behavior Research and Therapy*, vol. 23, pp. 635-640.

Levison, P.K., D.R. Gerstein, and D.R. Maloff (eds.), (1983). *Communalities in Substance Abuse and Habitual Behavior.* Lexington, MA: D.C. Heath.

Lieberman, H.R., J.J. Wurtman, and B. Chew (1986). Changes in mood after carbohydrate consumption in obese individuals. *American Journal of Clinical Nutrition*, vol. 44, pp. 772-778.

Mangan, G.L. and J.F. Golding (1984). *The Psychopharmacology of Smoking.* Cambridge, MA: Cambridge University Press.

Marlatt, G.A., C.F. Kostum, and A.R. Lang (1975). Provocation to anger and opportunity for retaliation as determinants of alcohol consumption in social drinkers. *Journal of Abnormal Psychology*, vol. 84, pp. 652-659.

Marlatt, G.A. and J.R. Gordon (eds.), (1985). *Relapse Prevention: Maintenance Strategies in the Treatment of Addictive Behaviors.* New York: Guildford Press.

Marques, K. and C. Nelson (1989). Understanding and preventing relapse in sex offenders. In M. Gossop (ed.), *Relapse and Addictive Behavior.* London: Tavistock/Routledge.

McAughtrie, L. and R.I.F. Brown (1988). Addiction recovery as bereavement and as liberation. In W.R. Eadington (ed.), *Gambling Research: Proceedings of the Seventh International Conference on Gambling and Risk Taking.* Reno: University of Nevada

MaCulloch, M.J., P.R. Snowden, P.J.W. Wood, and H.E. Mills (1983). Sadistic fantasy, sadistic behavior and offending. *British Journal of Psychiatry*, vol. 143, pp. 20-29.

Mello, N.K. and J.H. Mendelson (1965). Operant analysis of drinking habits of chronic alcoholics. *Nature*, vol. 206, pp. 43-46.

Mello, N.K., H.B. McNamee, and J.H. Mendelson (1968). Drinking patterns of chronic alcoholics: Gambling and motivation for alcohol. *Psychiatric Research Report No. 24.* Washington D.C.: American Psychiatric Association.

Milkman, H.B. and S. Sunderworth (eds.), (1987). *Craving for Ecstacy: The Consciousness and Chemistry of Escape.* Lexington, MA: D.C. Heath.

Miller, W.R. (ed.), (1980). *The Addictive Behaviors: Treatment of Alcoholism, Drug Abuse, Smoking and Obesity*. Oxford: Pergamon Press.

Morris, W.N. and N.P. Reilly (1987). Towards the self-regulation of mood: Theory and research. *Motivation and Emotion*, vol. 11, pp. 215-249.

Norwood, R. (1985). *Women Who Love Too Much*. New York: Simon and Schuster.

Olds, J. and P. Milner (1954). Positive reinforcement produced by electrical stimulation of septal areas and other regions of rat brain. *Journal of Comparative and Physiological Psychology*, vol. 47, pp. 419-427.

Orford, J. (1985). *Excessive Appetites: A Psychological View of Addictions*. Chichester, U.K.: Wiley.

Peele, S. (1975). *Love and Addiction*. New York: Taplinger.

Peele, S. (1985). *The Meaning of Addiction: Compulsive Experience and It's Interpretation*. Lexington, MA: Lexington Books.

Rosenthal, N.E., M.J. Genhart, B. Cabellero, F.M. Jacobsen, R.O. Skwerer, J.J. Wurtman, and B.J. Spring (1986). *Carbohydrate craving in seasonal affective disorder*. Paper presented at the annual meeting of the American Psychological Association, Washington, D.C.

Ross, C.A. (1989). *Multiple Personality Disorder: Diagnosis, Clinical Features and Treatment*. New York: Wiley.

Routtenberg, A. (1968). The two-arousal hypothesis: Reticular formation and limbic system. *Psychological Review*, vol. 75, pp. 51-80.

Roy, A., B. Adinoff, L. Roehrich, D. Lamparski, R. Custer, V. Lorenz, M. Barbaccia, A. Guidotti, E. Costa, and M. Linnoila (1988). Pathological gambling: A psychobiological study. *Archives of General Psychiatry*, vol. 45, pp. 369-373.

Ruderman, A.J. (1986). Dietary restraint: A theoretical and empirical review. *Psychological Bulletin*, vol. 99, pp. 247-262.

Russel, J.A. and M.A. Mehrabian (1975). The mediating role of emotions in alcohol use. *Journal of Studies in Alcohol*, vol. 29, pp. 355-363.

Scolarios, D. and R.I.F. Brown (1987). *Biased evaluation of the outcome of bets in a real casino*. Unpublished manuscript, Department of Psychology, University of Glasgow.

Scolarios, D. and R.I.F. Brown (1988). *A classification of gambling superstitions.* Unpublished manuscript, Department of Psychology, University of Glasgow.

Siegel, S. (1979). The role of conditioning in drug tolerance and addiction. In Keehn, J.D. (ed.), *Psychopathology in Animals: Research and Treatment Implications.* New York: Academic Press.

Stepney, R. (1980). Smoking behavior: A psychology of the cigarette habit. *British Journal of Diseases of the Chest*, vol. 74, pp. 325-344.

Stockwell, T., R.J. Hodgson, and H. Rankin (1982). Tension reduction and prolonged alcohol consumption. *British Journal of Addiction*, vol. 77, pp. 65-73.

Thayer, R.E. (1987). Energy, tiredness and tension effects of a sugar snack versus moderate exercise. *Journal of Personality and Social Psychology*, vol. 52, pp. 119-125.

Thayer, R.E. (1989). *The Biopsychology of Mood and Arousal.* New York: Oxford University Press.

Wagenaar, W.A. (1988). *Paradoxes of Gambling Behavior.* Hove, U.K.: Lawrence Erlbaum Associates.

Warburton, D.M. and K. Wesnes (1983). Mechanisms for habitual substance use: Food, alcohol and cigarettes. In A. Gale and J.A. Edwards (eds.), *Physiological Correlates of Human Behavior.* London: Academic Press.

Wittman, G.W., N.P. Fuller, and J.I. Taber (1988). Patterns of polyaddictions in alcoholism patients and high school students. In Eadington, W.R. (ed.), *Gambling Research: Proceedings of the Seventh International Conference on Gambling and Risk Taking.* Reno: University of Nevada.

Wray, I. and Dickerson, M.G. (1981). Cessation of high frequency gambling and "withdrawal" symptoms. *British Journal of Addictions*, vol. 76, pp. 401-405.

Addictive Behavior: An Informal Clinical View

Julian I. Taber

Having devoted almost every working day between 1978 and 1990 to addictive disorder patients, I have arrived at what seem to be obvious and simple conclusions about people who suffer from chronic addictions. My conclusions are that such people:

- are in many ways very childish;
- are exceedingly unhappy most of the time;
- almost always have more than one serious addiction;
- having stopped one addictive behavior, almost always either intensify other addictive behaviors or develop new ones;
- in nearly every case, show an almost phobic aversion to normal adult values, attitudes and habits; and
- as a result of all these traits, are not normal people.

During my work, I have also formulated certain equally unflattering impressions about the tenders of the flock, those dedicated and single-minded therapists and researchers like myself who make their livings on the promise that, in some important and usually unspecified fashion, the burden of the afflicted shall be lightened because of their efforts. This is not, of course, the occasion upon which I should dwell on my concerns about the mental health of my fellow workers. Inevitably however, whether or not it is proper to do so, I shall insult their sacred dogmas.

THE MIND OF THE CHRONIC ADDICT

My simplistic view of addicted people calls for some elaboration and justification. The only qualifier I must add to my experience, and so to my perceptions, is that my patients have been what one might call *end-stage* addictive disorder patients. I have not been privileged to work with the merely inconvenienced, the problem over-consumer, or the worried well. By the time gamblers, alcoholics and drug abusers turn up in public sector programs, such as those in Veterans Administration facilities, they have usually lost everything, including family, home, job, and physical health. The average patient has had about three prior formal treatment programs and has nowhere else to turn. Having worked mostly with extremes, my thinking may be extreme; I personally would want it no other way. The examination of the limiting case — of extremes — has always been a productive method in research and in clinical practice.

The childishness of the addiction-prone individual becomes quickly apparent in almost any clinical interaction beyond the most superficial of conversations, and it manifests itself in many fundamental areas such as perception, cognition, affect, problem solving, human relations, impulse control and self-image. I think that this childishness is not caused by addictive behavior but, to the contrary, is the pattern that makes addiction possible.

Perception is often limited or restricted to idiosyncratic needs which exclude many of the subtleties that enrich the more objective mind. Chronic addiction people see what they want to see and hear what they want to hear. Extending this self-preoccupation to cognition, they remember what they want to remember and often distort what they saw, heard, or did. Their thinking is simplistic, often characterized by "splitting" past events or potential considerations into dichotomous categories such as good and bad, easy and impossible, beautiful and ugly, etc.

There are usually strong expectations of specialness and entitlement along with magic thinking. Usually, one can notice what I call *delusions of normalcy, adequacy and competence.* Often, addiction patients are capable of unusual feats of accomplishment, but they achieve these for all the wrong reasons, seldom for the intrinsic values in work or play.

There is a strong *in order to* mentality; everything is done "in order to" get somewhere else. There is no joy in the here and now. No goal attained is ever good enough. No quest is ever long enough. And there is no life if there is no quest.

Affect is characterized as well by continued self-reference. Negative affectivity predominates and the individual suffers extreme and unmodulated anger, jealousy, fear, suspicion and yearning. Positive feeling tone is available only with addictives such as alcohol or gambling. Every addicted individual, regardless of the addiction, shows the same cycle of mood swings: preoccupation with "getting high," the false euphoria of being high, and the inevitable profound depression of rebound withdrawal. Time after time, the victim rescues himself or herself from this depression through again thinking about getting high or of getting "back into action." Then, once more, thought leads to action.

The problem solving style of the addiction-prone individual shows extremes that usually involve few choices between violent aggression and total flight or withdrawal. If no action is taken, inaction causes intolerable feelings of frustration, anger, and self-depreciation. Taking the path of violence or rage leads to the same result and adds a good measure of guilt.

If these were the only options open to everyone, everyone would be high most of the time. Mature, adult options such as discussion, debate, rational examination of alternatives, compromise and accommodation are not within the repertoire of the vulnerable individual.

Getting sober, clean or straight by no means assures the development of adult attributes; it only provides the opportunity for doing the work left undone in the developmental process. Unfortunately, there is no reason to think that, if it will take a ten year old child ten more years to learn efficient problem solving skills, it should take a physical adult any less time. It may, unfortunately, take the developmentally retarded adult even more time to learn some of the skills he or she might have learned at an earlier age. How ridiculous and dishonest it seems, then, for mental health professionals to offer 28 day "treatment" programs holding out the expectation that the consumer somehow will be made developmentally whole overnight. Condensing a four year medical school curriculum into 28 days makes about as much sense.

When I say human relations, I mean relationships between psychological grown-ups, relationships based on fair, consistent and rational rules. An adult does not confuse his wife with his mother, does not make a sexual partner of his child, does not expect others always to be fair, kind and understanding, and does not look to others for solutions to problems one ought to solve oneself. The addiction-prone individual always seems to want to be either in control or in the control of others. A calm and even give-and-take seems impossible. Most addiction patients like to think that their past failures in human relations must have been because of their addiction. On the contrary, it seems to me, their lack of basic skill for forming and maintaining normal relationships aggravates their chronic dysphoria and increases addictive behavior.

Having examined thousands of MMPI profiles of gamblers, alcoholics and drug abusers, I note that there is one scale that never fails to show a significant elevation. This is the old "psychopathic deviated" (PD) scale that we now know measures not antisocial personality disorder, but impulsiveness and authority conflict. In all areas of living, not just with overconsumption of euphorogenics, the individual tends to act without planning, without considering the needs of others, and without considering long term consequences. Concerning authority, the individual shows what may be the ultimate failure in human relations: no authority higher than one's self is recognized. If there is no elevation on the MMPI PD scale, then I would be very tempted to say that, while you may be seeing someone with an excessive appetite, the chances are great that there is no true addiction and possibly no developmental disorder.

Finally, there always seem to be serious problems in self-definition, self-acceptance and ego-mastery. The patient sees himself or herself as either wonderful or awful. He or she may spend much time and energy trying to convince oneself and others of personal merit, a continuing debate that never seems to come to resolution. He or she may be unable to see himself or herself accurately at all. Sometimes there is no clear boundary between self and others. Self attributes are freely assigned to others without justification, the motives and intentions of others are misunderstood, and the individual often feels out of control, helpless and overwhelmed.

One could go on and on listing developmental flaws of addiction-prone people. I often think, for example, that there is always a learning deficit. Addiction patients learn little from verbal instruction unless the subject is tied directly and concretely to immediate needs. They have a very difficult time accepting the views of others about themselves. They usually say that they need most to learn skills at which they already excel, and they least want to change what most needs changing. My main point is: Addictive disorders are primarily developmental disorders.

EXPLAINING THE ADDICTIVE PERSON

Simplistic, single cause theories of addiction are plentiful and tempting. While there is, without doubt, some influence by genetic and biochemical variables in the formation of addictive behavior, it seems unlikely that there will be found to be a specific factor for each of the growing list of addictions. So intense is the devotion of some theorists to biochemical mechanisms that they reject the possibility that non-substance addictions can be considered to be addictions at all. Gambling, work, sex, spending, and other antidysphoric activities cannot be addictions, they argue, because there is no chemical to which to become addicted. This position, I believe, reflects an empty, academic and clinically naive view.

Whatever the addiction, the mood cycle is the same, the progression of use is the same, the immature personality organization is the same, the withdrawal is similar, the social consequences are equally drastic, and the tendency to be multiply addicted is the same. In the author's own unpublished research, we have found a reliable and significant correlation between 22 substance abuse patterns and 18 non-substance abuse patterns in the same subject pool. Such evidence suggests the presence of a single, general disorder with multiple addictions as symptoms.

Other single cause theories have suggested specific vulnerabilities such as early exposure, attention deficit disorder, traumatic conditioning, alcoholic parenting, depression, life transitions, and so forth. I find such events to be common in the histories of patients, but not universal or even as common as one might think. I say *yes* to all of them and more, but *no* to any single cause as sufficient.

Single cause theories always remind me to think of people I have known outside the patient population. There are those with frequent severe depression, for example, who accept their depression with equanimity. They manage somehow to avoid becoming dysphoric when depressed, and they use depression as a time to relax, to engage in creative activity, or to reframe perspectives. They learn how to manage depression and limit its control over their lives.

Millions of people during World War II, as in other conflicts, were exposed to massive trauma, but the great majority emerged with the abilities needed to manage productive, addiction-free lives. Many thousands of American troops in Vietnam used high quality addictive drugs only to end illegal drug use promptly upon their return home. Some went on to abuse street drugs and alcohol, but most seem to have adjusted well to productive civilian life. I remember a very badly deformed and crippled man, one of my professors in graduate school, whom I regarded as brilliant. This man's stability, warmth, and acceptance of the unacceptable stood in stark contrast to two other of my professors who, though possessing vigor and health, subsequently died of alcoholism.

The notion of an "addictive personality" has not flourished because research and clinical experience show that a wide variety of personality structures and traits appear in any given addicted population. Personalities of those with addictive disorders differ on several critical dimensions and these differences should not be ignored. They will be useful in understanding individual addictive preferences and styles of use.

Some years ago, while searching for the ultimate "gambler profile," Dr. Alida Glen and I submitted 100 MMPI profiles from pathological gamblers to a complex computer analysis. A huge computer in Florida thought and thought. At length it advised us that there were probably no more than five different ultimate profiles in the profiles submitted. I had to agree with the computer.

TREATMENT OF THE ADDICTED PERSON

In the clinic, one sees all kinds of people. There are the anxious and the calm, the bright and the dull, the introverts and the extroverts, the skilled and the unskilled. The commonalities I see I have already mentioned; but I was not describing an addicted personality so much as I was describing a disorder.

One very troublesome model of addictions is the medical model. Diagnostic manuals in the United States already include many different addictions although they tend to be classified under different general headings. The medical establishment now claims to be able to treat eating disorders, substance abuse disorders, compulsive behaviors of all sorts, and even sexual perversions.

Thousands of specialized treatment facilities have sprung up to exploit the lucrative addictions market. Fifty years ago, few physicians or nurses would even consider alcoholics as sick. Few would voluntary specialize in their care. Drug dependent people were criminals and confined to prison when they proved troublesome. In the 1930s, Alcoholics Anonymous bootstrapped itself into existence by rediscovering principles of mature living and casting them into a form acceptable to some alcoholics. Health professionals have joined the party only in recent years, largely through the miracle of health insurance.

Those with medical training still do very little of the actual work of treatment themselves once life-saving interventions during early withdrawal are accomplished. They have used their power, in the United States, to garner insurance reimbursement for treatment programs of all sorts. These programs are often staffed by recovering people and by people who, although professionally trained, have personal or family reasons to be interested in addictions. Paradoxically, we seem to be saying that, in order to become an effective counselor, one should drink, take drugs or gamble for many years and then suddenly "see the light." A few weekend workshops and a state issued certificate then make one an expert. If you do not care to practice the necessary addiction for most of your life, you must then possess the bad judgment to marry an alcoholic and stay married long enough to suffer the degradation and pain of an alcoholic marriage before proclaiming yourself an expert.

The theory seems to be that only one who is similarly afflicted can "understand" the addicted individual. Early identification with recovering people is important, of course, but that was the whole point of starting self-help groups, and they were not supposed to charge a fee for being there.

I often tell patients that it is not so important that I understand them; what counts is if they can understand me, understand how I manage to live an abstinent, honest and responsible life. Wanting to get high is easy to understand, but being normal is far more difficult for the patient to grasp. I am not going to learn their language, values, or habits. They are going to have to learn mine if things are to be better for them.

For the most part, recovering people serve as *Judas goats* in the medical-economic establishment, accepting low pay, long hours, and minimal recognition while expanding the medical power base. What medical training contributes to the actual remediation of addictive disorders has yet to be shown. Most needed medical and psychological services could be obtained through contracting outside help at much lower cost than by allowing clinicians to run the show. For that matter, aside from offering cheap and willing labor, the value of the recovering counselor is still unproven.

THE DICK AND JANE THEORY OF ADDICTION

In my opinion, the reasons why the medical model is so troublesome are simple: Addictions are not primarily medical problems. They fit poorly into the disease model of specific disease, specific cause and specific cure. They do not have medical solutions. Medical practitioners have little interest in or training for helping people change values, habits and attitudes. In particular, except for a few psychiatrists, medical people have great difficulty accepting and being interested in non-substance addictions.

In the United States, the "alcoholism treatment establishment" encourages a very simplistic and uncritical addictions model that seems to place the blame for addictions upon the substances or activities that become the focus of treatment. Blaming alcohol or gambling for an addiction has important negative consequences. It leads to a prohibitionist mentality and encourages us to expect distilling companies and casinos to give guilt money for research and treatment. Worse, it allows the patient to focus on treatment and discharge plans that deal with everything except personal change. The least a treatment program should do is to provide the patient with a "laundry list" for personal change. However, the medical model plays into the patient's external locus of control and pathological wish to be fixed without personal effort and sacrifice.

I call this simple medical addictions model the *Dick and Jane Theory* of addiction. Dick and Jane are, or were, mythical siblings from middle class America of pre- and post-World War II days. Although chronically vacuous, Dick and Jane were active children with normal parents, a family car and a dog named Spot. They offended no one unless, of course, you were a minority group member who yearned to see a familiar face in your reading instruction book. The whole thing was a bit male dominant in orientation as well. Dick and Jane stories replaced the long familiar *McGuffey's Readers*, the many revisions of which were used for primary reading instruction in the United States from some time after our Civil War until well into the 20th Century. The old *McGuffey's Readers* inculcated, in addition to reading skills, all kinds of rules for everything from pronunciation to social conduct, and they were full of tales of heroic deeds, moral principles and noble scenes. They offended many people as well, and made no bones about the supposed superiority of certain races and classes over others. These reading manuals had their problems, but they had some virtues worth remembering.

The *Dick and Jane Theory* of addictions goes like this:

> Dick and Jane were wholesome young people who were skipping happily down the golden, sunlit path of life until one day they came to a gambling hall. They were usually well fed, loved and, above all else, they were normal, average and predictable. On this particular day, however, they were a bit hungry, angry, lonely and tired; skipping all the time, with all that sun, is certainly no bed of roses. Besides, they were always under the critical eyes of young readers everywhere.
>
> Well, they entered the gambling hall; they just had to because — you name it — the restaurant across the street was too expensive, they were lured in, they made a mistake, whatever. Dick began to play POOL with some local rowdies — shades of River City — and soon he was drinking BEER. Having no skill for playing pool, Jane put a coin in a slot machine and she was soon heavily involved in gambling. They stayed on there in that grimy little town for the next twenty-six years during which time Dick fell ever further into the pit of alcoholism. He began to beat Jane; he sold Spot for drinking money; he staggered through several bad marriages beating his children and holding no steady work. Jane passed the time selling her body and writing bad checks for gambling money.
>
> Right thinking saviors in white coats eventually intervened, and Dick and Jane went off to treatment and to self-help groups. Although now a bit old for such things, Dick and Jane were last seen skipping hand-in-hand off into the distance laughing, singing, and saying the Serenity Prayer.

Somehow little readers all over the world are supposed to convince themselves that this behavior is normal, average and predictable. So, if you believe all that, I have a bridge to sell you.

Bill W. and Dr. Bob did not, I think, have any kind of Dick and Jane theory in their minds as they formulated their plans for recovery. They recognized full well that alcoholism was a symptom of more pervasive life problems. The *Twelve Steps* and *Twelve Traditions* of Alcoholics Anonymous, now widely adopted for all sorts of addictive behavior, would never have predicted or called for the intrusions of the medical-economic establishment into what is properly a personal choice regarding how one will live a life. Rather, one of their first discoveries was: "The more we do for them, the worse they get. The more they can do for themselves, the better they get."

People in treatment for addictions, with proper support, should do all they can for themselves. They are quite capable, when organized around a constitution, to screen and admit new patients, pay the rent, deal with rule infractions, hire needed professional services, do the laundry, buy and cook the food, decide upon discharge, and so forth. Not to allow real responsibility early in treatment is to prevent recovery.

ADDICTIVE RESPONSE SYNDROME

One can easily envision a single, underlying disorder or problem that I prefer to call Addictive Response Syndrome (*ARS*). (It may be a sign of my own intellectual dependence that I use the medical word *syndrome*, but I hope that grown-ups can share words between specialties without getting into fights.) A syndrome is a pattern of emerging events or signs recognizable as a pattern in an individual. The pattern repeats itself with little variation in different lives.

If addiction is a syndrome, so is reading, writing and calculating. The word syndrome suggests ill effects, however. Reading and writing can be called habits because they are deemed to be desirable behaviors. Although the same developmental laws may account for good and bad habits, one must medicalize poor behavior and call it a syndrome. A person is supposed to be in control of good habits, but is supposed to a victim of bad ones. Nevertheless, outside assistance in the form of teachers and role models is necessary for both the formation and modification of most behaviors, good or bad. Sad to say, teachers of good habits get paid less than treaters of syndromes.

I hold that ARS always arises from some personal vulnerability acquired before the development of any specific addiction. Unless this developmental vulnerability is addressed during periods of sobriety or abstinence, it will not disappear. Stopping addictive behavior without changing personality structure only invites relapse, and it seems to me that the major cause of relapse to a primary addiction is almost always the practice of some substitute addiction.

Risk factors such as genetic predispositions, traumatic life events, stressful transitions, death of a loved one, and serious illness promote addictive behavior when, and only when, a given risk factor is dysphorogenic, i.e., it causes or promotes the development in the individual a chronic, pervasive and unrecognized state of negative affectivity. Thus, a risk factor becomes a vulnerability for addictive behavior when, and only when, because of the risk factor, the individual develops a dysphoric mood-mentation state.

What makes a thing or event dysphorogenic? Probably the level of one's skill in "processing" or psychologically managing bad and good fortune is a major factor.

Amazingly, good fortune can cause as much unhappiness as bad. In the right hands, sudden stardom, great financial success, achievement of power, or assignment of responsibility — any such unusual achievement can lead to addiction, just as surely as can trauma, loss, pain and deprivation. Maturity is everything. The *Twelve Steps* of A.A. are nothing if they are not a prescription for psychological maturity and growth.

Somewhere in some *McGuffey's Reader* it must say that attitude is everything, or words to that effect. How often it is we say and hear: "It's not as bad as you think. Snap out of it and get on with life. Roll with the punches. Tame your ego. Go with the flow. Take a slip lightly. Help others and you help yourself. Seek not so much to be understood as to understand." There is no shortage of prescriptive morality; just a shortage of people who will write the prescriptions and insist that the changes take place.

The dysphoric state is beyond personal modification, however, by the time it has become chronic. It is then, given this state of chronic "bad mood," that the individual is most subject to the mood/mind altering effects of addictive practice, be it a substance or an activity. Given the availability of a preferred addictive activity, and given some social sanction for its use, an addiction will inevitably form in any individual with this chronic dysphoric state.

Negative affectivity is a idea introduced into the literature some years ago, and it has since been called "bad mood" disorder. So varied are the forms and dimensions of negative affectivity that the concept will probably remain for now just a theoretical formulation. Many dimensions characterize it and vary in intensity from individual to individual. Some are predominately angry, some anxious, some self-depreciating, some paranoid, and so forth. Personalities of addicted people vary widely. The dysphoria is common to all.

Thus, it seems to me, there is but one addictive disorder with many manifestations in overconsumption or overuse. This disorder — ARS — is primarily a developmental disorder, one that requires a holistic analysis and comprehensive lifestyle modification. Substances and addictive activities have little to do with the causes of ARS, and nothing at all to do with their remediation.

REAL TREATMENT OPTIONS

What can we do for, to, or about those who destroy their lives though addictive behavior? The following are my suggestions.

From the start, the "treater" should not be obsessed with addictive substances or activities, either professionally or personally. There are few antidotes that are very useful in withdrawal, and we should be in no haste to relieve painful withdrawal symptoms with medical interventions. A few days of librium therapy ease the pain of alcohol withdrawal, but, short of life-saving interventions, pain can be a friendly teacher. Pain and the discomfort of withdrawal may not be as fatal as the addiction.

Why should we be in such haste to remove so valuable a teacher? It is during withdrawal that the alcoholic may be most open to hearing wise messages. The blessed sleep of librium makes learning difficult.

For many, withdrawal from heroin is no more painful than a bad case of influenza. A child makes the pain go away by causing pain for the parent who, in order to get a little sleep, gives the wailing baby whatever it wants. Withdrawal is better when monitored medically, but we should not forget that pain intolerance is a primary symptom of ARS. The wise treater does not easily remove the pain because teaching tolerance for pain and frustration is the heart of the matter. Recovering people can be very helpful at this critical time in caring for addiction patients and in carrying the message to them.

We should not call our programs "Alcohol" or "Drug" or "Gambling" programs, for these titles put the emphasis back on "Demon Rum" instead of on the inadequacy of the patient's personality. Unsalable as the program titles would be, we should be offering "Immature People" programs.

Lectures on the "Physical Aspects of Alcoholism" further illustrate the treater's obsession with illusory causes. Such lectures are generally properly ignored by sleeping patients since fear is a poor therapy for addictions.

I do not accept the patients' common language for addiction, words or phrases such as "crack," "long shot," "half in the bag," "slamming" or "doing dope." I insist that patients use my language to explain to me what they have been doing. The drug patient, after all, usually knows much more than I care to know about pharmacology. I know and care very little about addictive practice (except in the area of food, which has been a lifelong obsession) and I usually begin therapy by insisting that it take place in my territory, in the world of normal speech, thought and action.

The "therapist" can first and always be a role model, and use whatever positive transference there may be to induce positive change. The therapist must strive, in all aspects of living, to be sober, honest and responsible. As the innocent child can accurately read the real motives of the parents in spite of all parental denial, so the addictions patient is keenly sensitive to any personal weaknesses of the therapist. The patient may not mention our shortcomings and is more likely to join us in deception than to oppose us. The child wants to see parental figures as perfect, wise and eternal. This should not surprise us. If we are mature, we can understand that and, starting there, help the patient toward more realistic expectations.

I try to remain open and to encourage patients to give me feedback if they care to do so. If I want them to become open to constructive criticism, I must model that behavior myself. The therapist who accepts and glories in the status of a "guru" commits a serious error.

In addition to being "good parent" role models, we can and must hold a well thought out value system that works in the adult world. We must be willing to be judgmental about what is right to do and what is wrong to do, and we should be willing to teach this ethic to our patients. Again, the *Twelve Steps* and *Twelve Traditions* of Alcoholics Anonymous would be a good place to start if the therapist needs guidance. These steps and traditions are but rediscoveries of basic and primitive realizations about the nature and meaning of life. They suggest, as do most "enlightening" religions, that we seek out and practice certain fundamental tools for living: humility, reflection, simplicity, honesty, responsibility, sensitivity, service, self-denial, self-acceptance, perseverance, reverence for life, tolerance and love. In case you were in doubt, that is what I think normal should be.

I have some books from the original *McGuffey's Reader* series that I bought some years ago at an Ohio farm auction for a few dollars. I will not lend them to anyone, but I will tell you that they have all been reprinted. The reprints sell as curiosities, for much more money than the originals went for, to a generation that cut its intellectual teeth on dear old Dick and Jane. What, do you suspect, are the buyers of these reprints looking for?

Evidence Supporting a General Theory of Addiction©

Durand F. Jacobs

Extensive comparable information was collected and analyzed about populations of compulsive/pathological gamblers, alcoholics, and compulsive overeaters who are characterized by excessive behaviors over which they have shown lapses of control (Jacobs, Marston and Singer, 1985). The matrix design also included data from adolescents and normal adults who had responded to the same basic Health Survey instrument (Jacobs, 1984). To the best of this author's knowledge, this approach is the first in which information regarding similar indices has been collected and systematically compared across several different types of addicts as well as normative samples.

This strategy is designed to produce further refinements in theory development and testing. The ultimate goal is to construct descriptive models that will provide a better understanding of the addictive process, as well as facilitate early identification and prompt intervention for persons at high risk for developing addictive patterns of behavior.

As predicted by Jacobs' general theory, a common dissociative-like state has been found to prevail among compulsive gamblers, alcoholics and compulsive overeaters when they were indulging in their respective addictive behaviors. These dissociative-like reactions significantly differentiated them from normative samples of youth and adults who also had indulged in the same activities and substances. The dissociative state has been termed "an altered state of identity" (Jacobs, 1982).

SYNOPSIS OF THE GENERAL THEORY OF ADDICTIONS

The General Theory of Addictions emphasizes the presence of two sets of interacting *predisposing* factors that are held to determine whether an individual is at risk of maintaining an addictive pattern of behavior. The first of these two sets of predisposing factors is a *unipolar physiological resting state* that is chronically and excessively either suppressed or excited. The lifelong persistent state of hypo or hyperarousal is believed to predispose the individual to respond differentially to a rather narrow window of stress reducing, but potentially addictive, substances and/or activities (Elia, 1992).

The literature has referred to a minority of persons at either extreme of the normally distributed range of resting arousal levels as "reducer" or "augmenter/enhancer" types (Petrie, 1967, 1978; Ogborne, 1974). Either of these extreme arousal states is held to be aversive (Petrie, 1978). Consequently one would expect that those at either pole would attempt to seek and engage in activities that would make them feel better.

Not all reducers and enhancers are prone to acquiring an addiction according to the general theory. The persistence of what is subjectively perceived as an *aversive physiological arousal state* is only one of the two necessary predisposing conditions for developing an addiction.

The second precondition that theoretically must exist before the stage is fully set for acquiring an addictive pattern of behavior is a childhood and adolescence marked by deep feelings of inadequacy, inferiority, shame, guilt, and low self-esteem, plus a pervasive sense of rejection by parents and significant others. Such feelings would be expected to stimulate behaviors and activities that would produce relief from this psychological distress.

The general theory predicts that persons with a chronically abnormal arousal state who also tend to respond to feelings of inferiority and rejection by flight into denial and compensatory fantasy are at the highest risk for acquiring an addictive pattern of behavior. Such persons would be particularly vulnerable during adolescence, a developmental period when high levels of both physiologic and psychosocial stresses prevail. Given these two interacting predisposing conditions *in a conducive environment*, Jacobs' theoretical position is that whatever the potential addictive substance or activity chosen, its continued use into a frank addictive pattern of behavior will depend largely on its possessing the following three attributes:

- *It blurs reality testing.* Specifically one's attention is temporarily diverted from the chronic aversive arousal state. This may occur as a result of the physiologic effects of an ingested substance and/or by the manner in which an activity (such as gambling) so completely concentrates one's attention on a series of specific *here and now* events that coexisting aversive aspects of one's physical, mental and/or social life situation are "blurred out."
- *It lowers self criticism and self consciousness.* This is accomplished through an internal cognitive shift that deflects preoccupation from one's self-perceived inadequacies. Often this is supported and reinforced by the special circumstances that prevail where the addictive pattern of behavior is ordinarily pursued — such as with peers in a bar, gambling casino, race track, restaurant, or party. Each of these environs tends to accord acceptance, even encouragement, to behaviors that would be frowned upon or rejected in other company or in other settings.
- *It permits complementary daydreams about oneself.* These wish-fulfilling fantasies which surface as a natural aftermath of the first two attributes serve to facilitate the assuming of an altered identity

> wherein, while indulging in the chosen potentially addictive behavior, one perceives his or her self-image as greatly enhanced and his or her related social interactions and performances as highly successful.

Whether the addictive pattern of behavior is practiced in solitary of social settings, as the number and intensity of these three attributes increase, so does the likelihood that the person will actually "cross over" into a frank dissociative-like state. The relative frequency, intensity and extent of measures suggested to tap this dissociative-like state may well constitute key pathognomic "hard signs" that will differentiate potential and actual addicts from those who indulge in an abusive manner. Jacobs has proposed that, theoretically, it is the intent to achieve and act out an *altered state of identity* that distinguishes the true addict from the superficially similar excesses of the abuser.

It is important to note that, while the general theory proposes a marked transformation in the addict's self-image and behavior when indulging, this does not necessarily mean there is a total dissociation from his former customary self. Even while fully engrossed in the altered identity, like an accomplished actor in a play, the addict is not totally disengaged from his former self. Jacobs proposes that a demonstrable conscious channel of awareness remains open between the customary self and the altered self through the entire transition into, during, and after the period of addictive experiences. Consciousness of one's usual and customary self state is not fully relinquished when one becomes involved in the addictive self state and vice versa. (See "A Neodissociation Interpretation of Divided Consciousness," in Hilgard, 1986).

The general theory postulates that, once established, a given individual's addictive pattern of behavior represents that person's deliberately chosen means for entering and maintaining a dissociative-like state. The general theory recognizes that, as with dissociative states in general, an element of functional amnesia or memory blackouts is to be expected. Typically, however, such memory losses also are expected to be incomplete and even then to be volitionally reversible to a large extent under proper therapeutic conditions.

METHOD AND RESULTS

A questionnaire was constructed to initiate a program of research designed to test selected aspects of the General Theory of Addictions (Jacobs, 1980). Over a four year period, data were collected anonymously from known groups

TABLE 1

DISSOCIATIVE-LIKE REACTIONS EXPERIENCED BY ADDICTS AND NORMALS WHEN INDULGING IN GAMBLING, DRINKING AND OVEREATING									
*Dissociative-like reactions *reported "occasionally" to "all the time":*	*When Gambling*			*When drinking*			*When overeating*		
	% Gamblers N=121	% Adults N=168	% Adolescents N=843	% Alcoholics N=203	% Adults N=168	% Adolescents N=843	% Overeaters N=83	% Adults N=168	% Adolescents N=843
Trance	79	5	2	62	17	29	41	5	7
Different person	79	21	5	73	36	39	44	21	13
Outside self	50	8	2	34	12	23	30	7	10
Blackout	38	4	1	73	15	21	14	4	2
Median dissociative score:	64	6	2	67	16	26	35	6	8
*Reactions reported "rarely" are not included above									

of compulsive gamblers, alcoholics and compulsive overeaters and later compared with responses from normative samples of adolescents and adults. In all, more than 400 addicts and more than 1,000 normals were surveyed. This report is limited to discussing the responses of each of these groups to the four "dissociative items." A summary of results is presented in Table 1.

As predicted, moderate to high frequencies of each type of dissociative-like experience were reported by each addict group. Compulsive gamblers and alcoholics consistently reported a higher incidence of these reactions than did compulsive overeaters ($p>.01$). Each of the three addict groups reported significantly more ($p>.001$) dissociative-like reactions on each indicator than did normative groups. Normative groups reported dissociative-like reactions most often when drinking, next when overeating, and least when gambling. High school students reported significantly more dissociative reactions when drinking than did adults ($p>.01$). Adults reported significantly more dissociative-like reactions than high school students when gambling ($p>.01$).

These findings provide impressive support to the general theory's prediction that, when indulging, persons known to be addicted to different substances or activities will tend to share a common set of dissociative experiences that by virtue of the relative frequency of their combined occurrence will clearly differentiate them from non-addicts.

A more recent study by Kuley and Jacobs (1988) comparing groups identified as "social" and "problem" gamblers replicates and extends the earlier findings noted above which had indicated an extremely high prevalence of dissociative-like reactions while gambling among known compulsive gamblers. Kuley and Jacobs found that "problem" gamblers reported a significantly greater number of dissociative-like experiences than "social" gamblers on each of the four "dissociative" questions ($p<.01$). Fifty-four percent of problem gamblers reported they felt "like a different person" occasionally to all the time when gambling in contrast to ten percent of the social gamblers. Forty-three percent of the problem gamblers reported that "they felt like they were in a trance" occasionally to all the time during a period of gambling as compared to only three percent of the social gamblers. Thirty-three percent of the problem gamblers "felt outside themselves watching themselves as in a dream" occasionally to all the time when gambling in contrast to only four percent of the social gamblers. Finally, fifty percent of the problem gamblers reported that they "experienced memory blackouts" occasionally to all the time following an episode of gambling, whereas only three percent of the social gamblers reported this experience.

Kuley and Jacobs also noted highly significant correlations ($p<.001$) between high scores on each of the four dissociative items and high scores on the Gambler's Anonymous Twenty Questions. This represents the first documented evidence that subjects who admitted to more real life problems as a result of their gambling behavior on the Twenty Questions also tended to report a high frequency of dissociative like experiences.

Moreover, the average number of days per week subjects reported gambling correlated highly with the frequency of dissociative-like experiences. Correlations between extent of gambling and each of the dissociative-like experiences ranged from .46 to .60 ($p<.001$). The highly significant correlations between dissociative-like reactions with an independent listing of gambling related problems, and self-reports of the extent of real life gambling behavior, lend impressive support to the theory's contention that problem gamblers can be confidently discriminated from social gamblers by the nature of their answers to the four rather simple, nonincriminating "dissociative" questions describing what happens to them when they gamble.

CONCLUSIONS

One may confidently conclude from the studies reported here that addicts of markedly disparate types share a common dissociative-like experience when indulging that clearly sets them apart from normal groups of adolescents and adults who also indulge in the same types of substances or activities. The findings that addicts (particularly compulsive/pathological gamblers) reported a significantly higher frequency for experiencing dissociative-like reactions when indulging than did normals may have clinical as well as forensic utility for differentiating addicts from other excessive indulgers or abusers who present themselves or who are referred by families, employers, or the courts to health professionals for evaluation and treatment.

Further research undoubtedly will explore the incidence and prevalence of dissociative-like reactions among still other types of addicts. Meanwhile, the type and extent of dissociative-like experiences associated with a given form of indulgence may serve as a clinical "hard sign" for early identification of high risk adolescents and adults *before* they become enmeshed in addictive patterns of behavior. The ultimate goal of the author's entire program of research is to augment and encourage systemization of the knowledge base about addictions, so that one day timely interventions can be designed to prevent them.

REFERENCES

Elia, C.J. (1992). *Stimulus reduction and boredom in pathological gamblers.* Doctoral dissertation, California School of Professional Psychology, San Diego, California.

Hilgard, E.R. (1977, 1986). *Divided consciousness: Multiple controls in human thought and action.* New York: Wiley and Sons.

Jacobs, D.F. and Wright, E.T. (1980). *A program of research on the causes and treatment of addictive behaviors: Using the compulsive gambler as the prototype subject.* Loma Linda, CA: Veterans Administration Hospital. Unpublished.

Jacobs, D.F. (1982). The addictive personality syndrome (APS): A new theoretical model for understanding and treating addictions. In W.R. Eadington (ed.), *The Gambling Papers: Proceedings of the Fifth National Conference on Gambling and Risk Taking.* Reno: University of Nevada.

Jacobs, D.F. (1984). Study of traits leading to compulsive gambling. In *Sharing Recovery Through Gamblers Anonymous.* Los Angeles, CA: Gamblers Anonymous Publishing, Inc.

Jacobs, D.F., Marston, A.R. and Singer, R.D. (1985). Testing a general theory of addictions: Similarities and differences among alcoholics, pathological gamblers and compulsive overeaters. In J.J. Sanchez-Soza (ed.), *Health and Clinical Psychology.* Amsterdam, The Netherlands: Elsevier Science Publishers B.V.

Jacobs, D.F. (1986). *Early identification and prevention of health-threatening behaviors in adolescents.* Paper presented at the Twenty-First International Congress of Applied Psychology, Jerusalem, Israel.

Jacobs, D.F. (1987). A general theory of addictions: Application to treatment and rehabilitation planning for pathological gamblers. In T. Galski (ed.), *Handbook of Pathological Gambling,* 169-194. Springfield, IL: Charles C. Thomas.

Jacobs, D.F. (1989). A general theory of addictions: Rationale for and evidence supporting a new approach for understanding and treating addictive behaviors. In H.J. Shaffer et al. (eds.), *Compulsive Gambling: Theory, Research and Practice.* Lexington, MA: Lexington Books.

Kuley, N.B. and Jacobs, D.F. (1988). The relationship between dissociative-like experiences and sensation seeking among social and problem gamblers. *Journal of Gambling Behavior*, 4:3, 197-207.

Ogborne, A. (1974). Two types of heroin reactions. *British Journal of Addictions*, 39, 237-242.

Petrie, A. (1967, 1978). *Individuality in pain and suffering.* Chicago, IL: University of Chicago Press.

The Dynamics of Shame-based Addiction

James D. Gray

The intent of this analysis is to share the author's interpretation of shame-based addiction. This approach has provided significant insight into addictive behavior and is based upon the works of John Bradshaw, John and Linda Friel, and Terry Kellogg, to mention a few.

It is important to note that this approach is very much incorporated into the St. Luke's Gordon Recovery Center's (SLGRC) 12-step model of treating chemical dependency, compulsive gambling, and eating disorders. Shame-based addiction also complements SLGRC's understanding of primary disease and enhances our understanding to recovery. Of significance is a new perspective that this model has provided into understanding the dynamics of prevention in regards to substance abuse and high risk behavior among youth. This model has enhanced our ability to structure more effective and comprehensive strategies in approaching primary and secondary prevention. That topic in itself would constitute another complete analysis. Variations of this model are used as an educational tool with patients, with family members, and in professional in-services.

ADDICTION

In addressing the issue of addiction, a good place to start is with a definition of addiction.

> A pathological relationship with any mood-altering substance or activity that leads to life-damaging consequences (Bradshaw, 1988).

This is a functional definition as it refers to two types of addictions: substances and activities. Following is a brief list of both types of agents.

Substance	Activity
Alcohol	Gambling
Drugs	Sex
Nicotine	Work
Sugar	Religion

With the exception of nicotine and illicit drugs, the majority of agents, in moderation, are not harmful. Therefore, the agent is not the issue; rather it is the relationship of the individual with the agent (Friel and Friel, 1988).

It can be said that with the majority of addictions, there are shared or common elements. Following is a list and brief description of several common elements:

Pain Killers	Preoccupation
Alters Mood	Progressive
Trust/Control	Medical
Cover-up	Family

Each of these is briefly discussed below.

A. Pain Killers

One concept that is fairly easy to understand but often misunderstood by many is that addictions perform a function — they kill pain, either directly through the use of the substance, or through the distraction of the activity.

B. Alters Mood

The agents can alter mood by creating a sense of euphoria or by distraction from pain. The point to be made is that an attempt will be made to mood alter from pain by use of an agent that works.

C. Cover-Ups

Addictions are secrets. Denial and delusion are at the center of this element. Not only is this a dynamic for the addict but also for the family. Therefore, you will see the entire family pretending there is no problem; disguises will abound to protect the secret.

D. Preoccupation

The addict will have a mental obsession with the agent when the addict is not acting out. Another dimension to this element is inattentiveness. When one is preoccupied, one is inattentive to one's own needs as well as inattentive to the needs of others.

E. Progressive

Similar to cancer, if untreated, the addiction becomes progressively worse. Like cancer, addictions have stages, and the type of treatment varies depending upon time of diagnosis and stage of the disease.

F. Medical

There are numerous medical consequences from addictions. Mood altering individuals are exposed to high risk behavior. Preoccupied persons are prone to accidents. Substances can take a heavy toll on the body resulting in serious physical disorders and death. This element also includes activity addictions, as excessively high levels of activity create a highly stressful environment in which to survive.

G. Family

It is impossible to talk about addictions without talking about them being a family disease. I believe an easy way to help people understand that any addiction is a family disease is to relate the following "elephant story."

THE ELEPHANT STORY

About four years ago, I was working with a group of children, aged from 7 to 12 years, who came from alcoholic homes. We had an book for children of alcoholics, titled *An Elephant in the Living Room*, by Jill Hastings and Marion Typpo.

Based on this book, we asked the children to imagine their living room at home. In the middle of this room is the great big elephant. The elephant is Dad, who is an alcoholic. What we related to the children is that many times when they come home, they have found out that the elephant is predictably unpredictable. Sometimes when they come home, he is happy-go-lucky, but sometimes he is pretty nasty. Not knowing which way he is going to act, the children have a tendency to skirt around the elephant and to stay out of his way. They do not want to get stepped on by the elephant nor do they want to get hit by his trunk.

The children really do not know how they got the elephant, but they soon find out that the elephant is a secret. One day the child comes home and says, "Mom, I told my best friend that we have this great big elephant in our living room." Mom hits him against the head and says, "We don't talk about the elephant to anybody; it's a secret" (Hastings and Typpo, 1984).

It is important to understand that when children are living with an elephant it is a very frightening, scary, unpredictable environment in which to live. Our therapy staff who work with children who have been raised with elephants relate that there are two layers of trauma that such children experience. They get beat up, they get kicked down the stairs, they get physically or sexually abused. That's one form of trauma — abuse. They also experience another level of trauma — the inability to express the trauma that they have experienced. One is the physical abuse to which they have been exposed or have experienced; the other is the inability to share what is happening or has happened to them.

What we have learned from the story and the children is that the dynamics we see in an alcoholic family are very similar to the dynamics we see in a workaholic family, a compulsive gambling family, or a family in which there is an eating disorder. We are recognizing more commonalities than differences among addictions.

ADDICTIONS ALTER MOODS

It is necessary at this point to expand briefly on one previously discussed element shared in addictions. The dynamic of "mood altering." Mood altering is normal and can occur intentionally or unintentionally. It can be graphically demonstrated by the use of Johnson's Feel Chart (Johnson, 1976). The range of human emotions can be illustrated as follows:

An individual can experience emotional pain due to the death of a loved one or the loss of a job. The same individual can experience emotional euphoria due to a job promotion, the birth of a child, or due to recreation. There is a flow of feelings in both directions due to life events and a return to normal. Persons who have experienced healthy child development would not only experience and share their feelings, but would also have a higher likelihood to possess positive belief systems about themselves. Such persons would also be less likely to act in ways that are destructive to themselves or to others. This "healthy mood altering" can be illustrated graphically as follows:

Cognitive — "I'm valued; I can make a mistake; I'm not God."

Affective —

Behavior — "I act in ways that are healthy and not self-destructive."

John Bradshaw would refer to this type of individual as a "Healthy Shame Person" (Bradshaw, 1988).

Not all individuals mood-alter in the same way. Another way in which this can be illustrated is as follows:

The point to be made is that some individuals may mood-alter from a point of pain to normal/euphoria and move back to pain. This individual represents a high likelihood of being raised in a family system where addiction (elephants) were present — raised in an environment that was dysfunctional, unhealthy, and not conducive to normal, healthy human development. This individual will have a strong motivation to want to remove oneself from the pain. This individual is high risk for addictions. For this person, the pain is a state of being rather than a feeling. The individual normally will have a negative belief system and will act out in self-destructive ways to mood-alter out of pain through the use of addictive behavior. This process of "toxic mood altering" can be illustrated as follows:

Cognitive — "I'm worthless; I'm a mistake; Why was I born?"

Affective —

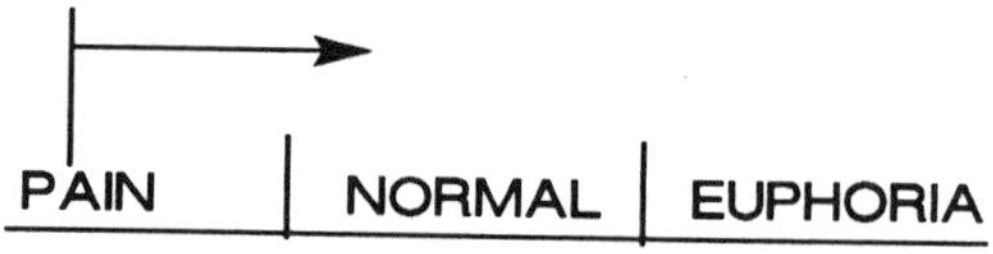

Behavior — "I act in ways that help kill my pain, even if it works only temporarily; when my pain returns, I will act out again."

John Bradshaw would refer to this type of individual as a "Toxic Shame Person." Toxic shame is primarily internalized *pain*; this can occur by ages five to seven for children. It develops as a result of being exposed to a family system living out an addiction — living with elephants. Therefore, toxic shame develops due to common elements in addictions being acted out. This state of toxic shame sets up an environment producing high risk, destructive, mood altering behavior, either through substances or activities (Bradshaw, 1988).

ADDICTIONS THROUGH THE EYES OF A CHILD

One caution must be made when it comes to understanding the nature of addictions. Many times, as adults, the dynamics of addiction are not understood as we tend to look at addictions through the eyes of an adult. It is useful to attempt to see these dynamics in action by looking at addiction through the "eyes of a child."

Three common elements of addictions are discussed in more detail and will be shared as seen through the "eyes of a child." What will be seen in the common elements of addictions is the abuse of the child — and the abuse occurs repeatedly and over a prolonged period of time. The three commonalities to be discussed are: preoccupation, cover-ups and the elephant story.

Graphically, a journey from birth into toxic shame and addictions can be represented as follows:

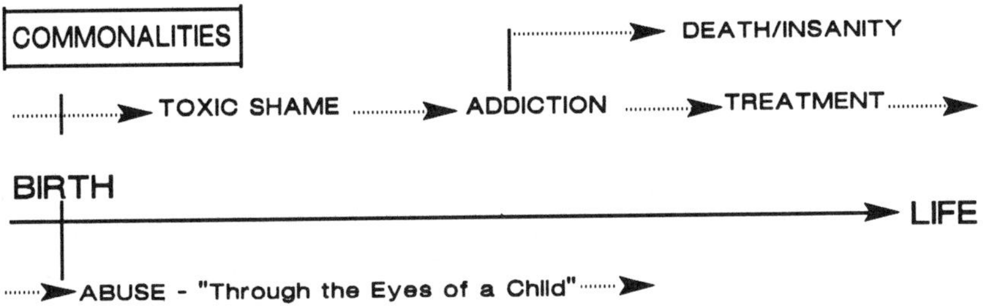

A. Preoccupation/ Inattentiveness

The first commonality to be discussed is preoccupation and inattentiveness. Consider the following scenario. Dad is preoccupied with alcohol; Mom is preoccupied with Dad because he drinks too much. Both are inattentive to the needs of the children. They may or may not be physically there but, emotionally, they are unavailable.

Consider two types of elephants — a workaholic and an alcoholic elephant. The alcoholic elephant comes home after work and goes out and gets drunk five nights a week. The workaholic elephant comes home after work, has supper, and goes back to work five nights a week. Through the eyes of a child, Dad is never there. The child will say:

> "Dad has never been to school activities ... he's never been to any basketball games ... I must not be worth his time, because if I were really worth his time, he would be there."

The child will not walk up to Dad and say he misses Dad or say he wishes Dad were around to spend more time with him. The child will not tell Dad to knock off the alcohol or the work. What children will do is to see the issue in terms of themselves and internalize it as:

> "There must be something wrong with me. If I were really special and he really loved me, he would spend more time with me."

One thing we have observed of children from alcoholic homes versus children from workaholic homes is that many times the children from workaholic homes have more guilt. What often occurs is that the child will say to Mom, "I really miss Dad; and I wish he were here." Mom responds by saying, "Hey, you've got the nicest car in town; we have the nicest clothes." What Mom has just done is stolen the child's feelings. What the child said is that he misses his Dad and wishes Dad were there. Mom added guilt to the child's need to have his father. However, the key point is that the child will define the issue in terms of himself.

When we think about preoccupation and inattentiveness, we need to realize that these are of a much larger scope. When we are inattentive to the needs of the child, we abandon their right not to be sexually, physically, emotionally, and psychologically abused. We also abandon their right to be educated, because education is a learning process between one another — between a parent and a child. When a parent is preoccupied and inattentive to the needs of a child, the child will tell himself or herself, "I must not be worth their time and I must be worthless."

B. Cover-ups

An easy way to understand cover-ups is to understand that addictions are secrets. It is a secret that not only the addict tries to cover up, but the family as well. Cover-ups are developed to protect the secret — the elephant — in the living room. Denial and delusion are the cores to this commonality. Family members, including the elephant, pretend — cover up — that a secret is being acted out. Therefore, you will see many disguises by the family members to protect themselves and other family members.

One element that evolves from cover-ups is perfectionism. In other words, the family attempts to look good, at all costs, to the community in order to disguise how alcoholic or addicted the environment is at home. Also, individuals are valued or not valued based on their ability to act in a way that promotes "looking good."

In an environment where perfectionism is the family virtue, there is extreme criticism to ensure that the cover-ups are done correctly, even to some degree at an unconscious level. Perfectionism also teaches that one must always be right, one cannot make mistakes, and therefore, one must be in control of all external events. One must not only plan ahead, but must guarantee the outcome. Being in control teaches one to be a manipulator, again to ensure the outcomes. Changing your mind is not taught, as this would indicate that you might have been wrong in the first place. Mistakes are not tolerated. Perfectionism teaches "enough is never enough."

In this environment, children soon realize that there is no way they can be perfect. "Since I can't be perfect, there are a couple of things I can do. I can pretend to be perfect, or I can lie."

It is interesting to note that a child can have other extreme behavioral reactions to perfectionism. The child will attempt to become the perfect child, the perfect student, the perfect son or daughter; or the child will say that it is impossible to be perfect, so why try at all.

What we see is the traditional "hero" or "scapegoat" developing, both out of the same dynamic. Both develop out of fear and anger. The scapegoat "knows" that he or she has no value. The hero "knows" that if he or she continues to do the right thing, they will continue to have value. Both individuals will internalize, "I'm only of value if I do the right thing."

C. The Elephant Story

Another common element that can be seen in all addictions is the denial of all feelings. That is the essence of the "elephant story." Living with the elephant is a very frightening environment. We are taught that it is a secret. We cannot share our pain; we cannot share our fear. We cannot share our apprehensions.

In my opinion, one positive emerging value in our society is a greater understanding that our feelings are very, very real. Our feelings are energy. The next time you observe somebody cry, look at the energy that comes out of them. When you see somebody angry, look at the energy that is coming out of them. We know that our feelings are very real and natural — they are energy. It is important to understand that if people are not taught that feelings are energy, often the energy will manifest itself in one of two ways: either it will appear in the form of physical ailments, or it will appear in the form of obsessive, compulsive, addictive behaviors.

Consider the following example. A child just broke their favorite toy and walks up to Mom crying. Mom responds by saying, "Shut up and grow up!" When we are talking about children living with an elephant, this absence of having somebody spend time with them to share feelings happens repeatedly over long periods of time. So what occurs is that a child's feelings are repeatedly stolen. The parent is telling them that their feelings do not exist; they do not count. Additionally, a child will internalize, "There must be something wrong with me because I feel something inside of me." There is this energy; they may not know what to call it, but it is real to them. Since part of living with an elephant is not acknowledging, displaying, or discussing feelings, the child will internalize, "There must be something wrong with me."

The type of abuse that the child is exposed to as a result of the commonalities of addiction being acted out is the dynamic of co-dependency. Toxic shame is the result of being raised in the co-dependent environment. Robert Subby describes co-dependency as:

> "An emotional, psychological, and behavioral condition that develops as a result of an individual's prolonged exposure to, and practice of, a set of oppressive rules — rules which prevent the open expression of feelings, as well as the direct discussion of personal and interpersonal problems" (Subby, 1987).

This definition is another version of the elephant story.

CYCLES OF ADDICTION

Figure A graphically presents the dynamics of addictions. The gray line represents toxic shame, the result of the commonalities of addictions being acted out. The black line represents the initial efforts by the child to cover up the shame — the internalized pain. The cover-ups can take on many forms, such as excessive use of anger, humor, perfectionism, or being withdrawn. Any attempt that works to cover up the feelings of inadequacies, of being a mistake, of worthlessness, will be pursued.

For some individuals, these initial cover-ups will work indefinitely throughout their life. For many others, the initial cover-ups may not be sufficient to cover up the pain. These individuals will discover through life's events that other types of substances or activities will relieve the pain, if only temporarily. This cover-up of pain is the addiction represented by the darker gray line.

In the recovery process, the process of "Last In, First Out" is followed. The initial concern in treatment is the active addiction, secondarily dealing with the layers of cover-ups, and eventually confronting the toxic shame and related

FIGURE A
ADDICTION MODEL

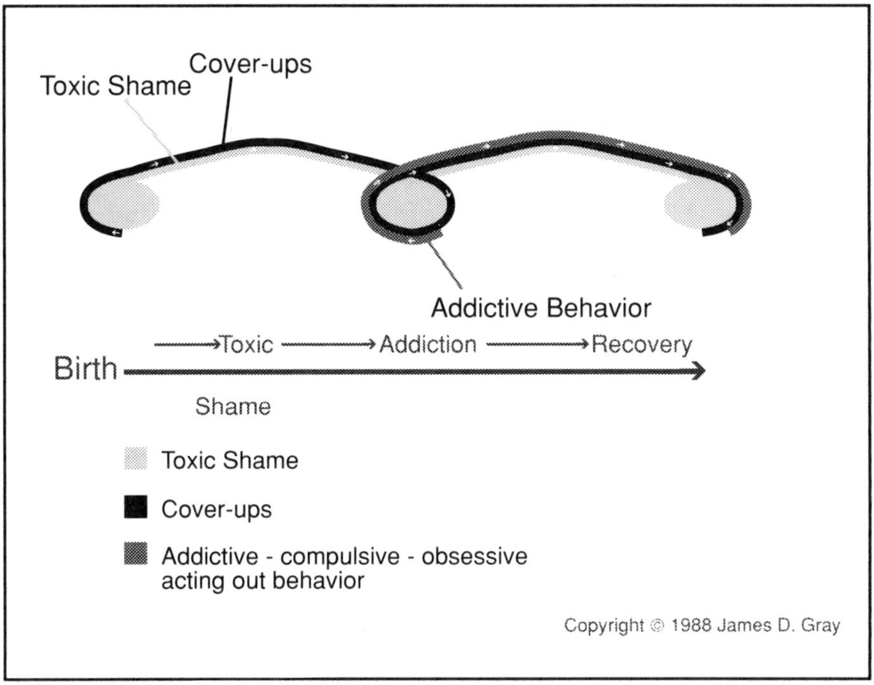

family-of-origin issues. It is important to note that many individuals are receiving treatment who have not developed some of the more traditional addictions, but due to toxic shame and layers of cover-ups, are seeking professional help.

THE TWO-HEADED DRAGON

There are two sets of similar dynamics which have been described as the two-headed dragon. This refers to the two layers of shame, guilt, and cover-ups, experienced by the addict. Individuals living out an addiction develop intense senses of shame and guilt. Behavior, many times, is not congruent with value systems. They get drunk when they did not plan to, they break promises they planned to honor, they embezzle from their employer, they mortgage the home to pay off gambling debts. Cover-ups are developed to protect one from these dynamics. Cover-ups also are developed to hide the secrets, which include the addiction itself.

It is important to understand that there is another layer of shame, guilt, and cover-ups that were developed prior to the active addiction. This additional layer of shame represents the attempts to protect — to cover up — oneself as a child from the abuse, abandonment, neglect, and the resulting shame and guilt of being raised with elephants. This is a classic example of denial represented in the original elephant story.

What we understand today is that relapses can and do occur due to this first, deeper layer, which was internalized as a child. Relapses can and do occur since this deeper layer was not dealt with in the recovery process, even though the primary addiction was addressed. It is important to note that additional, post-childhood, traumatic life events — rape, war, disfigurement, discrimination — only compound and enhance the intensity of these dynamics. As any one of these additional traumas occur, it adds another layer to the ones already present. In the recovery process, the added layers must be dealt with somewhat individually, layer by layer. The two dynamics are shown in the following diagram.

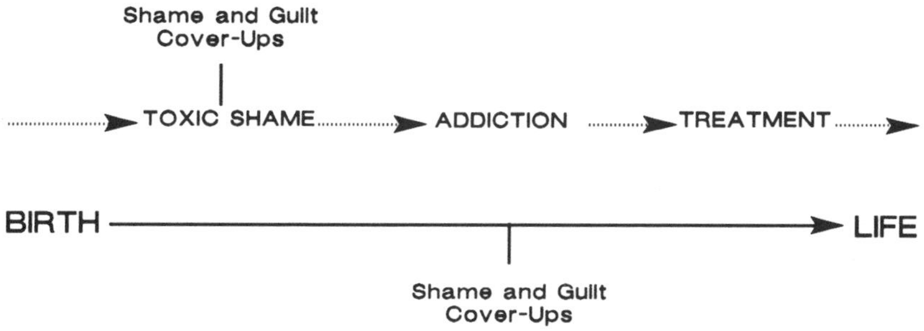

Finally, what occurs with a shame-based individual from one generation to the next is important to consider. First, the individual will make attempts to cover up the shame. Second, if necessary, the individual will mood-alter from the shame, with substances and/or activities. Third, the shame-based person will pass on the shame to whoever is the closest and most available to them. One important observation must be noted — the child as the victim will be the perpetrator as an adult.

SUMMARY

The understanding of shame-based addiction can be summarized as follows. A child being raised in an environment of repeated abuse will not be provided with the time or the nurturing to grieve the abuse and to heal. The child will move through life with on-going accumulations of unresolved trauma.

Post-traumatic stress syndrome, in combination with a primary active addiction, would be a most apt description of this child as an adult, if some form of intervention does not occur.

Another important perspective of this shame-based addiction model has been left unaddressed in this analysis — it remains for a future analysis and presentation. The additional perspective is our understanding of the cultural environment in which we each live and grow. Major elements of our cultural environment do not promote healthy human development and serve to perpetuate self-destructive behavior patterns.

Through an understanding of the dynamics of the shame-based addiction model and through holistic insights into the dynamics of our cultural environment, we can address the destructive inter-generational patterns of behavior that impact the individual, the family systems, and the greater society. Therein rests the healing, the hope, and the salvation for the future.

REFERENCES

Bradshaw, J. (1988). *Healing the Shame That Binds You.* Deerfield Beach, FL: Health Communications, Inc.

Bradshaw, J. (1988). *Bradshaw on the Family: A Revolutionary Way of Self-Discovery.* Deerfield Beach, FL: Health Communications, Inc.

Friel, J. and Friel, L. (1988). *Adult Children: The Secrets of Dysfunctional Families.* Deerfield Beach, FL: Health Communications, Inc.

Hastings, J.M. and Typpo, M.H. (1984). *An Elephant in the Living Room.* Minneapolis, MN: CompCare

Johnson, V. (1976). *I'll Quit Tomorrow.* San Francisco, CA: Harper and Rowe.

Subby, R. (1987). *Lost in the Shuffle: The Co-Dependent Reality.* Pompano Beach, FL: Health Communications, Inc.

Neuropsychological Assessment of Attention Deficit Disorder in Pathological Gamblers©

Loreen J. Rugle and Lawrence Melamed

A significant body of literature has been recently developed demonstrating the persistence of childhood Attention-Deficit Hyperactivity Disorder (ADHD) into adulthood, and measurement of neuropsychological deficits in such adults has been achieved (Ackerman, Dykman and Peters, 1977; Cohen, Weiss and Minde, 1972; Quitkin and Klein, 1969). Also, evidence has been accumulating linking childhood history of ADHD with vulnerability for development of adult addictive disorders. Until very recently the research on this connection has focused on alcoholism and ADHD. However, within the past few years, studies have also explored cocaine dependence and pathological gambling with respect to ADHD. In part, such evidence has included the similarities of neuropsychological and

© Reprinted with permission from Williams & Wilkins. Rugle, L. and Melamed, L. (1993). *Journal of Nervous and Mental Disease*, Vol. 181, 2, pp. 107-112.

behavioral dysfunction found in addicted individuals and those of ADHD subjects.

Until quite recently, in regard to substance abusers, neuropsychological deficits were generally assumed to be secondary to substance abuse (Carlin, 1986; Parsons and Leber, 1981; Tarter, Alterman, and Edwards, 1985; Tarter and Ryan, 1983). However, increasingly, the question has been raised as to whether some neuropsychological impairment has pre-dated substance abuse and is one aspect of a genetic, neurobiological substrate which increases risk for development of adult addictive behavior. Therefore, one way of investigating the involvement of ADHD as an "at risk" factor in the development of addictive behavior would be to employ pathological gamblers as a non-substance abusing, addictive group as this would eliminate the confounding effects of chronic use of a neurotoxic substance on neuropsychological functioning.

The research on pathological gambling has gone from theorizing about the psychodynamics responsible for the behavioral loss of control (Bergler, 1957; Freud, 1961) to investigating personality variables (Custer, 1978; Glen, 1979; Graham and Lowenfeld, 1986; Moravec and Munley, 1983; Roston, 1965; Taber, 1983) and, most currently, to exploring possible neurobiological factors underlying addictive gambling (Blaszczynski, Winter and McConagy, 1986; Carlton and Goldstein, 1987; Goldstein, Manowitz, Nora, Swartzburg and Carlton, 1985; Wolkowitz, Roy and Doran, 1985). As part of this evolution, theories are developing that encompass gambling, alcoholism, and substance abuse within a general theory of addictive behavior (Dell, Ruzicka and Palisi, 1981; Jacobs, 1986).

The characteristics of pathological gamblers that seem to recur conspicuously in the research are high energy level, impulsivity, low stress and frustration tolerance, poor judgment, difficulty learning from experience, labile affect, poor planning and goal setting, opposition to authority, underpinnings of inadequacy and insecurity, and shallow relationships (Custer, 1978; Glen, 1979; Graham and Lowenfeld, 1986; Taber, 1983). Along with this there is considerable evidence that pathological gamblers have significant commonalities with other addictive groups, both in terms of personality traits and co-incidence of substance abuse among gamblers (Dell et al., 1981; Glen, 1979; Ramirez, McCormick, Russo and Taber, 1983).

These characteristics, temperament patterns and potential for addictive disorders are found in individuals with childhood histories of Attention-Deficit Hyperactivity Disorder (ADHD) and adults with residual manifestations of this disorder (ADHD, residual state) (Gittleman, Mannuzza, Shenker and Bogare, 1985; Mann and Greenspan, 1976; Quitkin and Klein, 1969; Weiss, Hechtman, Perlman, Hopkins and Wener, 1979). Furthermore, at least one study has suggested neurological similarities between gamblers and ADHD subjects, presenting gamblers' EEG and childhood history data consistent with ADHD patterns (Carlton and Goldstein, 1987; Goldstein et al., 1985). To expand upon this line of research, the current study was designed to assess current attention function in pathological gamblers along with looking at childhood history of behavior symptomatic of ADHD. Also, the present study sought to control for any history of alcohol or substance abuse among gambling and control subjects.

In order to assess attention, it was felt important to consider prior research on patterns of neuropsychological impairment in other addicted groups as well as ADHD subjects.

To briefly summarize, the types of activities where both alcoholics and ADHD subjects present the most consistent impairment are on tasks that have a significant visual/spatial component and tasks that are often referred to as involving abstracting ability. However, what encompasses tasks in both these areas are the abilities described by Posner and Presti (1987) as involving higher order attentional capacity.

According to these authors, attention is not a unitary function, but is comprised of a variety of abilities on several levels that need to be assessed across sensory systems. These authors suggest that the ability to engage attention (alertness, the ability to focus on a stimuli) is the first level of attentional processing. At a higher level, selective attention involves that capacity to engage as well as then the mental flexibility to release attention from one focus to shift and re-engage on another stimulus. At even more complex levels of attention, Posner and Presti (1987) contend that the frontal cortex plays a major role in the "executive" aspects of attention which include maintaining coherent goal oriented programs, the capacity to plan and sequence and the ability to sustain inhibitory control over distracting sensory events.

As has been suggested by other authors, these executive functions are highly relevant in assessing ADHD (Douglas, 1984; Kinsbourne, 1984) and neuropsychological impairment in alcoholics (Ryan and Butters, 1983 and 1986). Some researchers have documented deficits among ADHD subjects and alcoholics on tasks that seem mainly to assess lower level attentional processing (Ackerman, Dykman, and Peters, 1977; Cohen and Douglas, 1975; Douglas, 1984; Elmasian, Neville, Woods, Schuckit and Bloom, 1982; Garfinkle, 1984; Goldstein and Shelly, 1981; Parsons and Leber, 1981). However, findings in this area of basic attention are somewhat inconsistent. What is repeatedly reported in assessment of both groups is that task demands are critically significant in determining which instruments are likely to differentiate between alcoholics or ADHD subjects and normal controls (Ackerman et al., 1977; Elmasian et al., 1982; Garfinkle, 1984).

Similarly on basic learning and memory tasks, no consistent differences have been found between ADHD subjects or alcoholics and controls. Douglas (1983) reports ADHD subjects have been found to display no significant impairment on both verbal and non-verbal memory tasks. Also, alcoholics have displayed intact abilities on such tasks as the Wechsler Memory Scale and Benton Visual Retention Test (Ryan and Butters, 1986; Tarter and Ryan, 1983).

However, what has been evidenced in both ADHD and alcoholic groups is that ADHD-normal and alcoholic-normal differences have been found on tasks that require purposeful effort and organized strategies for the efficient encoding, learning and retention of material (Brandt, Butters, Ryan and Bayog, 1983; Douglas, 1983; Ryan, 1983; Ryan and Butters, 1980; Weingartner, Rapoport, Ebert and Caine, 1980).

SUMMARY OF RESEARCH PLANS AND EXPECTATIONS

In the present study, non-substance abusing pathological gamblers were evaluated as to current attention abilities and childhood histories of behaviors symptomatic of ADHD. Non-substance abusing, non-gambling subjects were utilized as a comparison group.

In assessing attentional deficits in pathological gamblers, it was felt important to assess attention across sensory systems, verbal and non-verbal modalities and particularly across levels of attentional processing. Nine attention measures were selected to meet these criteria: Embedded Figures Test (EFT), Wisconsin Card Sorting Test (WCS), Porteus Maze Test, Trails B, Symbol Digit

Substitution Test (SDST), Knox Cube Test, Primary Memory with Distraction Test (Prime), Seashore Rhythm Test, and a multi-trial List Learning Test (List).

Given the nature of findings in ADHD subjects and substance abusers, it was expected that the strongest results would be with instruments that assessed the more executive aspects of attention involving the capacity to organize and focus on mental contents while inhibiting responses to incorrect or irrelevant sensory input and the ability to flexibly engage and disengage attention while maintaining overall cognitive set and respond to feedback. It was also anticipated that the amount of effort (quantity and complexity of material to be processed) required by an instrument would contribute to its discriminatory ability. Furthermore, it was anticipated that a higher number of childhood behaviors consistent with ADHD would be reported by gamblers than controls. Finally, it was hoped that some correlational agreement between childhood symptoms and current attention assessment would be found.

METHOD

A. Subjects

This study included sixty-six subjects, thirty-three gambling subjects and thirty-three non-gambling control subjects.

All subjects met the following criteria:

i. a negative history of substance abuse;

ii. no current medication with anti-psychotics, anti-depressants, sedatives or tranquilizers, or history of hospitalization for major psychiatric disorder;

iii. negative history of neurological disorder (other than ADHD) or trauma or other major medical condition that might contribute to cognitive deficits;

iv. caucasian and male (this was included because the population of recovering gamblers whether in GA or inpatient treatment is largely white and male. Including non-whites and females in such an initial study would seem to contribute to error variance unnecessarily); and

v. estimated IQ within the low normal range or higher.

Along with these overall criteria, control subjects had to present no history of problem gambling and gambling subjects had to report abstinence from gambling for at least two weeks prior to assessment.

The age range for the remaining sixty-six subjects was 23 to 62 years (mean = 41.12, standard deviation = 9.68) and the range of education was from 10 to 20 years (mean = 13.91, standard deviation = 2.16). Gambling and control groups were matched for age and educational levels.

Gambling subjects were recruited from the inpatient Gambling Treatment Program (GTP) at the Veterans Administration Medical Center of Brecksville, Ohio and from Gamblers Anonymous (GA) groups.

The age range for gambling subjects was 26-62 years (mean = 41.42, standard deviation = 9.52) and range of total years of education was 12 to 20 years (mean = 13.96, standard deviation = 2.28).

Control subjects were recruited from local veterans organizations, and other community groups.

The age range for control subjects was 23 to 61 years (mean = 40.81, standard deviation = 9.97) and range of years of education was 10 to 18 (mean = 13.85, standard deviation = 2.06).

B. Instruments

All subjects were administered a brief medical history questionnaire. This instrument was designed to quickly assess any gross medical conditions or events that might compromise cognitive functioning.

Screening for substance abuse utilized the short form of the Michigan Alcohol Screening Tests (SMAST) (Selzer, 1971; Zung and Charalampois, 1975). A modified version of the SMAST was also used for screening subjects for drug addiction (SMAST-D). The questions remained essentially the same other than the substitution of the word drug(s) for alcohol. The SMAST and SMAST-D were also employed for telephone interviews with collaterals to verify subjects history of alcohol and drug use.

The South Oaks Gambling Screen (SOGS) (Leseiur and Blume, 1987), was utilized to assess histories of pathological gambling. In addition to the standard items on this form, gambling subjects were also asked when they had last gambled.

To rate subjects' childhood behavior, the Self-Control Rating Scale (SCD) (Kendall and Wilcox, 1979) was employed. This test has been found to correlate significantly with children's performance on tests of impulsivity and attention such as the Matching Familiar Figures Test and Porteus Maze Test and to behavioral observations. Furthermore, factor analysis of this scale presented one major factor that accounted for 71.7% of the variance. This one factor was labeled cognitive-behavioral self-control (Kendall and Wilcox, 1979). This is significant as most other instruments utilized to assess ADHD confound attentional/activity factors with those of aggressiveness/ conduct disorder (Hinshaw, 1987). For the purposes of this study, it was felt particularly important to use an instrument that focused on the attentional factor rather than on the conduct disorder dimension.

The Shipley Institute of Living Scale was employed to assess general intellectual ability as a brief and valid measure that allowed for differential scores of verbal and abstract abilities.

The Beck Depression Inventory was employed to control for possible effects of depression on neuropsychological test performance (DeObaldia, Parsons and Yohman, 1983).

Nine tests were employed to assess a complete range of attention across levels of functioning (Posner and Presti, 1987), visual and auditory sensory systems and verbal and non-verbal modalities.

The Embedded Figures Test (EFT) is a nonverbal, visual/perceptual test that invokes the type of executive, frontally mediated aspects of attention, including extracting and using information (Shade, 1984), engaging and disengaging attention, and sustaining inhibitory control while mentally concentrating on relevant sensory input (Douglas, 1984; Falcone, 1985).

The Wisconsin Card Sorting Test (WCS) is a visual perceptual task that like the EFT is employed as a measure of the more executive aspects of attention. As such, it has gained wide acceptance as a test that is particularly sensitive to frontal impairment (Robinson, Heaton, Lehman and Stilson, 1980). The WCS is described as measuring the ability to selectively attend and respond to one aspect of a stimulus while inhibiting response to other sensory aspects of the stimulus and an ability to attend to and benefit from feedback with regard to accuracy of a response set and then the ability to shift attention to a new response set.

The Porteus Maze Test (Porteus) is a visually mediated, nonverbal measure of attention. For the purposes of this study, Form VII was used as an example and Forms XII-Adult were presented. This was done as evidence suggested that the less complex forms would be of little use in discriminating cases of subtle deficits (Porteus, 1965).

The Porteus has been found to be responsive to medication in groups of hyperkinetic children and to frontal lesions in adults (Porteus, 1965). The Porteus is widely held to assess the capacity to plan, attend and make appropriate decisions (Porteus, 1965; Riddle and Roberts, 1978), to measure focused attention, visual scanning, perceptual tracking and the ability to maintain focused attention on one's mental contents while following a sequence of ideas or problem solving (Johnston, 1986). Successful performance on this test also involved ability to inhibit incorrect responses (Douglas, 1984).

The Trail Making Test, part B (Trails B), was employed as a visual/verbal test of attention. This measure involves the ability to engage and disengage attention and visual scanning. While Trails B is also often included in batteries to assess frontal deficits (Reitan, 1986), it seems to be mediated more by the engaging/disengaging dimension rather than the conceptual/planning aspect observed in the WCS or Porteus.

The Symbol Digit Substitution Test (SDST) forms 1-3 was employed as a task of sustained attention. This is a task requiring encoding, memory storage and visual search among alternatives (Royer, 1971).

The Knox Cube Test (Knox) was utilized as a nonverbal visually mediated task measuring attention span (Stone and Wright, 1980). This test is therefore a measure of a rather basic level of attention, or as Stone and Wright (1980) state, "the first and most elementary stage of mental activity."

A Brown-Peterson type distraction task, the Primary Memory with Interference Test (Prime) is a visual/verbal task which involves the subject recalling nonsense trigrams following a 15 second distraction interval during which the subject counts backward from a number as quickly as possible. This task measures ability to inhibit distracting sensory and mental input and the capacity to engage and maintain attention.

A cued list learning task (List) was included as an auditory, verbal attentional measure. Subjects were asked to listen to a list of twelve words and repeat all they remembered. Five trails were given with subjects being cued after each trial on any words not remembered on that trial. Words were semantically related in three categories giving this task a potentially organizational component as well as involving basic engaging and sustaining attention.

The Seashore Rhythm Test was employed, which is an auditory, nonverbal task that measures alertness and focused attention at a basic level (Reitan, 1986).

C. Procedure

All subjects were initially contacted and the general requirements of participation were explained in terms of time commitment and assessment procedures. Those willing to participate were then scheduled for a two to three hour assessment session. All subjects with the exception of one gambler and one control subject completed all attentional measures in one session.

All subjects were administered the Shipley-Hartford prior to attentional tasks. Attention tests were presented in randomized sequence to each subject to avoid order effects. Following administration of five of the nine attention tests all subjects were given a break of approximately ten minutes.

All collaterals except two (who were available in person) were contacted and interviewed over the telephone. 95% of collateral respondents to the SCS were first degree relatives of subjects (59% parents, 36% siblings). The remaining 5% were friends or grandparents. For verification of substance abuse and gambling, 42% of collaterals were first degree relatives (24% parents, 18% siblings), 55% were wives, and 3% were friends.

RESULTS

Table 1 presents means and standard deviations for demographic variables, substance abuse data, SOGS, childhood history information (SCS and SCS-Collateral), and Beck and Shipley scores. As is indicated, there were no significant differences in age, education level, substance abuse ratings (per self and collateral reports), or Shipley verbal score between gambling and control subjects. As would be expected, there were significant differences between gamblers and controls on the SOGS on both self and collateral report. Furthermore, gamblers, as was hypothesized, obtained higher ratings on SCS and SCS-Collateral, indicating greater number and intensity of childhood behaviors consistent with ADHD. Beck scores were also significantly different, reflecting more depressive symptoms among gamblers.

TABLE 1

Means and Standard Deviations for Variables Other Than Attention Measures				
Variable	Gambler Mean	S.D.	Control Mean	S.D.
Age	41.424	9.523	40.818	9.967
Education	13.970	2.284	13.879	2.118
MAST	.061	.242	.030	.174
MAST-D	.030	.74	.030	.174
[a] SOGS	17.879	2.382	.152	.508
Collateral MAST	.030	.174	0	0
Collateral MAST-D	.030	.174	.030	.174
Collateral SOGS	16.879	2.583	0	0
[a] SCS	122.515	34.022	98.333	29.644
[a] Collateral SCS	108.970	39.702	83.576	29.748
ETOH Amount	2.242	.614	2.152	.712
Collat. ETOH Amount	2.121	.545	2.030	.529
Hx. ETOH	3.242	.751	3.182	.882
Drug Amount	1.092	.292	1.121	.332
Collat. Drug Amount	1.061	.242	1.061	.242
Hx. Drug	1.606	.704	1.576	.751
Last Gambled (mos.)	27.958	39.406		
Collat. Last Gamb.	26.958	37.673		
Shipley Verbal	52.030	7.265	53.394	5.820
Shipley Abstract	57.515	7.835	60.788	6.030
Shipley Total	55.485	7.225	58.455	5.740
[c] Est. I.Q.	103.545	9.481	108.121	8.158
[b] Beck	10.788	8.806	5.818	5.971

Note: MAST = Michigan Alcohol Screening Test, MAST-D = Michigan Alcohol Screening Test for Drug Use, SOGS = South Oaks Gambling Screen, SCS = Self Control Scale (Childhood history), ETOH Amount = current amount of alcohol use (on rating scale of 1-4), Hx. ETOH = Greatest alcohol use during lifetime, Hx. Drug = Greatest drug use during lifetime, Beck = Beck Depression Inventory.

a = $p < .005$; b = $p < .01$; c = $p < .05$

Table 2 presents means and standard deviations on attention measures. As can be seen, all mean differences are in the anticipated direction with gamblers attaining mean scores consistent with poorer attentional performance on all measures.

TABLE 2

Means, Standard Deviations and Univariate F's for Attention Measures

Variable	GAMBLER Mean	S.D.	CONTROL Mean	S.D.	F	P
Knox Total	12.667	3.388	13.273	2.764	.634	.429
*EFT	983.727	474.167	629.848	392.776	10.901	.002
List Learning	20.970	2.257	21.424	2.450	.615	.436
*Trails B	69.515	27.033	68.333	29.671	.029	.866
Porteus	15.333	2.157	16.121	.857	3.803	.056
Seashore	26.273	2.503	27.121	2.559	1.854	.178
Prime	35.758	8.136	37.091	6.779	.719	.400
SDST Total	126.515	21.665	131.576	26.582	.523	.472
*WCS Total	107.333	22.352	88.879	18.991	13.064	.001

Note: EFT = Embedded Figures Test, Prime = Primary Memory with Interference, SDST Total = Symbol Digit Substitution Test (Total across three forms), WCS Total = Wisconsin Card Sorting Test (total correct score).

* Poorer performance indicated by higher scores. On all other tests poorer performance is reflected in lower scores.

Table 3 presents correlation data. Significant levels are indicated using Bonferoni adjustment for family-wise error rates.

All Shipley measures are significantly intercorrelated as would be anticipated. Also, education correlates significantly with all Shipley measures. It also is significantly correlated with the Knox and Trails B. The only significant correlation among the drug and alcohol measures is that between current amount of drug use and greatest lifetime amount of drug use.

Among attention measures, EFT correlates significantly with Trails B, SDST, and WCS. Trails B also is significantly correlated with SDST, Knox and Seashore. This lack of intercorrelation among attention measures suggests that the various measures are assessing separate processes. Correlation between self report and collateral ratings on SCS was also computed and found to be significant ($r = .513$, $p < .001$).

Since differences on all attention measures were in the hypothesized direction (gambling subjects obtained scores indicative of poorer performance), they were all included in a MANOVA which was significant ($F = 2.148$; $p < .04$). Univariate tests were also calculated (Table 2). WCS reached significance ($F = 13.064$, $p < .001$) indicating that gamblers took significantly more trials to criteria than controls. EFT ($F = 10.901$; $p < .002$) also attained significance reflecting gamblers attained significantly longer time scores for figure identification. Porteus was significant at $p < .06$ ($F = 3.803$) suggesting gamblers made more errors and attained lower age scores. These results indicate that these measures most influenced MANOVA results. It is also significant that all three of these measures reflect higher order attentional processes.

All nine attention measures were utilized in an initial discriminant analysis to assess the ability of the whole battery to significantly discriminate gamblers from controls. This results in a subject: variable ratio of approximately 7 to 1, which exceeds that suggested by both Adams (1979) and Fletcher, Rice and Ray (1978). A Wilk's Lambda of .743, $F = 2.147$ $p < .04$ was obtained, as reported earlier. As group differences were significant using the complete variable set, the nine variables were examined for their relative discriminating power (canonical coefficients) and correlations with the overall discriminant function (canonical loadings), as presented in Table 4.

Along with relative discriminating ability and correlation with overall discriminant analysis, the intercorrelations between variables were considered to reduce the variable set and avoid an artificially high level of classification that is possible if too many correlated indices of performance are included (Adams, 1979). Furthermore and most importantly, the theoretical relevance of the variables in the overall assessment of attention was considered.

TABLE 3

Intercorreleations Among Attention Variables, Shipley, Beck, Substance Use, Gambling, Childhood Data, Age and Education

	AGE	EDUC	SHIPLEY V	SHIPLEY A	SHIPLEY T	BECK	AMT ETOH	AMT DRUG	HX ETOH	HX DRUG	SOGS	SCS	KNOX	EFT	LIST	TRAILS	PORTEUS	SEASHORE	PRIME	SDST	WCS
AGE	1																				
EDUC	-0.156	1																			
SHIPLEYV	0.106	[a]0.451	1																		
SHIPLEYA	-0.093	[a]0.468	[b]0.485	1																	
SHIPLEYT	-0.056	[c]0.537	[c]0.764	[c]0.930	1																
BECK	-0.002	-0.201	-0.109	-0.281	-0.244	1															
AMT ETOH	-0.247	0.010	-0.082	-0.235	-0.191	-0.201	1														
AMT DRUG	-0.158	-0.056	0.015	0.007	0.009	-0.133	-0.028	1													
HX ETOH	-0.292	0.148	0.147	0.140	0.169	-0.224	0.264	0.031	1												
HX DRUG	-0.395	0.058	0.062	-0.003	0.029	-0.094	0.139	[a]0.471	0.281	1											
SOGS	-0.036	0.035	-0.118	-0.229	-0.227	0.337	0.071	-0.055	0.035	0.017	1										
SCS	-0.048	-0.144	-0.056	-0.192	-0.158	0.267	-0.009	-0.004	0.069	0.018	0.363	1									
KNOX	-0.263	[a]0.454	0.318	0.393	0.420	-0.143	0.124	-0.013	0.046	0.105	-0.106	-0.168	1								
EFT	0.199	-0.161	-0.260	[a]-0.476	[a]-0.453	0.152	0.058	-0.017	-0.113	-0.144	0.372	0.111	0.369	1							
LIST	-0.359	0.150	0.234	0.181	0.240	0.127	0.014	0.076	0.155	0.275	-0.118	0.085	0.228	-0.201	1						
TRAILS B	0.256	[c]-0.513	-0.380	[b]-0.490	[c]-0.517	0.189	-0.022	-0.105	-0.083	0.171	0.010	-0.064	-0.514	[a]0.457	-0.191	1					
PORTEUS	0.265	0.246	0.212	0.377	0.378	-0.246	-0.027	0.056	0.128	0.097	-0.226	-0.172	0.235	-0.354	0.282	-0.299	1				
SEASHORE	-0.118	0.153	0.276	0.243	0.297	-0.008	-0.046	0.041	-0.013	0.132	-0.164	-0.084	0.379	-0.433	-0.052	[a]-0.465	0.177	1			
PRIME	-0.379	0.228	0.101	0.359	0.313	-0.324	-0.014	0.166	0.165	0.244	0.097	-0.277	0.271	-0.262	0.271	-0.209	0.191	0.157	1		
SDST	-0.420	0.427	0.347	[a]0.461	[c]0.496	-0.173	0.124	-0.060	0.295	0.16	-0.102	0.055	0.421	[c]-0.515	0.376	[c]-0.604	0.375	0.292	0.367	1	
WCS	0.118	-0.379	0.383	[c]-0.502	[c]-0.532	0.122	0.162	0.145	-0.151	-0.093	0.379	0.247	-0.309	[c]0.537	-0.160	0.261	-0.286	-0.309	-0.335	-0.265	1

[a] $p < .05$
[b] $p < .01$
[c] $p < .005$

TABLE 4

Dependent Variable Canonical Coefficients and Canonical Loadings for All Attention Measures	
Canonical Coefficients	
EFT	0.613
KNOX	0.029
LIST	-0.084
TRAILS	-0.492
PORTEUS	-0.278
SEASHORE	-0.134
SDST	0.091
WCS	0.601
PRIME	0.142
Canonical Loadings	
EFT	0.703
KNOX	-0.169
LIST	-0.167
TRAILS	0.036
PORTEUS	-0.415
SEASHORE	-0.290
SDST	-0.180
WCS	0.769
PRIME	-0.154

The final variable set arrived at in this way included EFT, Porteus, Trails B, List and Seashore. The discriminant analysis using these five variables resulted in a Wilk's lambda of .800, approximate $F = 2.998$, $p < .02$). The canonical coefficients and canonical loadings are displayed in Table 5.

TABLE 5

Dependent Variable Canonical Coefficients and Canonical Loadings for Reduced Data Set	
Canonical Coefficients	
EFT	-0.929
TRAILS	0.630
PORTEUS	0.357
SEASHORE	0.213
LIST	0.070
Canonical Loadings	
EFT	-0.826
TRAILS	-0.042
PORTEUS	0.488
SEASHORE	0.341
LIST	0.196

Table 6 presents the classification matrix. Overall, 77% of all subjects were classified correctly. Looking at classification rates per group, 73% of gamblers and 82% of controls were correctly classified. Only six of the 33 controls were incorrectly classifed as gamblers and nine of the 33 gamblers were incorrectly classified as controls. This suggests these variables classify both gamblers and non-gamblers comparably well.

TABLE 6

Classification Predictions for Gambling vs. Control Subjects

(Rows = actual group membership; Columns = group membership per discriminate analysis classification)

	GAMBLER	*CONTROL*	*TOTAL*
GAMBLER	24	9	33
CONTROL	6	27	33
TOTAL	30	36	66

DISCUSSION

The main objective of this study was to determine whether adequately sensitive measures of attention would discriminate pathological gamblers from non-gambling control subjects. The data obtained support this contention. The final discriminate analysis was able to classify 77% of all subjects accurately.

The original group of attention measures was chosen in order to cover a comprehensive spectrum of attention functions. These ranged from lower order capacities of engaging and sustaining attention to higher order capacities of planning, sequencing, flexibly shifting attention, selectively attending and organizing perceptual input. These abilities were measured through visual and auditory systems and verbal and nonverbal modes. Based on prior research on neuropsychological deficits in alcoholics and ADHD subjects (Tarter and Ryan, 1983; Ryan and Butters, 1983; Ackerman, et al., 1977; Hopkins, et al., 1979; Douglas, 1984) it was anticipated that tests assessing the more executive aspects of attention would produce the most significant findings.

This expectation was born out. Based on analysis of variance, EFT, WCS and Porteus mazes which are all sensitive to the executive aspects of attention were most significant in differentiating gamblers from controls. All three measures have been associated with frontal lobe function (Robinson, et al., 1980; Pendleton and Heaton, 1982; Porteus, 1965) which would be consistent with Posner and Presti's (1987) view of the executive aspects of attention being mediated via the frontal cortex.

The data obtained in this study would be consistent with the conclusion of other researchers in the area of ADHD that executive aspects of attention are critical in the assessment of ADHD (Douglas, 1984; Kinsbourne, 1984).

The findings of this present study are also consistent with many of the conclusions of studies of neuropsychological impairments of alcoholics and other substance abusers. Interestingly, Ryan and Butters (1983) in discussing neuropsychological deficits of alcoholics echo Cohen, et al.'s, (1972) summary of ADHD, residual state subjects' impairment. Ryan and Butters (1983) state alcoholics' "failure to approach novel, challenging, relatively unstructured problems in a systematic, planful manner, succinctly captures the nature of the primary neuropsychological deficit associated with chronic alcohol ingestion" (p. 499).

The second hypothesis proposed for this study was that gambling subjects would endorse more childhood behaviors consistent with ADHD. The data obtained supported this proposition as gamblers achieved significantly higher ratings than non-gamblers on the SCS per both self and collateral report. The validity of this retrospective data is affirmed as self and collateral reports were significantly correlated for all subjects. This finding corroborates and strengthens other research on childhood symptoms of ADHD in compulsive gamblers (Carlton and Goldstein, 1986) by finding similar symptom histories in gamblers who present no history of alcohol or drug abuse. Furthermore, it is important to recall that the SCS focuses on a dimension of cognitive/behavioral control, rather than aggressiveness/conduct disorder. This offers support for the contention that differences in childhood history between gamblers and controls is founded in behaviors related to overactivity, distractibility and difficulty inhibiting conflicting behaviors, rather in angry, acting-out behaviors.

The SCS data however, did not provide support for the third hypothesis of this study: that childhood history data would correlate with current functioning on measures of attention. As with most negative findings, it is difficult to interpret what this means. It may be that the measures were simply not sensitive enough to allow for positive findings. Alternatively, these findings may suggest that the SCS assesses a separate aspect of functioning that may contribute to development of addictive behavior, but that is independent from attentional problems.

Certainly further study needs to be done to clarify and specify what the progression from childhood disorder to adult impairment and/or pathology actually is. In this regard, Douglas' (1984) formulation of spiraling effects of ADHD seems quite useful. She posits that basic predispositions of ADHD include: (1) impaired ability to modulate arousal or alertness to meet situational demands; (2) impaired ability to inhibit responding to irrelevant or incorrect stimuli; (3) unusually strong inclination to see immediate gratification and/or stimulation; and (4) weak ability to invest attention and effort in demanding tasks. At this point, the similarity between these primary predispositions Douglas outlines for ADHD and Tarter et al.'s (1985) temperament traits contributing to a vulnerability to alcoholism needs mention. Tarter's traits include a soothability/emotionality factor which coincides with Douglas' arousal dimension. Tarter also presents a sociability dimension which, as he describes pre-alcoholic extraversion, is not "a true sociability, but instead stems from an inability to exercise inhibitory control" (p. 336). This relates to Douglas' disinhibitory predisposition. Tarter also includes in his characteristics of pre-alcoholics a deficit in attention span-persistence and excessively high activity level which compare to Douglas' predispositions of inattentiveness and stimulus seeking. Douglas (1984) and Tarter et al. (1985) go further to explore how these basic predisposing traits effect subsequent learning and experience. Douglas specifically holds that as a result of these primary predispositions an ADHD child is likely to be impaired in building the store of knowledge and skills necessary to develop effective problem solving strategies and a sense of effectance. This spiral contributes to failure experiences which further exacerbate arousal, inhibitory and attention problems. It is significant that Douglas includes not only cognitive problem solving skills in her formulation, but addresses the issue of effectance and motivation in this spiral. This suggests the negative emotional consequences of ADHD.

Certainly a study to replicate present findings and test the discriminating power of the variables utilized in this study is indicated. Also, studying other addictive groups such as overeaters and individuals addicted to nicotine along with gamblers, alcoholics and drug abusers might prove interesting in looking at how basic attention deficits are affected by a variety of addictive substances.

Another intriguing avenue of research involves the question of biological versus learned patterns of adaptation. While the present study supports the long term nature of attention deficits and a neurologically frontally mediated dysfunction contributing to current attention impairment, it really does not specifically answer the basic question of which came first, the biology or the learned behavior. While it is tempting to assume the biology must be the initial factor, learning paradigms could also explain the development of ineffective problem solving, inattention and inhibitory defects. For example, a learned helplessness paradigm (Seligman, 1975) could explain a child's response to a chaotic, unpredictable family environment. Alternatively, a high level of life stress and/or repeated trauma could result in physiological as well as cognitive and psychological changes and pathology (Selye 1956, 1969).

As has been suggested by many authors (Douglas, 1984; Tarter et al., 1985; Tarter and Ryan, 1983; Weiss, 1983) there is likely to be a biopsychosocial interaction operative in the development of addictive behavior and in the adult outcome of ADHD. Beginning to unravel the specific contributions of each sphere is important to developing the most effective treatment interventions. As has been the case with ADHD children, biological, educational and psychosocial interventions have all been devised (Douglas, 1983; Garfinkle, 1983). Furthermore, for example, as the literature on medical approaches to the treatment of ADHD suggest, treatment directed at only one domain is not apt to represent a long term or comprehensive solution (Gauthier, 1984; Mattes, Boswell and Oliver, 1984; Wender, Reinhart and Wood, 1981). What is therefore needed is research to assess an individual's current cognitive functioning, emotional and psychological status, social/environment system as well as learning history (whether an ADHD child, gambler or substance abuser), and to evaluate specific treatment interventions designed to address each problem area.

In summary, this study was designed as an initial exploration of attentional problems in a non-substance abusing group. As such, it presents evidence to support the contention that measures of attention deficit will discriminate gamblers as a non-substance abusing addicted group from non-gambling, non-addicted controls. The results of this study further indicate higher rates of childhood behaviors consistent with attention dysfunction are found among gamblers than controls. This suggests that attention deficits and the behavior problems associated with them have been a long term problem in this addicted group, and that the attention problems may well have pre-existed the addiction.

REFERENCES

Ackerman, P.T. (1977). Teenage status of hyperactive and non-hyperactive learning-disabled boys. *American Journal of Orthopsychiatry*, 47, 577-596.

Bergler, E. (1957). *The Psychology of Gambling*. New York: Hill and Wang.

Blaszcynski, A.P., Winter, S.W. and McConaghy, N. (1986). Plasma endorphin levels in pathological gambling. *Journal of Gambling Behavior*, 2, 2-14.

Brandt, J., Butters, N., Ryan, C. and Bayog, R. (1983). Cognitive loss and recovery in long-term alcohol abusers. *Archives of General Psychiatry*, 40, 435-442.

Carlton, P.L. and Goldstein, L. (1987). Physiological determinates of pathological gambling. In T. Galski (ed.), *A Handbook of Pathological Gambling*. Springfield, IL: Charles C. Thomas.

Cohen, N., Weiss, G. and Minde, K. (1972). Cognitive styles in adolescents previously diagnosed as hyperactive. *Journal of Child Psychology and Psychiatry*, 13, 203-209.

Custer, R.L. and Custer, L.F. (1978, December). *Characteristics of the recovering compulsive gambler: A survey of 150 members of Gamblers Anonymous*. Paper presented at the Fourth National Conference on Gambling and Risk Taking, University of Nevada, Reno.

Custer, R.L. and Milt, H. (1985). *When Luck Runs Out*. New York: Facts on File Publications.

Dell, L.J., Ruzicka, M.F. and Palisi, A.T. (1981). Personality and other factors associated with the gambling addiction. *The International Journal of the Addictions*, 16, 149-156.

DeObaldia, R. and Parsons, O.A. (1984a). Relationship of neuro-psychological performance to primary alcoholism and self-reported symptoms of childhood minimal brain dysfunction. *Journal of Studies on Alcohol*, 45, 386-392.

DeObaldia, R. and Parsons, O.A. (1948b). Reliability studies on the Primary/Secondary Alcoholism Classification Questionnaire and the

Hk/MBD Childhood Symptoms Checklist. *Journal of Clinical Psychology*, 40, 1257-1263.

DeObaldia, R., Parsons, O.A. and Yohman, R. (1983). Minimal brain dysfunction symptoms claimed by primary and secondary alcoholics: Relation to cognitive functioning. *International Journal of Neuroscience*, 20, 173-182.

Douglas, V.I. (1983). Attentional and cognitive problems. In M. Rutter (ed.), *Developmental Neuropsychiatry*. New York: Guilford Press.

Douglas, V.I. (1984). The psychological processes implicated in ADD. In L.M. Bloomingdale (ed.), *Attention Deficit Disorder: Diagnostic, Cognitive, and Therapeutic Understanding*. New York: Spectrum Publications, Inc.

Elmasian, R., Neville, H., Woods, D., Schuckit, M. and Bloom, F. (1982). Event related brain potentials are different in individuals at high and low risk for developing alcoholism. *Proceedings of the National Academy of Science*, USA, 79, 7900-7903.

Falcone, D.J. (1985). Laterality and field dependence. *Perceptual and Motor Skills*, 61, 651-657.

Freud, S. (1961). Dostoevsky and parricide. In J. Strachey (ed.), *The Standard Edition of the Complete Psychological Works of Sigmund Freud*, vol. 21. London: Hogarth Press.

Garfinkel, B.D. (1984). Neuroendocrine and cognitive responses to amphetamine in adolescents with a history of ADD. In L.M. Bloomingdale (ed.), *Attention Deficit Disorder: Diagnostic, Cognitive, and Therapeutic Understanding*. New York: Spectrum Publications, Inc.

Gittelman, R., Mannuzza, S., Shenker, R. and Bonagura, N. (1985). Hyperactive boys almost grown up — I. Psychiatric status. *Archives of General Psychiatry*, 42, 937-947.

Glen, A.M. (1979, August). *Personality research on pathological gamblers*. Paper presented at the American Psychological Association Annual Convention, New York.

Goldstein, L., Manowitz, P., Nora, R., Swartzburg, M. and Carlton, P.L. (1985). Differential EEG activation and pathological gambling. *Biological Psychiatry*, 20, 1232-1234.

Goldstein, C. and Shelly, C. (1980). Neuropsychological investigation of brain lesion localization in alcoholism. In H. Beglieter (ed.), *Biological Effects of Alcohol.* New York: Plenum Press.

Graham, J.R. and Lowenfeld, B.L. (1986). Personality dimensions of the pathological gambler. *Journal of Gambling Behavior*, 2, 58-66.

Hinshaw, S.P. (1987). On the distinction between attentional deficits/hyperactivity and conduct problems/aggression in child psychopathology. *Psychological Bulletin*, 101, 443-463.

Hopkins, J., Perlman, T., Hechtman, L. and Weiss, G. (1979). Cognitive style in adults originally diagnosed as hyperactives. *Journal of Child Psychology and Psychiatry*, 20, 209-216.

Jacobs, D.F. (1986). A general theory of addictions: A new theoretical model. *Journal of Gambling Behavior*, 2, 15-31.

Johnston, C.W. (1986). The neuropsychological evaluation of attention deficit disorder. *Psychiatric Annals*, 16, 47-51.

Kendall, P.C. and Wilcox, L.E. (1979). Self-control in children: Development of a rating scale. *Journal of Consulting and Clinical Psychology*, 47, 1020-1029.

Lesieur, H.R. and Blume, S.B. (1987). The South Oaks Gambling Screen (SOGS): A new instrument for the identification of pathological gamblers. *American Journal of Psychiatry*, 144, 1184-1188.

Mann, G.B. and Greenspan, S.I. (1976). The identification and treatment of adult brain dysfunction. *American Journal of Psychiatry*, 133, 1013-1017.

Mattes, J.A., Boswell, L. and Oliver, H. (1984). Methylphenidate effects on symptoms of attention deficit disorder in adults. *Archives of General Psychiatry*, 41, 1059-1063.

Moravec, J.D. and Munley, P.H. (1983). Psychological test findings on pathological gamblers in treatment. *The International Journal of the Addictions*, 18, 1003-1009.

Parsons, O.A. and Leber, W.R. (1981). The relationship between cognitive dysfunction and brain damage in alcoholics; Causal interactive or epiphenomenal. *Alcoholism: Clinical Experimental Research*, 5, 326-343.

Porteus, S.D. (1965). *The Porteus Maze Test: Fifty Years of Application.* Palo Alto, CA: Pacific Books.

Posner, M.I. and Presti, D.E. (1987). Selective attention and cognitive control. *Trends in Neuroscience*, 10, 13-17.

Quitkin, F. and Klein, D.F. (1969). Two behavioral syndromes in young adults related to possible minimal brain dysfunction. *Journal of Psychiatric Research*, 7, 131-142.

Ramirez, L.F., McCormick, R.A., Russo, A. and Taber, J.I. (1983). Patterns of substance abuse in pathological gamblers undergoing treatment. *Addictive Behaviors*, 8, 425-428.

Reitan, R.M. (1986). Theoretical and methodological bases of the Halstead-Reitan neuropsychological test battery. In I. Grant and K.M. Adams (eds.), *Neuropsychological Assessment of Neuropsychiatric Disorders.* New York: Oxford University Press.

Riddle, M. and Roberts, A.H. (1978). Psychosurgery and the Porteus Maze Tests. *Archives of General Psychiatry*, 35, 493-497.

Robinson, D.L., Heaton, R.K., Lehman, R.A.W. and Stilson, D.W. (1980). Utility of Wisconsin card sorting test in detecting and localizing lobe lesions. *Journal of Consulting and Clinical Psychology*, 48, 605-614.

Roston, R.A. (1965). Some personality characteristics of male compulsive gamblers [Summary]. *Proceedings of the 73rd Annual Convention of the American Psychological Association*, 263-264.

Royer, F.L., Gilmore, G.C. and Gruhn, J.J. (1981). Normative data for the symbol digit substitution task. *Journal of Clinical Psychology*, 87, 608-614.

Ryan, C. and Butters, N. (1980a). Further evidence for a continuum of impairment encompassing male alcoholic Korsakoff patients and chronic alcoholics. *Alcoholism*, 4, 190-198.

Ryan, C. and Butters, N. (1980b). Learning and memory impairments in young and old alcoholics: Evidence for the premature aging hypothesis. *Alcoholism*, 4, 288-293.

Ryan, C. and Butters, N. (1983). Cognitive deficits in alcoholics. In B. Kissin (ed.), *The Pathogenesis of Alcoholism, Biological Factors, Vol. 7, The Biology of Alcoholism*. New York: Plenum Press.

Ryan, C. and Butters, N. (1986). The neuropsychology of alcoholism. In D. Wedding, A.M. Horton and J. Webster (eds.), *The Neuropsychology Handbook: Behavioral and Clinical Perspectives*. New York: Springer Publishing Company.

Seligman, M.E.P. (1975). *Helplessness: On Depression, Development and Death*. New York: S.F. Freeman.

Selye, H. (1956). *The Stress of Life*. New York: McGraw-Hill.

Selye, H. (1969). Stress. *Psychology Today*, 3, 24-26.

Selzer, M.L. (1971). The Michigan Alcoholism Screening Test: The quest for a new diagnostic instrument. *American Journal of Psychiatry*, 127, 1653-1658.

Shade, B.J. (1984). Field dependency: Cognitive style or perceptual skill. *Perceptual and Motor Skills*, 58, 991-995.

Stone, M.W. and Wright, B.D. (1980). *Knox Cube Test Instruction Manual*. Chicago: Stoelting Company.

Taber, J.I. (1983, February). *Common characteristics of pathological gamblers and some interventions which seem to help*. Paper presented at the 14th Annual Convention of Divisions 23 and 26 of the American Psychological Association, White Sulphur Springs, West Virginia.

Tarter, R.E., Alterman, A.I. and Edwards, K.I. (1985). Vulnerability to alcoholism in men: A behavior-genetic perspective. *Journal of Studies on Alcohol*, 46, 329-356.

Tarter, R.E. and Ryan, C.M. (1983). Neuropsychology of alcoholism: Etiology, phenomenology, process and outcome. In M. Galanter (ed.), *Recent Developments in Alcoholism*, vol. 1. New York: Plenum Press.

Weiss, G., Hechtman, L. and Perlman, T. (1978). Hyperactives as young adults: School, employer, and self-rating scales obtained during a ten year follow-up evaluation. *American Journal of Orthopsychiatry*, 48, 438-445.

Weiss, G., Hechtman, L., Perlman, T., Hopkins, J. and Wener, A. (1979). Hyperactives as young adults: A controlled propective ten year follow-up of seventy-five children. *Archives of General Psychiatry*, 36, 675-681.

Wender, P.H., Reimherr, F.W. and Wood, D.R. (1981). Attention deficit disorder (minimal brain dysfunction) in adults. *Archives of General Psychiatry*, 38, 449-456.

Wolkowitz, O.M., Roy, A. and Doran, A.R. (1985). Pathological gambling and other risk-taking pursuits. *Psychiatric Clinics of North America*, 8, 311-321.

Zung, B.J. and Charalampous, M.D. (1975). Item analysis of the Michigan alcoholism screening test. *Journal of Studies on Alcohol*, 36, 127-132.

Causes of Pathological Gambling

Robert Ladouceur

In 1979, Loto-québec asked me to evaluate the psychological consequences or the pros and cons of implementing casinos in the Belle Province de Québec. After careful perusal of the literature, I was struck by the fact that I could find only a handful of empirical studies published on the topic, especially in the area of decision theory. We knew very little about the fundamentals of the psychology of gambling, or as I prefer to say, about normal or social gamblers. I asked Loto-québec for money to establish a laboratory. The first objective was to understand the fundamentals of this phenomena. So for the past 10 years, I devoted a large portion of my research time and personal energy to this laudable goal.

As a cognitive-behaviorally trained therapist, my hunches were that a better understanding of why normal people gamble despite persistent monetary losses, why they maintain gambling activities and why some of them become addicted, would provide crucial information for the treatment of pathological gamblers. Furthermore, this information would help us to design thoughtful prevention programs for gamblers at risk and to provide strategies for the maintenance of therapeutic gains for recovered pathological gamblers. This paper discusses the main conclusions of this effort.

Our research endeavors have been focused on three dimensions of gambling behavior: (1) behavioral, (2) cognitive and, (3) physiological. The findings to be discussed are the conclusions that I drew from over 50 empirical studies conducted both in the laboratory and in natural settings.

BEHAVIORAL DIMENSIONS

A. Monetary risk behavior increases as a function of exposure to gambling. Within a single session, the individual bet more and more heavily as the game progresses (Ladouceur and Mayrand, 1986, 1987).

B. Between sessions, monetary risk behavior does not return to baseline: Its progressive effect is transferred to the next session (Ladouceur, Mayrand and Tourigny, 1987).

C. If you block this progressive increase of monetary risk by limiting the number of tokens permitted on each trial, the player will rapidly find another way of increasing the level of risk behavior such as shifting his bet on higher odds (Ladouceur and Gaboury, 1988).

D. The very last bets of each gambling session are extremely high compared to the limits usually fixed at the beginning of the game.

COGNITIVE DIMENSIONS

While conducting these studies, we wanted to identify what was going in the gamblers' head while gambling. After using many techniques to evaluate the cognitive dimensions, one technique proved to be very successful, the thinking aloud method. While gambling, the player verbalized all thoughts, images, impressions.

A. More than 80% of game-related verbalizations were irrational or inadequate concerning the issue of the game (Gaboury and Ladouceur, 1989).

B. This result was found for different types of gambler and for all games studied (roulette, blackjack, video poker machine, fruit machine).

C. Cognitive restructuring was an effective technique not only to correct these inadequate perceptions but also to produce a decrease in:

   i. gamblers' interest and motivation for gambling, and

   ii. gambling activities for certain individuals. (Ladouceur, R., Gaboury, A. and Duval, C. 1988; Ladouceur, R., Sylvain, C., Duval, C., Gaboury, A. and Dumont, M., 1990).

PHYSIOLOGICAL DIMENSIONS

Physiological arousal (increased heart rate) was associated with the number of irrational thoughts (Coulome, Ladouceur, Desharnais and Jobin, 1990).

IMPLICATIONS FOR TREATMENT.

A. Individuals are generally not aware of these patterns.

B. Regardless of our theoretical orientation, any treatment package should include this behavioral, cognitive and physiological information.

REFERENCES

Gaboury, A. and Ladouceur, R. (1989). Erroneous perceptions and gambling. *Journal of Social Behavior and Personality*, 4, 411-420.

Ladouceur, R. and Gaboury, A. (1988). Effects of limited and unlimited stakes on gambling behavior. *Journal of Gambling Behavior*, 4, 119-126.

Ladouceur, R., Gaboury, A. and Duval, C. (1988). Modification des verbalizations irrationnelles pendant le jeu de roulette américaine et prise de risque monétaire. *Science et Comportement*, 18, 58-68.

Ladouceur, R. and Mayrand, M. (1986). Caractéristiques psychologiques de la prise de risque monétaire des joueurs et des non joueurs è la roulette. *International Journal of Psychology*, 21, 433-443.

Ladouceur, R. and Mayrand, M. (1987). The level of involvement and the timing of betting in gambling. *Journal of Psychology*, 121, 169-175.

Ladouceur, R., Mayrand, M. and Tourigny, Y. (1987). Risk-taking behavior in gamblers and non-gamblers during prolonged exposure. *Journal of Gambling Behavior*, 3, 115-122.

Ladouceur, R., Sylvain, C., Duval, C., Gaboury, A. and Dumont, M. (1990). Correction des verbalizations irrationnelles chez les joueurs de vidéo-poker. *Revue Internationale de Psychologie.*

Self-Reported Withdrawal Symptoms and Pathological Gambling

Richard J. Rosenthal and Henry R. Lesieur©

This article is dedicated to the memory of Robert L. Custer, M.D.

The DSM-III-R criteria for pathological gambling were patterned on those for substance dependence (American Psychiatric Association, 1987). This was done without empirical testing, a failing that those working on DSM-IV are attempting to correct (Lesieur, 1988; Rosenthal, 1989; Lesieur, 1991; Lesieur and Rosenthal, in press). Although the literature on pathological gambling frequently assumes it to be an addiction, and although tolerance (item 3) and withdrawal (item 4) figure prominently in the criteria, to date there have been only two studies of withdrawal symptoms among pathological gamblers (Wray and Dickerson, 1981; Meyer, 1989). Both studies reported primarily on psychological symptomatology while acknowledging that some subjects did experience physiological symptoms.

Wray and Dickerson (1981) noted the similarity to alcohol withdrawal but failed to ask subjects about concurrent alcohol or drug use. This appears to be a serious omission because various studies (Ramirez, McCormick, Russo, et al., 1984; Linden, Pope and Jonas, 1986; Lesieur and Blume, 1990) show that between 39% to 52% of pathological gamblers abuse alcohol and/or other drugs.

All of Wray and Dickerson's (1981) subjects were men and, except for four who were casino players, all were horse players. The Meyer (1989) study is also limited with regard to gambling type; it is based on German gambling machine players (similar, perhaps, to American slot or video poker machine players) and a second group who favored roulette. Again, the sample was primarily male (95%). One-third of the pathological gamblers in the U.S. are female (Volberg, 1988), and it is known that female pathological gamblers are quite different from their male counterparts (Lesieur and Blume, 1990). These facts raise questions about generalizability.

Further, neither study contained a control group. This article attempts to correct these shortcomings while examining whether a connection exists between the experience of so-called withdrawal symptoms and gambling behavior patterns, gender, the presence of other addictive disorders, and the diagnostic criteria for pathological gambling.

METHODS

This study was part of a survey conducted primarily to test the DSM-III-R criteria for pathological gambling. Most items related to different wording of potential criteria and the associated features and predisposing factors listed in DSM-III-R. Items included were based on the clinical experience of one of the authors (R.J.R) and a critical assessment of the DSM-III-R criteria (Rosenthal, 1989). The questionnaire included demographic questions, gambling preferences, age of onset of gambling problems, length of time spent gambling (hours "in action"), and self-identification as alcoholic, drug addict, or compulsive overeater.

Three questions related to the major hypothesis of this study were placed in different parts of the survey. The first, to be answered yes or no, asked subjects whether they felt restless or irritable when they cut down or stopped gambling. (Those who had never cut down or stopped were instructed to check no.) A second asked whether subjects agreed or disagreed with the statement that "when not gambling (they) had a persistent urge to gamble — 'cravings.'" Finally, there appeared a listing of 12 symptoms with instructions to check only those that applied. The question was worded as follows: "For those who have stopped gambling at some point, in the first days or weeks of stopping did you experience any of the following more than you usually do?"

Questionnaires were distributed by treatment professionals in eight states to their patients and to Gamblers Anonymous (GA) members. Two hundred twenty-two pathological gamblers and 104 substance-dependent controls participated in the study. The majority of the subjects were from Nevada, California, and New Jersey, with the rest from Iowa, Montana, New York, Ohio, and Virginia. A large majority (87%) of the pathological gamblers had been to GA, and 74% had seen a therapist for a gambling problem. These pathological gamblers satisfied the proposed DSM-IV diagnostic criteria for pathological gambling. All substance-dependent controls were contacted through therapists who made the determination. None of the controls fulfilled the proposed DSM-IV diagnostic criteria for pathological gambling but all were self-identified as having alcoholism or drug addiction and were at the time of their participation in an inpatient or outpatient treatment program for substance dependence. The two groups did not differ by gender (74% of gamblers were male versus 76% of controls; chi-square= 0.15, df=1, p= 0.69). However, the gamblers were older (mean age was 41.8 years old; s.d.=11.8) than controls (mean age 32.2 years old; s.d.=8.8); (t=7.34, df=322, p<.001); more likely to be married (54% married versus 36% for controls; chi-square=18.4, df=5, p<.005); and had higher income (group median=$46,406 versus $22,224 for controls; chi-square=64.99, df=4, p<.001).

The first gambling preferences of the pathological gamblers were parimutuel wagering on horses and dogs (20%), cards (20%), casino [other than slots or video poker] (18%), sports (16%) and slots and poker machines (14%), with lottery, dice, stock market, bingo and pull tabs following in that order. The controls were more likely to favor cards (25%), lotteries or numbers (20%), games of skill (15%), and parimutuel wagering (10%), with casino,sports, bingo, dice, slots and pull tab following. The mean age when pathological gamblers began to experience problems was 24 years of age (s.d.=9.8). Subjects were asked how many hours they would typically gamble when they were in action. The mean length of time was 12.4 hours for pathological gamblers (s.d.=12.9) compared with 2.4 hours for controls (s.d.=2.6); (t=6.5; df=275; p<.001).

Twenty-four percent of the pathological gamblers described themselves as alcoholic and 18% as drug addicts. Ninety percent of the controls described themselves as alcoholic and 59% as drug addicts.

RESULTS

Sixty-five percent of the pathological gambler respondents experienced at least one of the following psychosomatic withdrawal-like symptoms: insomnia (50%), headaches (36%), upset stomach or diarrhea (34%), loss of appetite (29%), physical weakness (27%), heart racing or palpitations (26%), shaking (19%), muscle aches or cramps (17%), difficulty breathing (13%), sweating (12%), and chills or fever (6.5%). Only 2% of controls said they experienced one or more symptoms, including upset stomach or diarrhea (1%), heart racing or palpitations (1%), and difficulty breathing (1%). In addition, 91% of the gamblers stated they experienced cravings (versus 1% of controls) and 87% of the gamblers (versus 6% of controls) stated they felt "restless and irritable" when attempting to cut down or stop gambling. Only 4% of the pathological gamblers (versus 92% of controls) stated they experienced neither physiological nor psychological withdrawal symptoms.

When examining only the pathological gamblers, the number of psychosomatic withdrawal-like symptoms reported was not associated with age, gender, religion, occupation, education, type of gambling, age of onset of problems, extent of alcohol or drug use while gambling, or self-identification as alcoholic or drug addict. Withdrawal was, curiously, correlated with income ($r=.13$, $p. <.05$); it was also associated with the number of hours spent in action ($r=.15$, $p<.05$) and the longest number of hours spent in action at any one time ($r=.17$, $p<.01$).

Four dissociative-like states experienced while gambling (Jacobs, 1988) were examined for possible inclusion in the DSM-IV. These items were correlated with pathological gambling (being in a trance, $r=.58$, $p<.001$; feeling outside of oneself, $r=.44$, $p<.001$; experiencing memory blackouts, $r=.38$, $p<.001$; and feeling like a different person, $r=.58$, $p<.001$). The number of physiological withdrawal symptoms was significantly correlated with feeling outside oneself ($r=.14$, $p<.05$) and experiencing a memory blackout while gambling ($r=.27$, $p<.001$). Feeling outside oneself was significantly correlated with sweating, loss of appetite, heart racing or palpitations, and having difficulty breathing; whereas experiencing a blackout was significantly correlated (or there was a trend in the relation) with all the physiological symptoms. Both also were associated with restlessness, irritability, and cravings.

There are currently nine criteria tentatively selected for inclusion in DSM-IV (Lesieur and Rosenthal, 1991; Lesieur and Rosenthal, in press). These can be summarized as follows: 1) progression and preoccupation; 2) need to gamble with an increasing amount of money to achieve desired excitement; 3) restlessness and irritability if unable to gamble; 4) gambling as a way of escaping from problems or intolerable feelings; 5) returning another day in order to win back one's money ("chasing losses"); 6) lying or concealing extent of involvement with gambling; 7) committing illegal acts to finance gambling; 8) jeopardizing relationship, job, educational or career opportunity because of gambling; and 9) reliance on others to provide money to relieve a desperate financial situation caused by gambling ("bailout").

The number of physiological symptoms of withdrawal was significantly correlated with all of the proposed DSM-IV criteria with the exception of "chasing losses" ($r=.11$, $p=.06$) and "bailout" ($r=.07$, n.s.). Gambling as a way of escaping from problems or intolerable feelings was the most strongly correlated with the number of symptoms ($r=.31$, $p<.001$). It was also the only criterion correlated with virtually all the withdrawal symptoms (the exception is chills, which were not significantly correlated with any of the proposed DSM-IV criteria). Cravings were correlated with all the DSM-IV criteria with the exception of "bailout."

DISCUSSION

The results of this study support the hypothesis that pathological gamblers are more likely to experience physiological (psychosomatic), withdrawal-like symptoms when attempting to stop gambling than are substance-dependent controls. In addition, the hypothesis that these symptoms may be explained by dual addiction (i.e., to gambling and alcohol or another drug) is not supported by the data. Although it appears that the withdrawal is not explained by the presence of concurrent substance dependence, the presence of withdrawal itself does support the idea of commonality among various forms of these dependencies.

Meyer (1989) found a positive correlation between withdrawal-like symptoms and an "excitation during gambling" variable. Wray and Dickerson (1981) also had discovered a positive correlation between number of disturbances reported and measures of attempts to increase the excitement of the gambling situation, rating it hard to stop, and the number of relapses after attempting to quit. Although our study did not measure subjects' attempts to stop or number of relapses, there is some support for the connection between a drive for excitement and withdrawal symptoms. The second DSM-IV criterion (the need to gamble an increasing amount of money to achieve the desired excitement) was significantly correlated with the number of physiological withdrawal symptoms ($r=.13$, $p<.05$). This criterion was specifically modeled after the tolerance phenomenon in psychoactive substance dependence (Lesieur, 1988). It is possible that, as with subjects with alcohol disorders (Miller, 1980), the greater the tolerance developed, the greater the withdrawal symptoms, difficulty in quitting, and number of relapses. Further research is needed to examine this hypothesis.

For some it is possible that, like their counterparts with alcohol disorders (Seixas, 1982), with tolerance and progression into the disorder come increased memory blackouts. The correlation with withdrawal is noted above. For others who spend long hours gambling, blackouts may be produced by sleep-deprivation. Their etiology needs to be examined.

The only finding that does not suggest a relationship between progression into increasingly serious problems and withdrawal is the connection between escaping from problems and withdrawal. It may be that there are two forms of escape — related gambling (Lesieur and Blume, 1990): escaping from problems that predate gambling and escaping from gambling-produced problems. It is possible that the correlation found was produced by the latter and not the former. If so, it suggests a "progression-related" scenario for withdrawal and pathological gambling. However, Meyer (1989) found a positive correlation between gambling as a "substitute/flight relationship" and withdrawal-like symptoms. Further research is needed to test whether both varieties of escape are correlated with withdrawal.

The results could conceivably have several interpretations. They do not form a clear pattern and could be a result of conditioned reactions to the stress from stopping gambling. Alternatively, they may be variable because individual physiological responses to situational extinction differ.

This was a retrospective study which demonstrated the presence of physiological withdrawal symptoms among pathological gamblers. Because of the nature of the study and the other two like it, prospective confirmation is needed. Patients entering an inpatient treatment facility for pathological gambling need to be systematically observed through the course of their treatment for symptoms of withdrawal.

REFERENCES

American Psychiatric Association Work Group to Revise DSM-III (1987). DSM-III-R in Development, Draft 10/5/85. Washington, D.C.: American Psychiatric Association.

Jacobs, D. (1988). Evidence for a common dissociative-like reaction among addicts. *Journal of Gambling Behavior*, 4:27-37.

Lesieur, H.R. (1988). Altering the DSM-III criteria for pathological gambling. *Journal of Gambling Behavior*, 4:38-47.

Lesieur, H.R. and Blume, S.B. (1990). When lady luck loses: The female pathological gambler. In Van Den Bergh, N. (ed), *Feminist Perspectives on Treating Addictions*, pp. 181-196. New York: Springer.

Lesieur, H.R. and Rosenthal, R.J. (1991). Pathological gambling: A review of the literature (prepared for the American Psychiatric Association Task Force on DSM-IV Committee on Disorders of Impulse Control Not Elsewhere Classified). *Journal of Gambling Studies*, 7:5-39.

Lesieur, H.R. and Rosenthal, R.J. (in press). *Pathological gambling* - in *Source Book for DSM-IV*. Washington, D.C.: American Psychiatric Association.

Linden, R.D., Pope, H.G., and Jonas, J.M. (1986). Pathological gambling and major affective disorder: Preliminary findings. *Journal of Clinical Psychiatry*, 47:201-203.

Meyer, G (1989). *Glucksspieler in Selbsthilfegruppen: Erste Ergebnisse Einer Empirischen Untersuchung*. Hamburg: Neuland.

Miller, P.M. (1980). Theoretical and practical problems in substance abuse assessment and treatment. In Miller, W.R. (ed), *The Addictive Behaviors*, pp. 265-290. Oxford: Pergamon Press.

Ramirez, L.F., McCormick, R.A., Russo, A.M. et al. (1984). Patterns of substance abuse in pathological gamblers undergoing treatment. *Addictive Behavior*, 8:425-428.

Rosenthal, R.J. (1989). Pathological gambling and problem gambling: Problems of definition and diagnosis. In Shaffer, H.J., Stein, S.A., Gambino, B., and Cummings, T.N. (eds), *Compulsive Gambling: Theory, Research, and Practice*, pp. 101-125. Lexington, MA: Lexington Books.

Seixas, F.A. (1982). The course of alcoholism. In Estes, N.J. and Heinemann, M.E. (eds.), *Alcoholism: Development, Consequences, and Interventions*, pp. 67-77. St. Louis: C.V. Mosby.

Volberg, R.A. and Steadman, H.J. (1988). Refining prevalence estimates of pathological gambling. *American Journal of Psychiatry*, 145:502-505.

Wray, I. and Dickerson, M.G. (1981). Cessation of high frequency gambling and 'withdrawal' symptoms. *British Journal of Addictions*, 76:401-405.

ACKNOWLEDGEMENT

The authors acknowledge the help of Valerie C. Lorenz, Ph.D., Mary Lou Strachan, Robert Hunter, Ph.D., Nadia Kuley, Ph.D., Betty George, Mona Sumner, Jim Overland, Dan Stamatelos, Donald Thoms, and the participating members of Gamblers Anonymous.

This research was partially funded by grants from Charter Hospital, Las Vegas, and Thomas N. Cummings.

IV

Pathological Gambling: Studies of its Prevalence in Society

A Preliminary Exploration of a Two-Stage Methodology in the Assessment of the Extent and Degree of Gambling Related Problems in the Australian Population

Mark Dickerson

Issues and methodological problems associated with establishing prevalence rates for pathological gamblers were critically reviewed, including the problem of base rates, the identification of cases, the time frame used in defining cases or problems and the importance of distinguishing between different forms of gambling. The psychometric properties of the existing measures were reviewed and empirical data presented illustrating some of the problems involved in using these measures in the general population. An alternative paradigm to illness prevalence methodology was outlined as a preferred research approach to the assessment of the extent and degree of gambling related problems.

At present in Australia all states derive 9-11% of their revenue from gambling taxation. It is one of the most popular leisure activities and is more readily available in Australia, in a wider range of forms, than in any other country. Each of the different legalized forms of gambling represents a major industry, and per capita expenditure by Australians probably exceeds that of most other developed countries (Haig, 1985).

Seminal work in the United Kingdom, Australia and the United States by Moran and Allcock and Blaszczynski, Custer and Lesieur, respectively, has established beyond dispute that for a proportion of those who gamble the behavior may develop addictive-like qualities and generate a range of problems, personal, financial, familial, vocational and legal. Although excessive gambling, variously labelled as "pathological" or "compulsive" has been classified amongst the other addictive behaviors since the early 1980s (Marlatt, 1979; Miller, 1980) and included in the American Psychiatric Association's Diagnostic and Statistical Manuals since 1980, there have been no national surveys in any country in the world to assess the extent and degree of gambling related problems. Case studies indicate that the individual excessive gambler may generate much disharmony about them, in their families and at work, but at present there exist no empirically derived estimate of their impact on Australian society generally.

Throughout the last decade in Australia, whenever a state has considered introducing an additional form of gambling, particularly when it involved casinos or poker machines, inquiries were conducted to evaluate the likely effects on the community. All such inquiries, whether in Victoria, Southern Australia (SA), Western Australia (WA) or New South Wales (NSW), have noted the lack of research evaluating the impact of gambling availability on the individual and family. All of these inquiries have recommended that national studies examining the relationship between different forms of gambling and the putative deleterious effects on the individual and family should be completed. Apart from the pilot work described below no studies have so far been completed or funded in Australia. A similar situation exists in the UK. Limited telephone surveys have been conducted in the US (Culleton, 1989; Volberg and Steadman, 1988) and it was not until mid 1988 that the first major study, by Rachel Volberg, was funded by a grant from the National Institute of Mental Health (N.I.M.H.).

The case accepted by all state inquiries in Australia has been that if governments gather revenue by the legalization of gambling, then the state is responsible for the provision of some form of safety net, education, counselling or whatever, for those individuals who respond to the availability of gambling with excess. The failure of all Australian states to provide any such services (with the exception of WA where some minimal funding for limited services has recently been made available) has, to a large part, been a function of the rejection of alarmist views concerning the size of the problem and the absence of any descriptive data base on which to formulate policy.

Given the rapidly developing nature of the Australian gambling industry, e.g., the introduction of sports betting to Victoria and poker machines into Queensland and Tasmania, it has become imperative that a national study be carried out for the following reasons:

- to establish the extent and degree of gambling related problems in the Australian population;
- to establish whether such problems are differentially associated with the availability of particular forms of gambling; and
- to establish a data base for state and federal policies concerning the need, or otherwise, for educational and counselling services for people who report gambling related problems.

In an earlier paper (Dickerson and Hinchy, 1988), discussion of some of the methodological issues involved in establishing what have typically been referred to as prevalence rates of pathological gamblers lead to the consideration of a two-stage approach and the suggestion that research in the area move away from attempts to identify "cases" adopting a more fundamental descriptive approach. This paper sets out to reinforce this proposal. Existing measures and methodologies currently in use in the United States will be reviewed in the context of various criticisms and arguments together with some illustrative data gathered in a recent pilot study.

The paper is structured as follows:

1. Base rate issues;
2. Cases or a continuum of involvement;
3. Time frame in defining problems;
4. Forms of gambling; and
5. Measures:
   a) Inventory of Gambling Behavior,
   b) South Oaks Gambling Screen — some empirical data.

BASE RATE ISSUES

Culleton (1989) criticizes the South Oaks Gambling Screen (SOGS) (Lesieur and Blume, 1987) as a measure for use in prevalence studies as it fails to account for the increase in false positives when used with a general population sample as opposed to the original validation groups. The aim here is merely to illustrate this point as a part of the overall argument that the identification of cases is a hazardous business and one perhaps best avoided given our current state of knowledge.

A basic textbook in clinical psychology such as Gathercole (1968) provides illustrations of the "efficiency" (Meehl and Rosen, 1955) of psychological tests designed to identify diagnostic categories such as "brain damage." Table 1 provides a similar illustration for pathological gamblers (PG) and others (NPG).

It can be seen that the efficiency of the SOGS falls from 0.93 in the validation study to 0.22 in the hypothetical "real life" situation. In other words, if the prevalence rates proposed by Kallick, Suits, Dielman and Hybels (1979) are assumed to provide a bench-mark for the general population in the United States then surveys using the SOGS will over-estimate the number of pathological gamblers by a factor of five.

Figure 1 provides an illustration of what seems likely to be a case in point where the use of the SOGS has resulted in a high rate of false positives. The data were gathered during the development of a test of betting skill (Solonsch, 1989). Although it is possible that the results represent the true state of the Australian gambling universe, as the figures when extended to the general population give a prevalence figure of 10.1% pathological gamblers for this form of gambling alone, it seems a little unlikely. It is possible that the problem of discriminating between regular gamblers and those with problems is particularly difficult. For example, many regular gamblers may chase their losses but have learned strategies to limit the extent to which they do so. At present, there exist no measures that permit such distinctions to be made.

CASES OR A CONTINUUM OF INVOLVEMENT

It has frequently been assumed that there are two clearly distinguishable groups of gamblers: excessive or pathological and infrequent social gamblers. However, even when considering the phenomena central to the concept of pathological gambling, i.e., impaired control over the gambling, empirical data from gamblers in treatment and regular gamblers from the general population shows considerable overlap (Dickerson, 1985). One might well be justified in paraphrasing Marlatt's (1979) much quoted comments about alcoholics; pathological gamblers differ from other gamblers only in terms of the size of their debts and the degree of related harmful effects.

TABLE 1

Illustration of the change in efficiency with which the South Oaks Gambling Screen (SOGS) discrminates between Pathological Gambler (PG) and Non-Pathological (NPG) from the validation study (A) to a hypothetical general population (B)

(A) VALIDATION (LESIEUR, 1988)				
		ACTUAL		
		PG	NPG	efficiency (Meehl & Rosen, 1955)
SOGS SCORE	PG	221 (98% of 226)	19 (3.6% OF 536)	p.PG = 0.93 221/240
	NPG	5 (2% of 226)	517 (96.4% of 536)	p.NPG = 0.99
Base Rate		226	536	N = 762
(B) 'REAL LIFE'/GENERAL POPULATION (E.G., KALLICK ET AL., 1976)				
		ACTUAL		
		PG	NPG	efficiency
SOGS SCORE	PG	1 (98% of 1)	4 (3.6% of 99)	p.PG = 0.22
	NPG	0 (2% of 1)	95 (96.4% of 99)	p.NPG = 1.0
Base rate		1	99	N=100

FIGURE 1

Distribution of Scores on SOGS (Solonsch 1989)

				Problem Gamblers		*Pathological Gamblers*						
SOGS Score	0	1	2	3	4	5	6	7	8	9	10	11
% Subjects	11	9	12.6	20	17	6.5	2	6.5	6.5	2	2	4.6
					(37%)					(30.4%)		

Line Chart of the Distribution of Scores on SOGS of a Sample of People Betting on Course and in Off-Course Agencies (Solonsch, 1989)

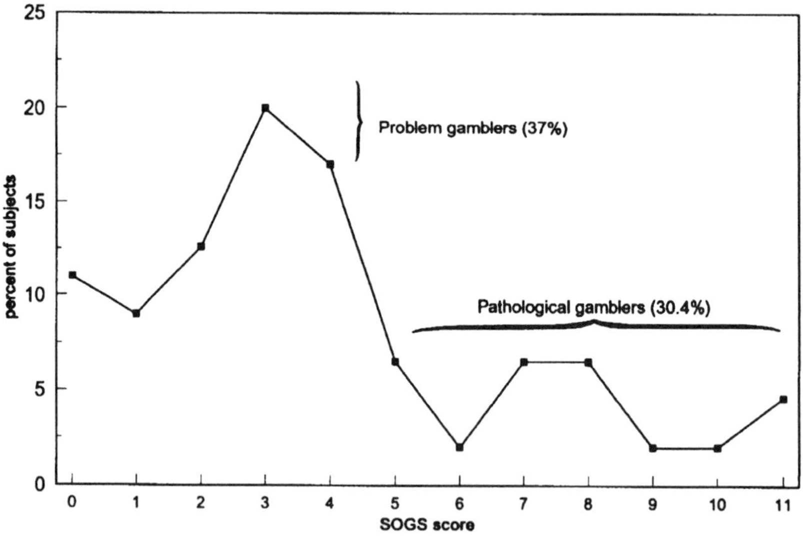

A case can be made that the criteria spelled out in the DSM III-R (American Psychiatric Association, 1987) are based on an atypical sample of people with gambling related problems (Volberg and Steadman, 1988). Most of the characteristics considered important in the identification of pathological gamblers have been culled from people seeking help from Gamblers Anonymous (GA)

or other treatment programs. Given the generally very limited availability of these forms of help, it is quite likely that the sample of people entering them are less than representative of the population of individuals with gambling related problems.

Even if the existing criteria for pathological gamblers were "correct," then, at present, there have been no studies examining the reliability with which the criteria may be used whether in the form of a psychometric test or in a psychiatric interview. Leaving aside the fundamental criticisms that have been made of the illness model of personal problems (Schacht and Nathan, 1977), adopting a pragmatic stance illustrates another difficulty in identifying cases. Even if a reliable method of measuring cases was to be developed, what of those individuals who just fail to meet the criteria? Do we ignore these people when assessing the extent and degree of gambling related problems in a particular population?

It can be argued from the existing empirical data, limited though it is, that if one considers levels of involvement in gambling, measured in terms of time and cash spent in the activity, then as involvement increases so too does the likelihood of impaired control and the incidence of gambling related problems. This approach directly parallels contemporary work in relation to alcohol (Pols and Hawks, 1989), although the situation is more complex as obviously no one level of gambling can be said to be harmful. The advantages of adopting the idea of a continuum rather than attempting to identify cases is expanded upon in the discussion section of this paper.

TIME FRAME IN DEFINING PROBLEMS (CASES)

In keeping with the Gamblers Anonymous assumption that once a compulsive gambler then always a compulsive gambler, both of the existing measures used in prevalence studies (Culleton, 1989; Lesieur and Blume, 1987) preface their questions concerning pathological characteristics with a phrase such as, "At any time in the past have you . . .." From the literature on alcoholism (Saunders and Kershaw, 1979), it can confidently be predicted that people will move into and out of "pathological" levels of gambling without the assistance of a treatment agency. If the major concern of prevalence studies of pathological gamblers is to establish the current level of gambling related problems in a particular community, then to assume that all past cases should be included in the estimates is something of a nonsense.

It is not so easy to be confident about what is the appropriate time frame within which to assess gambling related problems. The empirical work described below used a one-month window within which subjects were asked to limit their answers. For the purposes of accurate recall this is acceptable, but whether it is the right time frame for the research task is debatable.

FORMS OF GAMBLING

It has been argued elsewhere that it is an error in psychological research into gambling to assume that gambling is a homogeneous set of activities (Dickerson, 1987, 1989, 1990). As foreshadowed at the beginning of this paper, from the perspective of gambling related problems it is quite conceivable that different forms of gambling may be differentially associated with different levels and types of problems. Research in this area may need to include information about the preferred forms of gambling used by individuals.

At the very least, preferences should be categorized into continuous versus non-continuous forms where the latter are forms such as lotto and lotteries where single sequences of stake, play and determination are spaced out over several hours or days, and the former are types of gambling such as poker machines, off-course betting and most casino gaming. As it appears that it is the within session dynamics of continuous forms that may be the major source of impaired control (Dickerson, 1990), then it would be predicted that these forms would be associated with more gambling related problems.

MEASURES OF PATHOLOGICAL GAMBLING

A. Inventory of Gambling Behavior (IGB) (Zimmerman, Meeland and Krug, 1985)

The original validation study involved eighty-three (83) compulsive gamblers (69 men) who had attended at least one Gamblers Anonymous' meeting — they were clearly a sample of convenience as were the comparison group of sixty-one (61) local community service volunteers. Both groups completed a 122 item questionnaire; these items were developed from the criteria for DSM III (1980) and from the Gamblers Anonymous "20 questions." Using eight scores derived from a factor analysis, the authors found that a subsequent discriminant function analysis gave a significant separation of the groups.

Since this first study, a shortened version (29 items) has been used by Culleton in a series of telephone surveys and recently published in the context of a review of prevalence methods in which he recommends the use of the test in the context of a disease prevalence approach, the Cumulative Clinical Signs Method (CCSM) (Culleton, 1989).

The questions in both versions of the test refer to any time in the informants' past, and there is response bias with positive responses all scoring in the direction of pathology. In the short version, items were allocated to five scales by a panel of experts on the basis of content. Visual inspection of the 23 items presented by Culleton (1989) suggests weak face validity for the allocation of some items particularly in the Personal, Interpersonal and Vocational scales. No reliability data for either test has been published, and no further validation studies have been completed to verify the short form scales or the efficiency of that test. From a traditional psychometric viewpoint (Anastasi, 1976), it is a very weak test, and this evaluation holds regardless of whether it is used as a single screening device or within the methodological frame of CCSM. The latter approach cannot correct the IGB's inherent psychometric weaknesses.

B. South Oaks Gambling Screen (SOGS) (Lesieur and Blume, 1987)

The SOGS, despite a far more comprehensive sequence of validation studies, is very similar to the IGB. Although consisting of only 13 items, it has achieved some respectable discriminant function results in separating controls from pathological gamblers. From a psychometric standpoint, the reliability or internal consistency of the test is not known. The questions do not limit subjects to any time frame when recalling gambling related experiences and all positive responses score in the direction of pathology. Some of the problems of the efficiency of the test when used with general population samples have been illustrated above.

The evaluation of the SOGS and of the traditional prevalence approach to assessing the extent and degree of gambling related problems will now be considered in the light of some empirical data from a pilot study completed in Canberra, Australia.

METHOD

SUBJECTS

Stage 1 (1988) — 497 (246 women) probability sample.

Stage 2 (1989) — 56 (19 women) from 140 who at Stage 1 reported gambling once per week or more often.

NOTE: The gap of one year between the two phases of the study arose because the first was completed as a part of a Social Impact Study into the proposed Canberra Casino, and the second could only be completed once funding had been obtained from the Australian National University Faculties Research Fund. The usual method of completing a two-phase design would be for each to run concurrently. In this study, there were problems in ensuring that the person interviewed in the second stage was the same as the person originally contacted by telephone. Some informants at Stage 1 had moved inter-state by Stage 2. This study is therefore only an exploration of a method and cannot be said to have generated secure population estimates.

MEASURES

SOGS A: Essentially the original questionnaire but with certain words altered to fit with the Australian context.

SOGS B: All questions limited to a one month time frame and half of the questions redrafted to give reverse scoring.

PROCEDURE

Stage 1: A random telephone survey using a standard set of questions about current use of legalized forms of gambling (Caldwell et. al., 1988).

Stage 2: Domiciliary interview with informants randomly allocated to either of the two forms A or B. The interview also repeated the initial questions about current level of gambling, whether the person only used non-continuous (lotto) forms and limited demographic data.

NOTE: All data collection by The Roy Morgan Research Centre Pty. Ltd.

RESULTS

The sex and age distribution by SOGS A or B is given in Table 2 and Figure 2 respectively.

TABLE 2

Distribution of Subject by SOGS A & B			
Sex	*SOGS A*	*SOGS B*	*Total*
Female	8	11	19
Male	20	17	37
Total			56

FIGURE 2
Bar Chart Showing Age Distribution by SOGS A & B

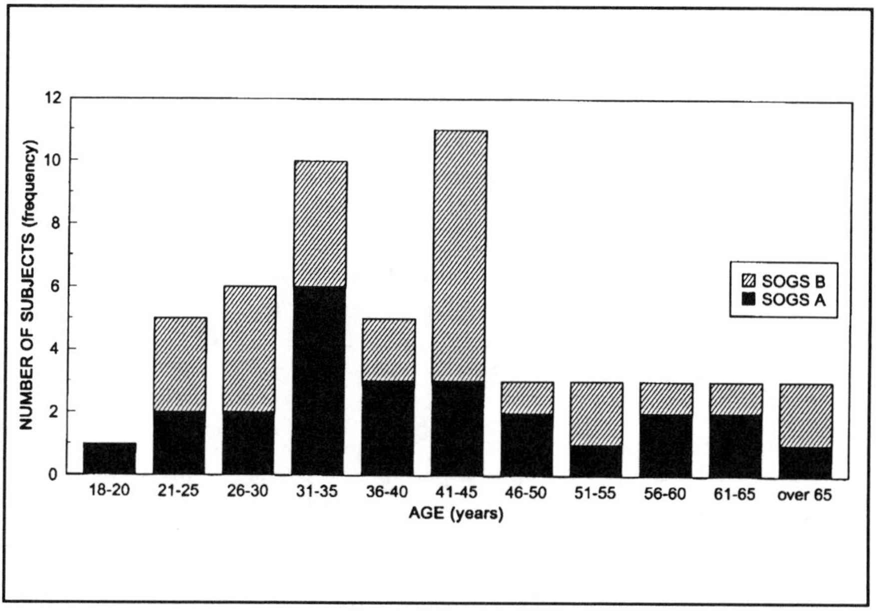

Table 3 gives the means and standard deviations for continuous versus non-continuous gamblers for both SOGS A and SOGS B. The difference between the two types of gamblers is significant as measured by the SOGS A (t=3.38,

$p < 0.01$ two-tailed). SOGS B shows a similar difference which is significant only if a directional hypothesis is assumed.

TABLE 3

Mean Scores (and Standard Deviations) for SOGS A & B for Continuous (N = 34) and Non-Continuous (N = 22) Forms of Gambling

	Continous	*Non-Continuous*
SOGS A	2.50 (2.83)	0.20 (0.42)
SOGS B	1.19 (1.72)	0.33 (0.65)

Table 4 is simply to be provocative and to illustrate what a difficult proposition it is to establish accurate prevalence rates for a phenomena that occurs at a very low frequency in the general population. For the sake of argument, it has been assumed that the 28 in each subgroup are representative of the total 140 people who reported at Stage 1 that they gambled at least once per week. In fact, as the two samples were selected to ensure that the two types of gambling were equally represented, the much less common continuous gamblers were almost all interviewed. As this type of gambler generates significantly more "cases," the prevalence figures may require further correction down as well as, that illustrated in the table, assuming that the SOGS overestimates by a factor of five. It is open to debate what such corrections mean when there are only one or two cases in the cells in question.

DISCUSSION

The pilot nature of the study limits the generalizations that may be drawn. Nonetheless, two results merit comment and add to the preceding debate.

Firstly, it appears that to limit the time frame within which informants recall gambling related problems (together with the elimination of the response bias which given the design does not permit separation from the time factor) results in significantly lower scores and hence prevalence rates. This is not unexpected, but highlights the problem should the prevalence methods using SOGS be challenged, for example, by government agencies from whom treatment funding is being sought or by the gambling industry itself in the context of a social impact study concerning the legalization of a new form a gambling. Further work needs to be done to separate the two effects but at this stage it might be assumed that the change in the time frame is the strongest effect. Even if good arguments can be developed against the use of a one-month time frame, it seems unlikely that the "at any time in the past" approach can be successfully defended. Solutions need to be established within the research literature or we may face a significant loss of validity in the eyes of the public.

TABLE 4

Estimated Prevalence of Problem Gambling Measured by SOGS A & SOGS B

SOGS A			
Test Score	*Subjects*	*Prevalence*	*'Corrected'*
≥ 2	10	10.05	2.01
≥ 3	6	6.00	1.20
≥ 4	4	4.00	0.80
≥ 5	3	3.00	0.60
SOGS B			
Test Score	*Subjects*	*Prevalence*	*'Corrected'*
≥ 2	3	3.00	0.60
≥ 3	2	2.00	0.40
≥ 4	1	1.00	0.20
≥ 5	1	1.00	0.20

The second result of interest is the significant difference in SOGS A scores between informants who use only discontinuous types of gambling such as lotto and those who prefer forms such as off-course betting and poker machines. This substantiates the common assumption that it is the latter, providing the opportunity within a single session for many repetitions of stake, play and determination, that are associated with higher levels of gambling related problems. Future research, by including information about the preferred forms of gambling, may develop profiles of related costs and benefits for each form.

If these findings are considered in the context of the other issues raised, it would seem that research in the area is faced with an important choice: either much more work in carefully refining psychometric instruments that will reliably detect cases in the general population or to adopt a different strategy. If there was agreement amongst researchers on the characteristics of a "case" of pathological gambling or even that an illness model was the appropriate paradigm then the former would be the more likely course of action. However, the conceptual issues around "cases" and the illness model remain contentious (Blaszczynski and McConaghy, 1989; Volberg and Steadman, 1988).

As foreshadowed by the title of this paper, a preference for an alternative paradigm will be discussed. An atheoretical position is one that defines the research problem as one of assessing the personal and social costs (and benefits) associated with the increasingly popular leisure activity of gambling. Thus, the main dependent variables are the costs attributed by an informant to their level of involvement in some form or forms of gambling.

It is fairly generally accepted that these costs may be roughly classified into five domains:

1. Personal, self-esteem, well-being, depression;
2. Relationships, marital, family, friends;
3. Financial;
4. Employment, productivity, promotion; and
5. Legal, contemplation — crime.

The difficult task remains of assessing the gambling related costs in each of these areas as accurately as possible. Ideally, the approach would be to use established psychometric measures in each of the five domains together with a detailed interview to confirm that the attribution of these costs was accurate, i.e., that the assessed level of problems were indeed caused by the person's involvement in gambling. Given the complexity and expense of such an approach, it seems more likely that short self report scales, reliable and consistent, for each of the five domains need to be developed. [Additional research in those social agencies listed by Nadler (1985) could examine the validity of such scales.]

The study of costs as the main dependent variable in a framework that also included some or all of the following as independent variables would have both theoretical and social policy implications:

1. Level of involvement in gambling (the product of average losses per session and frequency per week);
2. Measure of control of gambling;
3. Form(s) of gambling preferred;
4. Individual difference measures;
5. History of gambling experience; and
6. Demographics, i.e., age, sex, income, etc.

As regards methodology, if it is accepted that a face to face interview plus some corroborative information from a significant other is the preferred approach, then this is sufficiently expensive to suggest that some form of two-phase method has advantages. From our own experience, we would suggest the use of a random door-knock first stage rather than accepting the bias inherent in the population of telephone accounts. For example, it is relatively cheap to add two questions defining involvement in gambling by form to weekly market research surveys and then to complete a domiciliary interview with a random subset of those who gamble as the second stage.

This research approach, with an emphasis on accurate description and the avoidance of theoretical assumptions, has the potential to generate data with good face validity. For example, in the present situation in Australia where the Queensland Government intends making poker machines legally and generally available in social clubs and hotels, the above methods would inform policy makers and planners, should they be interested, of the kinds and levels of gambling related problems that would be predicted for the community at large for each level of involvement in poker machine play, once a month, once a week, etc. Such profiles of problems may well differ in content and degree from one form of gambling to another. It is obvious that this approach to the "prevalence" problem will also generate data of theoretical interest.

REFERENCES

American Psychiatric Association (1987). *Diagnostic and Statistical Manual*, 3rd edition, revised. Washington, D.C.: American Psychiatric Association.

Anastasi, A. (1976). *Psychological Testing*, 4th edition. New York: Macmillan.

Blaszczynski, A.P. and McConaghy, N. (1989). The medical model of pathological gambling: Current shortcomings. *Journal of Gambling Behavior*, 5, 42-52.

Caldwell, G., Young, S., Dickerson, M.G. and McMillen, J. (1988). *Social Impact Study* (Civic Section 19, Development and Casino). Australia: Commonwealth of Australia, Canberra.

Culleton, R.P. (1989). The prevalence rates of pathological gambling: A look at methods. *Journal of Gambling Behavior*, 5, 22-41.

Dickerson, M.G. (1985). The characteristics of the compulsive gambler: A rejection of a typology. In G. Caldwell, M.G. Dickerson, B. Haig and L. Sylvan (eds.), *Gambling in Australia*. Sydney: Croom Helm.

Dickerson, M.G. (1987). The future of gambling research: Learning the lesson of alcoholism. *Journal of Gambling Behavior*, 3, 248-256.

Dickerson, M.G. (1989). Gambling: A dependence without a drug. *International Review Journal of Psychiatry*, 1, 157-172.

Dickerson, M.G. (1990). Internal and external determinants of persistent gambling: Implications for treatment. In N. Heather, W. Miller and J. Greeley (eds.), *Self-Control and the Addictive Behaviors*. Australia: Pergamon.

Dickerson, M.G. and Hinchy, J. (1988). The prevalence of excessive and pathological gambling in Australia. *Journal of Gambling Behavior*, 4, 35-51.

Duncan-Jones, P. and Henderson, S. (1978). The use of a two-phase design in a prevalence survey. *Social Psychiatry*, 13, 231-237.

Gathercole, C.E. (1968). *Assessment in Clinical Psychology*. London: Penguin.

Haig, B. (1985). Expenditure on legal gambling. In G. Caldwell, M.G. Dickerson, B. Haig and L. Sylvan (eds.), *Gambling in Australia*. Sydney: Croom Helm.

Lesieur, H. and Blume, S. (1987). South Oaks Gambling Screen (SOGS): A new instrument for the identification of pathological gamblers. *American Journal of Psychiatry*, 144, 1184-1188.

Marlatt, G.A. (1979). Alcohol use and problem drinking: A cognitive-behavioral analysis. In P.C. Kendall and S.D. Hollon (eds.), *Cognitive Behavioral Interventions, Theory, Research and Procedures.* London: Academic Press.

Miller, W.R. (ed.) (1980). *The Addictive Behaviors: Treatment of Alcoholism, Drug Abuse, Smoking and Obesity.* Oxford: Pergamon.

Nadler, L.B. (1985). The epidemiology of pathological gambling: Critique of existing research and alternative strategies. *Journal of Gambling Behavior*, 1, 35-60.

Pols, R.G. and Hawks, D.V. (1987). *Is there a safe level of daily consumption of alcohol for men & women?* Canberra: Australian Government Publishing Service.

Saunders, W.M. and Kershaw, P.W. (1979). Spontaneous remission from alcoholism — a community study. *British Journal of Addiction*, 74, 251-265.

Schacht, T. and Nathan, P.E. (1977). But is it good for the psychologists? Appraisal and status of DSM III. *American Psychologist*, 32, 1017-1025.

Volberg, R. and Steadman, H. (1988). Refining prevalence estimates of pathological gambling. *American Journal of Psychiatry*, 145, 502-505.

Zimmerman, M.A., Meeland, T. and Krug, S. (1985). Measurement and structure of pathological gambling behavior. *Journal of Personality Assessment*, 49, 76-81.

Estimating the Prevalence of Pathological Gambling in the United States*

Rachel A. Volberg

Since the 1970s, legalized gambling has gained in popularity and legitimacy in the United States. Private sector gaming industries have grown rapidly, as have state-sponsored gambling activities. Increasingly, states experiencing financial problems have legalized lotteries, parimutuel racing, and off-track betting. Between 1964 and 1989, 33 states authorized lotteries. In 1976, New Jersey became the second state to legalize casinos, and the first state to do so since Nevada legalized casinos in 1931. In 1988, the federal government passed the Indian Gaming Regulatory Act, intended to legislate relations between state governments and American Indian tribes regarding gambling on tribal lands. In 1989 and 1990, Iowa, Illinois and Mississippi legalized riverboat casinos; Louisiana followed in 1991.

*This work was funded by Research Grant MH-44295 from the Violence and Traumatic Stress Research Branch of the National Institute of Mental Health.

In 1989, shipboard casinos were operating on cruise ships sailing out of American ports in California, Florida and the Gulf states (Even and La Fleur, 1990).

In 1989, Americans wagered $290 billion in total handle on legal and illegal games, including parimutuels, lotteries, casinos, legal bookmaking, card rooms, charitable games, Indian high stakes bingo, and illegal games such as the numbers and sports betting; gross win (total revenues from gaming) for operators was approximately $25 billion. Two-thirds (67%) of the money wagered was gambled at slot machines and casino tables in Nevada and Atlantic City. Parimutuel wagers, including jai alai as well as on- and off-track wagering on horses and dogs accounted for 6% of the gross annual wager. Lotteries accounted for another 7% of this sum. Americans have increased the amount they wagered by nearly $140 billion between 1982 and 1989. Since 1982, gambling has outpaced the American economy in terms of the percentage of personal income spent on wagering compared to other goods and services (Christiansen, 1990).

In spite of the fact that gambling has become an important part of the American cultural landscape in the past two decades, there has been little recognition that gambling might cause problems for individuals or society. Until the 1980s, excessive losses by gamblers, like excessive drinking, were regarded as an individual failing rather than as a medical or social problem. Although several psychoanalysts published case studies of individual compulsive gamblers early in the century, there was almost no interest among researchers and mental health professionals in the problem of compulsive gambling until the 1950s when Bergler (1974) published his analysis of the case histories of 60 compulsive gamblers. While his theory that compulsive gamblers suffer from a masochistic urge to lose has been largely discredited, the psychiatric perspective has "set the agenda for gambling research in the United States" (Rosecrance, 1988, p. 58).

Prior to the 1970s, Gamblers Anonymous was the only group in the United States providing any form of treatment for troubled gamblers. Established in 1957, Gamblers Anonymous has grown almost as rapidly as legalized gambling in the United States. The number of chapters grew from 16 in 1960 to 130 by 1970 and to 600 in 1988 (Lesieur, 1990). Like Alcoholics Anonymous, Gamblers Anonymous is a twelve-step organization whose purpose is to aid its members in their efforts to abstain from gambling (Rosecrance, 1988).

In 1972, the efforts of Dr. Robert Custer and Monsignor Joseph Dunne led to the establishment of the first inpatient treatment program for compulsive gambling at the Veterans Administration Hospital at Brecksville, Ohio, as well as the founding of the National Council on Compulsive Gambling (now the National Council on Problem Gambling). In 1980, the American Psychiatric Association included pathological gambling in the *Diagnostic and Statistical Manual*, 3rd Edition (commonly referred to as DSM-III).

In the wake of increasing legalization of gambling since the 1970s, there has been an increase in the number of treatment programs for compulsive gambling. Funding for many of these treatment programs was established by state legislatures to placate the opponents of legalized gambling. As of 1990, there were treatment programs for compulsive gamblers in eleven states, including Connecticut, Iowa, Maryland, Massachusetts, Minnesota, Montana, Nevada, New Jersey, New York, Ohio and Pennsylvania. These programs offer psychotherapeutic treatment in a variety of settings, including inpatient programs in private psychiatric hospitals as well as outpatient programs in general hospitals and community mental health centers. There are a few psychologists and psychiatrists, whose private practices are focused on compulsive gamblers. The majority of the treatment programs are staffed by professional and medical personnel, many trained by Dr. Custer and his associates. These programs either require or strongly advocate attendance at Gamblers Anonymous meetings as part of their therapeutic regimen and most stress abstinence as their primary treatment goal.

Basic information on the cost of such programs, their effectiveness, and even the nature of the problem itself, is just now becoming available in the United States. For example, in 1985 I was hired to direct an evaluation of New York State's compulsive gambling treatment programs, which are administered by the Office of Mental Health. This evaluation included the collection and analysis of uniform data on all clients in these programs as well as several specialized research initiatives. One such initiative was a prevalence survey of pathological gambling in the general population of New York Sate conducted in 1986. The results of that survey showed that there were significant differences in the characteristics of the clients entering treatment for pathological gambling and pathological gamblers in the general population (Volberg and Steadman, 1988).

In April, 1988, I began work on a three-year project, funded by the National Institute of Mental Health (NIMH), to investigate discrepancies between the characteristics of pathological gamblers in the general population and those entering treatment in five states around the country. The study states in this project were New Jersey, Maryland, Massachusetts, Iowa and California. Prevalence surveys were completed in all five states.

This analysis will first discuss, in some detail, the methods used to collect and analyze these data. Then, the most important results of that analysis will be presented. Finally, some of the implications of this work for the future of the field of problem gambling research will be outlined.

METHODS

The New York prevalence survey, as well as the NIMH-funded surveys, have used the South Oaks Gambling Screen (Lesieur and Blume, 1987). The South Oaks Gambling Screen is a twenty item scale derived from the diagnostic criteria for pathological gambling published in the DSM-III. For the purposes of the prevalence surveys, this instrument was slightly modified for use in telephone interviews with randomly selected respondents in each state.

The number of interviews completed in each state was determined by balancing available resources with the size of each state's population. In California, 1250 interviews were completed. One-thousand interviews were carried out in New Jersey. Seven-hundred fifty interviews were carried out in Maryland, Iowa and Massachusetts. The database consists of completed interviews with 5500 respondents from 6 states, inclusive of the interviews carried out in New York.

The sampling design in all of these surveys was carefully constructed to ensure that inferences could be drawn between the samples and the population over the age of eighteen in these states. The samples from each state were stratified to proportionally represent county populations on the basis of 1980 census figures. For counties where the population was less than 1% of the state total, counties were clustered geographically and respondents were drawn from any one of the cluster counties. Random digit dialing and random selection of respondents within households were used. Up to ten attempts were made to contact each number and up to five callbacks were made to complete an interview with each selected respondent. The response rate was 73% in California, 65% in New Jersey, 66% in Maryland, 69% in Massachusetts and 76% in Iowa. These response rates are similar to the response rates for telephone surveys on other sensitive topics in the United States.

The samples were compared with demographic data collected by the U.S. Bureau of the Census. There were some differences in the demographics of the states and our samples. In Iowa and California, men were undersampled. In New Jersey and California, the Hispanic population was undersampled. In New Jersey and Massachusetts, the population over 65 years of age was undersampled.

Rates of problem and pathological gambling are highest among men and non-white respondents. While the direction of the undersampling in these surveys may have contributed to an underestimation of the rate of problem and pathological gambling in the general population, it is difficult to determine the size of any such underestimation. In addition, since the census data were collected in 1980, some of the differences between these samples and the census figures may be due to changes in the demographics of the states' populations over the prior nine years.

RESULTS

Consistent with prior uses of the South Oaks Gambling Screen, respondents scoring 3 or 4 out of a possible 20 points were classified as "problem gamblers" and those scoring 5 or more points were classified as "probable pathological gamblers."

A. Differences Among States in Rates of Pathological Gambling

Prevalence rates for problem and probable pathological gambling in New Jersey, Maryland and California were very close to the rates found in our initial New York survey. Prevalence rates for probable pathological gamblers were much lower than the New York rate in Iowa and noticeably higher than the New York rate in Massachusetts. Findings are summarized in Table 1.

TABLE 1

PREVALENCE RATES OF PROBLEM & PATHOLOGICAL GAMBLING IN THE UNITED STATES				
State	Population Over 18	Sample Size	Problem Gamblers	Pathological Gamblers
New York (1986)	12.8 million	1,000	2.8%	1.4%
California (1990)	19.9 million	1,250	2.9%	1.2%
New Jersey (1988)	5.7 million	1,000	2.8%	1.4%
Maryland (1988)	2.9 million	750	2.4%	1.5%
Massachusetts (1989)	4.2 million	750	2.1%	2.3%
Iowa (1989)	2.9 million	750	1.6%	0.1%

Three of the survey states were Eastern seaboard states, with similarly heterogeneous populations. California, like the Eastern seaboard states, has a heterogeneous population. Among the study states, Iowa had the most homogeneous population. The prevalence rate of problem and probable pathological gambling in the East Coast states and California, where a broad range of legal wagering opportunities has been available for many years, is nearly twice the rate of problem and probable pathological gambling in Iowa, where wagering opportunities were more limited and where legal wagering had been available for less than 10 years.

These data provide substantiation for an important assertion made by clinicians about pathological gambling. There has been for some time "a general consensus among researchers that . . . increasing the availability of gambling opportunities will . . . eventually lead to an increase in problem gambling" (Rosecrance, 1988). The data from the NIMH-funded surveys are the first non-clinical evidence that there may indeed be a link between the availability of wagering opportunities and the prevalence of pathological gambling. In order to confirm the validity of this finding, it will be necessary to carry out a prevalence survey in another state or states similar to Iowa, where the opportunities for legalized wagering are as new as they were in Iowa.

B. Differences Between the General Population and Problem Gamblers

In addition to questions about differences among states in the prevalence rate of problem and probable pathological gambling, we were interested in whether there were significant differences between the general population and those respondents who scored as problem or probable pathological gamblers. In order to carry out this analysis, we combined the respondents who scored as problem gamblers with those who scored as probable pathological gamblers. We did this because our chief concern was to determine if there were differences between respondents without gambling problems and those with moderate to severe problems. Significance was statistically determined using chi-square analysis.

Differences between the overall samples and those respondents who scored as problem and pathological gamblers varied slightly from state to state. In order to determine the overall differences between the general population and those who scored as problem and probable pathological gamblers, the samples from all of the study states were combined. There were significant differences between the samples and those respondents who scored as problem and probable pathological gamblers along several dimensions.

SEX: Men constituted 43% (N=2275) of all of the respondents but 70% (N=147) of the problem and probable pathological gamblers (x^2=57.26, df=1, p<0.01).

AGE: Although 26% (N=1375) of the overall sample was under the age of 30, 37% (N=78) of the problem and probable pathological gamblers were in this age group (x^2=13.31, df=1, p<0.01).

ETHNICITY: While 18% (N=952) of the overall sample was non-white, 36% (N=76) of the problem and probable pathological gamblers were non-white (x^2=38.28, df=1, p<0.01).

EDUCATION: Although 11% (N=582) of the overall sample had not completed high school, 21% (N=44) of the problem and probable pathological gamblers had not completed high school (x^2=16.39, df=1, p<0.01).

MARITAL STATUS: While 55% (N=2909) of the overall sample was married, only 43% (N=90) of the problem and probable pathological gamblers were married (x^2=11.43, df=1, p<0.01).

Not surprisingly, the variables that discriminated most clearly between the overall sample and those who scored as problem and probable pathological gamblers were those related to wagering activities. For example, while 5% (N=265) of the overall sample stated that they had wagered very often in the last year, 34% of the respondents who scored as problem and probable pathological gamblers stated that they had wagered very often in the last year (x^2=294.13, df=1, p<0.01). The respondents who scored as problem and probable pathological gamblers were significantly more likely than the overall sample to have wagered on all types of gambling. However, there were several types of wagering that these respondents were far more likely than the overall sample to have tried, including card games, games of skill (such as bowling, pool and golf), dice and sports.

C. Comparing Treatment Populations and Problem Gamblers

Pathological gamblers in the United States have been treated in a variety of settings, including VA and general hospital inpatient programs, community mental health centers, private practices, and self-help groups. Assumptions about the characteristics of pathological gamblers are largely based on information collected from these treatment populations. Based on available information, health professionals as well as the general public assume that pathological gamblers are primarily middle-class white males in their forties and fifties.

Problem and pathological gamblers in the general population do not fit this profile. Problem and probable pathological gamblers are significantly younger than the clients entering treatment in all of the states surveyed for the NIMH study. They are more likely to be women, to be non-white, and to have less education than clients entering treatment in all of these states. In New York, 36% of the problem and probable pathological gamblers in the general population were women and 43% were non-white. Among the outpatient treatment programs in New York, 13% of the clients in 1987 were women and 14% were non-white. In New Jersey and Maryland, 32% of the problem and probable pathological gamblers in the general population were women and 36% were non-white. At John F. Kennedy Hospital, New Jersey's largest treatment program for pathological gamblers, 8% of the clients entering the program in 1987 were women and 9% were non-white. At Maryland's Taylor Manor Hospital, a private, inpatient treatment facility, 8% of the gambling clients entering between 1984 and 1987 were women and 11% were non-white (Ciarrocchi and Richardson, 1989).

DISCUSSION

This discussion focuses on some theoretical and methodological issues that must be considered as we move forward in studies of the nature and prevalence of problem and pathological gambling. Consideration of these issues will substantially strengthen the scientific and policy value of our work.

A. Theoretical Issues

There are clearly many questions that need to be answered in the field of problem gambling research. Some of the questions that will probably be critical in the next few years include the following:

1. The Social Context of Gambling

As Rosecrance (1988) has pointed out, and as Dickerson (1993) has also made clear, pathological gambling lies along a continuum that includes all types of gamblers, from the most occasional and innocuous lottery player to the most frequent and involved sports and horse bettors. Gambling as an ordinary activity that connects the individual to his or her social and familial worlds has rarely been a subject of serious research. It is time for researchers to comprehensively investigate the full range of gambling activities in society, as well as the ways in which individuals encounter and overcome difficulties with their gambling.

As I have argued elsewhere (Volberg and Steadman, 1988), problem and pathological gamblers are far more heterogeneous than previously expected. The results reported here point to the need for additional research focused on types of social gamblers as well as on types of problem gamblers. Such research will fill in the context within which problem gambling develops, in the United States and abroad.

A related issue that requires investigation is the relationship between gambling and the abuse of substances such as alcohol, cocaine and anti-depressants. Individuals' wagering strategies may be significantly affected by their consumption of alcohol and other drugs. However, little is known about the specific effects of alcohol or drug consumption on wagering levels or strategies.

Better information about the relationship between wagering and substance use and abuse can help the gaming industry provide improved service to their customers as well as assist mental health treatment professionals in diagnosing and planning for the treatment of problem gamblers.

Finally, there is a need to link the physiological, neurochemical and biological research that has been carried out with problem gamblers to the sociological and psychological research that has been done. Without an understanding of the interaction between body and mind, we cannot hope to fully comprehend the ways in which individuals gamble, both normally and pathologically. With a fuller understanding of the many levels at which gambling affects individuals and society, we can develop better plans for the prevention and treatment of problem gambling.

2. International Studies

It has been said that gambling is endemic to every human society. It is my belief, however, that gambling serves different purposes in different cultures. As we consider the implementation of cross-cultural studies, we must be sensitive to these potential differences and to the likelihood that gamblers who encounter difficulties may be dealt with quite differently in different societies. It may be that problem gamblers, even when they can be accurately diagnosed, seek and obtain very different types of help for their problems. Such help may range from traditional medicine to mental health treatment programs to self-help groups. As plans for international comparisons of gambling behavior and gambling pathology develop, we must be careful to guard against the ethnocentrism characteristic of so much Western, medically-oriented research.

B. Methodological Issues

In addition to these theoretical issues, there are several methodological issues to consider as we move forward with studies of social, as well as problem, gambling. These issues are particularly important in light of current efforts to plan and implement an international epidemiological study of problem and pathological gambling.

1. Classification

Issues of classification straddle the realms of theoretical and methodological discourse (Volberg, 1983). Over the last ten years, the issue of whether problem, compulsive or pathological gambling is in fact a medical illness has been raised numerous times. The tendency to classify problem gambling as a medical problem may reflect the political realities of obtaining organizational resources rather than a fundamental truth. As efforts continue to assess the impact of gaming legalization and legitimation around the world, we must pay careful attention to the assumptions implicit in our definitions of problem and pathological gambling. We must also pay attention to the ways in which our definitions shape the methods that we develop to measure all forms of gambling.

2. Screening

Recent debates in the area of prevalence surveys of pathological gambling (Culleton, 1989; Volberg and Banks, 1990) point to the importance of carefully considering the methods that we adopt. There are presently very few methods for determining the prevalence of problem and pathological gambling in the general population. In reviewing the available methods, I have concluded that the model advocated by Dickerson (1993) represents the most viable approach to determining the prevalence of pathological gambling in the general population.

There are a variety of arguments in favor of this type of two-stage methodology, including the enhanced sensitivity and specificity of this approach, the greater amount of information that can be obtained in face-to-face interviews, and the cost savings that are associated with the use of a short screening instrument combined with a longer interview with a small subset of respondents. Another benefit to such a two-stage methodology is the enhanced accuracy in identification that is possible with this approach. Finally, as I have pointed out elsewhere (Volberg and Banks, 1990), prevalence studies in other areas of medical and psychological research are based on this two-stage model. Adoption of a two-stage methodology will enhance the scientific value of prevalence research in the area of pathological gambling.

3. Validity

Perhaps the crucial issue in the field of gambling research is the question of the validity of the information we collect about people's gambling and problem gambling behavior. There is strong anecdotal and clinical evidence that problem and pathological gamblers lie systematically and that this is a characteristic feature of their gambling problem. The issue facing researchers is how to determine whether a respondent is lying and how to adjust for this as we collect and analyze our data. Obtaining information from collaterals may not be as reliable with this population as with other populations, since problem gamblers also lie to their spouses, children and families. Observing the behavior of these individuals outside the interview situation is not always feasible and when it is, it can be prohibitively expensive. It will be necessary for the research community to tax its collective imagination as we attempt to respond to this critical issue in carrying out research on problem gambling.

CONCLUSION

Although gambling in the United States has increased rapidly in the past two decades, relatively little has been done to investigate gambling behavior. The prevalence data reported here represent the first multi-state study of problem and pathological gambling as well as the first federally-funded research in this area. The results of this research suggest that problem gambling is a greater problem in those states where legal wagering has been available for some time. The results further indicate that problem and pathological gamblers are significantly more likely to be men, to be under the age of 30, to be non-white and to have lower education than the general population. Finally, the results demonstrate that problem gamblers entering treatment in a variety of settings represent only a small proportion of the full range of problem gamblers in the general population.

I believe that we have reached the crest of an initial wave of research on problem and pathological gambling. As we consider the future, our focus must shift toward issues such as the social context of gambling, the similarities and differences between "normal" and "pathological" gambling, the relationship between physiological and psychological responses to gambling, and the relationship between problem gambling and substance abuse. We must consider gambling and problem gambling from an international perspective, making every effort to avoid the pitfalls of an ethnocentric world-view in our efforts. Finally, we have an opportunity to discuss, if not resolve, some of the methodological questions that have plagued our efforts in the past.

The last point to be made regards funding. We must recognize the reluctance of federal and state government agencies to fund research on gambling and problem gambling. Unless proposals are framed very narrowly in terms of gambling as a pathology or as an addiction, it is unlikely that these agencies will commit funds to research in this area. It is time for the gaming industries and their regulators to recognize the importance of sponsoring research on normal and pathological gambling in order to obtain much-needed data on the individuals they serve and to demonstrate their willingness to act in a socially responsible manner. It is also time for researchers in this area to think imaginatively about our research agendas in order to develop information that will contribute to our understanding of the "risky business" with which we all are associated.

REFERENCES

American Psychiatric Association (1980). *Diagnostic and Statistical Manual of Mental Disorders*, 3rd Edition. Washington, D.C.: Government Printing Office.

Bergler, E. (1974). *The Psychology of Gambling.* London: International Universities Press.

Christiansen, E.M. (1990). 1989 U.S. gross annual wager. *Gaming and Wagering Business*, 11:7, 1 and 7-30.

Ciarrocchi, J. and Richardson, R. (1989). Profile of compulsive gamblers in treatment: Update and comparisons. *Journal of Gambling Behavior*, 5, 53-65.

Culleton, R.P. (1989). The prevalence rates of pathological gambling: A look at methods. *Journal of Gambling Behavior*, 5, 22-41.

Dickerson, M. (1993). A preliminary exploration of a two-stage methodology in the assessment of the extent and degree of gambling-related problems in the Australian population. In W.R. Eadington and J.A. Cornelius (eds.), *Gambling Behavior and Problem Gambling.* Reno, NV: Institute for the Study of Gambling and Commercial Gaming, University of Nevada.

Even, M. and LaFleur, T. (1990). 1989 Gaming at a glance. *Gaming and Wagering Business*, 11:7, 52-55.

Lesieur, H.R. (1990). Working with and understanding Gamblers Anonymous. In T.J. Powell (ed.), *Working with Self-Help.* Homewood, IL: Dorsey Press.

Lesieur, H.R. and Blume, S. (1987). The South Oaks Gambling Screen (SOGS): A new instrument for the identification of pathological gamblers. *American Journal of Psychiatry*, 144, 1184-1188.

Rosecrance, J. (1988). *Gambling Without Guilt: The Legitimation of an American Pastime.* Belmont, CA: Wadsworth.

Volberg, R.A. (1983). *Constraints and commitments in the development of American botany, 1880-1920.* Ph.D. Dissertation. University of California, San Francisco.

Volberg, R.A. and Banks, S.M. (1990). A review of two measures of pathological gambling in the United States. *Journal of Gambling Studies*, 6, 153-163.

Volberg, R.A. and Steadman, H.J. (1988). Refining prevalence estimates of pathological gambling. *American Journal of Psychiatry*, 145, 502-505.

Prevalence Estimates of Pathological Gamblers in Québec, Canada©

Robert Ladouceur

Gambling has been practiced among many cultures for thousands of years (Abt, Smith and Christiansen, 1985). We all know that this phenomenon is widespread. More than two-thirds of the adult population in the United States and in Canada engage regularly in some form of gambling (Olivier and Gagnon, 1984; Gallup, 1980; Kallick, Suits, Dielman and Hybels, 1979; Skolnick, 1979). While most people gamble moderately, some become addicted. Those gamblers become emotionally dependent on gambling and lose control of the personal, family and vocational dimensions of their lives (Custer, 1982).

© A version of this article has been accepted for publication in the *Journal of Primary Prevention*, (1993). Permission to reprint has been granted by the author and publisher, ©Human Sciences Press, Inc.

Clinical observations show that many pathological gamblers began their gambling activities during their adolescence (Custer, 1982; Dell, Ruzicka and Polisi, 1981). In the United States, Lesieur and Klein (1987) surveyed 892 adolescents to learn about their gambling behavior and problems. According to the authors, 91% of these students gambled at least once and 32% gambled regularly during the year preceding the experiment. Additionally, 5.7% of them were considered to be pathological gamblers.

Ladouceur and Mireault (1988) surveyed gambling behaviors of high school students in the Québec area with a French version of the questionnaire developed by Lesieur and Klein (1987). Three-quarters (76%) of the 1612 respondents had gambled at least once and 24% gambled at least once a week during the year before the survey. Furthermore, 3.6% of adolescents were identified as pathological gamblers according to Lesieur and Klein's (1987) criteria.

Few studies on the prevalence of pathological gambling have been conducted with adults. These studies are needed if we want to know the extent of pathological gambling disorder. These results would indicate the nature of needs related to problem gambling and justify the development of new treatment programs for pathological gamblers (Volberg and Steadman, 1989b).

Though prevalence studies have been conducted in only a few states in the United States, such studies have just recently or are in the process of being conducted in some provinces in Canada. The present study evaluates the prevalence of pathological gambling among the adult population of the Québec province.

METHOD

The South Oaks Gambling Screen (SOGS) developed by Lesieur and Blume (1987) was used. This instrument is a 20-item scale derived from the DSM-III criteria for pathological gambling (A.P.A., 1980). For the purposes of telephone surveys, Volberg and Steadman (1988) slightly modified this instrument. Since most of the people in Québec are French speaking, the instrument was translated into French.

The sample was stratified to proportionally represent the population of each area in the province (over the age of 18). Random selection of phone numbers in phone books and random selection of respondents within households were used. There were 1,002 interviews completed. Respondents were contacted and interviewed by four research assistants trained by an employee of a survey research firm located in Québec City. Interviews were conducted between the weekday hours of 4 PM and 9 PM and Saturdays between 12 noon and 6 PM. Up to five attempts were made to contact each number. The refusal rate was 32%. It was higher among urban respondents.

RESULTS

Respondents scoring 3 or 4 out of 20 points on the South Oaks Gambling Screen were classified as "problem gamblers" and those scoring 5 or more points were classified as "probable pathological gamblers" (see Volberg and Steadman, 1988). In the present survey, 2.6% of the Québec sample were identified as "problem gamblers" and 1.2% of the Québec sample scored as "probable pathological gamblers."

The next step in our analysis was to identify if there were significant differences between the overall sample and those respondents who scored as problem and probable pathological gamblers. In order to carry out this analysis, the responses of the problem and probable pathological gamblers were combined and compared to respondents without gambling problems.

Significance was statistically determined using chi-square analysis. Significant differences ($p<.05$) between the total sample and the respondents classified as problem and probable pathological gamblers were found on several dimensions:

GENDER: While 46% of the respondents were male, 75.9% of the problem and probable pathological gamblers were men ($X^2 = 11.43$, df=1, $p<.01$).

AGE: While 31% of the respondents were under the age of 30, 41.6% of the problem and pathological gamblers were under 30; and while 17.5% of the respondents were between 40 and 49, 33.6% of the two gambling-impaired groups were between 40 and 49 ($X^2 = 12.78$, df=4, $p<.01$).

EDUCATION: While 42.2% of the respondents have graduated from high school, 58.4% of the problem and probable pathological gamblers earned a high school degree ($X^2 = 8.21$, df=3, $p<.05$).

MARITAL STATUS: While 32.8% of the respondents were single, 40.2% of the problem and probable pathological gamblers were single; and while 53.7% of the respondents were married, 36.7% of the two gambling-impaired groups were married (X^2 = 11.48, df=4, p<.05).

No differences between the general population and the two gambling-impaired groups were found in religious preferences. However, with regard to age of onset, analysis of the data showed that problem and pathological gamblers tended to start wagering at an earlier age than other gamblers. Ten percent of all the respondents who gambled began wagering before the age of 15. In contrast, 26.4% of the problem and probable pathological gamblers began wagering before the age of 15. The interval between the age at which problem and pathological gamblers began wagering and the age at which they became preoccupied about the amounts they were wagering was 8.8 years.

A small percentage (11.5%) of the problem and probable pathological gamblers have already received help for gambling. Most respondents who received help for gambling were those who scored as probable pathological gamblers (8.9%), while only 2.9% of those who scored as problem gamblers received help.

During the year preceding the survey, 52.2% of the respondents have wagered money. Since lotteries are the most popular legalized gambling activity in Québec, it is not surprising that 88.3% of the respondents have bought a lottery ticket before, leaving only 11.5% of them who have never participated in lotteries.

DISCUSSION

Prevalence rates in the province of Québec survey showed that 2.6% of the sample were identified as problem gamblers and 1.2% of the sample scored as probable pathological gamblers. The results also showed that 88.3% of the respondents have participated in a gambling activity at least once in their life and 55.2% of them have gambled more than once during the year preceding the survey.

These results suggest that gambling activities are widespread in Québec. The prevalence rates for problem and probable pathological gamblers found here were very close to the rates reported by Volberg and Steadman (1988, 1989a) in New York, New Jersey and Maryland. Since lotteries, horseraces and bingo constitute the only legalized forms of gambling in the Province, we can suppose that many gamblers engage at one time or another in some form of illegal gambling.

The majority of the respondents who developed a problem with gambling were male and most of them began to wager at an earlier age than other gamblers. These results are consistent with clinical observations which show that many pathological gamblers are mostly men who began to wager during their adolescence (Custer, 1982; Custer and Milt, 1985; Dell et al., 1981). Furthermore, prevalence surveys among high-school students showed that a substantial number of students who gamble on a regular basis can already be classified as pathological gamblers (Ladouceur and Mireault, 1988; Lesieur and Klein, 1987). This suggests that for many of the respondents, problem or pathological gambling may have begun at an earlier age.

In our survey, only 11.5% of the problem and probable pathological gamblers received help for their gambling problems. Many gamblers are probably not aware of their gambling problems or they do not know where to seek help. In fact, it seems that very few people know about pathological gambling and its negative consequences. This suggests that people should have more information regarding the nature of pathological gambling and the resources available to help them cope with this problem.

Knowing more about the prevalence of problem and probable pathological gambling could bring about a better understanding of this pathology and lead to the establishment of programs for the treatment and prevention of pathological gambling. Many authors have suggested that the increasing availability of gambling opportunities could lead to more problem gambling among adult population. The present results should be considered when legislators have to decide whether or not to legalize new gambling activities such as casinos.

REFERENCES

Abt, V., J.F. Smith, and E.M. Christiansen (1985). *The Business of Risk: Commercial Gambling in Mainstream America.* Lawrence, KS: University of Kansas Press.

Custer, R.L. (1982). An overview of compulsive gambling. In P.A. Carone, S.F. Yolles, S.N. Kieffer and L.W. Krinsky (eds.), *Addictive Disorders Update*, 107-124. New York: Human Science Press.

Custer, R.L. and H. Milt (1985). *When Luck Runs Out.* New York: Facts on File Publications.

Dell, L.J., M.E. Ruzicka, and A.T. Palisi (1981). Personality and other factors associated with gambling addiction. *The International Journal of Addictions*, 16, 149-156.

Gallup, G. (1980, November 29). 78% des canadiens aiment parier. *La Presse*. Montréal.

Ide-Smith, S.G. and S.E.G. Lea (1988). Gambling in young adolescents. *Journal of Gambling Behavior*, 4, 110-118.

Kallick, M., D. Suits, T. Dielman, and J. Hybels (1979). *A Survey of American Gambling Attitudes and Behavior.* Ann Arbor, MI: Survey Research Center, Institute for Social Research, University of Michigan.

Ladouceur, R. and C. Mireault (1988). Gambling behavior among high school students in the Québec area. *Journal of Gambling Behavior*, 4, 3-12.

Lesieur, H.R. and S. Blume (1987). The South Oaks Gambling Screen (SOGS): A new instrument for the identification of pathological gamblers. *American Journal of Psychiatry*, 144, 1184-1188.

Lesieur, H.R. and R. Klein (1987). Pathological gambling among high school students. *Addictive Behaviors*, 12, 129-135.

Olivier, A. and C. Gagnon (1984). *Etude de la pénétration des loteries dans le marché montréalais: "Pénétration VIII."* Montréal: Multi-Reso, Inc.

Skolnick, J.H. (1979). The social risks of casino gambling. *Psychology Today*, 7, 52-64.

Volberg, R.A. (1989). *Prevalence rates of problem gambling in three states.* Remarks presented at the Fourth National Conference on Compulsive Gambling, Des Moines, Iowa, June 1-3.

Volberg, R.A. and H.J. Steadman (1988). Refining prevalence estimates of pathological gambling. *American Journal of Psychiatry*, 145, 502-505.

Volberg, R.A. and H.J. Steadman (1989a). Prevalence estimates of pathological gambling in New Jersey and Maryland. *American Journal of Psychiatry*, 146, 1618-1619.

Volberg, R.A. and H.J. Steadman (1989b). Policy implications of prevalence estimates of pathological gambling. In H.J. Shaffer, S.A. Stein, B. Gambino and T.N. Cummings (eds.), *Compulsive Gambling*, 163-174. Toronto: Lexington.

V

Gambling and Youth

Underage Gambling in New Jersey

Michael L. Frank

A three year survey of college students was conducted to ascertain the frequency and preferences of student gambling at nearby casinos in Atlantic City, New Jersey. The data suggest that gambling by underage college students is quite common and indicates that age controls at casino entrances is quite poor. An additional finding of differential memory for wins and losses suggests the need for an information processing analysis of memory for gambling outcomes.

UNDERAGE GAMBLING IN ATLANTIC CITY CASINOS

When casino gambling was first introduced in Atlantic City, New Jersey, the major concern of most public officials was that the casinos operate without any corruptive intervention by organized crime. Since 1978, that promise has been kept according to available data. Another equally pressing concern, however, was to control access to the casinos by underage gamblers. Originally, the statutory minimum age to gamble in Atlantic City was 18 years. On

January 1, 1983 the minimum age to drink alcoholic beverages in New Jersey was raised to 21, and subsequently the minimum age to enter the casino gaming area was raised to 21 on April 13, 1983. Due to a grandfather provision in the original statute, no one under 21 years of age was permitted to gamble in Atlantic City casinos after 1985. Since 1985, according to figures compiled by the New Jersey Casino Control Commission, almost one million youths have been prevented from entering gaming areas and over 140,000 have been ejected from the casino floor after they passed security guards stationed at the entrances to the gaming areas.

Over the past several years, the concern about underage gambling at Atlantic City casinos has been growing. An annual survey was begun at Stockton State College, a local four-year undergraduate institution close to Atlantic City, in order to ascertain the incidence and frequency of undergraduate student gambling. The college has an enrollment of approximately 5,000 students. The proximity of the campus to Atlantic City casinos makes it a unique place to study the relationship between travel distance and gambling behavior. The campus is highly residential and over 50% of the students live on or very close to campus.

METHOD

Students were sampled over the three years of the survey to get a representative mix from the entire college. The specific technique was to sample from large introductory courses given during one particular meeting-time module. This assured that no student over the three years of the survey would be sampled twice, the survey could be administered to fairly large groups, and the return rate would be reasonably high. Since enrollment data indicated that over 95% of students who graduate from the college take at least one introductory course in the social or behavioral sciences, the sample was chosen from this segment of the curriculum. The i)approach assured a sampling procedure which was both representative and reliable. A total of 636 students completed the survey over a three year period of time.

The survey form consisted of 48 questions concerning gambling behavior, employment, demographic information, and gambling preferences. Also, a copy of the South Oaks Gambling Screen — *SOGS* — (Lesieur and Blume, 1987) was included in the second and third administration of the survey; the first time the students were surveyed a copy of the SOGS was not included. This was, in fact, the only difference among the three administrations.

RESULTS

The results were analyzed by running several cross-checks to ascertain if, in fact, the sampling strategy produced a sample of respondents which was representative of the entire student body. The proportion of men to women, the age distribution, and class standing were all subjected to goodness of fit tests to those of the over-all institution. All tests indicated each of the samples were representative of the demographics of the student body. The 1988 sample was almost 69% under 21 years at the time of the survey, whereas in 1987 and 1986 the proportion of under-age students was 38% and 46% respectively. This is somewhat related to the month of sample selection with the 1988 sample selected in the fall and previous samples selected during the spring semesters.

Some of the findings of the study were striking. First of all, 59% of the 1988 sample had gambled within the previous year, 42% within the past six months, and 24% within the past month. The data from the 1987 survey show 78% of the sample gambled within the previous 12 months, 56% within the past six months and 19% within the past month of the survey. The 1986 data show that 73%, 51%, and 26%, of the students gambled during the respective intervals. This suggests that undergraduate gambling behavior is fairly stable and does not seem to vary significantly over time. Although there was a notable decrease in the number gambling over the past 12 months in the third administration of the survey, it was neither a large nor a stable decline.

It should be mentioned that college students' gambling mirrors the rate of casino gambling behavior for most adults in the northeast. This was true even though 69% of the current sample was under the minimum legal age of 21 years required to enter an Atlantic City gambling casino. This large number of under 21-year-old survey participants may also account for the decline in rates of casino participation as mentioned previously, with the proportion of under 21-year-olds in previous samples showing 38% and 46%, respectively, over the last two administrations. The relationship between gambling and age was examined more closely. It was surprising to find no significant relationship between age and gambling. The samples showed that age is not connected with gambling behavior in undergraduate populations. Of the students who gamble, 66% were under age, which is not appreciably different from the 68% of under 21-year-old students who do not gamble.

At the minimum, this is a clear indication of ineffective age controls in Atlantic City casinos. It seems then, that casino gambling is both common and is unrelated to age. These findings suggest that underage gambling among undergraduates is quite common and, if anything, the casinos serve as a magnet as much as anything else for very young college students.

Data were examined to assess if there were any demographic or behavioral variables associated with casino gambling behavior. No relationship was found with subject's sex, family size, or parental marital status. Surprisingly, no relationship was found with employment either. Although more than half the sample were employed at least part-time, whether they worked or not was unrelated to whether they gambled. This is particularly interesting because it suggests that income is not a primary variable in predicting college students' gambling. Similarly, casino gambling is not a social class phenomenon as it was unrelated to parental home ownership, parental education, or parental income.

There was, however, a class of variables associated with, and predictive of, the likelihood of casino gambling. These variables were related to other gambling or risk taking activities. Almost 75% of the respondents who gambled in a casino in the past year also played the New Jersey State lottery, whereas less than half of non-casino gamblers reported that they played the lottery. (Over-all, about 59% of students reported playing the New Jersey State Lottery.) The same sort of relationship also holds for sports betting — most of which is illegal — and for betting on horses at racetracks. This suggests that college students who gamble in casinos also tend to engage in other sorts of gambling activities — both legal and illegal.

An additional significant relationship with speeding tickets was found. Casino gamblers were more likely to have received a summons for exceeding the speed limit than were non-casino gamblers. This suggests either casino gamblers get caught more often or they actually drive faster than non-casino gamblers. In the author's view, this is an indication of fundamental propensity towards risk taking in general. Interestingly, these relationships hold up for students both above and below the legal minimum age to gamble which is suggestive of the underlying personality differences between gamblers and non-gamblers.

It is important to note that these general findings are quite stable. Additional research may turn up a "golden nugget" by exploring the propensity gamblers show for other, non-gambling risks.

Whatever the attraction of casino gambling, students who gamble indicate that they intend to continue to do so, with 47% saying they will probably or definitely return to an Atlantic City casino and only 33% saying they definitely or probably will not.

The specific attributes of gambling preferences for the group of students who gambled were also examined. Student gamblers prefer slot machines, blackjack and roulette to other casino games. Sixty-four percent report slots are their favorite game, 28% blackjack, and 6% reported a preference for roulette.

Student gamblers, by and large, play with modest amounts of money; 78% of the sample played with less than $50. It is interesting, however, that a small portion of the sample (7%) reported playing with more than $100. Most students, however seem to play with less money than they have on their person which suggests most gambling is, in fact, recreational and controlled.

The usual bet size at table games is $5, but a few people (8% of the sample) reported placing usual bets of $25 or more. This is larger action than expected in an undergraduate population. In fact, when asked what the biggest bet they have ever made was, 24% responded *more* than $25. This represents larger size betting behavior than previously reported in a college population.

Respondents were asked how they were doing, and the classical pattern was observed. About 66% of the respondents reported they were winning or breaking even! This pattern is common in surveys of the general population and suggests that either people are lying on anonymous survey forms, or they are misremembering their win/loss record. It is not reasonable to believe that most people who gamble do not lose money in the long run. In fact, all casino games represent a negative expected value gamble. Additionally, considering the particular gaming preferences reported, and the house advantage of casino games, the reported mean win of $39 compared to a mean loss of only $14 is highly unlikely.

It is reasonable to believe that this pattern of results is best explained by respondents remembering the wins and forgetting the losses. If this bias in memory is in fact occurring, it may be important in explaining the persistence of gambling behavior in the face of financial loss. Of course, this finding could be an artifact of public spectacle, rather than private rationalization, in which case it is far less interesting. This selective memory would, of course, raise interesting questions about the road to pathological gambling.

A few respondents in the sample indicated they visited a casino to gamble once a week or more on average in the past month. About four percent of the sample reported weekly or more frequent gambling activity. This behavior is rare among the undergraduate population and may serve as an estimate of those people who are "at risk" of developing into problem gamblers.

Student gamblers report that they usually drink alcoholic beverages when they visit a casino to gamble. Gamblers report a mean of 1.4 drinks consumed per visit. Further, an overwhelming majority of student gamblers gamble with friends; over 95 percent report gambling with others. It is interesting that the four percent who report gambling alone is roughly the same proportion who report gambling with abnormally high frequency. Additional analysis, however, indicated that only seven of the same individuals were involved in these groups and were also making large bets.

Data reported on the South Oaks Gambling Screen (SOGS) were also analyzed. These numbers suggested an interesting pattern. Six percent of the students scored five or higher on the SOGS, suggesting that six percent of the students in the survey were having significant difficulty with respect to their gambling, and could be classified as potential or probable pathological gamblers. It is important to remember that this six percent figure is from a young, college-age, general population and is alarmingly high, seemingly higher than the proportion in the larger population.

DISCUSSION

These data are useful for a variety of purposes and may suggest some direction for continued research. These are three major points which emerge from the data. First of all, it is clear that the age controls in Atlantic City casinos are considerably less effective than they need to be. The large number of underage gamblers ejected from casinos of course represent an unknown fraction of those who were actually on the casino floor and less than 21 years old. The data clearly indicate that a fairly large number of underage gamblers were permitted through security checks. When one considers the frequency of drinking while gambling in addition to the age limits, there is clearly a significant social problem. These data do not focus on whether controls at some casino hotels are more effective than others and should not be construed to indicate that all casinos are equally porous. Clearly, more study is called for in this regard.

An additional finding of clinical interest is the small but consistent proportion of the sample who report frequent gambling, betting with sizable amounts of money, and gambling in a nonsocial context. This suggests the need for closer scrutiny of the undergraduate population for potential pathology of gambling behavior.

Finally, the anomalous finding that most people report winning or breaking even is suggestive of support for an information processing model to account for persistence of gambling in the face of financial hardship. Several important papers in the literature (Keren and Wagenaar, 1985; Gilovich, 1983; and Fischholf and Beyth, 1975) have suggested that information about gambling decisions is processed in a consistently biased manner which leads the gambler to make less than optimal choices. If one rejects the survey findings that 66% of people who gamble are winning or about even as impossible, the discrepancy between the reported casino win figures and the reported average win figures in this sample demand an explanation. One interesting and theoretically important possibility is that respondents are, in fact, remembering wins and losses differently. If the memory of the magnitude of a win grows with the passage of time, while the amount of loss shrinks, a cognitive reinforcement theory of persistence of gambling behavior may be valuable. Also, clinical interventions may be directed to focus on accuracy of recall over time. Of course, more systematic work is needed to validate or disconfirm this conjecture, but it is clearly a testable hypothesis of potential importance.

REFERENCES

Fischhoff, B. and Beyth, R. (1975). 'I knew it would happen': Remembered probabilities of once-future things. *Organizational Behavior and Human Performance*, 13, 1-16.

Gilovich, T. (1983). Biased evaluation and persistence in gambling. *Journal of Personality and Social Psychology*, 44, 1110-1126.

Keren, G. and Wagenaar, W.A. (1985). On the psychology of playing blackjack: Normative and descriptive considerations with implications for decision theory. *Journal of Experimental Psychology: General*, 14, 133-158.

Lesieur, H. and Blume, S. (1987). South Oaks Gambling Screen (SOGS): A new instrument for the identification of pathological gamblers. *American Journal of Psychiatry*, 144, 1184-1188.

Towards a Sociological Understanding of Slot Maching Gambling in Young People

Susan Fisher

The inordinate commercial success of slot machines has been described as "one of the most disconcerting enigmas posed by contemporary amusements" (Caillois, 1958). Since this statement was made, over thirty years ago, the dramatic growth in slot machines has proved to be one of the most pervasive trends in the gambling industry. While fruit machines are played by all age groups in the United Kingdom, their attraction is predominately for young people and declines with advancing age. As with other gambling forms, more young males participate than females.

Adolescent gambling is preeminently a sociological concern. The majority of young people participate, and many of these on a regular basis. Furthermore it is alleged that a minority of young people are persistently drawn to delinquent behavior as a consequence of their play. But in spite of growing evidence that juvenile gambling is ubiquitous, enduring, and frequently deviant to boot, it has an astonishingly meager tradition in sociology. An attempt is made here to establish when and how children are initiated into gambling behavior, to assess the importance of fruit machine playing *vis a vis* other gambling forms favored by children, and to discuss ways in which the attraction of fruit machine gambling for juveniles might be rendered sociologically understandable.

AGE AT WHICH GAMBLING FOR MONEY COMMENCES

Both in the United States and in the U.K., children report gambling for money while still in primary education. In the case of the U.S., the child who complies with the minimum statutory age threshold set by his/her state of residence is the exception rather than the rule. In a recent study, more than a third of the respondents reported gambling before they were eleven years of age, and 70% to 88% said they gambled before they were fifteen years old (Jacobs, 1989). In the U.K., where gambling on fruit machines is lawful and readily accessible to children in amusement arcades, cafes, fish and chip shops, and the like, the onset of gambling for money is likely to be even earlier with fruit machine gambling commonly starting at eight or nine years of age (Fisher, 1989).

The lack of public outcry in the U.S. against the open practice of a patently illegal activity by the majority of its children reveals the degree of societal acceptance of juvenile gambling. This acceptance, which finds endorsement in the statute book in the U.K., has been attributed to several possible bases of rationalization or misconception by adults. The first is the implicit faith in legal sanctions for the protection of children from "really serious gambling" so that parents need not worry. The second is that adults in society are reluctant to face up to their own crucial role in the socialization of children into gambling behavior. The third is that juvenile gambling (albeit illegal) is dismissable as merely "fun and games." Finally it is suggested that such rationalizations are simply grounded in ignorance, in a delayed awareness of this aspect of adolescent leisure (Jacobs, 1989, p. 250).

GETTING STARTED

Initiation into gambling arises from a number of influences. Some writers hold that parental gambling is an important predictor of adolescent participation (Downes, 1976; Cornish, 1978; Amati, 1981; Arcuri, 1985; Jacobs, 1989). Indeed much adolescent gambling takes place in the company of parents (Lesieur and Klein, 1987). In addition, the media — particularly television — reinforces societal acceptance of gambling by glamorizing of high risk gamblers and glitzy game shows (Smith and Abt, 1984; Griffiths, 1988). In the U.K. some recent (1990) examples include two drama serials, "The Gambler" and "Big Deal"; and game shows based on games of chance such as "Gambit," "Play Your Cards Right," "Bullseye," "Winner Takes All," and the current "You Bet".

As far as gambling on commercially provided games is concerned, these tend to be locale specific, so that participation depends upon supply [for example slot machines in arcades are supernormally available to U.K. children who reside in seaside resorts and to U.S. children, albeit illegally, who reside near jurisdictions that allow casinos (Fisher, 1989; Jacobs, 1989)]. Finally, it is suggested that gambling is essentially a form of play and as such is inescapably interwoven into the autonomous culture of children's games (Herman, 1976; Abt and Smith, 1984). This latter suggestion is explored in more detail below.

CHILDREN AT PLAY

Smith and Abt (1984) highlight the inherent contradiction of children's games: By definition they are pointless, and yet they are significant for the part they play in the socialization process. They offer respite from the demands of daily life, while expressing and transmitting the myths and values of the wider culture. They may also give a clue as to the male gender bias among child and adult gamblers.

While young females tend to play out caring roles and consensual contexts in their play, boys are inclined to adopt aggressive and heroic roles in games based upon competition (see also Opie and Opie, 1969). However, not all players are equally endowed with the appropriate attributes of strength and skill, so that games which combine a measure of talent with the random favors for chance are assured cultural success. Gambling-like games such as cards, marbles, picture card flipping, and — since the 1970s — video games, teach children the adult, societal values of commercialism and competition in the context of what Goffman terms a "fateful encounter" (Goffman, 1969).

Thus, as in adult gambling games, the primary reward of success in children's gambling and gambling-type games is not material, but a highly prized gain in "character" in Goffman's sense of the term. By taking risks in games, reputations are built and the winners earn important social rewards (Smith and Abt, 1984; Opie and Opie, 1969). Keill's observations on the demeanor of five adolescent boys playing poker illustrates the point:

> "The sub-surface habits, whether verbal or physical, which these adolescents brought to the poker table, are essentially those which they bring to the dinner table, their classroom, their other play. They are part of the maturative process. When the adolescent approached the card table, he brought his 'hidden manliness' with him. It is this kind of 'man-to-man' relationship, where adolescent striving for asserting maturity and achieving recognition thereof from his peers, can genuinely be observed, stripped of fraud, of role playing his adolescence in front of his seniors" (Keill, 1956, pp. 88-89).

Each game is immersed in its own subculture and is consequently rich in ritual and meaning. Thus a game of marbles may be a "rite of passage" for a child in a school playground, while a poker game simultaneously provides adolescents with relief from the tedium of daily life and an "opportunity to reflect the psychological traits which they feel should govern the rest of their lives" (Smith and Abt, 1984, p. 132). An understanding of the subculture surrounding each gambling or gambling type game would thus seem to be essential to a proper sociological understanding of it.

GAMBLING GAMES PLAYED BY YOUNG PEOPLE

The four favorite games played for money by American youth since the mid 1980s are cards with family or friends; lotteries (where available); games of skill such as golf, pool and bowls; and sports betting on football and baseball pools and offtrack betting — for the most part illegally pursued with a bookie (Jacobs, 1993). However, in the case of adolescents who live within striking distance of casinos the pattern is notably different:

> "These glitter palaces seem to have an irresistible lure for underage high school students that tends to preempt their gambling time and dollars" (Jacobs, 1989, p. 253).

Most of the casino betting is on slot machines — around two-thirds — with blackjack and roulette respectively as the second and third favorite activities (Arcuri et al., 1985; Frank, 1988). In the U.K., young people gamble with each other on cards, games involving skill, and a traditional children's game called "coins up the wall" (Moran, 1987; Ide-Smith and Lea, 1988). But overwhelmingly the most common form of commercial gambling is on slot machines, preferably in the social context of an amusement arcade (Fisher, 1989). Thus it is apparent that, where supply permits, fruit machines emerge as the gambling form most favored by young people, on both sides of the Atlantic.

THE PULL OF THE FRUIT MACHINE

If games reflect the culture of the players (Caillois, 1958) then fruit machines are the ultimate manifestation of commercialism in modern leisure products. Names such as "Cash Arena," "Loads'a'Money," "Action Bank," and Noteshoot" leave the player in no doubt that the game involves the wagering of cash for more cash.

The fruit machine of today is the achievement of nearly a century's development of Charles Fey's first fully automatic payout, three reel machine. It still often comprises three reels, each adorned with successive brightly colored pictures of fruit (e.g., an orange, cherry, or lemon). Once money has been inserted, the reels spin on a random ratio schedule for predetermined time cycles, i.e., the first reel spins for approximately three seconds, the second for four seconds, and the third for five seconds (Griffiths, 1988). The twenty-stop, twenty-symbol reel system in general use allows for eight thousand possible combinations of symbols and frequent wins to maximize play value for money (Costa 1988). Cash prizes are typically paid out when the middle line of a three-by-three symbol matrix reveals a winning combination of symbols, e.g., three oranges (Griffiths, 1988).

Visually, modern fruit machines are incomparably exciting, with brightly lit displays in vivid primary colors, which change at frequent intervals to attract the eye of potential players. In addition, a variety of "play features" increase the number of decisions a player has to make and greatly enhance the experience of play. For example, instead of the machine automatically playing out on a winning sequence, it may be necessary to first press a "collect" button, or make a decision to store the winnings to "collect" later (or use for further play once the original stake is spent) by pressing a "bank" button.

Other features give the impression that the player himself may influence the outcome. For example, many machines in the U.K. have a "nudge" button which, when lit, can be pressed to change the position of any one of the reels to achieve a winning sequence, after automatic play is over. Similarly a "hold" button can be pressed to retain the favorable position of a reel before automatic play begins. Some fruit machines have a "gamble" button, which may be pressed in response to the appropriate flashing graphics, to gamble winnings against various odds, e.g., double or quits. These are just some of a range of sophisticated play features on modern fruit machines.

In the absence of ethnographic research, there has been much speculation as to why young people are particularly attracted to fruit machines. Some of the possible motivations are discussed below.

A. Ego-enhancement

On the face of it, slot machines would seem to offer the least scope for interpersonal character contests (Downes, 1976). Fruit machine gambling is held to be purely aleatory (Herman, 1976; Downes, 1976), and it is portrayed by the image makers to be a "mindless" or "moronic" pursuit. Furthermore, fruit machine gambling is indisputably "petty gambling," wagering 10 pence or less per play for a maximum jackpot of £4. Thus on first examination there appears to be little scope for the gain of *character* through prowess of skill or courageous staking.

However, the idea that knowledge of a particular machine, or acquired skill, can alter the odds in favor of the player, has been perceived by manufacturers as having a powerful incentive effect on many players. Whether memorizing the reel sequences and gaining expert use of play features such as the "nudge" and "hold" makes fruit machine play more skillful or merely creates the illusion of skill is open to debate (Griffiths, 1988). However, in either case, the potential for ego enhancement is available. Furthermore, when these low stake machines are repeatedly played by children, huge amounts of money relative to income may be wagered and peers impressed by consequential risk taking (Fisher, 1989).

Herman's brief account of fruit machine gambling further endorses the relevance of applying Goffman's ego-enhancement theory to fruit machine gambling. He noted that when a machine pays out, the coins or tokens drop noisily into a metal receiving tray. Simultaneously, lights flash and electronic beeps and buzzes celebrate the win. The coins are not usually scooped out of the tray immediately, but are allowed to accumulate so that other players may observe and admire them (Herman, 1976).

Thus, it is suggested here that while the contest appears to be against the machine, indirectly the contest is usually against other members of a peer group, so that the machine becomes a vehicle for participation in a status game. Thus a specific subculture emerges which is organized around participation in an interpersonal contest, and which results in a hierarchy of performance and consequent status roles. It is further suggested that for a small minority of players mastery of the recurrent obstacles and techniques of the game supersedes social factors, so that beating the machine itself becomes a lonely obsession.

B. The social context of play

Fruit machines are frequently marketed within the specific social context of an arcade or "leisure center," or in casinos in the U.S. and other countries.

Some writers have stressed the primacy of the supply environment itself to the attraction of slot machine use for young people. Holmes' description of U.K. arcades captures the atmosphere which pervades:

> ". . . great fun palaces which are warmly carpeted and flashy . . . Rarely are they directly lit from overhead and the light beams and tubes would not be out of place in a disco. The sounds are interesting too — jingles, jangles, bleeps and zaps. Seductively, cash always seems to be falling and flooding out if only from change dispensers" (Holmes, 1985, p. 33).

The existence of a commercially provided cultural space, monopolized by young people, is not without precedent. Coffee bars and pool halls have similarly provided shelter from the surveillance of the authorities or institutions which govern teenagers' lives. Such social contexts facilitate the negotiation of status passages which accompany the transition from childhood to adulthood:

> "In these places teenagers can meet peers, relieve boredom, act on their emerging sexual identities and institute cultural practices that build peers into a stable, if temporary, form of social organization" (Panelas, 1983, p. 62).

Panelas further suggests that such premises have always attracted the concern of adults who necessarily equate venues where youth meet without supervision with the spawning of delinquency.

Clearly both the ego-enhancement and the "cultural space" aspects of adolescent attraction to slot machines need to be fully explored. So also do other possible motivations such as the economic, thrill seeking, problem solving, teleological and "protest against ethics" motivations first suggested by Devereux with respect to adult gambling (Devereux, 1947). It is likely that systematic sociological research will reveal a range of key orientations to fruit machine gambling by young people which will provide valuable insights into both "social" and "compulsive" pre-adult gambling. Enormous potential exists for sociological contributions in this field, both theoretical and empirical.

REFERENCES

Amati (1981). Juvenile delinquency and habit patterns. *Indian Journal of Social Work*, 44, 405-408.

Arcuri, A.F., Lester, D. and Smith, F. (1985). Shaping adolescent gambling behavior. *Adolescence,* 20, 935-938.

Caillois, R. (1958). *Man, Play and Games.* New York: Free Press.

Cornish, D.B. (1978). *Gambling: A review of the literature and its implications for research.* London: Her Majesty's Stationery Office.

Costa, N. (1988). *Automatic Pleasures: The History of the Coin Machine.* London: Kevin Francis Publishing Ltd.

Devereux, E. (1949). *Gambling and the social structure.* Doctoral dissertation, Harvard University, Cambridge.

Downes, D.M., Davies, B.P., David, M.E. and Stone, P. (1976). *Gambling, Work and Leisure: A Study Across Three Areas.* London: Routledge and Kegan Paul.

Fisher, S. (1989). The use of fruit machines by children. *Society for the Study of Gambling Newsletter*, 16.

Frank, M.L. (1988). *Casino gambling among college students: Three sequential years of data.* Presented at the Third National Conference on Gambling Behavior, May 19-29, New York City, New York.

Goffman, E. (1969). *Where the Action Is: Three Essays.* London: Allen Lane — The Penguin Press.

Griffiths, M. (1988). *The psychological deception and perception of slot machines.* Internal Report, Department of Psychology, University of Exeter.

Herman, R.D. (1976). *Gamblers and Gambling.* Lexington, MA: Lexington Books.

Holmes, G. (1985). Against the odds. *Youth in Society*, December.

Ide-Smith, S. and Lea, S.E.G. (1988). Gambling in young adolescents. *Journal of Gambling Behavior,* 4, 110-119.

Jacobs, D.F. (1989). Illegal and undocumented: A review of teenage gambling and the plight of children of problem gamblers in America. In H.J. Shaffer, S.A. Stein, B. Gambino, and T. Cummings (eds.), *Compulsive Gambling: Theory, Research, and Practice.* Lexington, MA: Lexington Books.

Jacobs, D.F. (1993). A review of teenage gambling in the United States. In W.R. Eadington and J.A. Cornelius (eds.), *Gambling Behavior and Problem Gambling.* Reno: Institute for the Study of Gambling and Commercial Gaming, University of Nevada.

Keill, N. (1956). The behavior of five adolescent poker players. *Journal of Human Relations*, 5, 79-89.

Lesieur, H.R. and Klein, R. (1987). Pathological gambling among high school students. *Addictive Behavior*, 12, 129-135.

Moran, E. (1987). *Gambling among schoolchildren: The impact of the fruit machine.* London: National Council on Gambling.

Opie, I. and Opie, P. (1969). *Children's Games in Street and Playground.* Oxford: Oxford University Press.

Panelas, T. (1983). Adolescents and video games: Consumption of leisure and the social construction of the peer group. *Youth and Society*, 15, 51-65.

Smith, J.F. and Abt, V. (1984). Gambling as play. *Annals of the American Academy of Political and Social Science*, 474.

The Use of Slot Machines by Young People in the U.K.: The Present Evidence©

Susan Fisher

The recent interest in fruit machine gambling among young people has arisen from growing concern that some children who play fruit machines become "problem" gamblers and behave deviantly as a consequence of their play. Press allegations have included attempted murder, suicide and child prostitution, as well as a widespread incidence of theft, truancy and vandalism. Headlines such as "Children become bandits for fruit machines" (*Independent*, p. 1, February 8, 1988); "Young being brainwashed by machines says doctor" (*Times*, September 1, 1987); and "Youth stole 94 times to finance gambling" (*Times*, December 12, 1987) are typical and ubiquitous.

© A more extensive version of this article has been published in the *Journal of Gambling Studies* (1991), 7(3), 217-247. New York: Human Sciences Press. Permission to reprint has been granted by the author and publisher.

The role of the press in fuelling public concern about stereotypes which are ultimately shown to provide false or inaccurate pictures of reality has been well documented elsewhere (see Cohen, 1972). Furthermore, deviant behavior by children engenders an emotive response from which researchers are not necessarily immune, despite their best efforts. These potential red herrings should be borne in mind when searching for the facts of childhood slot machine use.

Widespread "problem" fruit machine gambling is a relatively modern phenomenon in the United Kingdom, resulting from some unseen consequences of the *1968 Gaming Act*, which effectively legalized gaming for profit. The same act also made fruit machine gambling the only form of commercial gambling legally available to children under the age of 18 years. The business is very profitable and the supply of machines has increased dramatically, as has the number of "problem" users seeking help:

> "Opportunities for 'action' gambling abound for children and young people and in recent years there has been a small flood of this group into Gamblers Anonymous — **they now account for about one in four of all new members**" (Moody, 1990, p. 109, emphasis supplied).

The Home Office responded to increasing public concern by undertaking a:

> "preliminary investigation into the prevalence and character of amusement machine playing by young people under sixteen with a view to establishing the existence or otherwise of a significant social problem requiring legislation" (Graham, 1988, p. 1).

The research enquired into the use of video game machines as well as fruit machines. When the report was published in 1988 it contradicted the findings of all previous research (with the exception of one undergraduate project) by concluding that:

> ". . . the scale of the problem does not appear to warrant legislation. Very few young people are at risk of becoming dependent upon amusement machines and no evidence is found of any association between the playing of machines and delinquency" (Graham, 1988, p. iii).

Other completed research consists of one national survey by the National Housing and Town Planning Council (NHTPC); several local surveys, for example those undertaken by a youth worker, a Children's Society and an Institute of Higher Education (Ashdown, unpublished manuscript 1987; Spectrum Children's Trust, 1988; Barham and Cornell, 1987); two undergraduate projects (Ide-Smith and Lea, 1987; Waterman and Atkin, 1985); and indirect research carried out by the psychiatrist referred to in the headline above (Moran, 1987). Preliminary findings of postgraduate research by Griffiths have also been published which provide fresh insight into the psychology of "addicted" adolescent gamblers. As in the case of the Home Office research, some of these studies have considered the childhood use of both video and fruit machines. Although video machines are designed for amusement only and not gaming, they are often the first slot machines which children play and are held by some writers to act as precursors of fruit machines (Moran, 1987; Spectrum Children's Trust, 1988).

While these previous studies provide valuable descriptive data on, for example, the incidence and frequency of childhood amusement machine use, not all would claim academic rigor, and a systematic and analytical sociological approach has yet to be made. The difficulties and limitations of evaluating research initiated by parties such as the Home Office, a Children's Society and a third year undergraduate project are well understood and acknowledged by the author. However, it is suggested here that in a field characterized by a paucity of factual information, that which does exist warrants careful consideration. The analysis which follows is an attempt to review all available U.K. research in order to arrive at a synthesis of existing knowledge about children's use of amusement machines in the U.K. and to clarify indications for further research.

PREVIOUS RESEARCH

A. Incidence of Amusement Machine use by Children

All previous studies report that the playing of fruit machines is the most common form of gambling among school children. Indeed, by the time children are established in secondary education they are in the minority if they have not gambled on fruit machines. Previous surveys undertaken in schools report as many as 99%, 81%, 77%, 64% and 65% taking part (Ashdown, 1987; Ide-Smith and Lea, 1987; NHTPC, 1988; Barham and Cornell, 1987; Spectrum Children's Trust, 1987). These percentages are of course of little interest if on the whole they represent an occasional play for fun which is inconsequential for the life chances of the child. However, the *variation* in these percentages may point us in the direction of further research.

While the variation partly reflects differing sampling procedures, it may also reflect the different types of location surveyed. Moran's 1987 survey of all the head teachers in the London boroughs found that the number of schools reporting fruit machine playing and the number of children in each school who played, increased with the availability of sites. In particular, fish and chip shops and cafes providing fruit machines were more commonly found near schools reporting gambling than arcades. One headmaster at a secondary school in Devon reported a decline in school meal takings of up to £50 a week since fruit machines were installed in a cafe near his school, a decline which subsequently halted when the machines were removed (Griffiths, 1988b). This would suggest that if gambling by school children on fruit machines is to be viewed in a negative light, it is the fruit machine which is the culprit rather than the venue (Moran, 1987).

If this proves to be the case, there would be an argument for some further rethinking on the provision of licenses for cafes, fish and chip shops and other non-arcade sites. And an even more pressing case exists for examining the anomalous situation of young people who live in seaside towns where fruit machines are traditionally freely available for rainy day tourist entertainment, and, like cafes, not subject to British Amusement Catering Trades Association (BACTA) or other codes of conduct, restricting access to young people under the age of sixteen. The supernormal exposure of children who live in seaside resorts to the alleged ill affects of amusement machines is a central theme of this study which will be addressed below and under other headings.

B. Seaside Arcades

Amusement arcades are as endemic to the British seaside holiday as picture postcards and lettered rock. Yet there is growing evidence that these "amusement palaces," which together with cinemas have traditionally provided wet weather entertainment for holidaymakers, may provide a year-round facility for the resident population which is harmful to some members.

In response to a May 6, 1987 request by Douglas Hogg, then Parliamentary Under Secretary of State at the Home Office, the Gaming Inspectorate looked for evidence of fruit machine gambling by children under sixteen in 151 inland, and 25 seaside arcades. Inspectors were required to visit each of six selected arcades in the chosen location on three separate occasions during the survey period. The first visit was to be made on a weekday between 12 noon and 2 p.m.; the second visit was to be on a weekday between 4 p.m. and 6 p.m.; and the third visit was to be during any hour on a Saturday.

Drawing a dividing line between age groups by observation alone is bound to be fraught with difficulty on several counts. Nevertheless, the greater proportion of children under sixteen seen in seaside arcades compared with inland arcades is too large to be dismissed on methodological grounds alone — 31% of those present in seaside arcades were reported to be under sixteen compared with 11% of those present in inland arcades, and of these, "less than half" were accompanied by a responsible adult (Gaming Board for Great Britain, 1987, p. 9).

Seaside arcades were inspected both inside and outside of school holidays. During term time inspection, nearly 500 under-16 year olds were observed, two-thirds of whom were unaccompanied by an adult. Unfortunately we are not told how this number of children compares with that found outside of school holidays in inland arcades. Neither are we able to assess the impact on this number of "holiday" use by children who live outside of the area. Nevertheless, 500 children observed gambling during term time, in such a limited time for observation, provide, at the very least, an indication for further research. Similarly, a "far higher proportion" of under-16 year olds playing videos was observed in the seaside arcades (Gaming Board for Great Britain, 1987, p. 10).

Spectrum Children's Trust also examined slot machine playing by children in both inland (Taunton) and seaside (West Somerset) settings. They found that children from the West Somerset location exhibited marked differences in their play from children in the Taunton area:

> "West Somerset children tend to play more habitually and make more use of amusement arcades, and here the effect of the holiday resort of Minehead is probably critical" (Spectrum Children's Trust, 1988, p. 25).

Barham and Cormell's research in the south coast resort of Bognor draws attention to the year round use of amusement arcades by local children:

> "We knew the arcades were populated all the year round by young people, particularly of secondary school age, some admitting to spending over £10 per week" (Barham and Cormell, 1987, p. 10).

Similarly, in her survey of young people and amusement machines in the Devon seaside resort of Dawlish, an Education Welfare Officer notes that:

> ". . .Dawlish, the seaside town with its arcades, it is for the holidaymakers an opportunity for idle leisure and pleasure, but for the young people growing up in the town the arcades are the norm" (Ashdown, 1987, p. 5).

The Home Office survey included 10% of children from seaside resorts, a stratification produced by the Registrar General's Standard Regions. One wonders how different the overall conclusions might have been if the regions had been awarded proportional representation and stratified according to the availability of sites (available from the license records of H.M. Customs and Excise). Not surprisingly the author reports that, "playing of fruit machines was slightly more prevalent in seaside resorts and slightly less prevalent in rural areas, which probably reflects the extent of opportunities for playing fruit machines in these two kinds of location." The hypothesis that additional use accompanies the increased availability of fruit machines generates no further comment.

This is a serious omission of the Home Office research and surprising in view of the findings of the above studies and that of a previous major work on gambling in the U.K. in which the authors expressed their "belief in the importance of supply generated by historical causes as a determinant of demand" (Downes et al., 1976, p. 47).

C. Non-Arcade Sites

The idea that the fruit machine has an intrinsic attraction for young people irrespective of its venue is borne out by where children say they play them. While all previous studies found that most fruit machine gambling takes place in arcades (60%, NHTPC; 65%, Graham; 77%, Ashdown) a significant number of children said they gamble elsewhere. One survey found that nearly 20% of children played *only* in non-arcade sites, but that for most children these venues supplemented arcades rather than providing an alternative (Spectrum Children's Trust, 1988).

These non-arcade sites include cafes, fish and chip shops and — perhaps surprisingly, given the age group — pubs. The Home Office study reported 60% of their 10 to 16 year olds gambling in arcades, 14% in cafes and fish and chip shops, and 12% in pubs.

Where choice of venue is concerned, supply seems to influence demand with greater use of arcades in seaside locations and comparatively less in urban areas where there are fewer arcades per capita, and trade controls restrict access to children. This is particularly evident in London where trade association (BACTA) controls are generally strictly enforced and less children play in arcades and more in cafes and fish and chip shops than the national average (Graham, 1988).

The significance of this for future research is similar to the case made for further research into seaside arcades described above, and has been well expressed by John Graham:

> "It would be useful to establish whether there is an increasing trend towards playing in locations other than amusement arcades if only because BACTA's code of practice, which enables arcades to restrict to those under the age of sixteen, does not apply to establishments other than amusement arcades" (Graham, 1988, pp. 34-35).

D. Incidence of Video Game Playing

Since video games are played for amusement and not gain, they are not classified as gaming machines. However, they are sited together with fruit machines in arcades and, in many premises, videos are sited at the rear of the room so that children must first walk past the fruit machines with their enticing displays in order to reach them (Barham and Cormell, 1987). Most studies report similar proportions of children playing video machines as fruit machines, which presumably reflects the fact that they are usually sited in the same location.

E. The Gender of Children who Play Amusement Machines

All studies found a strong gender bias among child fruit machine gamblers. A greater percentage of boys play than girls in both arcades and other venues. They play more regularly, spend more money and are more likely to play alone (NHTPC, 1988; Ide-Smith and Lea, 1988; Barham and Cormell, 1987; Spectrum Children's Trust, 1988). One national study found that 70% of boys play machines in amusement arcades compared with 40% of girls, that they spent more than the girls during a typical visit and were twice as likely to play on their own (NHTPC, 1988).

The Home Office data reproduce this gender bias and also provide some interesting information on which types of machine boys and girls prefer. Girls of all ages preferred fruit machines and the proportion in each age group who said they only played fruit machines was larger than the group who said they played both types of machine. In contrast, more boys said they only played videos than said they only played fruit machines. Since video games overwhelmingly reflect the violent "pretend" games that boys traditionally play, this is, perhaps, not surprising. If it emerges that the playing of video games precedes fruit machine gambling for many children, particularly boys, then some understanding of the nature of childhood play and how it has been taken up and transformed by software engineers could be crucial to the understanding of the career path of a child fruit machine gambler.

F. The Age of Children who Play Amusement Machines

There now appears to have been a significant under-estimate of the age at which many children first gamble on fruit machines. This is to some extent inevitable given that most research has been carried out in secondary schools, thus precluding children under the age of 11 years. However some studies have asked children how old they were when they started fruit machine gambling and these point to the majority having started while still at primary school. One study reported a mean age at which fruit machine play commenced of 8 years 3 months for boys and 8 years 9 months for girls (Ide-Smith and Lea, 1988). Another reported that 44% of the children surveyed started gambling on fruit machines under the age of 10 and 84% under the age of 11 (Ashdown, 1987). Yet another reported that 21% of children started gambling before they were 9 years old (NHTPC, 1988).

Age of commencement to play fruit machines could prove to be a significant factor in the future career of an adolescent gambler. All of Griffith's "addicted adolescents" said they started fruit machine gambling before the age of eleven years and the NHTPC national survey found that those respondents who started gambling before they were 9 years old were more likely to gamble "very frequently" (four times a week). This notion is also supported by Huff and Collinson's survey of 100 males in a Youth Custody Center which distinguished between those youths who had stolen to finance declared habitual gambling and video machine playing and those who had not. The mean age of commencement of play for respondents who had stolen to finance their habit was less than 12 years compared with just under 14 years for those who had not.

While girls in each age group seem to prefer fruit machines, boys in different age groups play different types of machine according to peer group norms. The younger boys predominantly play video games, but this preoccupation peaks at about 12 or 13 years and then declines. It is considered to be socially inappropriate to play videos after a certain age and to do so "risks censure and even exclusion by one's peers" (Graham, 1988). Spending on fruit machines, however, increases with age, although most players "think they'll grow out of it." Adult play of fruit machines in arcades is looked down upon by young players and "a lack of respect bordering on contempt is often shown to adult patrons by their younger counterparts" (Graham, 1988). This is an interesting sociological phenomenon and one which is begging an explanation.

G. The Class of Children who Play Amusement Machines

None of the existing studies reports a clear class bias. The H.O. researchers found that their respondents who played amusement machines were quite evenly spread in terms of class background although classes C2 and DE (fathers in manual occupations) were "slightly over-represented." They did find that a slightly higher proportion of children from DE families played fruit machines than those from other class categories, but that such differences were not apparent with respect to video games.

H. Indications of Dependency

As yet little theoretical work has been undertaken by the authors of existing studies on the explanation of such concepts as "dependency" and "addiction" with respect to childhood gambling. Rather, they have been taken as given and used without further attempt to give insight into their meaning as for example in Barham's unexplained and unsupported use of the concept "addicted" in the following sentence: "Some are addicted and spend beyond their means" (Barham and Cormell, 1987, pp. 25-26; Graham, 1988, p. 7).

Such reticence on the part of sociologists is not altogether surprising since their task is to offer explanations of social action. As such, they cannot be expected to define *addiction* to gambling, or anything else for that matter, since any attempt to do so necessarily involves the inappropriate application of sociological theories to non-social (psychological and/or physiological) phenomena. However sociologists can suggest why different groups are attracted to different gambling forms, why some members of these groups spend more time and/or money on them than others, and why some of them consider themselves (or are considered by others) to be addicted to gambling, and so on.

The Home Office research attempted "some assessment of the extent to which young people are at risk of becoming dependent upon the playing of fruit and video machines" (Graham, 1988, p. 17) by asking respondents to state:

- how often they spent their own money on playing machines;
- how long they played for during a typical session;
- how much, as a proportion of their weekly income, they spent on machines;
- how frequently players spent more than £5 during a session; and
- at what stage during a session they decided to stop playing (fruit machine players only).

Group interviews also provided data on spending behavior and patterns of play.

Several methodological flaws are evident in this approach:

1) The nature of the questions being asked suggest that confidentiality is essential for frankness of response. However, the respondents were first required to give their own and their mothers' name, their full postal address and their telephone number!

2) The answers to the questions asked provide not an indicator *of* dependency, but of how much time and money children spend on amusement machines. Even in cases where this is considerable, it could be argued that such behavior does not necessarily indicate "dependency" and that children are entitled to spend their time and money as they chose within the confines of the law.

3) The children were asked how often they spent their own money on machines. The issue of when they spent money from other sources, e.g., school dinner money, was excluded.

4) No systematic attempt has been made to correlate the statistics provided from the answers. For example, it would be interesting to know how many of those children who gambled "two or three times

a week" or "nearly every day" also spent "more than £5" a session or a large proportion of their weekly income.

5) The method of reporting focussed on those who did not participate frequently, did not spend large sums of money, or did not behave deviantly in the course of their play. Attention was thus systematically attracted away from the minority of children whose play has given sufficient cause for concern to warrant a H.O. enquiry in the first place, resulting in the statement: ". . . only a small minority of young people are at risk of becoming dependent upon either fruit or video machines" (p. 18). Take away the word "only" and the statement which in its original form is almost dismissive of this group now focusses upon them. (A similar criticism has also been made by Moody, 1989, p. 17, in an unpublished document prepared for the Home Office.)

It is fair to note at this point that the Home Office research claims only *preliminary* investigative status (Graham, 1988, p. 1), the implication being that its findings are expected to generate further research. Furthermore, all who research the field of child amusement machine use in the U.K. navigate waters which are largely uncharted and teeming with methodological sharks. (Spectrum Children's Trust could be said partly to redress the balance by focussing only on those children who played frequently and/or behaved deviantly, with no mention of the majority of children whose play does not give rise to concern.)

The other national survey (NHTPC, 1988) collected data on frequency of participation and amount spent and also on "some of the symptoms most commonly associated with dependency on gambling." Children who gambled were asked whether they had ever stolen or borrowed money, used their dinner money, or played truant in order to play gambling machines. These results were then correlated with others on frequency, amount spent, age and sex.

The findings of previous research on variables which have been used to indicate dependency are examined in more detail below.

I. Frequency of Amusement Machine Use by Young People

One measure of an individual's commitment to a leisure activity is the proportion of resources utilized to support it. The two basic requirements for slot machine gambling are time and money. Analysis of data on frequency of amusement machine use by children is hampered by the varying and often inadequate operationalization of concepts such as "regular" and "occasional." For example, the Home Office study defines "regular" users as "those who play more than once a week" while another describes a similar group as those who "play often" (Barham and Cormell, 1987). Yet another leaves interpretation of the classification of "regular" open to the subjective assessment of the respondent (Spectrum Children's Trust, 1988).

It could be argued that the Home Office research employs a particularly nonstandard definition of "regular" compared with common usage. For example a grown man who goes to the "dogs" every Friday evening may be described as "a regular punter" or as "attending regularly." However in terms used by the Home Office report, a young person who visits an arcade once a week to play amusement machines is described as playing "not very often." Yet, later in the report the author refers to an arcade visit as constituting "the central focus of a social event" and we are told that "the most popular time for playing the machines appears to be Friday evening and Saturday." One interviewee is reported as saying:

> "The main day I go down there is Friday night. It's quite a good night — all my friends are down there" (Graham, 1988, p. 23).

Thus, for some young people at least, a Friday evening or Saturday visit to an arcade is a regular weekly occurrence of some importance, which may well be undervalued in quantitative and qualitative terms if the child is said to play amusement machines "not very often."

There are other ways in which the Home Office's method of data gathering and analysis understates the frequency with which young people gamble on fruit machines. The key question is framed as follows:

> QD8 How often do you spend your own money playing fruit machines nowadays?
>
> - less than once a month
> - about once a month
> - about 2-3 times a month
> - about once a week
> - about 2-3 times a week
> - nearly every day

Those children who responded positively to the first four options to this question were subsequently classified as those who played "not very often." The remainder, who said they played 2 or 3 times a week or nearly every day, were then defined as "regular" players (6% of fruit machine players and 10% of video players). One wonders what the Home Office criteria for those children who gamble "often" might be.

It is possible, however, to deduce from the statistics given, the number of children who play amusement machines once a week or more, and these amount to 23% of fruit machine players and 28% of video players. These results can then be compared with those of other studies which specifically reported on a frequency classification of "once a week or more." All of the results are shown in Table 1.

TABLE 1

PROPORTION OF YOUNG PEOPLE WHO PLAY AMUSEMENT MACHINES ONCE A WEEK OR MORE*

STUDY	*FRUIT MACHINE PLAYERS*	*VIDEO PLAYERS*
H.O. 101	23%	28%
NHTPC	22%	--
Ashdown	23%	both types of machine
Waterman and Atkin	9%	videos not included
Barham and Cormell	37%	machines in arcades
Spectrum Children's Trust	26%	25% (self-defined "regulars")

*These percentages are proportions of the final group chosen for study, i.e., those of the total sample who said they played amusement machines (as opposed to those who said they did not). Or, as in the case of the Home Office and Barham's studies, those who said they had played amusement machines in the last month/two months, respectively.

It can be seen that using the criterion of "once a week or more" to define regular play, a considerable degree of consensus is revealed among previous studies, with an average of about 25% of children who participate playing once a week or more.

The Waterman and Atkins study report differs in this respect with only 9% of their respondents falling into this category. But this is probably explained by the age group of children surveyed (14-18 year olds) and their own finding that "younger people are more likely to play on fruit machines, that is 14-15 year olds." In addition, that study is now over five years old and the number of fruit machines available to children has increased considerably since then (Fisher, 1989).

Barham's report of 37% of respondents playing in Bognor Regis arcades once a week or more is focussed on a seaside town where "the number of gaming machines available to young people is the largest in the whole county of West Sussex." Such large numbers participating again highlights the need for further research into the effects of relatively free access to amusement machines on children who reside in seaside towns.

Similar proportions of young amusement machine players who said they played very often, i.e., "four times a week or more" or "nearly every day," are also reported by previous studies. The results are shown in Table 2.

TABLE 2

PROPORTION OF YOUNG PEOPLE WHO PLAY AMUSEMENT MACHINES FOUR TIMES A WEEK OR MORE*		
STUDY	*FRUIT MACHINE PLAYERS*	*VIDEO PLAYERS*
H.O. 101	2%	3%
NHTPC	5%	--
Ashdown	4%	both types of machine
Barham and Cornell	3%	machines in arcades

*These percentages are proportions of the final group chosen for study, i.e., those of the total sample who said they played amusement machines (as opposed to those who said they did not). Or, as in the case of the Home Office and Barham's studies, those who said they had played amusement machines in the last month/two months, respectively.

While 3% or 4% of young people who gamble so frequently is a tiny minority of child fruit machine gamblers, nevertheless they constitute a significant number when considered nationally.

But, of course, regular or even very frequent gambling does not automatically imply negative consequences. It may be that for many young people it is the social context of the machines which is the focus of interest and not gambling per se, and that expenditure on gambling is controlled expenditure, purchasing admission to the chosen social milieu. Barham, Graham, NHTPC, Ashdown and Huff and Collinson all report aspects of the social context of play, such as "atmosphere" and "a good place to meet friends," as an important component of machine use in arcades. Further qualitative research is required to establish the extent to which this is, or is not, so.

J. Expenditure on Amusement Machines

The ratio of time to money required to gamble on fruit machines depends upon the payout rate of the machine and (to a limited extent, in the short term) the skill of the player, in using the various "nudges" etc. to prolong play. Interviews undertaken by the writer suggest varying ratios in the amount of "handle" of between £30 and £60 per hour of continuous play, and the present writer wagered £30.60 in one hour (with the aid of sponsorship from a local machine operator who supplied both tokens and machine). Certainly, all previous research points to fruit machine gambling being an expensive past-time for many children and one which has a positive income elasticity among participating adolescents. (See also Waterman and Atkin, 1985.)

In addition, the NHTPC study found a strong correlation between the amount spent during a typical visit and the frequency with which children gambled. Of the 22% of fruit machine players who said they played once a week or more, 15% spent more than £3 during one visit to an arcade and 10% spent more than £5. Over 33% of children who played at least four times a week spent more than £3 on each occasion, and nearly 20% spent more than £10 a session, i.e., *at least £49 a week on gambling.* Other studies which tested this hypotheses found a similar correlation between frequency of play and amount spent during a typical visit (Waterman and Atkin, Spectrum Children's Trust).

The Home Office asked their respondents how much money they usually spent on amusement machines in a week. Seventy-one percent of fruit machine players said they spent less than £1 a week, 17% between £1 and £2 a week and the remaining 12% spent more than £2 a week. It is not revealed how many of these spent between £2 and £5, or more than £5 although this information was gathered. Thus attention was focussed on those spending relatively small sums of money and drawn away from those spending more.

Information is however supplied on the proportion of income spent on fruit machines and videos by a subsample of Home Office respondents (432 fruit machine players and 402 video players). It reveals that 40% of fruit machine players and 41% of video players spent half or most of their income on playing machines. The players who said they spent "only a very small proportion of their income" on fruit machines or videos amounted to 35% of respondents in each case and are described as "those least likely to be at risk of becoming dependent." This is typical of the reporting of results of this survey with attention focussed on the least involved and, in this instance, no comment at all on the more heavily involved or (using the criteria employed by Graham) those most likely to be at risk of becoming dependent.

DELINQUENT BEHAVIOR BY YOUNG PEOPLE WHO PLAY AMUSEMENT MACHINES

All previous studies agree that a minority of children steal or truant to play amusement machines but disagreement exists as to the size and nature of the problem. To measure delinquency by young people who play amusement machines (other than theft of money), the Home Office researchers administered a self-report questionnaire to all participants in the group interviews. As Graham himself points out, the results need to be treated with caution because the sample (of about 50 children) is too small to be considered nationally representative.

A further drawback is that the delinquency questionnaire was borrowed from Riley and Shaw's 1985 study of parental supervision and delinquency and as such is insufficiently focussed on the study in hand to be of much relevance. (Items include for example: written or sprayed paint on buildings, broken windows in an empty house and dialed 999 for a joke.) Not surprisingly the author found little evidence of behavior which could have been motivated by a need to fund the playing of machines. Nevertheless Graham concludes that:

> "The lack of evidence to suggest playing amusement machines can lead to delinquency also needs further investigation" (Graham, 1988, pp. 32-33).

Barham and Cormell (1987) reports that some of his respondents thought it "fair game" to fiddle the machines and had developed a range of techniques to do so:

> ". . . they used strimming wire shaped to coins or to retrieve them, 'taped' 10p pieces to a 50p shape, created static to short the micro-circuits and even used brake fluid to gain credits" (p. 21).

Most of the other studies concentrate on the unsocial or illegal behaviors of borrowing, using school dinner money, truanting and stealing (to support amusement machine play) to measure related delinquency. The results are discussed below.

A. Borrowing

Borrowing and lending money is intrinsic to the economic life of all ages and, where reciprocity is involved, may well enrich social relationships. But borrowing money to finance gambling may be symptomatic of excessive play, as it implies expenditure beyond the means of the participant. Research has shown that the more frequently young people play amusement machines the more likely they are to borrow money to do so (NHTPC, 1988; Graham, 1988). The NHTPC reported 32% of children who said they played once a month or less borrowing money to play, compared with 76% of those who said they played three or more times a week.

B. Obtaining money from strangers

Obtaining money from strangers in arcades is another way by which some young people raise further money to gamble when their own money runs out. Regular players learn through practice whether they should "hold" one reel and "nudge" another, and having "learnt" the machine, sell the knowledge to others:

> "When you get skint you watch other people. If you watch them and you know the machines and you can help them sometimes they give you money" (Graham, 1988, p. 30).

C. School dinner money

Huff and Collinson found that more "criminal" video players had used school dinner money to fund play than "non-criminal" players. Other studies report that the spending of school dinner money on amusement machines is more common among frequent players (NHTPC, 1988; Moran, 1987). The NHTPC reported that 12% of children who play the machines once a month or less used their dinner money to do so, compared with 27%, who played weekly and 53% who play four times a week or more. (The NHTPC reported that dinner money was used more often for non-arcade machines than for arcade machines, in all categories of frequency, which supports the proposal by the Home Office that further research into machine playing by children in non-arcade sites is indicated.)

Regular players interviewed for the Home Office also said they spent money given to them for meals, clothing and fares on amusement machines:

> "I get my dinner money and money to spend at school and I just go and spend it all in there; I'd rather play on the machines"
>
> "(My mother) gives me money every day, and what I do is, I don't have dinner, I save it and go to the arcade" (Graham, 1988, p. 19).

Barham similarly reports:

> ". . . we know of children who spend their 'dinner money' on the machines and eat if they 'win'" (p. 30).

D. Truancy

Truanting to play amusement machines is reported by all previous studies which included truancy as a research item (Barham, NHTPC, Spectrum). Truancy appears to increase with frequency of play. The NHTPC report that 3% of children who gambled once a week or less missed school to do so, compared with 35% of children who said they played four times a week or more. The NHTPC similarly report truancy increasing with the amount spent during a typical session, with the worst offenders again playing in non-arcade sites. For example, 27% of children who spent between £3 and £5 a session truanted from school to do so, together with a staggering 67% of children who spent £10 or more (NHTPC, 1988).

E. Stealing

For analytical purposes a frail but discernible dividing line may be drawn between those forms of theft which come to be defined as illegal and those which remain merely dishonest. Previous research suggests that some of the money which young people spend on amusement machines is dishonestly expropriated from the home.

One recent police survey claims that such behavior exists but is frequently covert as:

> ". . . parents are able to financially cope with their child or have such a strong parental response that it does not come to (police) notice" (Yeomans, 1989, p. 5).

Ashdown's case study of a schoolgirl gambler illustrates the dilemma faced by one mother:

> "Sally took £80 from her mother's bag to follow her obsession. Sally already has the supervision of a social worker following a shoplifting spree to raise funds for a night on the machines. Her mother dares not tell the social worker about the theft of £80 in fear of Sally being taken back before the courts and the possible consequences" (Ashdown, 1987, p. 1).

Even within the family such behavior may be covert:

> "He has stolen from his mother and now his stepfather. His mother has paid back his stepfather without him knowing" (Spectrum's Children's Trust, 1987).

Again it is the *extent* of the problem which is most open to debate. The Home Office suggests that it is minimal. "With only a couple of exceptions," they found that their respondents acquired money to play amusement machines from regular sources such as pocket money, ad hoc gifts of money from parents for sweets etc., and part-time employment. However, it must be remembered that no confidentiality was given to their respondents, and the group interviews do suggest that child gamblers used other less regular sources. Nevertheless, we are told that rarely did their dishonesty amount to more than a petty act of defiance or bravado, for example, "They might at the outside force a parking meter or take money from their parents" (Graham, 1988, p. 30). The way in which certain behaviors related to amusement machine use are acknowledged dismissively by some researchers and reported with concern by others remains further avenue for sociological enquiry.

Other surveys did not distinguish between theft inside or outside of the home. Huff and Collinson found that 60% of their respondents in a Youth Custody Center gambled on fruit machines, and, of these, 23% had stolen specifically to fund their play. A similar proportion played videos and, of these, 22% had stolen to fund their play. Barham reported that 3% of his sample admitted stealing money to play on fruit machines, and 8% of Spectrum Children's Trust's respondents said they had taken money to play slot machines (twice as many boys as girls).

The NHTPC found a significant relationship between the amount children spent on gambling, the frequency with which they played, and the propensity to steal. Four percent of children who played once a month or less said they had stolen to play, compared with 38% of those who gambled four times a week or more. Similarly 4% of children who spent up to £1 during a visit to an arcade had stolen to do so, compared with 25% of those who typically spent between £5 and £10 and 67% of those who spent over £10.

One surprising and as yet unexplained statistic is that children who spent money on fruit machine gambling at non-arcade sites such as fish and chip shops were more likely in every expenditure category to steal to do so. Table 3 reproduces this information.

TABLE 3

AMOUNT SPENT ON FRUIT MACHINES DURING ONE VISIT ARCADES AND NON-ARCADES*

	up to £1	*£1.01 — £3*	*£3.01 — £5*	*£5.01 — £10*	*£10 or more*
Children who had stolen	4(5)	10(13)	17(33)	25(46)	67(74)

*The first figure refers to amusement arcades, while the figure in brackets refers to fruit machines outside arcades. All figures are expressed as percentages.
Source: NHTPG Survey

This finding reinforces the need expressed earlier for further research on child use of fruit machines in non-arcade sites which are freely available to children and not regulated by trade controls. The research evidence overall supports Graham's view that there should be further enquiry into a possible link between amusement machine use and delinquency.

OTHER SOCIAL ISSUES AND AMUSEMENT MACHINES

A. Dependency and Video Machines

Much less attention has been paid in most of the previous research to the use of video machines than fruit machines. An exception to this is the Home Office study which suggests that the initial motivation to play may be quite different, i.e., "... the playing of video machines is about personal skill and challenge, rapid reflexes and effective hand/eye coordination, rather than winning money." The challenging nature of the games also engenders a keen competitive spirit between players:

> "... players persistently compare their scores with their own previous performances and those of others. The manufacturers of video games have not been slow to cotton on to this and most video machines now display lists of the best performers' names" (Graham, 1988, p. 26).

Existing research tends to report any negative consequences of video machines as being indirect and due to their juxtaposition with fruit machines (e.g., Barham, 1987), or their tendency to act as precursors for fruit machines (e.g., Moran, 1987). The Home Office found that:

> "... there is little if any likelihood of becoming dependent upon video machines — the interviewee tended to scoff at the very idea" (Graham, 1989, p. 27).

However, 41% of the video players in the H.O. sample said they spent a half or more of their weekly incomes on video games and Huff and Collinson reported a number of their "criminal" video players as, "having problems associated with their playing in the past, in the present and also foresaw more in the future." They also had more relationship problems, took more time off work and neglected food to a greater extent than "non-criminal" players. Thus, further research on the largely unexplored phenomenon of child video machine playing in the U.K. is clearly indicated.

B. With Whom Do Children Play Amusement Machines?

Present evidence suggests that for most children a visit to an arcade is a *social* event enjoyed with siblings or friends. All previous research supports Graham's claim that amusement machine playing is:

> ". . . an essentially peer group centered activity (which) contrasts somewhat with the concept of the 'lone addict,' the solitary player entrapped by the machine's irresistible pull" (Graham, 1988, p. 21).

Indeed, the H.O. survey found that the peer group became a powerful regulating mechanism by which "dependency" was avoided by the majority:

> "If the playing of fruit machines goes beyond the boundaries of a social event and begins to impose upon the individual's or the group's life outside the arcade, then the peer group are likely to intervene" (Graham, 1988, p. 25).

However, for 24% of the boys and 17% of the girls in the H.O. sample, and 24% of the boys and 10% of the girls in the NHTPC sample, playing is not a social event but a solitary pastime, and as such is, one presumes, outside the sphere of intervention of the group. While solitary playing of games expressly designed for one player can hardly be described as *prima facie* evidence of pathological play by "lone addicts," the NHTPC survey found that the more frequently children played and the more money they spent on a typical visit, the more likely they were to play on their own.

C. The Social Context of the Arcade

In an excellent account of how young players perceive and experience the role of amusement machines in their lives, Graham highlights the social function of the arcade. For the majority, gambling is just one of the thrills on offer during an occasion when young people meet, away from the watchful eyes of adults, and immerse themselves in the complexity of norms and roles of their own peer group. For example:

> ". . . during breaks, individual players might watch their friends or other players at play, smoke a cigarette, or leave the arcade in search of refreshments and throughout the event there is a constant undercurrent of playful flirtation between the boys and girls in the group" (Graham, 1988, p. 23).

In this respect the amusement arcade offers a private sector environment for adolescent socializing akin to the coffee bars of the 1960s.

> "It presents young people with a social event not only in terms of providing a convenient place to meet, but also by supplying an environment in which they can explore the boundaries of adulthood

> within the relatively safe confines of their peer group" (Graham, 1988, p. 27).

However, one of the arguments commonly cited by those concerned with the adverse consequences of fruit machine gambling is that arcades provide an environment which is unsuitable and even hazardous for young people. Graham reports that young people were:

> ". . . aware of the presence of vague undercurrents of illegal and even dangerous activities in and around arcades. And it is this atmosphere of potential danger, combined with 'the forbidden,' which constitutes a powerful attraction for some: 'You feel like something is going to happen, like somebody is going to beat you up.'[and] 'It's fun; you always think it won't happen to me being attacked down there'" (Graham, 1987, p. 28).

The positive aspects of perceived potential danger on the human psyche are highlighted thus:

> "This perception of a constant threat of danger encourages camaraderie and the playing of gambling machines induces a sense of rebelliousness and defiance. It can even offer the opportunity to test one's survival skills — sometimes players end up spending their last penny and having to improvise a way of getting home" (Graham, 1987, p. 28).

Regrettably, the vital question of to what extent the perceived threat of danger is real or imagined is not properly pursued, but early findings of a new survey do suggest the need for such a study. Of 430 child visitors to amusement arcades in Birmingham:

- 24% had been approached by someone offering to lend money;
- 12% had been approached by someone asking them to steal;
- 21% had been approached by someone offering or selling items (watches, hi-fi, clothes etc.);
- 26% had been approached by a stranger who had made them feel ill at ease, embarrassed, or uncomfortable; and
- 5% had been approached by someone offering drugs (Wyatt, 1989).

Barham suggests that the safety or otherwise of the arcade depends very much on the management whose attitude of "friendliness" ranges from:

> ". . . active interest, protection from bullying and undesirables, even support offered to the youth, to passive disinterest, leaving the young people to their own devices with the provision that such devices be legal (which is not always the case!)" [Barham and Cormell, 1987, p. 23].

In view of the undoubted attraction of arcades as meeting places for young people, the safety of the environment provided warrants further research.

CONCLUSIONS AND RECOMMENDATIONS FOR FUTURE RESEARCH

Existing research clearly shows that the playing of amusement machines has become a major leisure pursuit for young people. Braham, in particular, has shown that the meanings attached to slot machine play by young people are vastly different from the "mindless, moronic pursuit" model adopted by most (non-playing) researchers and journalists to date. Further systematic exploration of the subcultures of both video and fruit machine use is required to establish the range of motivations which make the playing of slot machines so attractive to young people.

Existing research also shows that a small minority of young players become "addicted" to gambling on fruit machines. The statistical significance of this small minority remains obscure due to methodological difficulties associated with definition as well as problems with mass measurement — such as lack of confidentiality and inadequately framed questions. Further efforts are required on the part of psychologists and sociologists to give a clearer indication of the number of young people involved.

It has been claimed that young people who become "addicted" to fruit machines suffer the same character changes that mark all compulsive gamblers. The reported association between "compulsive" fruit machine gambling and delinquency similarly requires further empirical investigation.

Existing research reports that young people who demonstrate "symptoms of dependency" on fruit machines (such as the spending of supernormal amounts of time and money, borrowing, truancy and theft), are predominately male teenagers who are likely to have commenced play as young boys (under the age of ten years). Many play alone. What is now required is some sociological accounting for the characteristics of this subgroup.

Compared with fruit machines, research on the incidence and consequentiality of video machine play by young people in the U.K. is meager, although similar preoccupations clearly pertain. The present finding seems to be that young people in the U.K. do not become "addicted" to video machines. However, the lack of systematic investigation and the reliance on (conflicting) anecdotal evidence suggests caution in accepting this finding as definitive. Further research is indicated.

The relationship, if any, between video and fruit machine play among young people also warrants further investigation. In particular, it would be helpful to know whether or not the playing of fruit machines is contingent in some way upon the playing of video games. Is there, for example, a pattern for some young players which commences with video machine play and graduates to fruit machine gambling which may or may not become problematic for the child and society?

Finally, analysis of existing research highlights the existence of a group of children who are uniquely vulnerable to the potential problems associated with amusement machine playing. These are the children who reside in seaside towns who have uncontrolled access to amusement machines in tourist arcades (in addition to those in non-arcade sites) throughout the year. Enquiry into the additional impact of amusement machines (if any) on the lives of these children is of paramount importance.

REFERENCES

Ashdown, J. (1987). *Young people and gaming machines.* A report by an Education Welfare Officer, unpublished manuscript.

Barham, B. and Cormell, M. (1987). *Teenage Use of Amusement Arcades in Bognor Regis.* Bognor Regis: WSIHE.

Childs, D. (1987). *Amusement arcades — Young people and criminal behavior.* Internal report for NASPO, unpublished manuscript.

Downes, D.M., Davies, B.P., David, M.E. and Stone, P. (1976). *Gambling, Work and Leisure: A Study Across Three Areas.* London: Routledge and Kegan Paul.

Fisher, S. (1989). *Postwar legitimization and commercial development in the amusement machine industry*. Unpublished manuscript.

Gaming Board for Great Britain (1987). *Survey of under 16 year olds in inland and seaside arcades*. Special report.

Graham J. (1988). *Amusement machines: Dependency and delinquency*. Home Office research study no. 101. London: H.M.S.O.

Griffiths, M.D. (1988b). Adolescent gambling: Report of a workshop. *Society for the Study of Gambling Newsletter*, 14, 12-16.

Griffiths, M.D. (1988c). Fruit machine gambling in addicted adolescents. *Society for the Study of Gambling Newsletter*, 14, 1719.

Huff, G. and Collinson, F. (1987). Young offenders, gambling and video game playing. *British Journal of Criminology*, 27:4.

Ide-Smith, S. and Lea, S.E.G. (1988). Gambling in young adolescents. *Journal of Gambling Behavior*, 4, 110-119.

Moody, G. (1989). *Amusement machines: Dependency and delinquency — A personal appreciation*. Unpublished manuscript.

Moran, E. (1987). *Gambling among school children: The impact of the fruit machine*. London: National Council on Gambling.

National Housing and Town Planning Council (1988). *The use of arcades and gambling machines: A national survey*. London.

Spectrum Children's Trust (1988). *Slot machine playing by children*. Special report.

Waterman, J. and Atkin, K. (1985). Young people and fruit machines. *Society for the Study of Gambling Newsletter*, no. 7.

Wyatt, B. (1989). *Survey of young peoples gambling habits in Birmingham*. The Children's Society Youth Link Project (preliminary findings).

Yeomans, T. (1989). *Adolescent Gambling Survey, Plymouth*. Presented at the Adolescent Gambling Conference, Rees Center. Plymouth, U.K.: Devon and Cornwall Constabulary.

A Review of Juvenile Gambling in the United States©

Durand F. Jacobs

Many legally underage adolescents in today's society gamble. Yet, there seems to be little public recognition of or concern with juvenile gambling. The apparent unwillingness of adults in society to acknowledge gambling behaviors in their adolescents may reside in their belief that legal sanctions will discourage any "really serious" gambling among those under eighteen years of age — so, not to worry. Or perhaps it reflects the hesitancy of adult society to face up to its own role in fostering childhood and teenage gambling, since the overwhelming majority of young people who gamble were introduced to this recreational diversion by their parents or relatives. Could it be that underage gambling simply is dismissed as "harmless fun and games"? Or is it delayed awareness on the part of adults, including school authorities, about this component of the current adolescent experience? And finally, how big a problem can it be?

Over one third of the students surveyed in this author's 1989 review of teenage gambling in America stated they had gambled for money before they were eleven years of age; and that, by age 15, over 80 percent had placed wagers on a wide range of social games with friends and family, as well as bet on both legally sanctioned and illegal forms of gambling. Since the mid-1980s, the extent of juvenile gambling has increased steadily.

Over the past decade, the social zeitgeist in America has changed radically because of the greatly increased availability, promotion, and glamorization, not to mention the inflated payoffs, associated with commercial gambling.

After a decade of unbridled growth, it may well be time for American society to reexamine the long-range consequences of its love affair with legalized gambling.

THE POPULATION STUDIED

This first systematic review of gambling behaviors among high school age youth, average age 16.5 years, combines and interrelates data obtained during the period 1984-1988 from five independent surveys of fourteen high schools located in California, Connecticut, New Jersey, and Virginia. The total subject pool numbered 2,777 ninth- to twelfth-graders, all of whom completed the surveys anonymously in a classroom or other setting on the high school grounds (Jacobs, 1989).

THE SURVEY INSTRUMENTS

The Health Survey devised and used by Jacobs in 1984 and 1987 with his California samples and in 1987 with his Virginia sample consisted of seventy (70) items. The first eleven items sought demographic information (e.g., age, sex, nationality, education, employment) and items assessing life stress (i.e., loss of parent, suicide attempt, imprisonment, and pending legal problems). The next section enquired about health status, quality of life and psychological adjustment across a number of self-image and interpersonal dimensions. A major section of the survey asked about history and specific levels of involvement with health-threatening substances (e.g., nicotine, alcohol and other drugs) and activities such as overeating and gambling. A detailed subsection was devoted to asking about the extent of involvement in each item of an extensive list of gambling activities during the past twelve months and the total amount bet during the past year. The final section covered initial and subsequent reactions to drinking, drug use, overeating and gambling. Supplementing the latter section were items asking about dissociative experiences while indulging in each substance and activity, self-assessment of evidence for loss of control and self-control methods, and attitudes towards help-seeking and treatment. Each subject also received one of three scales developed by Alcoholics Anonymous, Overeaters Anonymous and Gamblers Anonymous to evaluate potential addiction in these behaviors.

The surveys independently devised by Lesieur, for his New Jersey sample, and by Steinberg, for his Connecticut sample, contained items that sought information very similar to that investigated by Jacobs. Subjects participating in each high school setting were believed to constitute a representative sample of their fellow students, although none of these independent unsponsored investigators had the resources to employ formal stratified sampling procedures.

SURVEY RESULTS

Highly consistent results across subsamples revealed a surprisingly early onset of gambling for money. Almost a third of these youths reported their first experience before age 11 and over eighty percent had gambled for money by age 15. This finding is paradoxical in light of uniform state statutes in the United States that make gambling by those under eighteen years of age illegal.

Although the prevalence rates varied in direct relation to the variety of gambling outlets readily accessible to each group of students, it was found that, nationwide, more than half of these youth had gambled for money in the past twelve months. The types of wagering by these students ran the entire gamut of games available to adults. Again, highly consistent findings across the subsamples showed that, in rank order, the five favorite games of high school age youth were:

- cards with family and friends (45%);
- the state lottery (43%);
- betting on their own games of skill (e.g., pool, bowling, golf, etc.) 34%;
- sports betting (football pools, offtrack betting, etc.) 30%; and

- bingo (22%).

It is noteworthy that across the five independent studies, five percent to thirteen percent of the students described one or both of their parents as a problem gambler. These percentages of problem gambling reported among parents tended to rise over the period 1984 to 1988.

A very disturbing finding was that between four and six percent of the overall high school sample (n=2777) met the criteria established by *DSM-III* for diagnosis of "pathological gambling" (American Psychiatric Association, 1980). The rate of these youngsters is more than three times the prevalence rate of adult pathological gamblers (1.4%) reported by a recent national study of problem gambling in America funded by the National Institute of Mental Health (Volberg, personal communication, 1990).

The above finding is internally consistent with other gambling related problems reported by students who had admitted to gambling for money in the last year. One in five of these students stated either they "would like to stop gambling but could not" or that they believed their "gambling was out of control." Among students who gambled, thirteen percent stated they had committed illegal acts to get gambling money or to pay gambling debts, and twelve percent reported that their gambling had harmed relationships with their families.

Four of the five studies noted above inquired whether subjects had sought an organized program such as Gamblers' Anonymous for professional help to stop gambling. Findings varied from two percent to five percent in Virginia and California and twelve percent in the 1988 Connecticut study. Independent reports from Gambler's Anonymous groups around the country consistently report that the age of persons first seeking membership in the groups has dropped precipitously over recent years, with some as young as fifteen years of age seeking help. However they also report that these young gamblers seldom continue coming to meetings.

At this time, professional treatment programs for teenagers with gambling problems are all but nonexistent, except in those cases where teenagers also have admitted problems with substance abuse or other addictive behaviors. Outpatient treatment facilities for teenage gambling problems are also few and far between and await additional training of mental health professionals regarding this particular problem before we can expect any major inroads for remediation.

CHILDREN OF PROBLEM GAMBLERS — FIRST REPORT ON AN AT RISK GROUP

A substantial but narrowly targeted literature has accumulated in recent years describing the kinds of health and behavior problems experienced by children of alcoholic parents (Jacobs, 1986, 1986a, 1989, 1990; Jacobs, et al., 1989; Tharinger and Koranek, 1989; West and Prinz, 1987). No systematic information, however, has been gathered on the vulnerability and risks of youth who describe their parent or parents as compulsive or problem gamblers. The following study was the first to be completed on a self-identified but anonymous group of adolescents in high school settings who described themselves as children of problem gamblers.

An anonymous seventy item Health Survey was administered to 844 randomly selected ninth- to twelfth-grade students in four Southern California public high schools. Gathered was systematic information about their general health, quality of life, school and work adjustment, involvement with a range of potentially addictive substances and activities, and indications of psychosocial maladjustment, including difficulties with the law and suicide attempts (Jacobs, 1986).

Self ratings of students who characterized one or both of their parents as "problem gamblers" (n=52) were compared with those of their classmates who had reported no problem gambling among their parents (n=792).

Without exception, when compared to their classroom peers, children of problem gamblers showed:

- higher levels of use for tobacco, alcohol and drugs, as well as more involvement with overeating and much earlier onset of gambling;
- almost twice the incidence of broken homes, more instances of legal action pending against them, and poor self ratings of the overall quality of their youth; and
- a consistently greater incidence of dysphoric mood indicators and twice the frequency of suicide attempts (12% vs. 6%).

It is estimated that as many as one in every 25 Americans may be the adult or juvenile child of a problem gambler (Jacobs, 1989).

These results reflect a definite link between parental problem gamblers and elevated risks for dysfunctional behaviors among offspring raised in what may be termed "pathologenic families." In this study, such families may be characterized by the presence of one or both parents who are so unable to deal with their own problems that they have turned to gambling (among other potentially addictive behaviors) to "self treat" their own chronic stress conditions. The finding that such marriages show a very high incidence (37%) of separation, divorce, or death of a parent before the children are fifteen years of age, underscores the instability of this childrearing environment. Family instability appears to have its greatest effect on the more vulnerable child and junior high school student (West and Prinz, 1987).

What is suggested by these findings are intergenerational effects wrought by highly stressed, preoccupied, inconsistent, and often absent parents who have provided seriously flawed parenting, sex, social, and occupational role models for their children. The results of this study indicate that deficiencies in the home life of children who described one or both parents as "having a problem with compulsive gambling" become evident among such youths by their greater involvement in a number of potentially addictive health threatening behaviors, coupled with a consistent pattern of inadequate stress management and inferior coping skills.

One cannot resist the conclusion that without early and competent intervention, children of problem gamblers: (a) will be seriously disadvantaged when attempting to solve their present and future problems of living, and (b) as a consequence are themselves high risk candidates for developing one or another form of dysfunctional behavior, including an addictive pattern of behavior.

POLICY IMPLICATIONS OF THESE RESULTS

The current projections that four to six percent of high school students across America could already be compulsive/pathological gamblers are very provocative. For the moment, results from the studies reviewed stand as the only available estimates of the possible scope and nature of this problem. Critics may justifiably question the validity, even the temerity, of projections based on five surveys of American high school students. They may label the collective results as no more than "straws in the wind." This too may later prove to be so as new information is assembled. Meanwhile, it is noteworthy that all the "straws" appear to be blowing in the same direction, and they bear essentially the same message: There is reason enough to acknowledge that gambling is well established among American high school age youth and that a minority of them already are in serious straits, and probably are at considerable risk of experiencing future mental, physical and social dysfunctional consequences of their gambling related activities.

Likely, these revelations will be met by a combination of fear and denial that typically constitutes the public response to alleged problems among youth. In the best case, this will stimulate a series of research projects that will scientifically verify or disconfirm the purported prevalence rates of juvenile gambling in America, as well as the extent and nature of gambling related problems among these youth. The author hopes that the findings reported here will spur initiation of even more ambitious longitudinal studies aimed at identifying those sets of familial and environmental circumstances that presage risk or resistiveness among as many as ten million adult and juvenile children of problem gamblers.

Over the past decade the social *zeitgeist* in America has changed radically because of the greatly increased availability, promotion, and glamorization, not to mention the inflated payoffs, associated with commercial gambling. *Gaming and Wagering Business Magazine* (October 1988) notes that, "The twenty-seven U.S. lotteries operating in fiscal 1988 grossed $14.8 billion, a 19.3% leap over the previous year. Net revenues accruing to state governments are estimated at almost $6 billion, up almost 15% over fiscal 1987" (page 30). By the beginning of 1992, the total number of lottery states in America was thirty-three plus the District of Columbia, with more additions expected in Texas and Louisiana; some of the remaining hold-out states such as Nebraska and Georgia were also considering a lottery.

Eadington (1988) reports that by the close of 1987 the casinos of Las Vegas and Atlantic City each generated annual gross revenues in excess of $7.5 billion per year. The creation and proliferation of riverboat gambling, mining town casinos, and Indian casino gaming seen since the late 1980s presage a veritable explosion of gambling in the United States during the 1990s.

WHAT CAN AND SHOULD BE DONE?

The author shares Eadington's opinion that:

> ". . .the gaming industries in the United States have been relatively insensitive to the existence of problem or pathological gambling, choosing to ignore it rather than trying to deal with it in any constructive mitigating way. Unless and until this issue is adequately addressed by the commercial gambling industries or the appropriate regulatory bodies, commercial gambling will not be able to achieve a level of acceptance and legitimacy comparable to other industries. However, given the general direction of the evolution of commercial gambling in the United States and in many foreign jurisdictions, it is likely the industry itself, or the regulatory body governing it, will realize the enlightened self-interest involved in adequately dealing with this issue" (1988).

In this author's view, after a decade of unbridled growth and the apparent continuing explosion of gambling currently taking place in the early 1990s, it may well be time for American society to re-examine the long range consequences of its love affair with legalized gambling. Public understanding of gambling problems is where our understanding of alcoholism was some forty years ago. Public education is the prime vehicle for generating widespread consciousness of the extent and potential negative consequences of juvenile gambling. It also may motivate involved youth to critically evaluate their own behavior. Greater awareness at governmental levels regarding the large numbers of underage youth who gamble and the potential harm associated with their gambling may lead to firmer enforcement of existing laws that set statutory age limits for gambling, and thereby reduce the accessibility of this activity to those who are more vulnerable to its impact. The gaming industry itself may generate more vigorous and effective methods for discouraging play by underage youth in their own corporate self-interest.

Long past due are periodic, state funded, independent social impact studies to identify the extent to which new and changing forms of legalized gambling contribute to gambling rates and, particularly, to rates of problem gambling among potentially vulnerable groups such as juveniles, females and minorities. The scientific literature consistently indicates that adolescents are most at risk for developing addictive patterns of behavior, including pathological gambling.

The already high rates of tenuously controlled problem gambling behaviors among high school youth reported in this study accentuate the need for early identification and enhanced educational, counseling, and preventive interventions for this high risk group of young Americans.

There is no consensus on how, if at all, youngsters should be prepared for participation in a society where most adults gamble. Results from ongoing scientific studies of gambling in America reveal that more then eighty percent of American adults have gambled at some time in their lives (Volberg, 1990). Best estimates available for gambling by adolescents under eighteen years of age indicate that since 1987 more than fifty percent have gambled within the previous twelve months (Jacobs, 1989).

The finding that four to six percent of the high school students reviewed in this study already show serious gambling related problems must be made known when educating sixth to twelfth grade students, as well as their parents and teachers, to the possible problems that may attend excessive gambling. Materials carrying this message could be included with ongoing educational programs about tobacco, alcohol, and drug use, since all of these behaviors appear to be fellow travelers among adolescents. The data discussed in this analysis about the surprisingly early age of onset of gambling make it imperative that educational programs be introduced at or before entry into junior high school. Indeed there is good justification for targeting early primary prevention efforts at the primary school level where preadolescents may be taught social skills, stress management and various coping skills and problem solving strategies that will anticipate and put them in better stead to deal with the physical, psychological, and social stresses that characterize the adolescent years.

Meanwhile, prompt availability of treatment must be organized for adolescents who already show serious problems related to their gambling behaviors. This resource could rather easily and economically be integrated into existing adolescent drug, alcohol, and overeating programs already functioning in hospital and outpatient settings.

Lying somewhere between treatment and prevention is a special need for programs directed at that forgotten population who are the children of problem gamblers. Virtually nonexistent for them are support groups like those established for children of other addicts, such as *Al-Ateen*. Meeting this need would require revitalizing and rapidly expanding the nascent *Gam-Ateen* movement in America. Our enthusiasm to identify and assist these youth must be tempered by care that such efforts avoid violating child and parent rights to privacy, and not create self-fulfilling prophecies by polarizing the expectations of parents, teachers and peers and thereby stigmatize the child.

The willingness of gambler parents to cooperate in family interventions is another problem inviting future close attention. In all these considerations, fruitful methods can be borrowed and progress can be accelerated by drawing on the examples and expertise provided by those who have long since been active in programs for children of alcoholics.

Since 1975, the University of Michigan Survey Research Center has been conducting a series a longitudinal "Monitoring the Future" studies of drug use among high school seniors. Results of the 1986 survey indicate that the downward trend noted since 1980 in the use of all illicit drugs continues, except for cocaine which remains a serious problem among high school youth. The cocaine problem is being attacked on an international front and the rate of increase of cocaine use has already begun to fall off. Reports from the U.S. Surgeon General indicate declining rates of cigarette smoking among high school youth. The use of alcohol by teenagers is also under fire. As a result of the AIDS epidemic, sex is seen to have its perils among experimenting adolescents. Soon these youth will wonder, "What's left that will provide recreation, relieve boredom and stress, and add excitement to my life?"

This author predicts that the 1990s will mark the historic heyday of legalized gambling throughout the world. How we in America plan to meet this eventuality will determine the extent to which future generations of our youth will be placed at risk.

REFERENCES

Eadington, W.R. (1988). Preface. In W.R. Eadington (ed.), *Gambling Research: Proceedings of the Seventh International Conference on Gambling and Risk Taking*. Reno: University of Nevada, Reno.

Jacobs, D.F. (1986). *High risk youth: Children of compulsive gamblers.* Invited address presented at the Western Conclave of GA/GAM-ANON, Palm Springs, CA.

Jacobs, D.F. (1986a). *Early identification and prevention of health-threatening behaviors in adolescents.* Paper presented at the Twenty-First International Congress of Applied Psychology, Jerusalem, Israel.

Jacobs, D.F. (1986b). Application of a general theory of addictions to treatment and rehabilitation planning for pathological gamblers. In T. Galski (ed.), *Handbook of Pathological Gambling.* Detroit, MI: Thomas Press.

Jacobs, D.F. (1989). Illegal and undocumented: A review of teenage gambling and the plight of children of problem gamblers in America. In H.J. Shaffer, S.A. Stein, B. Gambino, and T. Cummings (eds.), *Compulsive Gambling: Theory, Research and Practice.* Lexington, MA: Lexington Books.

Jacobs, D.F. (1990). Gambling behaviors of high school students: Implications for government-supported gambling. In C.S. Campbell and J. Lowman (eds.), *Gambling in Canada: Golden Goose or Trojan Horse?* Burnaby, B.C.: Simon Fraser University.

Jacobs, D.F. et al. (1989). Children of problem gamblers. *Journal of Gambling Behavior*, 5, 261-268.

Jacobs, D.F. and Wright, E. (1980). *A program of research on the causes and treatment of addictive disorders: Using the compulsive gambler as the prototype subject.* Unpublished research proposal. Jerry L. Pettis Memorial Veterans Hospital, Loma Linda, CA.

Tharinger, D., and Koranek, M. (1988). Children of alcoholics — at risk and unserved: A review of research and service roles for school psychologists. *School Psychology Review*, 17, 166-191.

Volberg, R. (1990). Personal communication.

West, M.O. and Prinz, R.J. (1987). Parental alcoholism and childhood psychopathology. *Psychological Bulletin*, 102, 204-218.

Preventing Pathological Gambling Among Teenagers

Anne Gaboury and Robert Ladouceur

Gambling behavior starts during adolescence. In a recent literature review, Jacobs (1989) estimated the prevalence of pathological gambling among American teenagers who gamble at 7%. Furthermore, 22% gamble at least once a week. In Québec, Ladouceur and Mireault (1988) reported 1.7% of high school students were pathological gamblers and 24% were regular gamblers. As a step towards the reduction of this widespread problem, the present study evaluated the effectiveness of a prevention program for gambling behavior.

Prevention programs exist for substance abuse, but none have yet been designed for gambling. Since gambling is also an addiction, the program discussed in this paper was inspired by alcohol and drug abuse prevention programs. Typically, these programs include information about the substance and the effects of consumption. Other programs provide subjects with coping skills, social and problem solving skills and ways to increase self-esteem. According to the prevention literature, school is the best place to talk about prevention. Further, a program designed for teenagers needs to include group activities.

The first goal of the program was to provide information on gambling. The authors measured the effect of receiving this information on four variables which will be discussed.

METHOD

Nine schools were contacted and five agreed to participate in the program. Figure 1 illustrates the experimental design of the study. A total of 289 students completed the study: 134 were in the intervention group and 155 in the control group. The students (half boys and half girls) were in grades 11 or 12, with an average age of 16 years old. However, descriptive data from the pre-test include 421 students.

FIGURE 1

EXPERIMENTAL DESIGN

OCTOBER 89		DECEMBER 89	JUNE 90
Pre-test		Post-test	Follow-up
01-Exp	X	02-Exp	03-Exp
9 groups	Program		
204 subjects		→ 134 subjects at the three sessions	
01-Control		02-Control	03-Control
9 groups	Program		
217 subjects		→ 155 subjects at the three sessions	
421 subjects			289 subjects

The program included three 75-minute sessions which took place during normal class time. The control groups were submitted to two 20-minute evaluations

evaluations at pre-test and post-test. The follow-up for both groups was conducted 6 months after the intervention.

The evaluation was the same for experimental groups and control groups but an appreciation evaluation was added for groups participating in the program.

The authors evaluated the groups on the following four variables:

1. Gambling behavior — frequency, amount of money bet, kinds of games played, and questions derived from the DSM-III-R criteria assessing pathological gambling.
2. Knowledge about the gambling industry, the psychology of gambling, and pathological gambling, in a questionnaire of 20 true or false questions — for example:

   In Québec, casinos are illegal: true or false?

   Anybody can stop gambling when he intends to: true or false?

   Only bad gamblers lose money: true or false?
3. Attitudes about gambling — We used eight questions similar to those that Rhodes and Jason (1988) used for drugs, adapted for gambling. For example:

   People who gamble look like big shots: strongly disagree, disagree, neither agree or disagree, agree, strongly agree.

   It's stupid to spend money on gambling. . ..
4. Spontaneously known skills for coping with gambling and for preventing pathological gambling, measured by the following question: Do you know some ways or tricks that help you to gamble less often, spend less money or to stop gambling?

THE PROGRAM

The program was divided into six sections. These are described below as well as the time allotted for each.

SECTION 1: This section introduced the program, a definition of gambling, legal and illegal in Québec and the consequences of participating in legal or illegal games. (30 minutes)

SECTION 2: During this section discussions were held on gambling as an industry which survives on the gambler's money. In groups, students created a casino game. The authors illustrated that on a long term basis, games are beneficial to the owner, and publicity about gambling focuses on aspects of the game that seem to the player's advantage. For example, the publicity shows the cost of participating, when it is a small amount, the prize when it is a very large amount, but the publicity never talks about the low probability of winning. (25 minutes)

SECTION 3: The students were given information about automatic behavior in gambling. The content of this part is based on our research findings. A short video was viewed in which a teenager is observed thinking aloud while gambling at a video poker machine. While observing him, two phenomena were noticeable. First, he progressively increased his bet (Ladouceur, Tourigny and Mayrand, 1986; Ladouceur and Gaboury, 1988), and second, he demonstrated inadequate thinking as he tried to find winning strategies (Gaboury and Ladouceur, 1989). In discussion with the students, it was explained how awareness of those phenomena can help to control gambling behavior. (35 minutes)

SECTION 4: Here, the concept of pathological gambling was introduced. A television program was shown in which anonymous pathological gamblers talked about how and when they started to gamble, how it became a problem, and what were the consequences of their pathological gambling. In the following discussion, students had to identify similar behaviors among the gamblers. Diagnostic criteria was also discussed. (45 minutes)

SECTION 5: Students were asked to identify strategies to control gambling habits and to prevent pathological gambling. For example: no chasing, watch for increasing bets, be assertive when they don't want to gamble, stop gambling after a big win, etc. (20 minutes)

SECTION 6: A quiz was administered which summarized and demonstrated how chance has nothing to do with skills. (30 minutes)

RESULTS

Descriptive analysis performed on the 421 subjects present at the pre-test revealed that 64% of subjects had gambled at least once in the last 6 months and 21% gambled once a week or more. The average money gambled per month was $8.50, which represented 5.6% of their personal income. Boys bet more than girls: $13 per month versus $3.33. Furthermore, according to DSM-III-R criteria, 6.7% would be considered pathological gamblers. Only one girl met DSM-III-R criteria.

Analysis of variance was performed on the four dependent variables. Results showed significant differences on knowledge and skills reported. The experimental group improved their scores on the knowledge questionnaire significantly more than the control group. Gains were maintained at the follow-up (Figure 2).

FIGURE 2

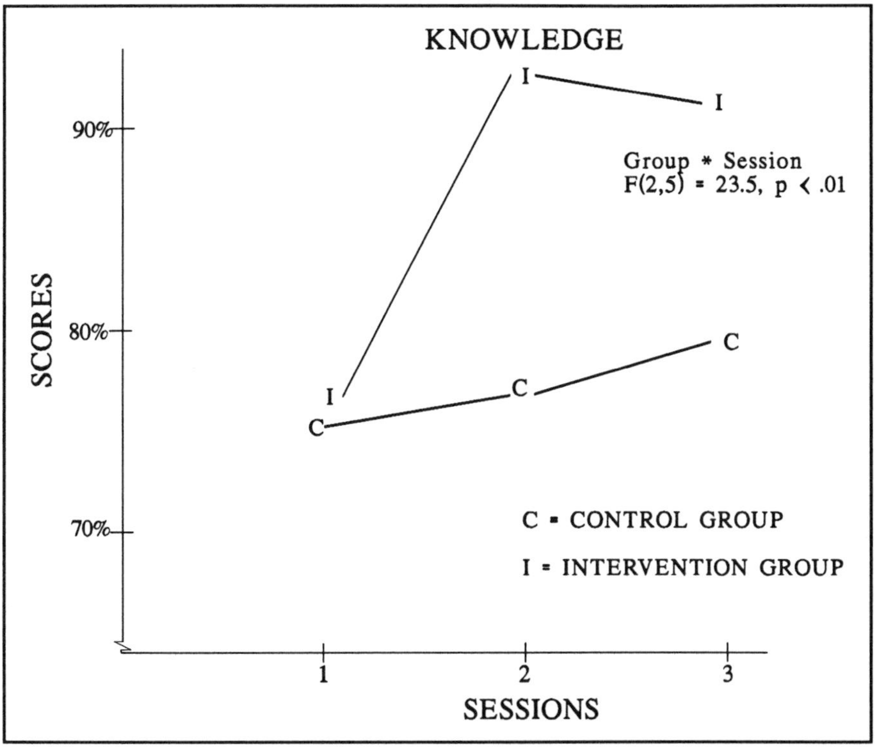

Significant differences were found on skills reported for coping with gambling behavior (Figure 3). The score is a mean for the group: total skills divided by the number of subjects by group. The intervention group reported more skills than the control group at the post-test but not at the follow-up.

FIGURE 3

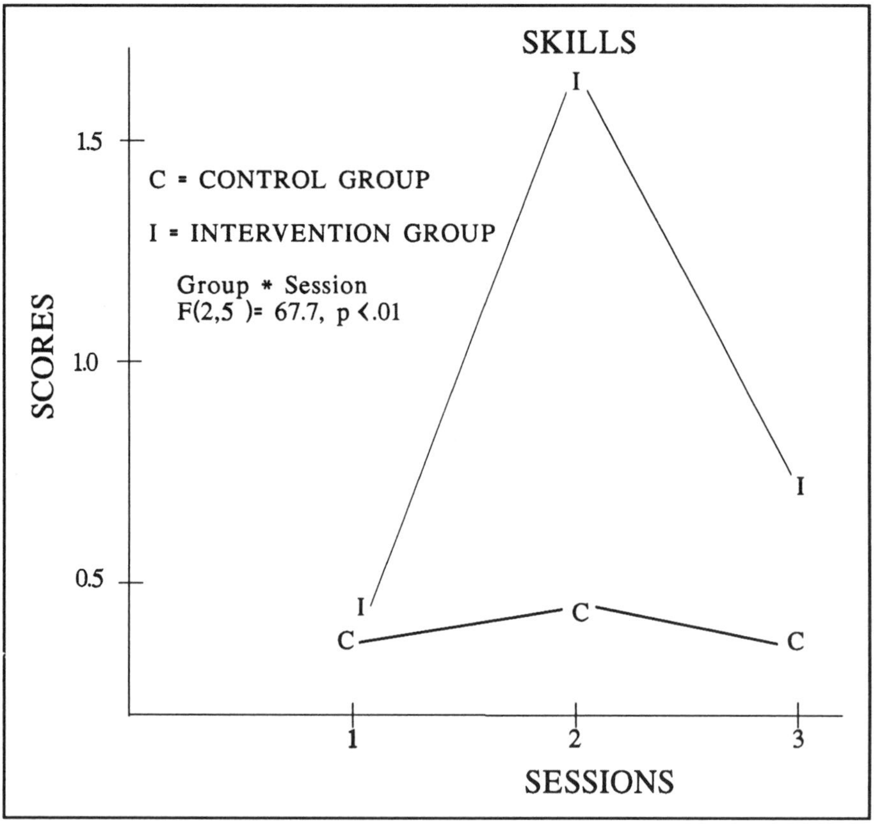

Analysis showed no impact of the program on gambling behavior and attitudes. The appreciation evaluation revealed that 77% of the subjects found the program interesting or very interesting and a qualitative analysis showed that, for 52% of the students who participated in the program, the information about pathological gambling was the most impressive.

DISCUSSION

The survey data are really impressive. The authors were expecting an increase in pathological gamblers since 1986 but to this extent. The increase can be explained by the fact that video-poker machines have become more popular in Québec and also by the use of new criteria.

Results partially confirm our hypotheses. The impact of the program was significant on two variables: knowledge and skills. However the newly known skills were not practiced. They were not maintained at follow-up. The authors succeeded only in increasing knowledge on gambling and pathological gambling in teenagers. Such knowledge is important and obviously needed. Teenagers gamble a lot, some of them have real problems with gambling, and they do not know that just like drugs, there are possible dangers of addiction.

No significant differences were found in attitudes and gambling behavior. Perhaps the impact will appear later. I think that to have an impact on attitudes and gambling habits the information has to be even more explicit. The fact that subjects in the intervention group couldn't recall coping skills at follow-up supports this hypothesis. The subjects didn't feel implicated, even if they were. The program was perhaps too short, not in content but in time. Perhaps it is the kind of information that would be transmitted better by a regular teacher who can repeat it. It would also be easier for a regular teacher to stimulate personal questionning, to speak at greater length on what they think about gambling, and to discuss the content of the program with them. Finally, gambling is an addiction. Perhaps it would be better to discuss it in a general prevention program on substance abuse. This type of solution needs to be explored in order to find ways to make teenagers feel more implicated by the information and more equipped to cope with this problem.

REFERENCES

Gaboury, A. and Ladouceur, R. (1989). Erroneous perceptions and gambling. *Journal of Social Behavior and Personality*, 4, 411-420.

Jacobs, D.F. (1989). Illegal and undocumented: A review of teenage gambling and the plight of children of problem gamblers in America. In H.J. Shaffer, S.A. Stein, B. Gambino, and T.N. Cummings (eds.), *Compulsive Gambling: Theory, Research and Practice*. Lexington, MA: Lexington Books.

Ladouceur, R. and Gaboury, A. (1988). Effects of limited and unlimited stakes on gambling behavior. *Journal of Gambling Behavior*, 4, 119-126.

Ladouceur, R. and Mireault, C. (1988). Gambling behaviors among high school students in the Québec area. *Journal of Gambling Behavior*, 4, 3-12.

Ladouceur, R., Tourigny, M. and Mayrand, M. (1986). Familiarity, group exposure, and risk-taking behavior in gambling. *Journal of Psychology*, 120, 45-49.

Rhodes, J.E. and Jason, L.A. (1988). *Preventive Substance Abuse Among Children and Adolescents*. New York: Pergamon Press.

Home Computer and Video Game Addictions in Relation to Adolescent Gambling: Conceptual and Developmental Aspects

R. Iain F. Brown and Seonaid Robertson[1]

Adolescent gambling has been an emotive and controversial issue in Britain, particularly in England. The major form of problem child gambling in the United States is the slot machines (Arcuri, Lester and Smith, 1985) and in Britain it is Amusement With Prizes (AWP) fruit machines (British Market Research Bureau, 1986; Ide-Smith and Lea, 1988). Young males, aged 16 to 31, are one of the two demographic groups most strongly represented in amusement arcades where many gambling machines are grouped together (Bentall, Fisher, Kelly, Bromley and Hawksworth, 1989).

The incidence of pathological or addicted gambling in adolescents was surveyed in the United States (Lesieur and Klein, 1987) and in Canada (Ladouceur and Mireault, 1988) and the various surveys in the United Kingdom have been extensively reviewed and evaluated (Fisher, 1989; Griffiths, 1989a, 1989b, 1990; Ides-Smith and Lea, 1988). A recent report from the British government's own research team (Home Office, 1988) proved very controversial (Griffiths, 1989).

AROUSAL IN MACHINE GAMBLING AND IN VIDEO AND COMPUTER GAMING

Although recent studies suggest that we ignore differences between those gamblers who express preferences for particular types of gambling at our peril (Shapiro, 1981; Blaszczynski, Winter and McConaghy, 1986; Adkins, Kruedelbach, Toohig and Rugle, 1988; Coventry and Brown, 1990), the arousal and sensation seeking components found in most other forms of gambling appear to be present in machine gambling as well. Brown (1988) monitored arousal as measured by changes in heart rate during play in two groups of normal gambling machine players (n = 12). There were steady rises in tonic heart rate over nine of the ten minutes of the recording period. Increases in heart rate over baseline averaged 26.75 beats per minute at the ninth minute of the game sequence which is similar to the increases found in poker machine players in Australia by Leary and Dickerson (1986). The high sensation seekers averaged 43 beats per minute increases at this point, significantly greater than the low sensation seekers. Average increases in heart rate over baseline were calculated for the three "stages" of "nudge," "lose" and "win." These were greatest at the "nudge" and lowest at the "lose." Machine gambling, then appears to involve potentially addictive increases in arousal like other forms of gambling (Anderson and Brown, 1984; Brown, 1986).

Potentially addictive rises in arousal have been monitored, again measuring heart rate, in the playing of a business simulation of the management of a sales force. In these, individuals have been found who were clearly so involved in computer gaming as to be "addicted" by most meanings of the concept (Brown, 1993).

VIDEO GAME ADDICTIONS IN A SAMPLE OF SCOTTISH SCHOOL CHILDREN

The relationship between addiction to video gaming (measured by items from Gamblers Anonymous "Twenty Questions") and commitment (as measured by proportion of available money spent playing) was investigated in a small study in Scotland in 1986. The subjects were 134 school children aged between 12 and 16 years who were given a questionnaire containing items probing aspects of their playing of non-gambling video games. Of the whole group, 44% were players and of these players 76% spent money playing on the video machines (the other 24% playing only on their computers at home). The items from the Twenty Questions used by Gamblers Anonymous to determine the presence of compulsive gambling (all answered Yes/No) were:

- Can you pass a Space Invaders machine without wanting to play a game?
- When you have played one game do you always want to play another?
- Do you some times spend more money than you were going to?
- Do you often leave only when all your money has run out?
- Do you often borrow money in order to play the machine?

As a validity check, the correlation between commitment (as measured by proportion of available **spare** time spent on playing both home computers and video games outside) and addiction (measured as above) was calculated. Since this result was low and insignificant (Spearman's Rho = 0.391, p = 0.769, n = 59), it was concluded that it would be invalid to use the extended sample including the home computer players. Accordingly, the following statistical analysis is confined to the smaller sample of video game players (n = 45) in which the correlation between commitment (as measured by proportion of available **money** spent playing) and addiction was high, positive and significant (Spearman's Rho = 0.4966, p = 0.001, n = 45) and was good evidence of validity.

Frequency histograms and percentile tables were computed to examine the distribution of addiction scores (Table 1). The modal score was 3 out of 6 times and it was found that 4.4% had achieved the highest possible addiction scores (5 items) and an additional 6.7% with only one item short of this (4 items out of five), giving 11.1% scoring highly on addiction (i.e., reporting themselves as often leaving only when all their money has run out and often borrowing money to play the machines). This suggested that a sizeable percentage of the general population of school children may have a significant addiction to video gaming alone.

TABLE 1

Distribution of Scores of Addiction to Video Gaming in a Small Sample of Scottish School Children

Frequency Tables of Addiction Scores

Addiction Score	Frequency	Percentage
0	7	15.6
1	6	13.3
2	9	20.0
3	18	40.0
4	3	6.7
5	2	4.4

Bar Chart of Addiction Scores

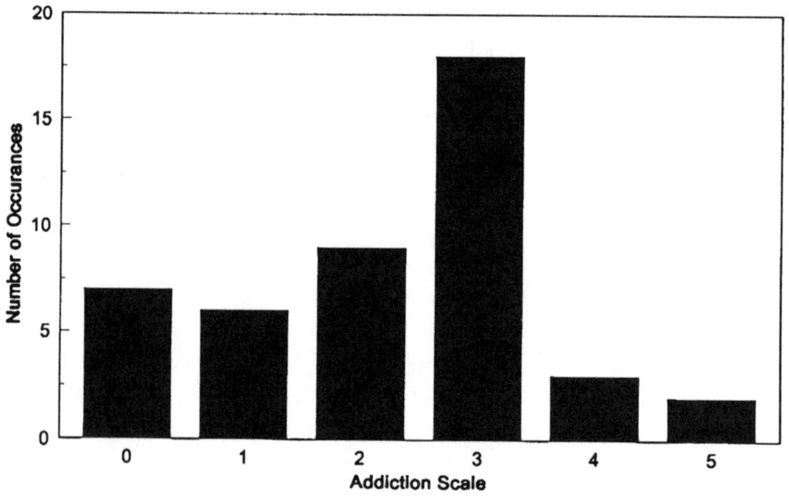

There is already evidence that over the age group 11 to 13 there is a regular escalation with increasing age of the proportions of children who attend amusement arcades who play the fruit machines as well as the video games alone (Roberts and Poole, 1988), and there as an apparent progression from borrowing money to play through using school dinner money to play, and stealing money to play to missing school to play (National Housing and Town Planning Council, 1988). This could make the examination of video gaming as a gateway to or a precursor of machine gambling a potentially urgent social issue.

RELATIONSHIPS BETWEEN HOME COMPUTER PLAYING, PLAYING OF VIDEO GAMES OUTSIDE THE HOME AND GAMBLING

The main study reported here differs from many previous studies in so far as it is one of the first, possibly the first, to attempt to examine systematically home computer, video game, and gambling game use in the same population of adolescents.

Subjects (n = 807) were obtained from two secondary neighboring schools in an urbanized area on the fringes of Greater Glasgow, covering the first to the sixth years of secondary school (the American equivalent is grades seventh to twelvth). Ages ranged from 11 to 18 years. Failures to complete the entire research protocol led to the reduction of the usable sample to 380.

A ten page questionnaire was administered assessing a wide range of variables. After the demographic variables such as age, sex and social class, total available leisure time and total available spending money were assessed for all subjects by a systematic survey of the week previous to filling in the questionnaire. The time and money spent in the past week on each of: video games played on computers at home; video games played on computers outside the home; and gambling games — was assessed in the same way. Questions were included for each activity about age of starting and about playing alone. Finally a number of questions about borrowing, stealing and truancy and their association with gaming were included. Within the questionnaire were embedded measurements of potential addictive involvement in each game playing activity using an addiction involvement scale.

The *Addiction Involvement Scale*, First Form (AIS I) is a questionnaire based on a general addictions paradigm which principally measures salience, conflict and social damage, but also includes questions about tolerance and withdrawals.

It consists of twenty questions, each answered as "never" (scored as 0), "occasionally" (scored as 1), and "quite often" (scored as 2). It has a maximum score of 40. It can be adapted to measure the intensity of an individual's involvement with any activity, and equivalent versions have been used with drinkers, eaters, gardeners, golfers, and other groups. It has a test-retest reliability of 0.62. The findings by the authors that it has differentiated addicted drinkers (clients seeking help for drinking problems from the Glasgow Council on Alcohol) from non-addicted drinkers (first year Psychology students at the University of Glasgow, and addicted eaters (members of Weight Watchers) from non-addicted eaters (first year Psychology students at the University of Glasgow) suggest that it has some construct validity.

Questionnaires were administered to the subjects in classes by their instructors within one extended period of the school timetable, usually taking about one hour to complete. Anonymity was strongly emphasized.

RESULTS

Subjects were classified in subsamples according to the games they did and did not play (Table 2). Since there were less than ten subjects in two of the categories, returns specific to those two categories are not reported in many of the following analyses.

TABLE 2

Distribution of Adolescents Across Game-playing Categories

Games Played	*N*
None	73
Home computer only	125
Video outside only	24
Gambling machines only	16
Both home computer games & video games outside	79
Both home computer games & gambling machines	7
Both video games outside & gambling machines	8
All types; home, video and gambling	48
Total	380

TABLE 2a

Percentages of Total Sample Playing Various Games	
Games Played	%
None	19.2
Home computer	68.2
Video outside	41.8
Gambling machines	20.8

With regard to demographic characteristics, although roughly equal numbers of boys and girls play gambling games exclusively or video games exclusively, more boys than girls play both (Anova $p < 0.00001$). The only significant difference in ages between game playing categories was that the "gambling machines exclusively" category were younger than the "video games exclusively" (Anova $p < 0.00001$). The only difference between social classes was that there were significantly fewer adolescents in social classes C1 (skilled working class) and C2 (small businessmen) who played gambling games exclusively (Anova $p < 0.00001$). There was no significant difference in available spare time between game-playing categories but adolescents playing gambling machines exclusively had the least available spending money, and those playing gambling machines and outside video games — but not home computers — had the most (Anova $p < 0.003$).

A. Time spent playing

There were significant differences between game categories in average proportions of available time spent playing (Table 3). Players of home computers exclusively spend more of their available time playing than any other single-game-playing category ($t = .04$, $p < 0.01$) and gambling exclusively players spend the least time ($t = 7.42$, $p < 0.01$). Adolescents playing both home computers and video games outside spend almost double the time playing home computers as opposed to video games outside, and those who play all game types spend significantly more time playing home computers than they do video games outside ($t = 4.3$, $p < 0.01$).

TABLE 3

Time Spent Playing Per Week as a Average Proportion of Total Leisure Time

Games Played		*Mean % of Total Time*	*SD*
Home computers only		41	60.3
Video outside only		39	20.0
Gambling machines only		8	3.5
Home computer & video			
(i)	home computer	41	64.7
(ii)	video	24	31.3
All types			
(i)	home computer	41	69.3
(ii)	video	3	8.5
(iii)	gambling	31	36.4

No adolescents who played gambling machines exclusively had played within the last two weeks before filling in the questionnaire, and only 4.7% of those who played all categories of games had played gambling games within the last two weeks; for 33% it had been more than a month since they last played. The highest percentage of people who had played recently (within a week) were in the category of those who played video games outside exclusively (38%).

There were significant differences between game-playing categories in the average length of the longest session spent playing. Adolescents who play video games exclusively spent significantly more time on their longest session than those playing gambling machines exclusively ($t = 4.12$, $p < 0.01$) or those playing exclusively home computer games ($t = 2.31$, $p < 0.05$). Those who play both home computer and outside video games also spent longer in their longest session on video games ($t = 2.49$, $p < 0.02$).

B. Those who play alone compared with those who play with others

Adolescents who describe themselves as playing mostly alone are compared with those who describe themselves as mostly playing with others in Table 4. Some comparisons could not be usefully made due to missing data, but from those that could be made, it can be seen that those adolescents "playing home computers exclusively" and "playing alone" devote almost 50% of their available spare time to them, and more than 2.5 times the proportion of their available spare time than those "playing with others" devote to them ($t= 4.7$, $p < 0.01$). Similarly, adolescents who "play exclusively video games outside alone" devote almost twice as much of their time compared with those "playing with others." Yet, by contrast, among those who play video games, those who "play outside video games with others" spend significantly more time compared to those who play alone ($t = 2.75$, $p < 0.01$). Among those who play all types of games, those who play with others devote more than twice the proportion of their available spare time to playing home computer games than do those who play alone ($t = 2.52$, $p < 0.02$), devoting almost 65% of their spare time to playing home computer games.

TABLE 4

Comparing Those Who Play Alone With Those Who Play With Others: Time Spent Per Week as an Average Proportion of Total Leisure Time

Games Played	*Play Alone Mean % of Total Time*	*SD*	*Play with Others Mean % of Total Time*	*SD*
Home Computers only	49.7	72.1	18.8	13.1
Video outside only	53.0	0.0	25.0	0.0
Gambling machines only	Missing		15.9	6.9
Both home computers & video games outside				
(i) home computer	42.5	61.0	45.0	83.3
(ii) video games outside	12.0	0.0	22.7	34.5
All types, home computers, videos and gambling				
(i) home computer	27.7	33.4	64.9	112.2
(ii) video games outside	Missing		31.9	45.6
(iii) gambling machines	Missing		28.2	40.2

There were significant differences between those who played alone and those who played with others in the average time spent per week by adolescents who played video games exclusively. Those playing with others spent an average of 5.5 hours per week compared with only 1 hour for those who played alone ($t = 4.45$, $p <$).01). Among those who played all types of games, the time spent on one session of gambling machines was twice as long (4 hours) as the average time spent by those who played gambling machines with others ($t = 11.98$, $p < 0.01$). Adolescents who played alone tended to have played more recently than those who played with others, but this trend did not reach significance.

C. Age of starting

The modal age at which the adolescents in each game-playing category began to play was the same for each game-playing category and sub-category: ten years of age. Comparisons were made between those adolescents who started playing before ten and those who started after that. In general, those who began playing earlier devote a greater proportion of their leisure time (Table 5). The differences between those who started playing earlier and those who started later are significant for those playing home computer games in the "home computer and video game-playing" category ($t = 5.38$, $p < 0.01$); for those playing video games in the "home computer and video game-playing" category ($t = 5.0$, $p < 0.01$); and those playing gambling machines in the category "playing all types" ($t = 11.6$, $p < 0.01$). The exception is those playing home computers exclusively. In this category, those starting to play earlier devote less time than those who started later. Those starting before age ten and playing all game types devote an average of more than 71% of their leisure time to playing gambling machines. But not far behind them are those starting early in the home computer and video category who devote an average 69% of their available leisure time.

There are few significant differences in average length of the longest session between those adolescents who started playing before age ten and those starting later. Among adolescents playing video games exclusively, those starting before ten play more than three times longer in the average longest session (6.6 hours) than those starting after ten ($t = 4.65$, $p < 0.01$). Among adolescents playing both home computers and video games, those starting before ten play almost four times as long in their average longest session (5.6 hours) as those starting after ten ($t = 6.4$, $p < 0.01$). There were no significant differences between those starting before and those after age ten in how recently they had last played.

TABLE 5

Comparing Those Who Started Before Ten With Those Starting Later: Time Spent Playing Per Week as an Average Proportion of Total Leisure Time

	STARTING BEFORE TEN		STARTING AFTER TEN	
Games Played	*Mean % of Total Time*	*SD*	*Mean % of Total Time*	*SD*
Home Computers only	34.6	27.0	34.7	29.0
Video outside only	Missing		Missing	
Gambling machines only	Missing		9.0	4.2
Home computer & video				
(i) home computer	68.6	86.3	16.0	10.0
(ii) video	46.6	0.0	9.6	6.5
All types				
(i) home computer	Missing		12.0	9.4
(ii) video	Missing		5.0	0.0
(iii) gambling machines	71.0	40.4	10.6	8.1

D. Money spent playing

Most adolescents spent between one and two pounds sterling per week on games, but 3.8% of those playing home computer and video games spent between eight and fifteen pounds a week.

E. Addiction/involvement scores

Means, standard deviations and ranges of the *Addiction Involvement Scale* (First Form) scores from the various game-playing categories are set out in Table 6, and normative data for comparison purposes are supplied.

TABLE 6

Preliminary Comparisons Between Game-playing Categories and Various Addictive and Non-Adictive Normative Groups:

A) MEANS, STANDARD DEVIATIONS AND RANGES OF ADDICTIVE INVOLVEMENT SCORES

Games Played	*Mean*	*SD*	*Range*	*N*
Home computers only	4.50	4.79	0—23	125
Video games only	4.94	6.72	0—19	24
Home computers & video games	7.52	6.72	0—27	79
All Types:				
Home vomputers & video outside	7.57	6.82	0—27	63
Machine gambling	3.67	5.20	0—20	63

B) NORMS FROM COMPARISON GROUPS

	Mean	*SD*	*N*
Addicted drinkers	17.9	11.7	20
Non-addicted drinkers	3.5	4.0	150
Addicted eaters	12.5	7.0	87
Non-addicted eaters	7.9	5.0	49

Some preliminary comparisons between addiction/involvement scores of game-playing categories and comparison groups of help seeking addicted drinkers and non-addicted students are set out in Table 7.

TABLE 7

Preliminary Comparisons Between Game-playing Categories and Various Addictive and Non-addictive Normative Groups:

C: STUDENT'S T-TESTS

Games Played	*Addictive Drinkers*	*Non-Addictive Drinkers*	*Addictive Eaters*	*Non-Addictive Eaters*
Home computers only	2.03*	1.96	1.99*	2.02*
Video games only	2.07*	2.01	2.03*	2.05*
Both home computers & video games outside	2.05*	1.98*	2.00*	2.01
All types:				
(i) Home computers & video games	2.05*	1.98*	2.00*	2.01
(ii) Gambling machines	2.05*	1.98	2.00*	2.01*

* Significant difference between game-playing category and normative sample — $p < 0.05$

DISCUSSION

The large numbers of protocols which had to be excluded and the prevalence of missing data in many others must be taken into account in the evaluation of the results. The majority of the exclusions arose from the failure of the subject to complete the last page of the questionnaire. Whether this arose from insufficient supervision from the instructors administering the questionnaire or from insufficient time given to complete it because of the timetable demands of the school environment is difficult to determine. However, each could have different selective effects on the sampling which are impossible to estimate.

The most widespread involvement of the adolescents in the sample were with home computers (68%) and video games outside (42%) but 21% of the sample also played gambling machines and the average proportion of leisure time —

71% — devoted to the gambling machines by those who had started before age ten strongly suggests the presence of the addictions found in other studies. The usual sex differences emerged and some social class differences in categories of games-played, although these could have been affected by class differences in failures to complete the questionnaire. Age effects in the playing of gambling games were unusual but these have not yet been analyzed in detail.

The main focus of this analysis, and therefore of this discussion, is not on whether gambling machine addictions in adolescents exist or not because this is well established (e.g, Lesieur and Klein, 1987; Ladouceur and Mireault, 1988). Nor is it on how widespread such addictions may be, or even on what the main independent variables governing the intensity of the addiction might be, although these will be mentioned. It is rather on the possible relationships between gambling machine playing (and therefore gambling machine addictions) and home computers and video gambling.

POSSIBLE FACTORS IN INVOLVEMENT WITH GAMES

There are obviously complex relationships between home computer gambling, outside video gambling, and machine gambling on the one hand, and between all of them and the proportion of total available time spent, length of time spent on longest session, age at which they started to play, and whether they are played predominantly alone or with others, on the other. There is a place here for several large analyses of variance with complex interactions. The independent variables would then be: playing alone versus playing together, and starting before ten versus starting after ten; the dependent variables would be: proportion of total spare time spent playing, average longest session spent playing, and time elapsed since last session played. This has not yet been done.

Anticipating that analysis, for the moment, it seems possible to suggest from these data that the strongest general effect seems to be associated with playing alone rather than with others. Loners play all types of games longer at any single session than those who play with others. Those who play home computer games exclusively devote 2.5 times the proportion of their total leisure time to playing compared with those who normally play with others. Those who "play outside video games exclusively and usually alone" devote twice the proportion of their spare time to them compared with those who mainly play together. Those who play all types of games predominantly alone, when they are playing gambling machines, report the average longest session as more than twice as long as those who play predominantly with others.

This effect seems to be reversed among those who "play combinations of game types," "play home computers and outside video" or "play all types" when they are playing video games outside with others. In this situation the average longest session is more than five times as long as among those who "play video games outside predominantly alone." This might suggest that, for adolescents, outside video gaming may be mainly undertaken as a social activity. Another discernable effect, even at this stage, is that the earlier starters appear to be more involved. Thus, early starters tend generally to devote a higher proportion of their leisure time to playing than late starters. The prominent exceptions to that trend are "home computer gamers" and "exclusively video game players" among whom early starters tend to play longer (6.6 hours average longest session).

THE PREDOMINANCE OF HOME COMPUTER GAMING

Not only are home computer games played by 25% more of the sample than any other game type, but those who play home computers (whether alone, or in conjunction with other game types) appear to spend more time on them than those who play any other type of games. The "home computer exclusive" players spend a larger proportion of their spare time playing than any other group exclusively playing a single type of game. When both home computer games and outside video games are played, players spend twice as much time on home computer games as on outside videos. When all types of games are played, the most time is spent on home computers.

An average of 58% of available leisure time is spent playing among those who "play home computer games exclusively and play predominantly alone." Among those who play all types of games, an average of 65% of their leisure time is devoted to playing home computer games, not gambling games. It is clear that within this sample of adolescents, home computer games command more of the adolescents' time than any other category of game, regardless of whether or not they are in competition with outside video games or gambling machines or both. If salience (filling the horizons of one's life) is the major characteristic of addiction (Brown, 1993) then home computer games appear to provide greater and more widespread dangers of addiction for the majority of adolescents than either outside video games or gambling machines.

Excessive involvement in home computer gaming may be no less damaging than excessive involvement in machine gambling, but it is much less obvious in the kind of damage it causes. With home computer gaming, there will probably be much less need for money with which to feed the video or the gambling machines, so the disruption to the rest of the family is minimal. However, damage to social skills development of the adolescent at a vital stage of growth and the damage to relationships with peers or even with parents may only be exceeded by the impoverishment of emotional experience available from a relationship with an electronic robot which consumes all available time.

ADOLESCENT MACHINE GAMBLING IN CONTEXT

Means, standard deviations and ranges on the *AIS I* are given for each game-playing category for which there was enough data in Table 6a and the norms from addicted and non-addicted samples are set out in Table 6b. From the standard deviations and ranges for each of the game-playing categories listed in Table 6a, it is clear that there are some, although few, individuals in each game-playing category (certainly those who are more than one standard deviation above the mean or who are at the top of the range) who score as highly on the *Addiction Involvement Scale* as the average addicted drinker or addicted eater. Not only do adolescent gambling machine addicts exist, but adolescent home computer playing addicts and adolescent outside video gaming addicts exist too.

From Table 7 it can be seen that no categories of game players are clearly differentiated from either the addicted norms or the non-addicted norms, suggesting that the average intensity of involvement of home computer gamers, video outside gamers and gambling machine players all lie somewhere between the typical normative samples of addicted drinkers and eaters and the typical non-addictive normative samples. There are certainly addicted machine gamblers, but there may be no more of them — and they may be no more involved with their addiction — than those addicted to home computer games or outside video gaming.

MAN-MACHINE RELATIONSHIPS IN A DEVELOPMENTAL MODEL

There may be many possible paths through which gambling addictions may develop in certain individuals. This model attempts to describe one of them. It proposes that: Young machine-gambling addicts will be found to have vulnerability to video and computer games as well as to gambling, probably previous to their involvement with gambling machines; and these vulnerabilities spring from a common base in an attachment to electronic video devices formed at an earlier critical period when the young child was left in the company of television as its major stimulus and companion for long periods at a time.

It is suggested that the vulnerability is first produced when the young child, at a critical point in its development, spends long periods with television as its main stimulus or sole company, or when it finds the figures on television more encouraging and less hostile and intrusive than its parents. The television becomes a caretaker and/or a companion figure, and a positive attachment is developed to it. This builds in a familiar precedent or template for later relationships with electronic robot figures. So these figures become one of the child's preferred caretaker/attachment figures.

Another way of describing what happens might be to say that for many children television becomes a transitional object. According to D.W. Winnicot (1958), a transitional object is a substitute for the mother, which serves a soothing function for the child. It is felt to be under his or her control. The usual examples are the blanket or the teddy bear but it can be anything — even a television. At this first stage, whatever its later effects, television fosters short attention spans, instant gratification and passive acceptance.

The second stage in this suggested model is when the child, now carrying the expectation of an attachment to, and a relationship with, electronic video screens (probably fostered and maintained by constant television watching) meets a video game, which is like a television that you can talk to and it answers back, one you can interact with instead of just being passive before. This acts as a superstimulus that excites unusually strong responses. In ethology, very large eggs lead to excessively zealous retrieval behavior by certain birds (Tinbergen, 1951) and are called "super-stimuli." A human equivalent might be a doll which shuts its eyes and wets the bed, superseding the dull old simple dolls which did neither of these things, only in turn to be superseded by a super-doll which also talks or sings.

Harlow's (1974) wire and cloth surrogate mothers for young monkeys also constituted such a progression of preferences. The vulnerable gambler-to-be, deprived of real human relationships with their healthy mix of security/comfort and stimulations, satisfies these needs in attachment to robot figures which generalizes to other robot figures and especially to the most lifelike, the superstimuli, rather as Harlow's cloth mother was preferred to the wire mother by the deprived infant monkeys in his experiments.

All this time, while the developing individual is so absorbed with machines, he is failing to learn how to interact with people, he is developing an unrealistically simplistic model of human interaction, and the complex skills needed for real human relationships are being neglected, making him yet more vulnerable to robot relationships at the next stage of development.

Finally, in the third stage of this suggested model, the heavily attached or even dependent video-game player gains access to amusement with prizes (AWP) machines and then to gambling machines with much more powerful reinforcements in terms of payouts. The super-super-stimulus has arrived in the player's deprived social milieu and all the old childhood needs for security and companionship are met once again, but now in combination with a new more powerful set of rewards such as effectiveness and approval.

The developmental process is now complete, and the television orphan has become the gambling machine addict. The useful and obedient machines we created and once welcomed as relieving the burdens of parenthood have turned Pied-Piper of Hamlyn on our children — or perhaps the Frankenstein analogy is a better one.

SUMMARY

There is no dispute in this analysis that the problem of adolescent machine gambling is real. No attempt has been made to quantify either its extent or its intensity in individuals. The importance of some factors associated with heavier machine gambling as opposed to lighter use have been confirmed and demonstrated in association with greater involvement with video gaming outside the home and the playing of games on home computers. But the main thrust has been to demonstrate that adolescent machine gambling occurs in a wider context of other, possibly equally powerful addictions, to video-gaming and especially to home computer gaming, and that it may have a developmental relationship to them as well.

ENDNOTES

[1] Parts of this analysis were prepared as part of the requirements of the Degree of B.Sc. from the University of Glasgow. A portion of the data for one of the studies was collected by Carol Galloway and Caroline Smyth and for another by Rhona Birrel and Mary Lawson.

REFERENCES

Adkins, B.J., Kruedelbach, N.G., Toohig, T.M. and Rugle, L.J. (1988). The relationship of gaming preferences to MMPI personality variables. In W.R. Eadington (ed.), *Gambling Research: Proceedings of the Seventh International Conference on Gambling and Risk Taking*. Reno: University of Nevada, Reno.

American Psychiatric Association (1985). *Diagnostic and Statistical Manual of Mental Disorders*, 3rd edition, clinical revision. Washington, D.C.

Anderson, G. and Brown, R.I.F. (1984). Real and laboratory gambling: Sensation seeking and arousal. *British Journal of Psychology*, 75, 401.

Arcuri, A.F., Lester, D. and Smith, F.O. (1985). Shaping adolescent gambling behavior. *Adolescence*, 20, 935-938.

Bentall, R.P., Fisher, D., Kelly, V. and Hawksworth, K. (1989). The use of arcade gaming in machines: Demographic characteristics of users and patterns of use. *British Journal of Addiction*, 84, 555-562.

Blaszczynski, A.P., Winter, S.W. and McConaghy, N. (1986). Plasma endorphin levels in pathological gamblers. *Journal of Gambling Behavior*, 2, 3-14.

British Marketing Bureau (1986). Gambling. *Mental Leisure Intelligence*, vol. 14. London: British Marketing Bureau.

Brown, R.I.F. (1986). Arousal and sensation seeking components in the general explanation of gambling and gambling addictions. *International Journal of Addictions*, 21, 1001.

Brown, R.I.F. (1987). Classical and operant paradigms in the management of gambling addictions. *Behavioural Psychotherapy*, 15, 11.

Brown, R.I.F. (1988). *Arousal during play in normal machine gamblers.* Unpublished manuscript, Department of Psychology, University of Glasgow.

Brown, R.I.F. (1993). Some contributions of the study of gambling to the study of other addictions. In W.R. Eadington and J.A. Cornelius (eds.), *Gambling Behavior and Problem Gambling.* Reno: Institute for the Study of Gambling and Commercial Gaming, University of Nevada.

Commission on the review of national policy towards gambling in America (1976). *Gambling in America.* Washington, D.C.: United States Government Printing Office.

Dickerson, M.G. and Adcock, S.G. (1987). Mood, arousal and cognitions in persistent gambling: Preliminary investigation of a theoretical model. *Journal of Gambling Behavior*, 3, 3.

Fisher, S. (1989). The use of fruit and video machines by children in the United Kingdom: An analysis of existing research. *Society for the Study of Gambling Newsletter*, no. 16, 13-33.

Griffiths, M. (1989a). Gambling in children and adolescents. *Journal of Gambling Behavior*, 5, 66-83.

Griffiths, M. (1989b). An analysis of "Amusement Machines, Dependency and Delinquency" (Home Office Research Study No. 101). *Society for the Study of Gambling Newsletter*, no. 16.

Griffiths., M. (1990). The acquisition, development and maintenance of fruit machine gambling in adolescence. *Journal of Gambling Studies*, 6, 193-204.

Harlow, H. (1974). *Learning to Love.* New York: Aronson.

Home Office (1988). *Amusement machines, dependency and delinquency.* Home Office Research Study No. 101. London: Her Majesty's Stationery Office.

Ide-Smith, S. and Lea, S.E.G. (1988). Gambling in young adolescents. *Journal of Gambling Behavior*, 4, 110-118.

Ladouceur, R. and Mireault, M.F. (1988). Gambling behavior among high school students in the Québec area. *Journal of Gambling Behavior*, 4, 3-12.

Leary, K. and Dickerson, M.G. (1985). Levels of arousal in high- and low-frequency gamblers. *Behavior Research and Therapy*, 23, 635.

Lesieur, H.R. and Klein, R. (1987). Pathological gambling among high school students. *Addictive Behaviors*, 12, 129.

National Housing and Town Planning Council (1988). *The use of amusement arcades and gambling machines: A national survey.* London.

Parliamentary Debates (Hansard) (1981). *Control of Space Invaders and other electronic games.* Sixth series, vol. 5, May 18-June 5th. London: Her Majesty's Stationery Office.

Roberts, J. and Pool, Y. (1988). *Slot machine paying by children.* Taunton Spectrum Children's Trust.

Schapiro, E.G. (1981). Preference for gambling at slot machines, keno, blackjack and craps: Who and why. In W.R. Eadington (ed.), *The Gambling Papers: Proceedings of the Fifth National Conference on Gambling and Risk Taking.* Reno: University of Nevada, Reno.

Shotton, M.A. (1989). *Computer Addiction: A Study of Computer Dependency.* London: Taylor and Francis.

Svebak, S. (1985). Psychophysiology and the paradoxes of felt arousal. In M.J. Apter, D. Fontana and S. Murgatroyd (eds.), *Reversal Theory Applications and Developments.* Wales: University College Cardiff Press, and New Jersey: Lawrence Erlbaum.

Svebak, S. (1988a). Psychogenic muscle tension. In M.J. Apter, J.H. Kerr and M.P. Cowles (eds.), *Progress in Reversal Theory.* Amsterdam: North Holland Press (Elsevier).

Svebak, S. (1988b). Personality, stress and cardiovascular Risk. In M.J. Apter, J.H. Kerr and M.P. Cowles (eds.), *Progress in Reversal Theory.* Amsterdam: North Holland Press (Elsevier).

Tinbergen, N. (1851). *The Study of Instinct.* London: Oxford University Press.

Wiesenbaum, J. (1984). *Computer Power and Reason.* New York: Harmondsworth Penguin.

Winnicot, D.W. (1958). *Collected Papers: Through Paediatrics to Psycho-Analysis.* London: Tavistock Publications.

Gambling and Pathological Gambling Among University Students*

Henry R. Lesieur, John Cross, Michael Frank Michael Welch, Carolyn White, Garry Rubenstein Karen Moseley and Marie Mark[1]

According to a 1974 study conducted by the Gambling Commission, approximately 61 percent of the U.S. population gambled (Commission, 1976). Since 1974, numerous states have legalized various forms of gambling. By 1989 a Gallup poll found 81% had gambled with 71% doing so in the past year and 31% doing it weekly (Hugick, 1989).

One consequence of the increasing legalization may be a higher incidence of compulsive or pathological gambling in the population. The Gambling Commission study, for example, found a significantly higher rate of probable compulsive gambling among Nevadans who had not moved to Nevada for

*Reprinted with permission from ©Pergamon Press Ltd. Lesieur, H.R. et al. (1991). Gambling and pathological gambling among university students. *Addictive Behaviors*, vol. 16, pp. 517-527. Oxford, England: Pergamon Press Ltd.

the gambling than is evident for the rest of the U.S. (Commission, 1976, p. 74). Similarly, recent surveys done in New York, New Jersey and Maryland demonstrated higher rates of problem gambling than a survey done in Iowa (Sommers, 1988; Volberg and Steadman, 1989, June).

Pathological gambling among Americans has been associated with family, job, financial and legal difficulties among those so addicted. In the family, excessive gambling is associated with increased stress, a pattern of lies and deception on the part of the gambling spouse, increased risk of divorce and other signs of family dysfunction (Lorenz and Shuttlesworth, 1983; Lesieur, 1984; Wanda and Foxman, 1971). On the job, pathological gamblers are likely to be less productive and to embezzle when employed by others; they have high rates of business failure when self-employed (Lesieur, 1984; Livingston, 1974). The evidence consistently shows that pathological gambling is associated with financial difficulties and illegal activities in order to support an increasingly expensive addiction (Custer, 1982; Lesieur, 1979).

The primary consideration for the present survey is the question of the extent of pathological and problem gambling among college and university students. Every major investigation of pathological (compulsive) gambling has demonstrated that the vast majority of males who become pathological gamblers in their adult lives start gambling in their teens (Custer, 1982; Livingston, 1974), while females tend to have a later, more telescoped career (Custer and Milt, 1985; Lesieur and Blume, 1991). In addition, problems with gambling frequently emerge in the teens.

In studies in New Jersey and Québec high schools, pathological gambling was found to be associated with cutting classes, low grades, and problematic gambling in parents (Lesieur and Klein, 1987; Ladouceur and Mireault, 1988). Moreover, in Jacobs' study of California high schools, compulsive gambling in these students was associated with use of addicting substances, other indicators of psychosocial maladjustment, and alcohol, substance abuse and compulsive gambling in parents (Jacobs, 1988). Each of these studies found rates of problematic gambling in high school students which were higher than for the adult population.

Pathological gambling has also been found to be present among college and university students at higher rates than among the general population (Frank, 1987; Lesieur, 1988). These studies were limited to the northeastern United

States. The present study is intended to examine this issue as well as the correlation between pathological gambling, other forms of deviant behavior and parental problems.

METHODS

A questionnaire was constructed using the South Oaks Gambling Screen (SOGS) as the primary indicator of the presence of pathological gambling. The SOGS is a valid, reliable screening instrument for the identification of pathological gamblers (Lesieur and Blume, 1987). In addition to the SOGS, questions from Jacobs' Health Survey (1986) were appended. These questions probe the extent of involvement with addicting substances and behaviors, incidence of psychosocial risk factors, and extent to which they believe their parents have mental health problems and problems with addicting substances and behaviors. Finally, the questionnaire asks about socio-demographic information.

Six colleges and universities from five states participated in this study. The colleges were chosen based partially on the extent of legalized gambling present in the state where the institution resides. Within the colleges, classrooms were randomly selected from required courses and were stratified based on class level and population proportionate to size bases.

The five states differ in the extent of legalized gambling available in 1988 (Davis and LaFleur, 1989; *Journal of Charity Gaming*, 1989). In three of them, it was readily available. New York has legal bingo, Las Vegas Nights run by charities, race tracks, off-track betting, and a wide variety of lottery and numbers games. Lottery and OTB outlets are in virtually every neighborhood in the state. New Jersey, like New York, has legal bingo and charity run gambling (legal raffles). There are also race tracks (which provide interstate intertrack wagering as well) and a wide variety of lotteries and numbers games in every neighborhood in the state. Furthermore, Atlantic City is easily accessible to both New York and New Jersey residents. Nevada, of course, has legalized casinos, sports wagering, off-track betting, card rooms and bingo. While Nevada does not have a lottery, slot machines are in most neighborhoods and gambling is easily available on a 24-hour basis.

The other two states had a minimal amount of gambling. Oklahoma had bingo and race tracks (with interstate intertrack wagering), while Texas only had legal bingo and charitable gaming. In neither of these states was legal gambling available to residents in grocery stores or off-track betting offices. Table 1 summarizes the differences in legalized gambling among the five states in 1988.

TABLE 1

Types of Legalized Gambling Available in Surveyed State (1988)

Form of Gambling	New York	New Jersey	Nevada	Oklahoma	Texas
Bingo	yes	yes	yes	yes	yes
Charitable gaming	Las Vegas nights	Raffles	no	no	GCTs
Lottery	Lottery, Lotto Numbers, Instant tickets	Lottery, Lotto Numbers, Instant tickets	no	no	no
Racetracks	yes	yes	no	yes	no
Off-track betting	yes	at race tracks	yes	at race tracks	no
Casinos	no	Atlantic City only	yes	no	no
Slot Machines	no	in casinos only	yes	no	no
Card rooms (poker)	no	no	yes	no	no
Sports betting	no	no	yes	no	no

Source: Davis & LaFleur, 1989; *Journal of Charity Gaming*, 1989

SAMPLE

The sample consisted of 1,771 students surveyed in the 1987-88 academic year. Almost 56% of the sample were female and 44.5% male; ages ranged from 16 to 57 with a mean age of 22.3 (s.d.= 5.1); 41% were Catholic, 43% Protestant, 2% Jewish, 10.5% another religion, and 4.5% agnostic or atheist.

Eighty-one percent of the sample were white (18% Irish, 11% Italian, 5% German, and a mixture of other non-Hispanic whites); 6% Black, 5% Hispanic, 4% Asian, 2% American Indian, and 1.5% mixed race. Eighty percent of the students were single, 12% married, 8% divorced or separated, and less than 1% widowed. Eighteen percent of the students came from families earning less than $25,000 per year — 12% from families earning $100,000 or more. Their median family income (based on grouped data) was $49,271.

For purposes of this study, post-stratification weights were applied to each academic year to make the sample representative of the student population of each college or university. In addition, each state was given equal weight in the overall analysis. SPSS-X was used for cross-tabluations, correlations and multiple regression.

GAMBLING AMONG COLLEGE STUDENTS

Eighty-five percent of the students have gambled, and 23% gamble once a week or more. Slot and poker machines were the most popular form of gambling — 54% of the students have played them. Playing cards for money was next in popularity (51%), followed by casino games (49%), numbers or lotteries (46%), games of skill (44%), bingo (43%), betting on horses or dogs (31%), sports betting (29%), dice games (24%) and the stock or commodities market (19%). Games of skill were the most frequently played games: 9% played once a week or more for money. Following in popularity were casino games (8%); numbers or lotteries (6%); slot or poker machines (5%); card playing for money (5%); stock or commodities market (4%); sports betting (3.5%); dice games (2%); bingo (2%); and betting on horses or dogs (1.4%).

The rate of gambling for each type of gambling varied by state. For example, students in Nevada gambled more often than those in New Jersey and New York, while students in those three states gambled more than students in Oklahoma and Texas. Predictably, New Jersey and Nevada had the highest rates of casino and slot/poker machine play, and New York and New Jersey had the highest rates of lottery and numbers gambling. Students in New York apparently experienced a neighboring effect from easy access to Atlantic City gambling, in that their rates of casino gambling were higher than those of Oklahoma and Texas. The four states with legalized race tracks or off-track wagering had higher rates than Texas, which has neither. More detail is provided in Tables 2 and 3.

TABLE 2

Gambling Among College Students by State (Percentages)						
Type of Gambling	New York (n=446)	New Jersey (n=227)	Nevada (n=219)	Oklahoma (n=583)	Texas (n=299)	5 State Average
Playing cards for money	3%	54%	53%	53%	42%	51%
Bet on horses, dogs	29	41	30	32	22	31
Sports betting	28	35	31	23	28	29
Dice Games	21	25	33	18	23	24
Casino games	39	75	84	27	20	49
Numbers or lotteries	69	66	42	30	20	46
Bingo	43	39	38	45	49	43
Stocks/ commodi-ties	15	23	19	18	18	19
Slot/poker machines	50	74	83	35	27	54
Pool, bowling, games of skill	40	51	41	43	42	44
Any gambling at all	90%	92%	91%	78%	75%	85%

TABLE 3

Weekly GamblingAmong College Students by State (Percentages)						
Type of Gambling	New York (n=446)	New Jersey (n=227)	Nevada (n=219)	Oklahoma (n=583)	Texas (n=299)	5 State Average
Playing cards for money	5%	6%	8%	1.50%	2%	5%
Bet on horses, dogs	3	2	1	1	0.4	1.4
Sports betting	5	3	5	2	3	3.5
Dice Games	2	3	2	1	0.5	2
Casino games	3	6	29	0.5	0	8
Numbers or lotteries	14	12	4	1	1	6
Bingo	3	2	1	1	1	1.6
Stocks/ commodities	3	4	7	2	2	4
Slot/poker machines	4	4.5	16	1	0.6	5
Pool, bowling, games of skill	12	11	8	7	8	9
Any gambling at all	27%	28%	39%	12%	11%	23%

Gambling rates varied enormously by gender; that is, males gambled more than females on all forms of gambling with the exception of bingo. Moreover, while 90% percent of males and 82% of females had gambled in their lifetimes, more than twice as many males (33%) as females (15%) gambled once a week or more. The differences apparent between the sexes for weekly wagering were highest for games of skill, casino gambling, cards, and sports betting. These data are presented for each state in Tables 4 and 5.

Table 4

Gambling Among College Students by State for Males and Females (Percentages)

	New York (n=446)		New Jersey (n=227)		Nevada (n=219)		Oklahoma (n=583)		Texas (n=299)		5 State Average	
	M	F	M	F	M	F	M	F	M	F	M	F
Playing cards for money	67%	42%	73%	40%	77%	31%	68%	39%	65%	28%	70%	36%
Bet on horses, dogs	41	21	48	36	47	13	29	34	24	20	38	25
Sports betting	51	10	50	22	51	10	35	13	50	14	47	14
Dice games	33	12	33	19	46	20	26	10	43	11	36	14
Casino games	44	35	79	72	88	79	30	24	28	16	54	45
Numbers or lotteries	72	68	69	64	44	41	33	28	22	19	48	44
Bingo	37	50	37	41	36	41	41	49	51	48	40	46
Stocks/ commodities	24	8	31	18	27	11	23	23	30	11	27	14
Slot/poker machines	56	46	77	72	88	78	41	29	35	22	59	49
Pool, bowling, games of skill	61	24	70	36	62	20	59	29	73	24	65	27
Any gambling at all	94%	88%	96%	90%	92%	89%	84%	74%	86%	69%	90%	82%

TABLE 5

Weekly Gambling Among College Students by State for Males and Females (Percentages)

	New York (n=446)		New Jersey (n=227)		Nevada (n=219)		Oklahoma (n=583)		Texas (n=299)		5 State Average	
	M	F	M	F	M	F	M	F	M	F	M	F
Playing cards for money	8.5%	2%	10%	3%	16%	1%	3%	.3%	4%	1.5%	8%	1.5%
Bet on horses, dogs	6	0	3	0	1	1	1	.3	1	0	2.5	.6
Sports betting	10	0	5	0	8	1	3	1	7	.3	7	.8
Dice games	5	0	5	1	3	.6	2	.3	.6	.4	3	.4
Casino games	5	1	9	3	41	17	.4	.6	0	0	12	4
Numbers or lotteries	20	9	11	12	6	1	.4	2	1	1	8	5
Bingo	3	3	2	2	0	1	0	1	0	2	1	2
Stocks/ commodities	7	.5	5	2.5	10	5	3	2	6	0	6	2
Slot/poker machines	6	2	5	4	23	9	1	.6	1	.3	8	3
Pool, bowling, games of skill	23	3	18	5	12	4	11	4	17	2	16	3.5
Any weekly gambling at all	44%	15%	35%	23%	52%	25%	16%	7%	20%	6%	34%	15%

PROBLEM AND PATHOLOGICAL GAMBLING AMONG COLLEGE STUDENTS

While 85% of the students have gambled, most do so with minimal amounts of money: 44% have gambled with $10 or more in one day; 12% have ventured $100 or more. Maximum wagers varied by state and gender. Specifically, students in Nevada gambled with more money than those in other states; students in New Jersey and New York followed in that order. Gender differences followed along similar lines with males wagering significantly greater amounts of money than females (eta = .35, $p<.001$). These results are depicted in Tables 6 and 7.

TABLE 6

Maximum Wager, Pathological and Problem Gambling by State (Percentages)

	New York (n=446)	New Jersey (n=227)	Nevada (n=219)	Oklahoma (n=583)	Texas (n=299)	5 State Average
Gambled with more than $10 in one day	41%	57%	55%	36%	33%	44%
Gambled with more than $100 in one day	12	13	19	8	6	12
Problem gamblers	18	16	16	11	12	15
Pathological gamblers	8	6	4	5	5	5.5%

Gambling created problems for some of the students; among them, interference with relationships, job, and school. Seven percent of the students said that someone had criticized their gambling; 3% argued with someone they lived with over gambling; 3% hid betting slips, lottery tickets or other evidence of gambling from family members; 4% cut classes in order to gamble; and 2% said they had lost time from work or school due to gambling. These students also experienced financial difficulties as 10% borrowed from household money, 3% from banks, 3% from credit cards, 3% from checking accounts, 1% from loan sharks and 2% sold personal property.

TABLE 7

Maximum Wager, Pathological and Problem Gambling by State and Gender (Percentages)

	New York (n=446)		New Jersey (n=227)		Nevada (n=219)		Oklahoma (n=583)		Texas (n=299)		5 State Average	
	M	F	M	F	M	F	M	F	M	F	M	F
Gambled with more than $10 in one day	63%	25%	71%	45%	72%	36%	49%	24%	54%	22%	62%	30%
Gambled with more than $100 in one day	24	4	21	6	30	9	12	6	15	1	20%	5%
Problem gamblers	30	9	26	8	20	12	19	4	18	8	25%	8%
Pathological gamblers	12	4	12	1	6	1.5	8.5	2	9	3	9.5%	2.3%

Using a score of 3 or higher on the South Oaks Gambling Screen (SOGS), 15% of the students experienced some problems in connection with gambling. Five and a half percent of the students scored in the pathological gambling range of the SOGS (i.e., they scored 5 or more on the index). A greater proportion of students in New York, New Jersey and Nevada could be classified as "problem gamblers" than students from Oklahoma and Texas (Cramer's V =.08, n=1771, p<.05). Ironically, while New York had the highest rate of pathological gambling (7.6%) and Nevada had the lowest (3.6%), these differences were not statistically significant.

Gender differences in rates of problem and pathological gambling were significant (r =.24, n=1767, p<.001). Twenty-five percent of males and 8% of females experienced some gambling problems, while 9.3% of males and 2.4% of females could be classified as pathological gamblers. In other words, approximately one-fourth of problem and one-fifth of pathological gambling college students are female. State by state information is included in Table 7.

In addition to gender, pathological gambling was also weakly correlated with age ($r=.05, n=1755, p<.05$), racial/ethnic background (Cramer's $V=.12, n=1724, p<.01$), and religion (Cramer's $V=.10, n=1700, p<.05$). Blacks, whites, and American Indians had lower rates (4-5%) than Hispanics (11%) and Asians (12.5%). Rates for Jews (11%), Catholics (7%), and other religions (7%) were higher than those for Protestants (4%) and atheists or agnostics (3%). Pathological gambling was not associated with academic year or marital status.

Curiously, scores on the SOGS were not significantly associated with the occupational status of the male or female head of the students' family and whether the parents own or rent their living accomodations; yet they were positively correlated with family income ($r=.09, n=1641, p<.001$) and negatively correlated with neighborhood status ($r=-.04, n=1756, p<.05$).

In addition to personal problems, pathological gambling students also had parents with problems. Four percent of students said their father had a gambling problem while 1.4% said their mother had a problem. When asked in a different way, 3% said their father (and 1% said their mother) was a compulsive gambler. Not surprisingly, students with compulsive gambling parents were more likely to show signs of pathological gambling (18.8%) than students without compulsive gambling parents (4.7%) (Cramer's $V=.13, n=1712, p<.001$). Parental overeating and excessive drugs use were also positively correlated with pathological gambling by students (Cramer's $V=.09, n=1712, p<.05$ for parental overeating; $r=.06, n=1771, p<.01$ for parental drug abuse). Parental alcoholism was not significantly associated with gambling problems in this study. SOGS score was positively associated with parental living arrangements ($r=.04, n=1752, p<.05$ where 0=not living together; 1=living together). This appears to be an anomalous finding as troubled parents are more likely to be living apart than untroubled parents.

CORRELATES WITH OTHER STUDENT BEHAVIOR

Scores on the South Oaks Gambling Screen were positively correlated with use of tobacco ($r=.10, n=1767, p<.001$), use of alcohol ($r=.05, n=1766, p<.05$), getting drunk ($r=.08, n=1764, p<.001$), use of illegal drugs ($r=.18, n=1755, p<.001$), arrest for non-traffic offenses ($r=.11, n=1756, p<.001$), the number of traffic tickets ($r=.04, n=1749, p<.05$) and parking ($r=.07, n=1741, p<.01$), and overeating ($r=.05, n=1765, p<.05$). Pathological gambling was also negatively associated with grade point average in college ($r=-.05, n=1734,$

$p<.05$). "Overeating and vomiting" was the only "substance abuse" type of behavior not associated with excessive gambling ($r=.00$, $n=1755$, n.s.). While 8% of pathological gambling students said they had attempted suicide compared with 6% of non-pathological gamblers, this difference was not statistically significant.

MULTIPLE REGRESSION

The socio-demographic, parental, and (non-gambling) student behavior variables were introduced into a multiple regression (using mean substitution for missing data) to see which would be best at predicting scores on the South Oaks Gambling Screen. Gender, the number of illegal drugs used, overeating, parental gambling problem, arrest for a non-traffic offense, getting drunk, being non-white, age, parental cohabitation status, being Asian, number of parking tickets received, and being non-Protestant were significantly correlated with SOGS score. The effect of the state and the socio-economic indicators are eliminated after controlling for the above variables. The overall Multiple R is .392 ($F=26.5$, $n=1771$, $p<.001$). This explains 15% of the variance (R-squared) in SOGS scores. When the behavioral variables are forced into the regression equation first, they explain 7% of the variance compared with 7% of the variance explained by the socio-demographic variables. Parental gambling problems explain only 1% of the variance whereas gender alone explains 6% of the variance. Results of the regression are summarized in Tables 8 and 9.

DISCUSSION

The results indicate that gambling is widespread among college students in the five states studied. Their overall participation rates are higher than for the adult population, while their weekly rates are lower than those for the adult population. In addition, rates of pathological and problematic gambling are four to eight times higher than reported for the adult population. Whether these youth are "sowing wild oats" or their high rates are a portent of things to come remains to be seen.

Jacobs (1989a) believes that a sizeable proportion of these students will end up with disastrous gambling careers when they grow older. However, we take a signal from the literature on drug use. This literature (see Kandel and Maloff, 1983) reveals much experimentation with drugs among those in the late teens and early twenties, which can be viewed as relatively normal behavior. It

TABLE 8

Multiple Regression of Variables with South Oaks Gambling Screen

	Beta	*Multiple R (stepwise)*	*Significance of Beta*
Gender (male=0; female=1)	-0.21	0.245	p<.001
Number of Illegal Drugs Used	0.08	0.292	p<.01
Overeating 0=never 1=rarely, lightly 2=sometimes, moderately 3=often, heavily	0.11	0.319	p<.001
Parents have gambling problem 0=neither 1=either or both	0.11	0.338	p<.001
Arrest for non-traffic offense (0=no; 1=yes)	0.09	0.349	p<.001
Got drunk 0=never 1=rarely, lightly 2=sometimes, moderately 3=often, heavily	0.11	0.358	p<.001
White (0=no; 1=yes)	-0.07	0.369	p<.01
Age (in years)	0.08	0.374	p<.001
Parental stuatus 0=not iving together 1=living together	0.06	0.381	p<.01
Asian (0=no; 1=yes)	0.06	0.384	p<.01
Number of parking tickets received in past three years	0.06	0.389	p<.01
Protestant (0=no; 1=yes)	-0.05	0.392	p<.05

TABLE 9

Multiple Regression of Blocks of Variables with South Oaks Gambling Screen

	Multiple R for Block of variables (forced entry)	*R Square*	*F*	*Significance of F*
Socio-demographic variables				
Gender, White, Asian, Age, Parental status and Protestant	0.275	0.075	28.8	p<.001
Behavioral variables				
Number of Illegal Drugs Used, Got drunk, Overeating, Arrest for non-traffic offense, Number of parking tickets received in past three years	0.271	0.074	28	p<.001
Modeling or possibly genetic variable				
Parents have gambling problem	.118	.014	24.9	p<.001
All significant variables	0.392	0.153	26.5	p<.001

is quite possible that gambling takes a similar form. Youthful gamblers may learn from their mistakes and lower the extent of their involvement with gambling as they mature. The question of whether the high rates of pathological and problem gambling found among youth is permanent or temporary can only be resolved through longitudinal analysis. While the question of the future of gambling problems needs to be resolved, some of these youths will go on to have disastrous lives and intervention is called for in light of this possibility.

While the rates of gambling, weekly gambling, highest amount of money spent gambling in one day and problem gambling were higher in the casino states and New York than in Oklahoma and Texas, the rate of pathological gambling was not predicted by the presence of casino gambling in the state.

Gender is a significant variable unearthed in this and other studies of youthful gambling behavior (see Griffiths, 1989; Ladouceur and Mireault, 1988; Lesieur and Klein, 1987). In the teens and early twenties, male pathological gamblers outnumber females by four to one, as compared to studies of adults (Sommers, 1988; Volberg and Steadman, 1989), which show a reduced two to one ratio. It is quite probable that gambling problems among women surface at an older age than among males as interviews with female Gamblers Anonymous members suggest (Custer and Milt, 1985; Lesieur and Blume, 1991). Additionally, females appear to be more likely than males to use gambling as a means of escape from relationship problems and life traumas in adulthood.

Another significant finding of this study is further support for the idea that addictive-like behaviors, including excessive gambling, excessive alcohol and drug use, and overeating, are associated with each other. It is uncertain whether these behaviors follow one another in sequence, coexist at the same time, or are causally connected to each other. It is possible that all three are true of different people. A portion may feel a physiological or psychological need for external stimulation from addictive-like behaviors; some may socially learn these behaviors from parents, peers, or the media; the behavior of others may be less subject to strict social control.

Gambling, getting drunk, illegal drug use, arrests for non-traffic offenses, and receiving parking tickets are indicators of a global pattern of risk-taking and anti-social behavior. These activities, in a more general sense, may satisfy needs for stimulation, may be socially learned, and might break out in the absence of social control. In any case, the troubles overlap and should not be treated as totally independent entities.

These problems may be symptomatic of other underlying problems. Adult pathological gamblers, for example, have high rates of depression, early life stress, and loss (McCormick, Russo, Ramirez and Taber, 1984; Linden, Pope and Jonas, 1986; Taber, McCormick and Russo, 1987; Glassman, 1990). It is possible that this is true of the college students who showed signs of pathological gambling. If so, gambling problems may be indicators of troubles which should be addressed in treatment.

There are limitations to the study design. In future research, a representative sample of U.S. colleges and universities should be chosen for generalizability. While caution should be taken in generalizing beyond the six colleges in this study, it is clear that there are troubled college students who need counseling for gambling-related problems in each of the schools surveyed and quite probably every college and university nationwide.

The impact of parental gambling problems are not as strong as indicated in other studies. However, because other investigations have shown that children of compulsive gambler parents are adversely affected by that experience (Jacobs, 1989b; Lesieur and Rothschild, 1989), this impact should be investigated further.

In this study, gambling-related problems are correlated with other behavioral difficulties which may have an adverse impact on academic performance as well as on life functioning. We do not yet know whether gambling problems are products, causes, or in some other way interconnected with these other problems. Research into this question is sorely needed. One thing appears clear. Whether they are cause or product, the gambling problems need to be addressed rather than be allowed to fester and grow.

It is imperative that college and university counselors be trained to identify pathological and problematic gambling behavior among students and their parents. Students can be screened using the South Oaks Gambling Screen, the same instrument used in this study.[2] Other research has demonstrated the value of screening alcohol and other drug abusers for gambling problems (Lesieur, Blume, and Zoppa, 1986; Lesieur and Heineman, 1989). It is our belief that all college youth in trouble as well as those with troubled parents or relationships be screened for potential problems with gambling.

ENDNOTES

[1] This research partially funded by the National Council on Problem Gambling, Inc. The authors would like to thank Mirian Asmar, Donna Hynes, Carmen Leichtle, Miriam Paulin and Lorraine Vargas for data coding and entry.

[2] The full screen and scoring are available in the article by Lesieur and Blume (1987).

REFERENCES

Commission on the Review of National Policy Toward Gambling (1976). *Gambling in America.* Washington, D.C.: U.S. Government Printing Office.

Custer, R.L. (1982). An overview of compulsive gambling. In P.A. Carone, S.F. Yoles, S.N. Kieffer and L. Krinsky (eds.), *Addictive Disorders Update: Alcoholism, Drug Abuse, Gambling* (pp. 107-124). New York: Human Sciences Press.

Custer, R.L. and Milt, H. (1985). *When Luck Runs Out.* New York: Facts on File Publications.

Davis, M.P. and La Fleur, T. (1989, July 15). U.S. and Canadian gaming-at-a-glance. *Gaming and Wagering Business*, 30-32.

Frank, M.L. (1987, September). *Youth: Casino gambling and college students.* Paper presented at the Fifth Annual Statewide Conference on Compulsive Gambling, Council on Compulsive Gambling of New Jersey, Asbury Park, NJ.

Glassman, W.E. (1990). *Female pathological gamblers: Early trauma and depression.* Ph.D. dissertation. The Professional School of Psychology, San Francisco.

Griffiths, M.D. (1989). Gambling in children and adolescents. *Journal of Gambling Behavior*, 5, 66-83.

Hugick, L. (1989). Gambling on the rise: Lotteries lead the way. *The Gallup Report*, 285, 32-41.

Jacobs, D.F. (1986). *Early identification and prevention of health-threatening behaviors in adolescents.* Paper presented at the 21st International Congress of Applied Psychology, Jerusalem, Israel.

Jacobs, D.F. (1988). Effects on children of parental excesses in gambling. In W.R. Eadington (ed.), *Gambling Research: Proceedings of the Seventh International Conference on Gambling and Risk Taking*, 5, 226-229. Reno: University of Nevada, Reno.

Jacobs, D.F. (1989a). Illegal and undocumented: A review of teenage gambling and the plight of children of problem gamblers. In H.J. Shaffer, S.A. Stein,

B. Gambino and T.N. Cummings (eds.), *Compulsive Gambling: Theory, Research and Practice.* Lexington, MA: Lexington Books.

Jacobs, D.F. (1989b). Children of problem gamblers. *Journal of Gambling Behavior*, 5, 261-268.

Journal of Charity Gaming (1989). Who plays what? 2, September 5, p. 6.

Kallick, M., Suits, D., Dielman, T. and Hybels, J. (1979). *A Survey of Gambling Attitudes and Behavior.* Ann Arbor, MI: Institute for Social Research, University of Michigan.

Kandel, D.R. and Maloff, D.R. (1983). Commonalities in drug use: A sociological perspective. In P.K. Levison, D.R. Gerstein and D.R. Maloff (eds.), *Commonalities in Substance Abuse and Habitual Behavior*, 3-27. Lexington, MA: Lexington Books.

Ladouceur, R. and Mireault, C. (1988). Gambling behaviors among high school students in the Québec area. *Journal of Gambling Behavior*, 4, 3-12.

Lesieur, H.R. (1979). The compulsive gambler's spiral of options and involvement. *Psychiatry: Journal for the Study of Interpersonal Processes*, 42, 79-87.

Lesieur, H.R. (1984). *The Chase: Career of the Compulsive Gambler.* Cambridge, MA: Schenkman Books.

Lesieur, H.R. (1988). Altering the DSM-III criteria for pathological gambling. *Journal of Gambling Behavior*, 4, 38-47.

Lesieur, H.R. and Blume, S.B. (1987). The South Oaks Gambling Screen (the SOGS): A new instrument for the identification of pathological gamblers. *American Journal of Psychiatry*, 144, 1184-1188.

Lesieur, H.R. and Blume, S.B. (1991). When lady luck loses: The female pathological gambler. In N. van den Bergh (ed.), *Feminist Perspectives on Treating Addictions* (pp. 181-197). New York: Springer Publications.

Lesieur, H.R., Blume, S.B. and Zoppa, R.M. (1985). Alcoholism, drug abuse, and gambling. *Alcoholism: Clinical and Experimental Research*, 10, 33-38.

Lesieur, H.R. and Heineman, M. (1988). Pathological gambling among youthful multiple substance abusers in a therapeutic community. *British Journal of Addiction*, 8, 765-771.

Lesieur, H.R. and Klein, R. (1987). Pathological gambling among high school students. *Addictive Behaviors*, 12, 129-135.

Lesieur, H.R. and Rothschild, J. (1989). Children of gamblers anonymous members. *Journal of Gambling Behavior*, 5, 269-282.

Linden, R.D., Pope, H.G. and Jonas, J.M. (1986). Pathological gambling and major affective disorder: Preliminary findings. *Journal of Clinical Psychiatry*, 47, 201-203.

Livingston, J. (1974) *Compulsive gamblers: Observations on Action and Abstinence.* New York: Harper and Row Publishers.

Lorenz, V.C. and Shuttlesworth, D.E. (1983). The impact of pathological gambling on the spouse of the gambler. *Journal of Community Psychology*, 11, 67-76.

McCormick, R.A., Russo, A.M., Ramirez, L.R. and Taber, J.I. (1984). Affective disorders among pathological gamblers seeking treatment. *American Journal of Psychiatry*, 141, 215-218.

Sommers, I. (1988). Pathological gambling: Estimating prevalence and group characteristics. *International Journal of the Addictions*, 23, 477-490.

Taber, J.I., McCormick, R.A. and Ramirez, L.R. (1987). The prevalence and impact of major stressors among pathological gamblers. *International Journal of the Addictions*, 22, 71-79.

Volberg, R.A. and Steadman, H.J. (1989). Prevalence estimates of pathological gambling in New Jersey and Maryland. *American Journal of Psychiatry*, 146, 1618-1619.

Volberg, R.A. and Steadman, H.J. (1989, June). *Prevalence estimates of problem gambling in three states.* Remarks presented at the Fourth National Conference on Compulsive Gambling, Des Moines, Iowa.

Wanda, G. and Foxman, J. (1971). *Games Compulsive Gamblers, Wives and Families Play.* Downey, CA: Gam-Anon, Inc.

VI

Gambling and Crime

Female Pathological Gamblers and Crime

Henry R. Lesieur[1]

According to the Commission on the Review of National Policy Towards Gambling, approximately 0.77% of the adult population in the U.S. were "probable compulsive gamblers" and another 2.3% were "potential compulsive gamblers" in 1974 (1976, p. 74). About one-third of "probable" and "potential" compulsive gamblers in the U.S. are female (1976, p. 74). More recently, statewide surveys have been conducted in Maryland, New Jersey, New York and Ohio. These studies estimate that between 1.4% and 3.4% of the adult population are "probable pathological gamblers" (Sommers, 1988; Volberg and Steadman, 1988; 1989). Again, they have found that one-third of these probable pathological gamblers are female. Despite the high incidence of this behavior among women, the overwhelming majority of research on pathological gambling has been done with primarily male populations. This is particularly true of studies of pathological gambling and criminal behavior.

Research on the connection between pathological gambling and crime is still in its infancy. Using the term "inveterate gambler," Julian Roebuck found that 157 out of 409 male prisoners (38 percent) "spent most of his leisure time at cards, dice, race tracks, lottery games, etc. A considerable amount of this gambler's earnings had to be spent in this activity" (1967: 279). Sewell, in a probe of 1,058 male inmates at Pentonville Prison in London (Royal College of Psychiatrists, 1977), found five percent of prisoners gambled heavily (56 subjects), using "more than their family approved" as the definition. Another five percent (54 subjects) were classified as compulsive gamblers. An added two percent (18 subjects) mentioned having a gambling problem in their past. The results were later confirmed by Borrill and Moran (Royal College of Psychiatrists, 1977).

Research by criminologists studying specific offenses shows a connection between gambling problems in males and embezzlement (Cressey, 1971), check forgery (Lemert, 1953), confidence games (Maurer, 1974) and armed robbery (Camp, 1968). Treatment professionals have also made the connection; Custer and Custer (1978), and Politzer et. al., (1985) uncovered arrests, prosecutions and convictions of male pathological gamblers for forgery, fraud, embezzlement and income tax evasion. A study of women who embezzle or defraud gives anecdotal attention to the issue (Zietz, 1981).

Studies by Livingston (1974) and Lesieur (1979; 1984) uncovered a wide variety of illegal behaviors among the male compulsive gamblers they interviewed. Livingston found compulsive gamblers involved in check forgery, embezzlement and employee theft, larceny, armed robbery, bookmaking, hustling, running con games and fencing stolen goods. Lesieur uncovered these patterns as well, and also found gamblers engaged in systematic loan fraud, tax evasion, burglary, pimping, selling drugs and hustling at pool, golf, bowling, cards and dice. According to Lesieur, compulsive gamblers are engaged in a spiral of options and involvement wherein legal avenues for funding are utilized until they are closed off. As involvement in gambling intensifies, options for funding become closed. Dependent on personal value systems, legitimate and illegitimate opportunities, perceptions of risk, the existence of threats (for example, loan sharks) and chance, the gamblers became involved in increasingly serious illegal activity (1984). For some, the amount of money appropriated runs into the millions of dollars.

Building on Lesieur's research, Brown found that the pattern of illegal activity in a Gamblers Anonymous sample more closely resembled that of drug addicts than of alcoholics (1987). That is, they were involved in financially-oriented crimes in an effort to support their gambling. Brown, however, did not collect information on the gender of his subjects. In another study which confirms the patterns found in earlier reports, Blaszczynski and colleagues found a relation between pathological gambling and crime even after controlling for antisocial personality disorder (1989). Although that study included 96 males and 13 females, the results were not reported separately for males and females.

In an earlier report on some of the data used herein, Lesieur compared the illegal behavior patterns of male and female prisoners identified as pathological gamblers (see Lesieur, 1987). Both females and males were involved in a wide variety of financially oriented crimes to pay for gambling or gambling related debt. The most common offenses were drug sales, gambling related hustles and cons, fencing stolen goods, burglary, and forgery. Males were more likely to be involved in burglary, card and dice hustling, and running con games and swindles to support their gambling, while females were more partial to passing bad checks, engaging in other forgery, and involvement in prostitution than their male counterparts.

There is evidence to date that connects pathological gambling to other addictions. Studies demonstrate that there is a high degree of overlap among pathological gambling, alcoholism and drug addiction. Pathological gamblers have high rates of substance abuse (Ramirez, McCormick, Russo and Taber, 1983; Lesieur, 1988) and substance abusers have high rates of pathological gambling (Haberman, 1969; Lesieur, Blume and Zoppa, 1986; Lesieur and Heineman, 1988). In addition, there is some evidence that problems associated with pathological gambling and substance abuse are more serious when the problems are combined than either is alone (Ciarrocchi, 1987). Since there is overwhelming evidence of the connection between chemical dependence and criminal behavior (Collins, 1981; Johnson et al., 1985), it is important to control for the influence of that on the compulsive gambling and crime nexus.

The purpose of the present study was to trace the sequence of events leading up to illegal activities in female pathological gamblers. In the process of addressing that question, the interviews revealed interaction among pathological gambling and other addictions. A collateral question for this study was to find out what type of impact multiple addiction has on illegal behavior patterns of female pathological gamblers.

METHOD

As part of a larger study of female pathological gamblers, fifty female members of Gamblers Anonymous (GA) were interviewed in depth. Snowball sampling was used with interviews conducted primarily in the northeast and western parts of the U.S. These women were asked questions about their early life and their entry and progression into increasingly destructive gambling, as well as their routes out of gambling. Topics specifically probed in depth were the relation between gambling and home life, gambling and work, the interaction between gambling and use of psychoactive substances, and the means of obtaining money for gambling. The study also probed for money acquisition methods, including legal as well as illegal means utilized in order to gamble or pay gambling related debts.

In a separate study, 114 female prisoners from New Jersey were administered a questionnaire asking about gambling behavior and legal and illegal money acquisition in connection with that behavior. A "gambling history test" was used to determine whether these women were probable compulsive gamblers. This test was previously validated in research given to 458 alcohol and drug abuse patients in an effort to determine what percent of them had a gambling problem. Among these patients, a correlation of .83 ($p<.001$) was found between the counselor's independent appraisal and assessments arrived at using the "gambling history test" (Lesieur et al., 1986). Thirty-four of the 114 women were deemed to be probable pathological gamblers using the test. In addition to gambling behavior and money acquisition methods, the survey used in the prison study asked about demographic characteristics, and self-identified alcoholism and drug addiction.

SAMPLE CHARACTERISTICS

Interviews with Gamblers Anonymous women bring out only a partial picture of the relationship between women, compulsive gambling and crime. In order to get a more complete picture, the prison women were included in the study and comparisons were made. A look at sample differences illustrates the value of the sample contrasts.

The fifty Gamblers Anonymous members ranged in age from 25 to 73 years (mean age = 43.8); the prisoners were much younger with a range from 20 to 42 years (mean age = 31.2). The marital status of the two samples also differed. Sixteen percent of the GA members were single (never married); 52% currently married; 30% separated or divorced; and 2% widowed. The prisoners were less likely to be currently married than their GA counterparts. Thirty-five percent were single (never married); 18% currently married; 44% separated or divorced; and 3% widowed.

The samples also differed in race, religion, education and income. The GA women were more likely to be white and Jewish, with higher education and income than the prison women. Specifically, 92% of the Gamblers Anonymous women were white; the rest (8%) were black. In contrast, 32% of the prisoners were white, 53% black, 12% Hispanic and 3% Asian. Thirty-eight percent of the GA members were Catholic, 28% Protestant, 24% Jewish, and 10% had no religious preference; forty-four percent of the prisoners were Catholic, 35% Protestant, 3% Jewish, 12% Islamic, and 6% had no religious preference. The mean years of education were 12.7 for GA women, and 11 years for the prisoners. Slightly less than half the prisoners (47%) had not graduated high school, while this was true of only 22% of the GA members. The median annual income for the GA members was $18,000 excluding their spouse's income ($32,500 including spouse's income), while the median was $12,500 for the prisoners, based on their annual income in year prior to prison; their spouse's income was not asked. However, since only 18% were currently married, this figure would probably increase only slightly had it been included.

The women differed in their gambling preferences with the GA women favoring card games, casinos, and slots while the prison women preferred numbers or other lotteries, cards, and horse race betting. These differences are reported in Table 1.

There were variances as well in the extent to which they had alcohol and other drug problems. Fourteen percent of the GA women and 36% of the prisoners were alcoholics; 22% of the GA members versus 59% of the prisoners were dependent on other drugs. Regarding the combination of alcohol and other drugs, 26% of the GA members were drug dependent compared with 71% of the prisoners. Using a "drug abuse" criterion (American Psychiatric Association, 1987), 56% of the GA women had a drug problem at some point in their life, and, while comparable data are not available, 88% of the female prisoners said someone else told them they had an alcohol or drug problem. More complete data on the type of drug are reported in Table 2.

TABLE 1

Gambling Preferences of Female Gamblers Anonymous Members Compared with Female Prisoners. Percent gambling once a week or more on each of the activities.

Type of Gambling	Female GA N=50	Female Prisoners N=34
Casinos	58%	23%
Horse Betting	32	41
Sports Betting	12	26
Card Games	64	50
Dice	2	29
Bingo	22	38
Slots	42	35
Numbers/Lotteries	34%	74%

Note: Percentages do not add up to 100% because of multiple responses.

The rates of alcohol and substance abuse of the GA members are two to three times higher than those for the adult female population (Robins et al., 1984). They are comparable to the rates found for hospitalized male compulsive gamblers (Ramirez et al., 1983). The rates for female prisoners are comparable to those of their male counterparts in prison (Lesieur and Klein, 1985).

Sixteen percent of the GA sample had been in jail or prison — only 4% for gambling related offenses. (The rest were for disorderly conduct, prostitution, drunken driving, drug crimes, etc.) Forty-one percent of the compulsive gambling prisoners said their present imprisonment was partially or totally gambling connected.

TABLE 2

Psychoactive Substance Dependence and Abuse, Self-reported by Female GA Members (N=50) and Female Prisoners (n=34)

	Gamblers Anonymous		Prisoners
Substance abuse	Abuse only[a]	Dependence[a]	Dependence
Alcohol	9 (18%)	7 (14%)	12 (36%)
Other Drugs	13 (26%)	11 (22%)	20 (59%)
Amphetamines	4 (8%)	6 (12%)	b
Cocaine	2 (4%)	—	b
Tranquilizers/ Valium	9 (18%)	5 (10%)	b
Heroin	1 (2%)	1 (2%)	b
Marijuana	2 (4%)	2 (4%)	b
Hallucinogens	1 (2%)	—	b
Any psychoactive substance	15 (30%)	11 (22%)	24 (71%)
Dependence and abused combined	28 (56%)		30 (88%)[c]

[a] DSM-III-R criteria used for Psychoactive Substance Dependence and Abuse (A.P.A., 1987)
[b] Information not available
[c] Figure for prisoners based on positive answer to question: "Others have said I have an alcohol/drug problem."

BACKGROUND CHARACTERISTICS OF THE GAMBLERS ANONYMOUS WOMEN

Intensive interviews with the Gamblers Anonymous members revealed problem childhoods, troubled marriages and troubled adult lives. Although the women's reports of their childhood experiences range from happy and healthy to severely disturbed, well over half had difficult early years.

Alcoholism in their parents was more common than was compulsive gambling. Included among other serious problems were parents who were mentally ill or who subjected them to physical or sexual abuse. As a result of these childhood experiences several mentioned getting married in order to escape their families. Table 3 indicates their statements about disorders in their parents. In addition, four women's childhoods were disrupted by World War II. Two lost their parents in the Nazi holocaust; the father of a third was imprisoned in a concentration camp; and the fourth survived the London blitz. These early life experiences definitely had an impact on their later gambling careers.

TABLE 3

Parental Pathology of Female Gamblers Anoymous Members

Type of Family Pathology	Number	Percent
Father alcoholic	14	28%
Mother alcoholic	5	10%
Father compulsive gambler or probable compulsive gambler	10	20%
Mother compulsive gambler	2	4%
Other serious problems	6	12%
Any of the above	30	60%

Source: Survey of 50 female pathological gamblers.

In addition to the subjects' gambling, other factors negatively affected their marriages as well. For example, 62% were married to troubled husbands who were pathological gamblers, alcoholics, drug abusers or had other problems, which are listed in Table 4. A common factor in many of the marriages was the husband's frequent absence from home. Apart from the problems noted in Table 4, 44% of the husbands were absent either because of evening or night shift work, or had jobs that involved travel, which gave rise to chronic loneliness among their wives. Twenty-nine percent had physically abusive husbands, most of whom were alcoholics.

More than half of the GA women stated that their gambling was initially looked upon as a means of escape from overwhelming problems, including trauma of the past, troublesome marital relationships and loneliness. I call these women "escape seekers" as escaping from problems is their prime motive for gambling. While half of the female GA members were "escape seekers," they overlapped with the "action seekers" described below.

TABLE 4

Problem Husbands of Female Gamblers Anonymous Member (N=42)		
Type of problem	Number	Percent
Married to pathological gambler	8	19%
Married to alcoholic	14	32%
Married to other drug abuser	4	10%
Married to mentally ill husband	4	10%
Married to "womanizer"	5	12%
Married to "workaholic"	9	21%
Married to any above	26	62%
Husband has none of problems above	16	38%
Total ever married	42	100%
Source: Survey of 50 female Gamblers Anonymous members.		

PHASES IN THE CAREER OF THE FEMALE PATHOLOGICAL GAMBLER

Custer describes three phases in the career of the compulsive gambler: the winning phase, the losing phase, and the desperation phase (1984; 1985). These adequately describe the male gambling pattern but need to be revised when discussing women. Gambling starts as a recreational activity for all who gamble. Compulsive gamblers are no exception to this rule. Like others, they win, lose, and break even; they win, lose, and break even. For about half of compulsive gamblers, an upsurge in gambling activity begins with a big win or a winning streak which frequently results in the equivalent of half a year's income or more. They become convinced that they can win a fortune by gambling, and simultaneously feel the thrill of being "in action." They are "smarter than the average sucker" out there. These gamblers can be called "action seekers."

While some women experience this early pattern, it is more common among male compulsive gamblers than females, many of whom never have a big win at all. More than half of the women stated that they initially looked upon gambling as a means of escaping from the overwhelming problems described above. A quote from an "escape seeker" illustrates this early pattern.

> In all honesty, I went out gambling when my husband was drunk so we wouldn't fight. By that time, my older kids were old enough to take care of the little ones if they were awake. I started out on the nickel slot machines and progressed to the dollar machines . . . Like I said, I started out allowing myself only so much money. And the money I had, gave me the time — time away, time of not thinking, the time of not worrying [Helen — slots player].

The intensive interviews with Gamblers Anonymous members uncovered two career styles which have different starting points but eventually merge into a common pattern: the "action seeker" and the "escape seeker." These are ideal types which represent two dimensions often found in combination.

All heavy gamblers seek "action" as well as money or a means of escaping from problems. Action is an aroused, euphoric state comparable to the "high" derived from cocaine or other drugs. "Action" means excitement, thrill, and tension. In short, the "adrenalin" is flowing:

> I'd need one number, the adrenalin would pick up, I'd get all numb, hoping and praying that number would be called [Hope B. — talking about bingo].

> I was a maniac in the casino . . . My adrenalin starts to go. Meaning, I start getting high, start getting nervous, looking forward, rushing compulsively. Ah, going up to the first table where I could get a spot right in the middle so I would have enough room to place my bets wherever I felt hot on a number [Sue M. — a roulette player].

The desire to keep the action going is so intense in later stages of compulsive gambling that many women discussed going without sleep for days, not eating, and not getting up from a seat until there was a desperate need to go. Being in action pushes out other concerns for these women.

Those who are escaping from some problem comment on gambling as being an "anesthetic" which "hypnotizes." Jacobs calls these phenomena, which many gamblers experience, "dissociative states" (1988). They include "memory blackouts," "trances," "out of body experiences" and the feeling of taking on another identity while gambling. Regular gamblers discuss these experiences as being "on tilt" (Browne, 1989). "Escape seekers" come to appreciate these feelings, particularly when they are combined with the euphoria of the action.

"Action seekers" derive an increasing proportion of their self-esteem from their handicapping abilities. Additionally more time is allocated in an effort to produce a winning system to beat the horses, sports, stock options, or numbers. When they experience a "bad beat," an unexplainable loss or losing streak produced by bizarre circumstances (see Rosecrance, 1986), many will *"chase"* their losses in an attempt to get even. They will try to get their money back and frequently become obsessed with doing so, as the losses represent a serious blow to their self-esteem. The consequent chasing produces irrational gambling and further losses (Lesieur, 1979).

"Escape seekers" gradually come to rely more and more on the action for a "time out" from their troubles. This "time out," however, is expensive. As costs rise, they also borrow and stretch their expenses to the limit. When they gamble on borrowed money, they chase their losses in an attempt to pay back the borrowed money. Now, not only do they have their original troubles to escape from, but they also have problems produced by their gambling which compound these troubles.

For both the "action seeker" and the "escape seeker," there is a gradual deterioration in the home, job and financial realms as the gambling progresses in the losing phase. Relationships suffer as family members and friends are borrowed from, and lies are told. Their jobs are exploited for what they can bring: time to gamble and money to pay for it. Eighty-six percent of the GA women were currently employed or had been previously. Only four women described themselves as "housewives"; two were disabled and one was a student. Compulsive gambling eventually led to financial problems. All of the women used both their own and their family's money to finance their gambling, typically delaying payment of household bills, exhausting bank accounts, borrowing from friends and family (including their own children), taking out small loans (sometimes forging their husband's signature), and spending their unemployment or welfare checks. Family possessions, savings, and legitimate sources of funding were exhausted.

In the process of obtaining money to gamble, various options utilized are typically dependent on income and access to credit. Use of options occurs in a repeated cycle with basically three stages: getting money, moving it, and the closure of options and consequent need to re-evaluate moral position. The process of getting money includes attempts to "con others with a sad story," making phone calls to friends, relatives, loan companies and others, taking advantage of available opportunities, and as one woman noted, "letting my brain start scheming" for ways of getting money to gamble or get out of trouble (for example, pay the electric bill, cover bad checks, replace borrowed or stolen money or keep things hidden from her husband or lover).

Table 5 summarizes the different legal resources which both the GA and prison women used to finance their gambling. The female GA members were more adept at using legal avenues for financing their gambling than the prisoners. They were also more likely to use household money and their children's money but less likely to say they borrowed from siblings. In addition, they seemed to have more access to legitimate credit and legitimate property to sell than prisoners. They were more likely to borrow from banks, loan companies, credit unions, credit cards, insurance policies, and cash in stocks, bonds and other securities, or sell property, than their imprisoned counterparts. On average, the GA members used 5.8 different sources of "legitimate" funds compared with 4.1 for the prisoners. This greater access to financial resources meant that the GA women could move, manipulate, or juggle money more readily from one source to another in order to "stay in action." They could stall one party while paying another; that is, they could "borrow from Peter to pay Paul" with greater facility. Greater money moving ability meant that fewer illegal options had to be utilized to finance gambling. However, some of the money moving involved illegal options — those of the "white collar" variety.

A typical sequence of events will illustrate what is meant by the term "moving money." Becca would write checks in a casino where she had check cashing privileges. She would borrow from the mortgage, gas, electric and telephone payments to cover the checks (i.e., she would move the money from the rent to the checking account). Eventually the rent became three months late.

TABLE 5

Financial Resources used by Female Gamblers Anonymous Members (n=50) and Female Prisoners (n=34) to Gamble or Pay Gambling Related Debts.

SOURCE OF MONEY FOR GAMBLING	GAMBLERS ANONYMOUS MEMBERS	PRISONERS
Borrowed from:		
household money	33 (66%)	17 (50%)
children	20 (40%)	3 (9%)
spouse	20 (40%)	17 (50%)
parents	20 (40%)	13 (38%)
siblings	18 (36%)	16 (47%)
other relatives	15 (30%)	12 (35%)
friends	30 (60%)	23 (68%)
loan company/bank	32 (64%)	1 (3%)
credit union	6 (12%)	1 (3%)
credit cards	19 (38%)	2 (6%)
loan sharks	11 (22%)	7 (21%)
insurance policies	6 (12%)	1 (3%)
cashed in stocks, etc.	12 (24%)	5 (15%)
sold personal property	32 (64%)	9 (26%)
Credit with casino	11 (22%)	8 (9%)
Credit with bookmaker	6 (12%)	6 (18%)
Average number of different sources used	5.8	4.1

Realizing this, she took overdraft loans to cover the bad checks but had to get a "home improvement loan" (note the irony and the loan fraud) from HFC to avoid prosecution for the bad checks. At one point she forged her husband's name to insurance and other checks that came in without his knowledge or acquiescence so he wouldn't find out about the checks that were bouncing all over the place. All of this sequence was complicated by periodic winning and losing streaks in her career. At one point, for example, she had won enough money to make three months payment on the mortgage. She gambled some more, lost all but $100, then won $4,000; she used $300 to cover bad checks and gambled with the rest (she was trying to pay off her loans as well as the mortgage); she lost her winnings and the bills went unpaid. After years of such manipulating she and her husband divorced and the bank foreclosed on the house.

As options were closed off, Becca had to resort to forgery and fraud. For her, the moral decisions she confronted were not that severe; as a result, she could easily justify the things she did. The bad checks were signed with the intention of covering them sooner or later. She believed she could win and cover them that way, or, if push came to shove, borrow the money to cover them. The loan fraud wasn't really "fraud" as she had every intention of paying the loan; signing her husband's name wasn't really "forgery" as it was her husband after all and "everybody does it" (conveniently forgetting that this may be true but justifiable only with the husband's consent — she stretches her moral understanding of the event). It would hurt her husband to find out but he doesn't have to know.

Skirting of the forgery and fraud laws was fairly common among the female GA members. Those who didn't engage in these activities defined false statements on loans as "fraud," called passing bad checks "illegal," and could not justify signing anyone's name other than their own to anything. Major value differences separated these women from those who used illegal options. These women also tended to have less fear of their husbands' reactions to debt. Consequently, they personally experienced less "threat" than those who engaged in illegality to "cover" financial difficulties.

Eventually, legal avenues (and possibly some illegal ones as well) become closed off (for example, banks close checking accounts and employees are fired for theft) and no longer provide the needed resources. Their options subsequently narrow to include fewer and fewer activities which can be easily and morally justified.

GAMBLERS ANONYMOUS AND PRISON WOMEN COMPARED

While GA women were more likely to use legal activities to finance gambling than the prison women, they were *less* likely to resort to illegal actions as a solution to their problems. Two-thirds of the GA women and all but one of the prisoners engaged in illegal activity to finance their gambling or pay gambling related debts. Table 6 compares the gambling-related illegal activities reported by the female GA members with those in the study of female prisoners. Crimes committed to finance drugs are specifically excluded unless those crimes financed gambling as well.

When compared with the GA women, the female prisoners had higher rates of check and other forgery, burglary, robbery, prostitution, procuring, drug sales, fencing stolen goods, hustling at games of skill, card and dice hustling, and running con games and swindles. The two groups had similar rates of employee theft, fraud, larceny, and employment in illegal gambling settings (this ranged from operating small-time card games and "cutting the pot" to being a bookmaker or working for "the mob"). The only offense categories in which the GA women exceeded the prisoners were those of income tax evasion and tax fraud. They also had higher rates of civil fraud in making loan applications (typically concealing debts, exaggerating income, or giving false reasons for the loan). The GA women averaged 2.3 types of illegal activities while the prison women averaged 4.9 types of illegal actions each to finance their gambling. This difference narrows only slightly (2.8 versus 5.0) if we include loan fraud.

Two major factors seem to explain the difference in criminal behavior between the GA and prison women. The first factor which seems to explain the differences in rates is the difference in alcoholism and drug addiction among the two groups. The GA women who were alcohol or drug dependent engaged in more forms of illegal behavior, an average of 3.6 different types of crimes, compared with 2.8 for substance abusers, and 1.4 for non-abusers. Among the prison women, alcoholics and drug addicts participated in 5.2 types of crime compared with 4.2 for the others. The GA women who were chemically dependent or multiple substance abusers (particularly of street drugs) had early histories of street crime (only those which were specifically for gambling are

TABLE 6

Illegal Activities and Civil Fraud Engaged in by Female Gamblers Anonymous Members and a Comparison Group of Female Pathological Gamblers in Prison.*

TYPE OF ACTIVITY	FEMALE GA N=50	FEMALE PRISONERS N=34
Loan Fraud (civil)	22 (44%)	2 (6%)
White-Collar Crime		
Check forgery ("bad checks")	22 (44%)	20 (59%)
Forgery	12 (24%)	12 (35%)
Embezzlement and Employee Theft	12 (24%)	7 (21%)
Tax Evasion	6 (12%)	1 (3%)
Tax Fraud	3 (6%)	—
Other Fraud**	9 (18%)	7 (21%)
Commonplace Crime		
Larceny	13 (26%)	8 (24%)
Burglary	1 (2%)	10 (29%)
Armed Robbery	1 (2%)	5 (15%)
Prostitution	6 (12%)	14 (41%)
Pimping — Procuring	—	4 (12%)
Selling Drugs	1 (2%)	18 (53%)
Fencing Stolen Goods	2 (4%)	14 (41%)
Gambling System Connected		
Bookmaking or Working in an Illegal Game	14 (28%)	8 (24%)
Hustling at Pool, Golf, Bowling or Other Sport	4 (8%)	17 (50%)
Hustling at Cards or Dice	4 (8%)	12 (35%)
Run a "con game"; Swindle Suckers	7 (14%)	10 (29%)
Engaged in Any of the Illegal Activities Above	33 (66%)	33 (97%)
Types of Crimes Engaged In:		
Average per person	2.3	4.9

* Offenses engaged in as a consequence of gambling only. Percentages listed in the table.

** Welfare fraud only for prison sample. Fraud for Gamblers Anonymous sample excludes false statements on loan applications.

included in Table 6). Heavy drug users are involved in street hustles in combination with other money acquisition methods (Johnson et al., 1985; Rosenbaum, 1981). When they gamble, part of their illegal money is channeled in that direction.

It is obvious that addiction itself does not account for all the difference apparent between the GA and prison women. Perhaps of equal or possibly greater importance are the higher levels of education and income found among GA women, who were also more likely to be married than the prisoners. As a result, they had greater access to legitimate credit and could therefore "move money" for longer periods of time. In this time span their luck could change, they could get the money legitimately from someplace else, or they could stall or otherwise delay impending problems. Some of those who did not engage in illegal options used bank accounts, had husbands or parents with substantial incomes, or had decent interest income sources or earned incomes themselves. In other words, their *options* were still open.

While gambling and drug abuse interact, they also have different impacts. The most common pattern for the GA women interviewed was the simultaneous use of drugs while gambling, with slightly more emphasis on drugs than on gambling, followed by a cycle out of drugs, with increased gambling then used as an alternative means of stimulation. In other words, they "switch" their primary addiction from chemicals to gambling. With this move, the types of crimes committed when they gambled altered in contrast to when they used alcohol or other drugs. They developed a preference for "white collar" crimes which would yield substantial amounts of money. The next most common pattern comprised a primary addiction to gambling and use of alcohol or drugs to "escape" from gambling produced problems. The combination of chemical dependence and compulsive gambling produced situations which exacerbated their problems. For example, people gamble more recklessly when drunk or high on drugs; reckless gambling increases losses.

Both legal and illegal sources of money are treated as a "big win" in that they enable the gambler to continue and possibly even escalate the gambling. Eventually however, the gambling takes on a desperate quality. Gambling is still exciting but the negatives outweigh the positives. Obsession with getting out of and escaping from trouble overtakes the desire for excitement as the principal motive for gambling. When the strategies fail as they often do, serious bouts of depression are experienced. In fact, 22% of the GA women made potentially lethal attempts at suicide. Arrest and imprisonment are also possibilities.

Several policy-related questions are raised by these data. First, what percent of the crimes which alcoholics and other drug addicts engage in are motivated by gambling or exacerbated by it? How much of stolen and otherwise hustled money is used for action and escape into what GA members call the "dream world" of gambling? If the figure is low, will it increase if the individual becomes abstinent from alcohol or drugs and yet still craves excitement? Secondly, to what extent does poverty interact with gambling to produce illegal behavior? Finally, what impact is the current rush to legalize gambling having on crime rates? In 1974 there was $17 billion in legal gambling. By 1988 this figure had risen to $210 billion (Christiansen, 1989), more than a 1,200 percent increase in legal gambling alone. Much of the recent wave of legalized gambling (lotteries, card games and casinos in particular) is attractive to women. To the extent that gambling becomes increasingly legitimized (see Rosecrance, 1988) we can expect ever larger numbers of people to become addicted to its excitement and anesthetizing qualities, eventually chase their losses, and become trapped in a spiral of options and involvement.

ENDNOTES

[1] The author would like to acknowledge faculty support from St. John's University and the assistance of the following students who transcribed interviews and acted as coders for this project: Noemi Balinth, Theresa Camelo, Esperanza Diaz, Vincent Ferri, Jerald Freeman, Maria Markou, Timothy McCorry, Joseph Palermo, Patrick Rameau, Theresa Romani and Catherine Toriello. The author would also like to thank Marie Mark who made comments on an earlier draft of this paper.

This research partially supported by grant C-000791 from the New York State Office of Mental Health. Research on prisoners partially funded by the Council on Compulsive Gambling of New Jersey, Inc.

REFERENCES

American Psychiatric Association (1987). *Diagnostic and Statistical Manual*, third edition, revised. Washington, D.C.: American Psychiatric Association.

Blaszczynski, A.P., McConaghy, N. and Frankova, A. (1989). Crime, antisocial personality, and pathological gambling. *Journal of Gambling Behavior*, 5, 137-152.

Brown, R.I.F. (1987). Pathological gambling and associated patterns of crime: Comparisons with alcohol and drug addiction. *Journal of Gambling Behavior*, 3, 98-114.

Browne, B.R. (1989). Going on tilt: Frequent poker players and control. *Journal of Gambling Behavior*, 5, 3-21.

Camp, G. (1968). *Nothing to lose: A study of bank robbery in America.* Unpublished Ph.D. dissertation, Yale University.

Christiansen, E.M. (1989). 1988 U.S. gross annual wager. *Gaming and Wagering Business*, 10, July 15, 8.

Ciarrocchi, J. (1987). Severity of impairment in dually addicted gamblers. *Journal of Gambling Behavior*, 3, 16-26.

Collins, J.J. (ed.) (1981). *Drinking and Crime.* New York: Guilford Press.

Commission on the Review of National Policy Towards Gambling (1976). *Gambling in America.* Washington, D.C.: U.S. Government Printing Office.

Cressey, D. (1971). *Other People's Money.* Belmont, CA: Wadsworth Publishing.

Custer, R.L. (1984). Profile of the pathological gambler. *Journal of Clinical Psychiatry*, 45, 35-38.

Custer, R.L. and Custer, L.F. (1978, December). *Characteristics of the recovering compulsive gambler: A survey of 150 members of Gamblers Anonymous.* Paper presented at the Fourth Annual Conference on Gambling, Reno, Nevada.

Custer, R.L. and Milt, H. (1985). *When Luck Runs Out.* New York: Facts on File Publications.

Haberman, P.W. (1969). Drinking and other self-indulgences: Complements or counter-attractions? *International Journal of the Addictions*, 4, 157-167.

Jacobs, D.F. (1988). Evidence for a common dissociative-like reaction among addicts. *Journal of Gambling Behavior*, 4, 27-37.

Johnson, B.D., Goldstein, P.J., Preble, E., Schmeidler, J., Lipton, D.S., Spunt, B. and Miller, T. (1985). *Taking Care of Business: The Economics of Crime By Heroin Users.* Lexington: Lexington Books.

Lemert, E. (1953). An isolation and closure theory of naive check forgery. *Journal of Criminal Law, Criminology, and Police Science*, 44, 296-307.

Lesieur, H.R. (1979). The compulsive gambler's spiral of options and involvement. *Psychiatry: Journal for the Study of Interpersonal Processes*, 42, 79-87.

Lesieur, H.R. (1984). *The Chase: Career of the Compulsive Gambler.* Cambridge, MA: Schenkman Books.

Lesieur, H.R. (1987). Gambling, pathological gambling and crime. In T. Galski (ed.), *Handbook on Pathological Gambling* (pp. 89-110). Springfield, IL: Charles C. Thomas Publishers.

Lesieur, H.R. (1988). The female pathological gambler. In W.R. Eadington (ed.), *Gambling Research: Proceedings of the Seventh International Conference on Gambling and Risk Taking* (pp. 230-258). Reno, NV: University of Nevada, Reno.

Lesieur, H.R., Blume, S.B. and Zoppa, R.M. (1986). Alcoholism, drug abuse, and gambling. *Alcoholism: Clinical and Experimental Research*, 10, 33-38.

Lesieur, H.R. and Heineman, M. (1988). Pathological gambling among youthful multiple substance abusers in a therapeutic community. *British Journal of Addiction*, 83, 765-771.

Lesieur, H.R. and Klein, R. (1985, April). *Prisoners, gambling and crime.* Paper presented at the Annual Meetings of the Academy of Criminal Justice Sciences, Las Vegas, Nevada.

Livingston, J. (1974). *Compulsive Gamblers: Observations on Action and Abstinence.* New York: Harper Torchbooks.

Maurer, D. (1974). *The American Confidence Man.* Springfield, IL: Charles C. Thomas Publishers.

Politzer, R.M., Morrow, J.S. and Leavey, S.B. (1985). Report on the cost-benefit/effectiveness of treatment at the Johns Hopkins Center for Pathological Gambling. *Journal of Gambling Behavior*, 1, 131-142.

Ramirez, L.F., McCormick, R.A., Russo, A.M. and Taber, J.I. (1984). Patterns of substance abuse in pathological gamblers undergoing treatment. *Addictive Behaviors*, 8, 425-428.

Robins, L.N., Helzer, J.E., Weissman, M.M., Orvaschel, H., Gruenberg, E., Burke, J.D. and Regier, D. (1984). Lifetime prevalence of specific psychiatric disorders in three sites. *Archives of General Psychiatry*, 41, 949-958.

Roebuck, J. (1967). *Criminal Typology*. Springfield, IL: Charles C. Thomas.

Rosecrance, J. (1986). Attributions and the origins of problem gambling. *The Sociological Quarterly*, 27, 463-477.

Rosecrance, J. (1988). *Gambling Without Guilt: The Legitimation of an American Pastime*. Pacific Grove, CA: Brooks/Cole Publishing Company.

Rosenbaum, M. (1981). *Women on Heroin*. New Brunswick, NJ: Rutgers University Press.

Royal College of Psychiatrists (1977). *Submission of Evidence To the Royal Commission on Gambling*. London: Royal College of Psychiatrists, mimeo.

Russo, A.M., Taber, J.I., McCormick, R.A. and Ramirez, L.F. (1984). An outcome study of an inpatient treatment program for pathological gamblers. *Hospital and Community Psychiatry*, 35, 823-827.

Sommers, I. (1988). Pathological gambling: Estimating prevalence and group characteristics. *International Journal of the Addictions*, 23, 477-490.

Volberg, R. and Steadman, H. (1988). Refining prevalence estimates of pathological gambling. *American Journal of Psychiatry*, 145, 502-505.

Volberg, R. and Steadman, H. (1989). Prevalence estimates of pathological gambling in New Jersey and Maryland. *American Journal of Psychiatry*, 146, 1618-1619.

Zietz, D. (1981). *Women Who Embezzle Or Defraud: A Study of Convicted Felons*. New York: Praeger.

Pathological Gambling and Criminal Behavior

Gerhard Meyer and Thomas Fabian

The ever increasing supply of gambling opportunities in the Federal Republic of Germany since the middle of the 1970s was followed — with some temporal delay — by an increase in the demand for professional counseling and therapy and the formation of self-help groups by gamblers.

According to statistics of ambulant institutions for counseling and treatment of addictive behavior, the percentage of male clients with non-substance related addiction — almost exclusively pathological gambling — has risen from 3.1 percent in 1987 to 5.4 percent in 1989. Their proportion therefore amounts to about the same as that of clients addicted to legal or illegal drugs — with the exception of opiates (Simon, Strobl, Ziegler, Bühringer, Helas and Schmidtobreick, 1990). Since the formation of the first self-help groups of "Gamblers Anonymous" in 1982, their number has risen to more than 70 groups today.

However, reliable data about the number of pathological gamblers in the Federal Republic of Germany are not available; recent estimates vary between 20,000 and 160,000 (Bühringer, Kunkel and Reye, 1985; Caritas, 1989).

At the same time we find on an international level an increasing acceptance of the specific clinical diagnosis "pathological gambling." The American Psychiatric Association (APA) has included this disorder in its diagnostic manual — the DSM-III and DSM-III-R (APA, 1980, 1987) — as a diagnostic category of its own. It will also be included in the next diagnostic manual of the World Health Organization (WHO), the "International Classification of Disease" (ICD-10) [WHO, 1987; Sartorius, Jablensky, Cooper and Burke, 1988].

Both diagnostic manuals mention the committing of illegal acts in order to obtain money for gambling as a characteristic problem of pathological gamblers.

The authors have attempted to explain why a gambler begins to resort to financially motivated criminal acts by taking into account the specific dynamics of pathological gambling (Meyer and Fabian, 1988): With the development of pathological gambling behavior and as a consequence of thereby intensified gambling, financial expenditure grows and the gambler experiences a progressive narrowing-down of his perception of the necessity to obtain money for continued gambling. When his own financial resources and legal means of obtaining money are exhausted, it still remains the pathological gambler's goal to obtain money because of his inability to abstain from gambling. The pressure to act then becomes so strong that he passes increasingly higher moral thresholds. He does not keep financial obligations and finally commits criminal acts in order to obtain the necessary financial means.

Passing a moral threshold is not a distinct event but the result of a continuing process during which alternative actions are again and again mentally gone through and discarded until the gambler sees no other way out. Even borrowing money from relatives and acquaintances under false pretenses means that moral thresholds must be passed, but it becomes easier and easier to surmount them. In the further course of the gambling career moral thresholds are lowered due to a habituation process. At the initial stage interiorized norms and values still have an effect on the gambler's actions. A delinquent gambler will often try to keep open a way to compensate for the damage caused by him. He might for example deposit stolen objects at a pawnbroker's, thereby maintaining the possibility to redeem and return them in case the hoped for winnings should come true. The delinquency of the pathological gambler is basically caused by the widening gap between the amount of money required to continue with gambling — for which he feels a compulsive desire — and the money which he can obtain by legal means.

Apart from the specific dynamics of pathological gambling which play a major role in the gambler's delinquency there are however other factors to be taken into account, such as the personality of the gambler, biography and conditions of socialization, previous delinquency, age and social context at the beginning of the gambling career and the degree of involvement with the gambling scene (Kreuzer, 1987).

So far in the Federal Republic of Germany only very little research has been done on gambling related delinquency. The aim of this study was to gain empirically based information about the delinquency of gamblers who commit illegal acts in order to obtain money for gambling. The data were also to be used for a first examination of causal relations between pathological gambling and delinquency. This was done on the basis of data collected in a comprehensive research project on gamblers in self-help groups (Meyer, 1989a, b).

METHOD

All then existing self-help groups for gamblers in the Federal Republic of Germany were contacted in 1987 and the group members were interviewed with standardized instruments. They consisted of a comprehensive questionnaire about a wide range of different aspects of gambling, which was developed for the purpose of this investigation, a list of adjectives (following Janke and Debus, 1978) for self-description of the emotional state while gambling, the Freiburg Personality Inventory (FPI-R) (Fahrenberg, Hampel and Selg, 1984) and questions concerning socio-demographic data. The scalability of the instruments was tested with a probabilistic scaling procedure (Mokken, 1971).

In this paper the authors will present selected results in respect to the question of gambling related delinquency.

Group comparisons (t-test, Chi-square test) were made between those interviewed who reported that they had obtained money for gambling through illegal means and those who denied this.

Furthermore, a multiple regression was computed through a path analysis to examine a hypothetical model of the causal structure of different aspects of pathological gambling in relation to delinquency. For the hypothetical model those scales from the gambling questionnaire, the emotional state questionnaire and the personality inventory were selected, which focus on emotional stress because it can be assumed that delinquent gamblers show a more pronounced problem behavior than non-delinquent gamblers.

Altogether nine variables were entered into the path analysis in the following sequence:

> age → personality scale "emotional instability" → scale "function of gambling as substitute and escape" → scale "experience of excitement during gambling" → scale "symptoms of pathological gambling" → duration of excessive gambling phase → gambling debts → neglect of financial obligations → delinquency.

A second path analysis was computed in which the scale "emotional instability" was substituted by the scale "aggressiveness."

SAMPLE

A total of 437 gamblers from 54 self-help groups were interviewed. The mean age of the mainly male (95%) interviewees is 31 years. In comparison with the age structure of the overall population the age group 20 to under 40 is overrepresented in this sample. The male interviewees had a better education, with respect to profession and monthly net income there were no substantial divergences from overall population.

RESULTS

A. Frequencies

Of the gamblers interviewed, 54.5 percent reported having obtained money for gambling through illegal means.

A total of 10.3 percent (N=45) of the interviewees had already been sentenced for criminal offenses committed in order to obtain money for gambling. These were mainly non-violent offenses against property, such as theft (42.2%), embezzlement (31.1%), fraud (26.7%), forgery of documents, tax evasion or manipulation of gambling machines (13.3%), but included also robbery or blackmail (15.6%).

B. Group comparisons

The group comparisons show that the group of interviewees who had admittedly committed criminal offenses gambled more often and longer. Their average stakes were higher and their losses larger. Their total gambling debts were about one and a half times higher. Their gambling behavior was therefore altogether more excessive than that of the non-delinquent group (Table 1).

TABLE 1

Variables of Gambling Behavior (N=437)

	delinquent group (n=238)		non-delinquent group (n=199)		t-test	
	M	s	M	s	t	prob
frequency (per week)	5.5	1.7	4.9	1.9	3.76	.000
duration per day (in hours)	4.4	2.0	3.8	1.8	3.59	.000
intensive phase (in months)	75.7	64.0	58.3	50.0	3.07	.002
average stake (in DM)	365.8	640.0	259.6	445.3	1.95	.050
highest loss (in DM)	2656.2	5990.9	1492.6	3533.2	2.40	.010
highest win (in DM)	5187.7	14740.6	2018.6	6443.2	2.81	.005
total losses (in DM)	115846.7	231381.2	59757.1	87956.6	3.20	.001
total debts (in DM)	33080.5	75242.9	21241.9	34355.2	2.02	.040

On the scale which describes symptoms of pathological gambling and also includes the diagnostic criteria of the DSM-III-R the group of delinquent interviewees shows a significantly higher mean score (Table 2). They also more often had a very strong subjective feeling of dependence on gambling (Table 3) and they more often described withdrawal-like symptoms such as sleep disorders, restlessness, irritability, sweating, nightmares or headaches. We found however no significant differences on the scale which describes attempts to abstain from or reduce gambling (Table 2).

TABLE 2

Variables of Pathological Gambling (N=437)

	delinquent group (n=238)		non-delinquent group (n=199)		t-test	
	M	s	M	s	t	prob
scale "symptoms of pathological gambling"	15.5	5.4	12.3	5.7	6.58	.001
scale "function of gambling as substitute or escape"	5.4	2.1	4.3	2.4	4.97	.001
scale "reduction of gambling"	3.4	1.8	3.1	1.7	1.42	n.s.
scale "happy mood while gambling"	13.3	9.5	10.6	9.1	2.98	.003
scale "excitement while gambling"	7.6	3.0	6.3	3.4	4.25	.000
scale "self-confidence while gambling"	3.4	2.6	2.4	2.2	4.48	.000
scale "dreaminess while gambling"	1.7	1.6	1.0	1.2	4.66	.000
scale "concentration while gambling"	3.2	1.7	2.8	1.6	2.63	.009
scale "negative withdrawal-like symptoms"	4.9	3.6	3.7	3.4	2.97	.003
personality scale "emotional instability"	9.0	3.4	8.0	3.7	2.84	.005
personality scale "aggressiveness"	5.6	3.0	4.4	2.6	4.63	.000

TABLE 3

Variables "Feeling of Dependency" and Problems Because of Gambling (N=437)				
	delinguent group (n=238)	CHI^2	D.F.	prob.
feeling of dependency on gambling	more frequent "very strong"	26.65	2	.000
degree of pschological problems because of gambling	more frequent "very strong"	14.72	6	.020
problems with partner because of gambling	more frequent "strong"	18.97	6	.004
problems with job because of gambling	more frequent "strong"	19.30	6	.003
problems with social contacts because of gambling	more frequent " strong"	21.39	6	.001
problems with leisure time because of gambling	more frequent "strong"	13.56	6	.030
loss of job because of gambling	more frequent	38.32	2	.000
loss of housing because of gambing	more frequent	11.41	2	.003
separation from partner because of gambling	more frequent	14.38	2	.000

There were significant differences with regard to motivating and maintaining factors. For the delinquent interviewees who, as mentioned above, had gambled more excessively, gambling had served to a greater extent as a kind of substitute or escape behavior. They more often described such motives for their gambling as trouble at home and in their jobs or depressive moods. Gambling was a significantly more positive experience for them — they felt happier, more excited, more self-confident, dreamier and more concentrated while gambling (Table 2).

A comparison of the two groups with regards to the psychological and social effects of gambling shows a more frequent very high degree of psychosocial stress for the delinquent interviewees (Table 3). They experienced more often problems concerning their partnership, jobs, social contacts or leisure time activities than the non-delinquent interviewees. They also reported more often separation from their partners, loss of job or housing (Table 3).

The two groups differ with respect to personality characteristics. The delinquent interviewees described themselves to a greater extent as emotionally unbalanced (Table 2).

C. Path analysis

For the model resulting from the path analysis only those path coefficients were considered to be relevant that were equal or higher than .10.

The results (Figure 1) show a strong correlation between an unstable personality and the function of gambling as an escape from reality. There is also a connection between the personality variable and the experience of pleasurable excitement while gambling. There are direct connections between the function of gambling as escape and experience of excitement while gambling and symptoms of pathological gambling, but there is no direct connection between the personality variable and the symptom scale, nor are there direct connections between the age variable and the personality or the three gambling variables.

FIGURE 1

Path Diagram of Age, Personality Variable "Emotional Instability," Pathological Gambling and Delinquency

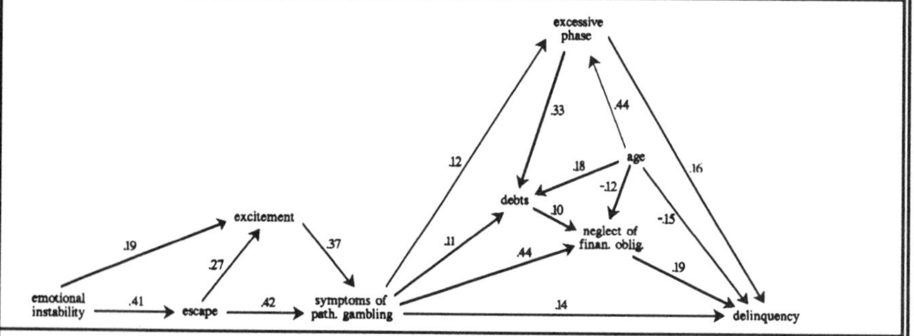

Residual variance (1-R^2): variable "emotional instability" .99, variable "escape" .83, variable "excitement" .84, variable "symptoms of pathological gambling" .58, variable "duration excessive phase" .80, variable "debts" .79, variable "neglect of financial obligations" .73, variable "delinquency" .85

Concerning the delinquent behavior of gamblers, this model shows that there are no direct connections between personality, escape behavior or the experience of pleasurable excitement and delinquency, but there is a relatively small correlation between symptom scale and delinquency. The correlation between the symptom scale and debts is also relatively small. The authors found no direct connection between debts and delinquency here. The correlation between neglect of financial obligations and delinquency is small, but there is a strong correlation between the symptom scale and neglect of financial obligations.

The model shows direct connections between the age variable and the duration of the intensive gambling phase and the amount of debts, and negative correlations between this variable and neglect of financial obligations as well as delinquency. Lastly, there is a direct connection between the symptom scale and the duration of the intensive gambling phase as well as between the latter and the amount of debts and also delinquency.

If the personality variable "emotional instability" is substituted with "aggressiveness" in the path analysis, the following changes result (Figure 2): The duration of the intensive gambling phase then shows no direct relation to delinquency, but there is a direct connection between "aggressiveness" and delinquency.

DISCUSSION

The results of the study show that there is a considerable degree of delinquent behavior among pathological gamblers. They also indicate a relation between delinquent behavior and the symptoms of pathological gambling.

The comparison of those interviewees who said that they had not committed criminal offenses for gambling with those who admitted to such acts shows that the latter were more excessive in their gambling behavior, experienced a higher degree of gratification through gambling and had more psychosocial problems. The question remains open, however, whether these problems are to be accounted for by gambling alone or whether they were aggravated by the illegal actions. It is interesting to note that the higher amount of problems experienced by the delinquent interviewees does not seem to have led to more attempts to abstain from or reduce gambling on their side. Possibly the illegal acts were a kind of "way out" which enabled them to continue to gamble.

FIGURE 2

Path Diagram of Age, Personality Variable "Aggressiveness," Pathological Gambling and Delinquency

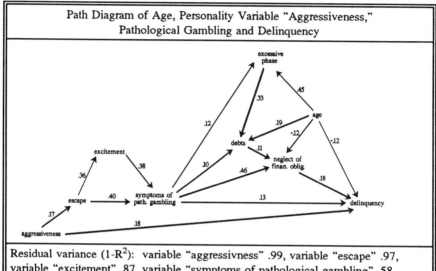

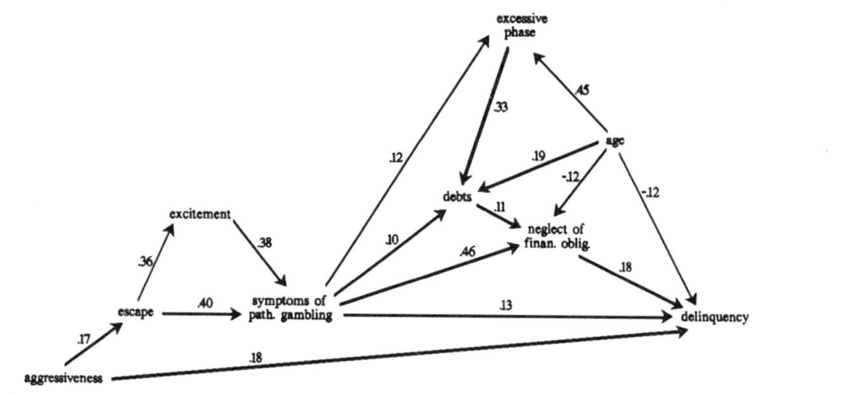

Residual variance (1-R^2): variable "aggressivness" .99, variable "escape" .97, variable "excitement" .87, variable "symptoms of pathological gambling" .58, variable "duration excessive phase" .79, variable "debts" .79, variable "neglect of financial obligations" .72, variable "delinquency" .83

In the path analysis neither emotional instability nor pathological gambling are age-specific. The direct connections between the age variable and the duration of the intensive gambling phase and the amount of debts seem plausible. The negative direct connections between the age variable and the neglect of financial obligations and delinquency can be explained by the fact that norms and values are not yet fully developed in young adults.

Considering the causes of delinquent behavior of gamblers, the path analytical model shows that emotional instability has no direct influence on delinquent behavior. The same applies to the amount of debts, which as such are not a phenomenon typical of gambling. Remarkable in this model is the considerable correlation between the symptoms of pathological gambling and the neglect of financial obligations. This can be explained by the increasing loss of responsibility and the retreat from social context shown by pathological gamblers.

The second model — in which the personality variable "emotional instability" was substituted by the variable "aggressiveness" — shows — in contrast to the first model — a direct connection between this personality variable and delinquent behavior, as is known from criminological investigations. In this model, the duration of the intensive gambling phase has no direct influence on delinquency.

The differences between the two models confirm the thesis that there is a group of emotionally unstable gamblers whose delinquent behavior can primarily be attributed to their problems with pathological gambling. Even though we must assume that other factors — above all socialization — contribute to the delinquent behavior, the dynamics of pathological gambling play a chief part in the delinquency of these pathological gamblers.

In the Federal Republic of Germany the recognition that certain illegal acts can be accounted for by pathological gambling is increasingly taken into consideration by criminal courts. According to our experiences as expert witnesses in more than forty trials many criminal courts today recognize diminished culpability for pathological gamblers (Meyer, Fabian and Wetzels, 1990). The highest criminal court in the Federal Republic of Germany — the federal court — has as well stated in a verdict that under certain conditions diminished culpability on account of pathological gambling — as in the case of drug abuse — cannot be ruled out.

Finally — with respect to crime prophylaxis — it would be worth considering whether the licensing of gambling should not be restricted rather than letting this market expand rapidly as is presently the case. For example, only a few months after the opening of the Berlin wall the first casino was opened in East-Berlin on May 18th, 1990. There is now another casino in Dresden and all over the German Democratic Republic, German-style-slot-machines are being installed in arcades, pubs and restaurants. On account of its potential danger, steps should be taken against the spreading of a need for gambling among larger parts of the population. The authors do not want to call for prohibition, but as one of the pioneers in the research on pathological gambling, Emanuel Moran, once stated:

> "Until it is recognized that social policy on gambling plays a fundamental role in the aetiology of pathological gambling, little will be achieved when dealing with this disorder" (Moran, 1979, p. 9).

REFERENCES

American Psychiatric Association (1980). *Diagnostic and Statistical Manual of Mental Disorders* (DSM-III), 3rd edition. Washington, D.C.: American Psychiatric Association.

American Psychiatric Association (1987). *Diagnostic and Statistical Manual of Mental Disorders* (DSM-III-R), 3rd edition revised. Washington, D.C.: American Psychiatric Association.

Bühringer, G., Kunkel, K. and Reye, I. (1985). Erste Ergebnisse zur Frequentierung von Unterhaltungsautomaten mit Gewinnmöglichkeit. *Suchtgefahren*, 31, 221-235.

Caritas (1989). Pressemitteilung anläßlich der Freiburger Sozialtherapiewochen. Manuscript.

Fahrenberg, J., Hampel, R. and Selg, H. (1984). *Das Freiburger Persönlichkeitsinventar* (FPI-R), revidierte Fassung. Göttingen: Hogrefe.

Janke, W. and Debus, G. (1978). *Die Eigenschaftswörterliste* (EWL). Göttingen: Hogrefe.

Kreuzer, A. (1987). *Jugend - Drogen - Kriminalität* (3. Auflage). Neuwied: Luchterhand.

Meyer, G. (1989a). *Glücksspieler in Selbsthilfegruppen*. Hamburg: Neuland.

Meyer, G. (1989b). Glücksspieler in Selbsthilfegruppen — erste Ergebnisse einer empirischen Untersuchung. *Suchtgefahren*, 35, 217-234.

Meyer, G. and Fabian, T. (1988). Abhängigkeit vom Glücksspiel und Beschaffungskriminalität. In C. Wahl (ed.), *Spielsucht*, (pp. 103-132). Hamburg: Neuland.

Meyer, G., Fabian, T. and Wetzels, P. (1990). Kriminalpsychologische Aspekte und forensisch-psychologische Wertung des pathologischen Glücksspiels. *Strafverteidiger*, 10, 464-469.

Mokken, R.J. (1971). *A Theory and Procedure of Scale Analysis*. The Hague: Mouton.

Moran, E. (1979). An assessment of the Report of The Royal Commission on Gambling 1976-1978. *British Journal of Addiction*, 74, 3-9.

Sartorius, N., Jablensky, A., Cooper, J.E. and Burke, J.D. (1988). Psychiatric classification in an international perspective. *British Journal of Psychiatry*, 152, (Supplement 1).

Simon, R., Strobl, M., Ziegler, H., Bühringer, G., Helas, I. and Schmidtobreick, B. (1990). *Jahresstatistik 1989 der ambulanten Beratungs- und Behandlungsstellen für Suchtkranke in der Bundesrepublik Deutschland*, Band 12. Freiburg: Ebis.

WHO (World Health Organization) (1987). *ICD-10, 1987 draft of chapter V — mental, behavioral and developmental disorders.* Genf: WHO.

VII

Approaches to Treatment of Problem Gambling

Treatment Strategies for Problem Gambling: A Review of Effectiveness

Michael B. Walker

Problem gambling, whether it is called compulsive, pathological, or excessive, is one of the social problems in Western societies which is most disruptive to individual well-being and family harmony. Furthermore, whether or not the number of problem gamblers is 2.0%, 1.0% or 0.1% of the adult population, as various writers have argued, there is a continuing need to find effective techniques for treating the numbers of people who have difficulty controlling their gambling.

CRITERIA FOR EVALUATION

The first dimension of the evaluation criteria is the point in time at which programs are evaluated. When claims are made for the effectiveness of a therapy or treatment, some kind of follow-up and statistic for long-term improvement is mandatory. While there is no established period of time for long-term follow-up, a minimum of two years would seem desirable for the treatment of pathological gamblers. For periods of up to one year and longer, the gambler may not gamble because of debts and loss of funds for gambling. Although the gambling debts may persist beyond two years, those debts will be less pressing. Furthermore, control of money in the family is likely to have been placed with the spouse initially. During the first year of abstention, gambling may not have occurred because of a lack of opportunity. After two years, the gambler may have regained some control over money and therefore may be in a position to start gambling again. Thus, the emphasis in this review will be on the maintenance of control over gambling two years after entry into treatment.

Establishing criteria for success is also important. *Successful treatment* means quite different things depending on the rationale and objectives of the therapy and the perspective of the investigator. At one extreme, Gamblers Anonymous regards success as lifelong abstention, and the emphasis, to date, in hospital programs within the United States has been on abstention, although some writers have argued for a more broadly based set of criteria (Franklin and Richardson, 1988). Controlled gambling as a treatment objective is becoming more popular in Europe and fits closely with the theoretical perspective of behavior modification. Recently, Blaszczynski (1988) has provided evidence that controlled gambling, relative to abstinence, is associated with positive indices of mental health. By implication, controlled gambling is a preferable criterion (where control includes abstinence). Finally, at the other extreme, Sartin (1988) has argued that gambling problems are not primarily about control but about losing strategies. By implication, financial criteria are the most appropriate. Since most of the results of therapy reported in the literature are based on the abstinence criterion, abstinence following therapy will be the focus of this review. However, the prospects for controlled gambling as a therapeutic objective will also be examined.

STATUS OF THE MAIN TREATMENTS: A BRIEF SUMMARY

The most widespread resource for problem gamblers is the Gamblers Anonymous organization. Until the 1980s there were very few alternatives to Gamblers Anonymous for gamblers seeking help. However, the period since 1980 has seen the development of a number of hospital-based programs involving various therapeutic techniques. Although the hospital-based approaches have relied heavily on group therapy, a number of programs have also incorporated behavior modification techniques as well. Treatments within a psychodynamic perspective are less common now and rely on the results achieved in an early program by Bergler (1958). The favored treatment of the 1960s, aversion therapy, appears to be less popular now. Finally, there are more unusual methods being used with problem gamblers which may possibly point to new directions in the future for this area of therapy.

A. Gamblers Anonymous

For Gamblers Anonymous members, compulsive gambling is regarded as a disease or illness which is progressive in nature. Gambling will ruin the life of the compulsive gambler unless the gambler can abstain from the activity. The compulsive gambler is different from other gamblers because he or she cannot control the gambling activity once started. A person is never cured of compulsive gambling but, at best, reaches a state of being in which he or she is able to avoid gambling despite the urge to gamble. Complete abstention from gambling is necessary if the compulsive gambler is to survive and build a happy and productive life.

For therapy, Gamblers Anonymous uses the strategies of mutual support, encouragement and holding the gambler to an honest, realistic accounting of his attitudes and behavior (Custer, 1985, p. 272). The compulsive gambler can only stop gambling if he or she makes a voluntary commitment to do so. Thus changes come about by an act of will. However, very few, if any, compulsive gamblers have the strength of purpose, unaided, to keep a commitment to avoid gambling. Regular attendance at Gamblers Anonymous meetings provides the support needed for the compulsive gambler to maintain abstinence.

Gamblers Anonymous supports the commitment to avoid gambling in a number of ways. Fully understanding the impact of one's gambling on the people in the gambler's life will strengthen the resolve not to gamble again. Gamblers Anonymous offers a supportive group context in which the gambler can fully state the extent of his or her gambling and the consequences of it for other people. The telling of personal stories of involvement in gambling is called *therapy.* By regularly retelling their stories, members strengthen their resolve not to gamble.

Gambling is a consequence of the urge to gamble. In order to avoid gambling, the gambler must be continually vigilant to recognize and cope with urges to gamble. One technique to cope with the urge to gamble is to immediately telephone another member. The commitment to avoid gambling must be renewed on a daily basis. Long term members of Gamblers Anonymous report that the urge to gamble again is always present and, even twenty years on, the need to take each day one at a time remains (Harry P., 1983).

Meetings focus on the twelve steps to recovery which are based on those used by Alcoholics Anonymous. Contemplation of the twelve steps strengthens the resolve not to gamble. Meetings also focus on the repayment of debts. In carrying out a plan for repayment, the gambler has overt evidence of his or her continuing resolve not to gamble.

The only major attempt at this time (1990), to evaluate the effectiveness of Gamblers Anonymous was the recent study of drop-outs and continuers in Britain by R. Iain F. Brown (Brown, 1985, 1986, 1987a, 1987b, 1987c). Brown made use of the fact that Gamblers Anonymous, unlike Alcoholics Anonymous, keeps minutes of each meeting showing who attended. In a retrospective study of three groups, Brown analyzed the minutes for a five year period. In all there were 232 new members in that period. Table 1 shows the lengths of time over which new members attended.

TABLE 1

Number of % attending for varying lengths of time		
Category of attendance	*Number*	*Percentage*
Only one meeting	52	22
2-9 meetings	109	47
10 - < one year pin	29	13
on - two year pin	4	2
still attending	38	16
		(From Brown 1985, p. 265)

The majority of new attenders (69%) dropped out after attending less than ten meetings. We do not know how many of these returned to gambling — though probably most — or how many began gambling again at a problem level. Brown counts these drop-outs as treatment failures for evaluation purposes, although he acknowledges the unknown status of this group.

Brown set the criterion for maintained improvement as two years of abstinence. With this rather strict criterion, we can ask, how effective was the program? What percentage of new members attain their two-year pin? Brown's figures for those members who potentially could have abstained for two years show that only 15% of the new members were actually awarded their two-year pin.

A 15% success rate is not high. Part of the reason for this low figure is the strict criterion of absence from gambling for two years. Perhaps some of those who leave before reaching the two-year pin do not return to gambling. Perhaps also, some return to gambling but not at the level which had caused them to seek help in the first place. However, this latter possibility is rejected by Gamblers Anonymous which regards compulsive gambling as an ever present threat for the kind of person whom they accept in the first place.

One important point needs to be made concerning the treatment provided by Gamblers Anonymous. Because the organization is voluntary, the cost to the community is negligible. Even if other treatment programs should prove more effective in preventing further pathological gambling, Gamblers Anonymous will remain the cost-effective alternative.

B. Group Psychotherapy

The perceived nature of problem gambling that suggests group psychotherapy is that pathological gambling is a psychological illness with psychological causes. The core aspect of pathological gambling is the inability of the gambler to resist the urge to gamble. The gambling is out of control. Inability to control the urge to gamble is part of a maladaptive personality. These personality traits precede the onset of gambling. Effective therapy will thus involve some change to these maladaptive personality traits. Treatment must not only support the patient's resolve not to gamble again but must help him or her to cope with everyday life. Given that the gambler is in difficulties financially, at home, in his or her employment, in interpersonal relations, and in his or her own psychological stability, it follows that therapy must be tailored to help the gambler deal with the problems in each of these areas.

Therapy must provide opportunities to practice and to learn the rewards of responsibility: acceptance, patience, self-discipline and sensitivity. These are the qualities which the process of group therapy is designed to bring out and foster — as it were, a training ground for tolerance (Spanier, 1987, p. 112).

Group psychotherapy uses group processes to bring about change in behavior and possibly change in the personality of the group members. Conflict within the group is bound to occur. Group therapy allows patients to confront one another about undesirable behavior. Change comes about because the gambler is too insecure to resist group pressure and stand up to group censure. A number of group techniques may be used to facilitate change. These techniques include *spoken autobiography* (Adkins, Taber and Russo, 1987) and *peer counseling*. Spoken autobiography involves a group member telling his or her story and the other members of the group commenting on aspects of the story as they see fit. Peer counseling involves the use of successfully treated pathological gamblers to help the gambler understand the nature of pathological gambling and to provide support through periods of crisis. Group psychotherapy is frequently complemented by individual and marital therapy and by education programs on addiction and health.

TABLE 2

The effectiveness of programs based on group psychotherapy

Centre	*Authors*	*Intake*	*Follow-up*		*Abstaining*	
		N	Period	N	N	%
Brecksville	Russo et al. (1984)	124	6 mth	60	33	
Brecksville	Taber et al.(1987)	66	6 mth	57	32	
Taylor Manor	Franklin et al. (1988)	80	1 yr	77	37	46

Although the success rate of these programs is very high, there are several reasons for caution:

1. Research design. The evaluation of these programs involve only before and after measures and not controlled trials where some gamblers, chosen randomly, receive the treatment program when others do not. The impact of this failure is that we know neither the spontaneous recovery rate nor the recovery rate for a placebo treatment program.

2. Confounding factors in the treatments offered. In both the Taylor Manor program and the Brecksville program, the gamblers are advised to attend

Gamblers Anonymous. Thus the group psychotherapy and its effects is augmented by whatever gains are achieved by attendance at Gamblers Anonymous. Taber, for example, states that: "Clearly, participation in Gamblers Anonymous, which was the primary aftercare resource for these patients, was an important factor in their continued abstinence" (Taber et al., 1987, p. 760).

3. Type of gambler treated. In the Taylor Manor study, it appears that at least 22 gamblers obtained low scores on the finance subscale on admission to the program. These gamblers were thus solvent and sometimes secure financially. This level of financial security is inconsistent with the image of the pathological gambler as someone concerned with getting money from wherever possible in order to have another gamble. A sizable proportion of the gamblers accepted for treatment at Taylor Major do not appear to have had severe gambling problems at the level generally reported by Gamblers Anonymous.

4. Period of abstinence. A six-month or one-year follow-up should not be regarded as conclusive where pathological gambling is concerned. The committed gambler may have to wait considerably longer before he or she is again in a position to resume gambling.

C. Conjoint marital therapy

The rationale for this approach notes that the pathological gambling of the gambler is often used as a defense against the stresses threatening the marriage. The gambler and spouse have worked out mutually dependent roles in a complex game which stabilizes the marriage. At the core of this game is the role of "martyr" for the wife and the "sick, compulsive gambler" for the husband.

Symptoms of pathological gambling must be understood in the larger context of an even more complicated marital symptom and interaction complex. Analogous to the individual intrapsychic dynamics, gambling in the marital relationship also serves the defensive function of stabilizing a pathological marriage at a level of minimal disequilibrium that is mutually tolerable by the marital partners (Boyd and Bolen, 1970, p. 89).

Therapy for the gambler without his or her partner is likely to be ineffective. Therapy must allow both partners to become less defensive and to face the problems in the relationship.

The group psychotherapy offered by Boyd and Bolen (1970) and by Tepperman (1985) differ considerably in structure and content. Boyd and Bolen's approach was exploratory and relatively unstructured whereas Tepperman structured his program around the twelve steps of Gamblers Anonymous. Boyd and Bolen's sessions took place once per week for a year whereas Tepperman held twelve sessions, each investigating the meaning of a different step. Tepperman ran two groups with ten couples in each group whereas Boyd and Bolen ran two groups with four or five couples in each group. However, despite these differences, the general aim was similar: to allow couples to begin working through their problems in a situation where each partner could be less defensive.

Measures of treatment effectiveness are summarized in Table 3.

TABLE 3

The effectiveness of programs based on marital therapy					
Authors	*Intake*	*Follow-up*		*Abstaining*	
	N	period	N	N	%
Boyd and Bolen (1970)	9	1 yr	8	3	37
Tepperman (1985)	20		10	no details given	

Since the same number of subjects dropped out of both the experimental and control groups, it can be concluded that the experimental treatment was not a clear advantage over Gamblers Anonymous alone in preventing a return to gambling. Both the Tepperman and Boyd and Bolen studies highlight a clear need for standardized measures of improvement. "Being near cessation" is difficult to interpret in the Boyd and Bolen study, and in the Tepperman study no statistics are given concerning persistence in attending Gamblers Anonymous and no details are given concerning the time and rate of improvement.

D. Psychoanalysis

From the perspective of psychoanalysis, gambling is but one of the long series of unconsciously self-provoked, self-created, and self-perpetuated, self-damaging tragedies in their lives (Bergler, 1957, p. 128). Psychoanalytic theory has produced not one but several explanations for pathological gambling. Various writers have urged that various early childhood factors are involved. Oral fixation (Maze, 1987), anal and oedipal complexes (cited in Halliday and Fuller, 1974), and masturbation have been linked with compulsive gambling. However, from the point of view of therapy, the most significant account is given by Bergler (1957) and it is Bergler's views which are summarized here.

The important aspect of gambling for the compulsive gambler is the losing and the consequences that follow from losing. Every compulsive gambler gambles for masochistic reasons. All of the overt reasons given by the gambler can be shown to be false: If one is gambling to win, then why continue when losing; and if one is gambling for the excitement or as an escape, then why do it at such a cost.

The explanation for the gambling will be found in the history of the gambler and especially in the childhood relations with parents. The gambler's problems go back primarily to the early relationship with the mother. This relationship is misperceived. When the mother refuses to offer the breast, she is perceived as being malicious. Essentially, the gambler grows up believing that the world is unjust. Time and again in therapy, Bergler exposes his patients as collectors of injustices. Gambling is an effective means of collecting injustice. Failed gambling is bad luck but brings a great deal of antagonism from the gambler's family, especially in the gambler's spouse.

The two main techniques in psychanalytic therapy are the use of *transference* and *resistance* as means to attack and breakdown the neurotic structures on which the patient relies. *Transference* is the name given to the situation in which the patient comes to treat the analyst as an important figure, and the patient uses the same neurotic displays and emotional pressures against him or her as are typical of the relationship with spouse or parent. The patient gains emotional insight into the neurotic behavior through the confrontations with the analyst. *Resistance* refers to the negative feelings brought about in the patient during interactions with the analyst. The analyst tries to upset the neurotic ritualized patterns of the patient. Since these rituals are the basis of the patient's stability, the analyst's words are dangerous and his arguments and assertions are therefore resisted.

Thus, psychanalytic therapy aims to uncover the real reasons for the gambling behavior and to show that the gambler's conscious thoughts about gambling are a cover for more important beliefs and goals. Since these beliefs and goals are unconscious, the gambler will not in general agree with the interpretations of the analyst. However, by showing how the patient uses the same limited range of strategems repeatedly despite their failure and by linking these strategems back to their use in childhood, the analyst hopes to give the patient insight into his or her own unconscious motivations. Once this insight has been obtained, the consciously organized rationalizations of the neurotic behavior become unnecessary. The gambling loses its meaning and its thrill, and the former gambler begins the task of learning new and more adaptive ways of interacting with the world.

According to one observer, "There are certainly no grounds for recommending that a gambler who wants to cease betting should enter psychoanalysis" (Dickerson, 1985, p. 101). The assessment of Bergler's effectiveness in treating compulsive gambling by psychoanalysis is made difficult by the fact that Bergler regards statistics of this kind as unreliable, and because Bergler himself does not provide exact numbers. Thus, the percentages stated in this section must be regarded as only roughly describing the effectiveness of psychoanalysis.

According to Bergler, 60 patients entered analysis and approximately 34 were completely cured of their neurosis, giving a success rate of 57%. This assessment is probably generous since many gamblers had enquired about treatment but only 60 began treatment (see Table 4).

Since Bergler does not give precise figures, it is easy to see that errors of interpretation might occur when assessments are made of his work. It appears that such errors have been made by Brown (1985) and by Blaszczynski (1988) who estimate that approximately 200 gamblers sought help and, of these, 80 entered therapy. These figures appear to misunderstand the intent of Bergler's assertion that 25% of patients were terminated after a four to six week trial period. In order for Bergler's statements to be consistent, these 25% must refer to a proportion of the sixty gamblers entering analysis and not to another group not included in the sixty. Dickerson (1984) provides estimates similar to those in Table 4 although he assumes that three gamblers receiving full analysis were not cured. There appears to be no basis on which to make this assumption.

In evaluating the effectiveness of psychoanalysis for the treatment of compulsive gambling, two problems occur in relation to Bergler's work. First of all, Bergler chose which gamblers were suitable for analysis. Thus, up to 25% of patients were not accepted past the four to six week trial period. By comparison, Gamblers Anonymous and the various hospital programs accept all compulsive gamblers who wish to stop gambling. Nevertheless, over 50% of all gamblers

TABLE 4

The effectiveness of psychoanalysis in the treatment of compulsive gambling. The estimates are based on the report of Bergler (1957).

	Number	% of total
Gamblers seeking treatment	160*	100
Gamblers who enter therapy	60	38
Gamblers discontinuing after 4 weeks	15*	10
Gamblers continuing after trial period	45*	28
Gamblers whose gambling only is cured	11*	7
Gamblers completely cured	34*	21

Note: * indicates that these figures are estimates based on Bergler's statements (Bergler 1957, pp. 128-134) and may be slightly inaccurate.

entering psychoanalysis with Bergler were cured of their neurosis. Secondly, Bergler provides no follow-up data. From the theory it is clear that a patient who is *cured* has no psychological need to gamble. However, we do not know if such gamblers abstained from gambling after the completion of therapy and we have no data concerning possible relapses. The five case studies provided by Bergler all suggest that gambling ceased for good, that the former gamblers did abstain, and that this abstinence from gambling was maintained over a period of years. It seems likely then that the *thirty-odd* gamblers whom Bergler reports as cured were indeed free of gambling for the rest of their lives but, unfortunately, we have no hard evidence on which to base this speculation. Nevertheless, the strength of the evidence presented by Bergler is sufficiently compelling for us to disagree with Dickerson's conclusion that psychoanalysis is ineffective.

Whereas the psychoanalytic perspective views compulsive gambling as a manifestation of a neurotic personality, behavior theories regard gambling as simply behavior which has been acquired by typical learning processes. It follows that gambling behavior can be extinguished by appropriate manipulation of the environment. Pathological gambling is maladaptive behavior which is maintained either by instrumental or classical conditioning. Instrumental conditioning refers to the variable ratio schedule of reinforcements provided by repetitive gambling activities such as occur in betting shops, casinos, and slot machine parlors. Classical conditioning refers to the pairing of the arousal or excitement associated with gambling with the cue structure of the gambling environment.

According to behaviorist accounts of gambling, pathological gambling is simply one extreme of a continuum of gambling behavior. Why one person gambles more than another will follow from a detailed analysis of their respective conditioning histories.

A range of behavioral techniques have been devised for the treatment of gambling problems. In order to extinguish the gambling, both imagined and real reinforcements have been used. Since imaginal procedures are conducted in the hospital or clinical rooms by a therapist talking to the gambler, they are not greatly different from psychotherapy in form. However, where psychotherapy focuses on the broader consequences of the gambling, behavior therapies focus on the details of the gambling behavior itself.

E. Aversion Therapy

Aversion therapy refers to interventions which produce a negative response when the undesired behavior is exhibited. Typically, the gambling behavior is paired with an electric shock. Repeated pairings diminish the pleasure associated with gambling and induce anxiety when the gambling behavior is initiated. Although electric shock is the aversive stimulus most frequently chosen in the treatment of compulsive gambling (Barker and Miller, 1988; Goorney, 1988; Seager, 1970; Cotler, 1971; Koller, 1972; and McConaghy et al., 1983), an intravenous injection of apomorphine, which induces nausea and vomiting, has also been tried with some success (Salzmann, 1982).

The timing of the unpleasant stimulation is very important. The electric shock or other aversive stimulus should immediately precede or be contiguous with the gambling behavior for maximum effectiveness. The aversive stimulus should be terminated when the gambling behavior ceases. Repeated pairings of the aversive stimulus with the gambling behavior induces conditioned aversion to the gambling behavior and associated stimuli.

The cues which elicit the pleasurable sensations and excitement should be located and used to define the times at which to apply the aversive stimulus. Goorney (1968), for example, identified the following events as ones which provided the patient with pleasurable emotions: buying the morning newspaper and making the selections for the day's races; fantasies concerning horses, prices and profits; anticipating and listening to the results of races which were given over radio in the late afternoon; and, where possible, watching the races on television.

Despite the variation in technique from study to study, it is likely that the best assessment of the effectiveness of aversion therapy will come from a summation of the results. However, since no single study appears to have used the therapy under ideal arrangements, it is perhaps fair to say that aversion therapy is at least as effective as the available figures show and may be more effective if used under ideal conditions. Table 5 summarizes the data currently available about the effectiveness of aversion therapy.

TABLE 5

Outcomes for aversion therapy in the treatment of gambling problems

Authors	*Sample*	*Follow-up*	*Abstaining*	*Improved*
Barker & Miller (1968)	3	2 years	1	2
Goorney (1968)	1	1 year	1	—
Seager (1970)*	16	1 to 3 years	5	3
Colter (1971)	1	1 year	—	1
Koller (1972)*	12	½ to 2 years	5	1
McConaghy et al. (1983)*	10	1 year	0	1
Blaszczynski (1988)*	10	2 years	0	1
Total	53		12	9

Note: * indicates studies in which some gamblers could not be followed-up. All such cases are treated as failures in the data given.

Table 5 reveals that the overall success rate for aversion therapy in producing abstention from gambling is about 23%. However, the reliability of this estimate for aversion therapy can be expected to be low. There are several reasons for expecting unreliability. First of all, there is the wide variation in actual techniques used. Secondly, the results obtained by McConaghy et al. (1983) and Blaszczynski (1988) may be inappropriately low because of the major differences between their techniques and the other studies with which they are being summed. Finally, in at least one study (Seager, 1970), the follow-up data is confounded by the availability of psychotherapy as an adjunct and the recommendation that the patients also attend Gamblers Anonymous meetings.

F. In Vivo Desensitization

With this approach, the therapist accompanies the gambler to the betting shop, casino, or slot machine parlor and enables the patient to experience all of the usual cues associated with gambling, but this time without actually gambling. This is probably not as difficult as might be expected because the gambler-patient is likely to have few or no funds with which to make a bet or to play a machine. The procedure might be conducted over a number of sessions and an extended period of time (Greenberg and Rankin, 1982) or repeated once a day for seven consecutive days (Blaszczynski, 1988).

The only controlled trials for in vivo desensitization are those reported by Greenberg and Rankin (1982) working at the Maudsley Hospital in London and Blaszczynski (1988) working at the Prince of Wales Hospital in Sydney, Australia. Table 6 shows the results of those studies.

TABLE 6

The effectiveness of in vivo desensitization		
	(Blaszczynski) in vivo sensitization	(Greenberg & Rankin) in vivo sensitization and behavior counselling
Stopped	2	0
Controlled	4	5
Variable control	—	7
Uncontrolled	4	14
Not known	10	—
Total	20	26
(Data from Blaszczynski (1988), p. 153; Greenberg & Rankin (1982), p. 365)		

Clearly, in vivo desensitization is not highly effective as carried out by either Blaszczynski or by Greenberg and Rankin. An abstention rate of 10% with a further 20% improved is reported by Blaszczynski if failure to contact at the time of the follow-up is counted as no improvement in gambling. Similarly, only 20% of the Greenberg and Rankin sample are exhibiting controlled gambling at the time of follow-up (nine months or more). Perhaps the main reason for the relatively poor showing of in vivo desensitization is that, even if the theoretical basis for treatment is valid, full extinction of the gambling behavior and associated excitement is unlikely to occur with such a short period of time in which extinction trials are held. An over-learned behavior such as gambling may take months or years of trials before it is extinguished.

G. Imaginal Desensitization

The use of imaginal desensitization as a treatment approach for pathological gambling has been pioneered by two Australian workers, Neil McConaghy and Alex Blaszczynski (McConaghy et al., 1983; Blaszczynski, 1985; Blaszczynski, 1988). Recently, Blaszczynski (1988) has completed a controlled test of imaginal desensitization. This is an important study because it is the first controlled comparison of different therapies.

The therapy is undertaken with each gambler being asked to describe scenes associated with gambling. These scenes are then reduced to the core components and rephrased so that they can be suggested to the gambler during therapy. Finally, the ending is changed so that, although the gambler has visualized a range of stimuli associated with gambling, he or she does not in fact complete the behavior. A typical scene is described by McConaghy et al.:

> You are going home from work and know your wife is away. You decide to go to the club and put a few dollars through the poker machines. You enter the club and find a free machine. You are about to put a coin in but feel bored. You leave without gambling (McConaghy et al., 1983, p. 368).

According to McConaghy et al., these instructions will increase the gambler's level of arousal substantially. Thus the imagined scene must be followed immediately by a relaxation procedure. The gambler is taught a relaxation technique based on tensing and relaxing muscles in the arms, legs and face. Following each scene, the gambler employs the relaxation technique and signals to the therapist when relaxation has been achieved. Therapy then proceeds to another scene and the process is repeated. Altogether, four scenes are dealt with in a fifteen minute session. The gambler may have three sessions a day over a short period of time such as a week. It is important to note that the gambling is imaginary and that the scenes are not placed in a hierarchical sequence of increasing arousal levels as would occur in systematic desensitization.

Controlled studies of treatment effectiveness for pathological gambling are rare. In 1988, as a part of his doctoral dissertation, Blaszczynski reported a controlled comparison between imaginal desensitization and a variety of other behavior therapies. Twenty gamblers were randomly allocated to imaginal desensitization or to the alternative treatment in each of six studies:

1. Imaginal desensitization versus aversion therapy;
2. Imaginal desensitization versus aversion therapy;
3. Imaginal desensitization versus relaxation therapy;
4. Imaginal desensitization versus relaxation therapy;
5. Imaginal desensitization versus brief in-vivo exposure; and
6. Imaginal desensitization versus prolonged in-vivo exposure.

It can be seen that this kind of research is hindered substantially by inability to follow-up over extended periods of time. However, for those gamblers who could be followed-up, imaginal desensitization performs better than the alternative therapies; 43% of gamblers receiving imaginal desensitization are known to have improved at follow-up compared with 30% for relaxation therapy, 30% for in vivo exposure, and 10% for aversion therapy.

An interesting aspect of these results is the implications they have for McConaghy's theory of behavioral completion mechanisms. McConaghy predicted that both aversion therapy and imaginal desensitization would be effective in reducing general arousal and thereby enabling the gambler to experience the gambling cues without succumbing. Table 7 shows that aversion therapy was clearly less effective than imaginal desensitization. Such a result does not invalidate the notion of a behavioral completion mechanism, but McConaghy is left with the problem of explaining the large difference in effectiveness for the two therapies.

H. Behavioral Counseling

With behavioral counseling, the basis of change lies in the ability of the therapist, in conjunction with the gambler and other significant people in the gambler's life, to arrange environmental contingencies in such a way that the gambler is less likely to come in contact with gambling venues, less likely to remain gambling when in such environs, and less likely to form relationships among other gamblers. If the opportunity to gamble is severely limited and if other enjoyable activities are arranged to replace gambling, then the rewards from the new activities and the relationships formed with other non-gamblers may be sufficient for the gambler to regain control over his or her life. These positive reinforcements for not gambling can be supported by negative reinforcement made salient in a behavioral contract between the gambler and a significant other (usually, the gambler's spouse).

TABLE 7

Imaginal desensitization versus alternative therapies					
	Original N	*Follow-up N*	*Abstinent*	*Controlled*	*No change*
Imaginal desensitization	60	33	10	16	7
Aversion therapy	20	6	0	2	4
Relaxation therapy	20	14	6	2	6
In-vivo exposure	20	10	2	4	4
(From Blaszczynski 1988, p. 153)					

Typically, the gambler agrees to a limited access to gambling in return for meeting certain obligations. Failure to meet obligations results in withdrawal of the gambling privilege. By meeting obligations, this unfavorable outcome can be avoided.

There is no standard treatment regime and, in fact, very few studies report the details of the behavioral contingencies arranged through counseling. Two single case studies (Dickerson and Weeks, 1979; Rankin, 1982) exemplify the approach. One interesting detail about these studies is that in each case the aim of treatment was control.

Both of these cited treatment programs were successful. At a follow-up fifteen months from the time of referral, Dickerson and Weeks found that all of the controls were still in place. The gambler now placed his own bets but only if time permitted. Marital arguments had decreased but the wife still maintained control over the family income. Even after the elapsed time, the couple still considered such a move too risky. In the case of the gambler treated by Rankin, follow-up was maintained for two years. The controls placed on this gambler were not as restrictive as those reported by Dickerson and Weeks. Perhaps for this reason, there were more relapses by Rankin's gambler.

I. Cognitively based treatment strategies

Cognitive therapies attempt to modify the thought patterns of an individual so that the undesired behavior is no longer triggered. Although a number of case studies can be found which use a variety of cognitive treatments, there appear to be no large scale studies of the kind reported for psychotherapy or behavior therapy.

One cognitive therapy is referred to as "thought stopping." In this case, it is believed that the urge to gamble is experienced as thoughts about gambling. Specifically, gambling behavior follows from the intention to gamble which is expressed in thoughts such as "I'll go down to the club and make some money on the slots." All gambling, whether pathological or not, follows from intentional thoughts. What distinguishes the problem gambler from other gamblers is the frequency of gambling-related thoughts and the extended period over which they are experienced.

As a therapy, the patient typically is instructed to monitor his or her impulses to gamble; when thoughts concerning the possibility of gambling are detected, one or more of a variety of thought-stopping or thought-replacement techniques is instigated. For example, a common thought-stopping routine involves the use of a rubber band on the wrist. When the impulse to gamble is detected, the gambler snaps the rubber band and says aloud, *stop*. The thought about gambling is then replaced by a previously rehearsed alternative. Thus, the gambler might replace, "I'll go down to the club and make some money on the slots," by "I'll go down to the library and borrow a really good thriller." Similarly, the thought, "I am so angry at my wife that I am going to gamble for a few hours," might be replaced by "I certainly am angry at my wife and after I have cooled down I will talk with her about my concerns."

According to Maurer (1985), it is important to include with thought-stopping procedures a range of other techniques to support the intention to cease gambling. First of all, it is important to develop a plan for repaying loans. Secondly, the gambler should learn mood management procedures such as stress management techniques, relaxation training, and self-hypnosis. Maurer has found that spouse involvement is a positive factor in maintaining the involvement of the gambler in the treatment program. Gamblers seen alone typically attend for three or four visits whereas couples average ten visits.

Finally, Maurer recommends attendance at Gamblers Anonymous meetings and marital therapy following the completion of treatment.

A second cognitive strategy is *cognitive restructuring*. "Much of what passes for pathology in gambling is relatively straightforward, mistaken belief that it is possible to win consistently even in games of pure chance" (Baucum, 1985, p. 201). The rationale for cognitive restructuring begins with the assumption that gambling is maintained by irrational thinking and thus treatment of gambling problems should focus on changing the relevant irrational beliefs to beliefs which are consistent with the reality of gambling (Baucum, 1985; Walker, 1985).

Pathological gamblers begin their gambling careers in the same way as other gamblers. However, they believe that they will succeed in making fortune where others fail. It is the strength of the belief that persistence will be rewarded that supports chasing of losses. The extent of the losses cause most of the other problems associated with pathological gambling.

Surprisingly, there does not appear to be a single case reported in the literature where cognitive restructuring has been used in the treatment of pathological gambling. Thus, in this section, one possible treatment strategy based on cognitive restructuring will be described.

The major steps in the successful treatment of gambling problems can be stated as follows:

1. the gambling must stop (whether or not it may be resumed at a later date);
2. alternative activities to gambling initiated or resumed;
3. a plan for repayment of debts must be initiated; and
4. the motivation to gamble must be moderated or eliminated.

Most programs for the treatment of compulsive or pathological gambling would endorse most or all of these steps. The main difference between a treatment strategy based on cognitive restructuring and other therapies is in the implementation of the fourth step. Whereas other treatment approaches may attempt to decondition the excitement attached to gambling, improve the relationship between the gambler and his or her spouse, eliminate character or personality defects, or simply bolster the gambler's resolve to stop gambling, cognitive restructuring attempts to change mistaken beliefs held by the gambler about his or her involvement in gambling.

In order to complete the fourth step, a detailed account of the gambling must be obtained. *Detailed* does not mean the details of frequency, duration, money lost, precipitating factors and so on that might be part of a detailed case history but, rather, the steps, procedures, strategies, rituals, and so on that the gambler employs when gambling. If the gambler is unable to remember or to recount this aspect of the gambling, it may be necessary to accompany him or her on a gambling session. Each form of gambling has its own structure and the therapist will need to be aware of this structure in order to accurately understand the significant features of the gambler's play.

It is possible to foresee some of the strategies the gambler will employ in order to win. These are listed below for slot machines. However, it is important to realize that each gambler may have his or her own special knowledge and that this material must be located anew for each new gambler.

Trying to extract personal slot machine strategies might involve posing the following questions to the gambler:

- Does the gambler have a favorite place and is this related to potential to win?
- Does the gambler have a favorite machine or type of machine?
- Does the gambler have any rituals associated with playing the machine?
- Does the gambler prevent others from playing this machine until he or she has finished with it?
- Does the gambler have any methods of play (for example, always maintain some minimum number of credits in the machine, press quickly for a fast spin, etc.)?
- Does the gambler think that he or she can predict when a big pay-out will occur?

UNUSUAL TREATMENT METHODS FOR GAMBLING PROBLEMS

Possibly because the mainstream treatment approaches have been far from fully effective in dealing with cases of problem gambling, a whole range of methods has arisen based on unusual conceptions of the nature of gambling problems. Some of these methods, such as hypnosis and logotherapy, appear to be similar in technique to methods which have been described earlier.

Hypnosis can be seen as an extreme form of imaginal desensitization whereas logotherapy requires a treatment with many of the behavioral features of satiation therapy. Similarly, the Adlerian approach seeks to uncover the hidden agenda of the gambler in much the same way as classical Freudian psychoanalysis. More unusual are methods such as win therapy, which seeks to transform "bad" gamblers into "good" gamblers, and brief therapy, which uses a form of "reverse psychology" to undermine the gambling behavior.

A. Hypnotherapy

There appears to be only one reference to the treatment of compulsive gambling by hypnosis (Griffiths, 1982). However, since this was a case where the gambling problems had become severe and where the therapy was spectacularly successful, it is important that the approach be considered.

The theory behind the use of hypnosis is similar to that explained for imaginal desensitization. It is assumed that the gambling is maintained by the excitement associated with the action of gambling. This excitement can be lessened or removed by hypnotic suggestion.

Griffith employed hypnosis based on eye-fixation with progressive relaxation and deepening procedures. He reports that the patient was a good subject for hypnosis, a statement which immediately raises the question of how widely applicable hypnotherapy would be in general.

The patient was a thirty-six year old man who had had a lifelong problem with gambling. At the time of treatment he was threatened by divorce, heavily in debt, pursued by creditors, and threatened by criminal charges. He received one session of therapy which aimed at deconditioning the excitement associated with gambling and rekindling the excitement associated with other activities. A second "reinforcement" session was the last received. At this final session the patient had lost all interest in gambling. No follow-up details are given but for the statement that, "Since this final session, no recurrence of the symptom has been seen to date."

B. Logotherapy

The technique of logotherapy is suggested by the following quote: "The neurotic who learns to laugh at himself may be on the way to self-management, perhaps to cure" (Allport, 1956). Anticipatory anxiety is a problem frequently encountered by people. Anticipatory anxiety may be experienced before important events such as examinations, speeches, and performances. This anxiety can be so intense as to threaten the ability of the person to complete the activity. Anticipatory anxiety becomes maladaptive when it brings about the failure which the person most fears. Pathological gambling may be an example of maladaptive anticipatory anxiety.

Frankl (1967) invented a technique, which he called paradoxical intentions, which would dissipate anticipatory anxiety. The technique involves instructing the client to exhibit the symptoms at their strongest level rather than trying to inhibit them. Victor and Krug (1967) report a case in which paradoxical intentions were used to treat compulsive gambling. The treatment consisted of the instruction to gamble for three hours and then to record the details in a diary. The patient was required to gamble each day. At the end of three weeks the patient had lost all of his ready money. The therapist suggested he sell his watch or a picture so that he could continue and instructed that as soon as he had the cash he was to let the therapist know and to resume gambling.

At the time at which the Victor and Krug paper was written, the gambler had abstained from gambling for "several months" (details not supplied). There was one notable exception to his loss of interest in gambling: He took a large bet of $700 with a gambling friend that he would not be seen again in the gambling joints!

C. Minimal interventions

Minimal intervention refers to any treatment of a problem which requires considerably less time from a therapist than is typically needed by psychotherapy. One of the main forms of minimal intervention is the self-help manual. With the aid of the manual the client becomes his or her own therapist.

With this treatment, pathological gambling is seen as essentially a failure of self-control. Self-control can be regained by practicing good behavioral management such as avoiding cues which invite participation in gambling and by becoming involved in alternative activities. Behavioral management of this kind can be specified in a manual. One additional benefit deriving from the use of a manual is that the problem gambler can attribute the success in gaining control over gambling to his or her own efforts. This would be a basis for increased self-esteem.

A self-help manual for people with gambling problems has been developed by Dickerson in Australia (Allcock and Dickerson, 1986; Dickerson, 1987). The manual is modelled on the one for drinking problems used by Robertson and Heather and provides advice under five headings:

1. Who is this manual for?;
2. Why do I gamble?;
3. How can I cut back?;
4. How can I stop gambling?; and
5. The future.

The manual allows the gambler to choose whether abstinence or controlled gambling is the goal. If the goal is control then the advice focuses on ways to limit the time and money spent on gambling, the need to maintain an accurate record of the gambling, thinking accurately about gambling expectations, and rewarding oneself for maintaining control over the gambling. Advice is also given about actual gambling behavior which is more controlled and therefore less dangerous financially.

Slightly different advice is offered if the goal is to stop gambling altogether. Most importantly, access to cash must be controlled. Wages must be collected by someone else or be paid straight into a bank account; withdrawal of money should depend on two signatures; only limited sums of cash should be kept in the house; and so on. Particularly in relation to access to money, it is important to have someone else involved.

Another important area is involvement in other activities. Since problem gambling typically absorbs most of one's free time each week, it is important to become involved in other activities that will enable attention and energy to be directed away from gambling. The use of relaxation techniques is advised as a way of keeping the gambling urge under control and the gambler should avoid things and places that might trigger the urge to gamble.

How effective is a self-help manual in dealing with problem gambling? Dickerson has reported on the characteristics of fifty problem gamblers who have received the self-help manual. The average losses for this group amounted to $30,000 per year. Gambling sessions typically lasted two hours or more and occurred on average three to five times per week.

Unfortunately, Dickerson has not published follow-up data to show what level of control or abstinence has been achieved by his program. Nevertheless, we should not have unrealistically high expectations for this approach. Its strength lies in the low costs involved. However, pathological gamblers may need more support in their endeavors to control their gambling than can be given in a self-help manual. Furthermore, although advice is given to think rationally about gambling, habitual gamblers may need persuasion that the expectations for gambling given in the manual apply in their particular case.

D. Brief therapy

Brief therapy does not refer to minimal intervention of the kind proposed by Dickerson. Although the one case study published required only two treatment sessions with the spouse of the gambler — and thus the therapy was brief in duration when compared to many other approaches — brief therapy refers to a specific theoretical base (Fisch, Weakland and Segal, 1982). According to the theory, problems such as compulsive gambling are interactional in nature and not individual. The central theme in relation to problems such as compulsive gambling is that the gambling problem is being maintained by the very same actions that the spouse or other significant persons are using to try and reduce or stop the gambling.

For example, the problems that arise between a husband and wife over gambling stem from their opposed views about what is happening. The wife views her husband's behavior as destructive and tries to make him realize this. The more she tries to make him stop, the harder he tries to prove he is right. The more he gambles, the more he loses. And the more he loses, the harder she tries to make him stop. Thus the two individuals are involved in an escalation of conflict. The financial problems that arise from heavy gambling are real but the more that the wife or significant other tries to stop the gambler from gambling, the worse the problem becomes.

Since the problem is interactional rather than located solely in the gambler, treatment can be effected through the spouse or significant other. In a case described by Walker (1985), the wife of the gambler tries without success to have her husband stop gambling. Significant features of her account include her belief that her husband will never change, that he will always be able to deceive her, but that she loves him and does not want to leave him. Therapy was built around a change in the central theme of the wife's interactions with her husband. Whereas previously she had used the approach, "You must change," she was encouraged now to use the approach, "You cannot change."

Her attitude to her husband was to be one of resigned acceptance of her husband's "incurable" condition. She was to behave as if hiding a great sadness behind a brave smile. In this way, the interactions between them could be changed dramatically and, if gambling has been maintained by the wife's efforts to make it stop, then the basis for gambling would have been removed and a decrease in gambling would be expected.

In the case reported by Walker, the husband reacted to the change, in his relationship with his wife, with indignation. He believed that the counseling received by his wife would be useless since there was nothing wrong with him. The wife pointed out that his response was exactly what people with this problem typically would say. Her sadness distressed him because this was exactly what he had been trying to prevent. He was told that regardless of what he might say, it was impossible for him to change. As you might expect, the husband was very angry with the counseling his wife had received. To prove he was right, the husband stopped gambling.

At a six-month follow-up, the husband was still not gambling. The wife was to report that the therapist was surprised though inflexible in his attitude. By eighteen months there appeared to have been no relapse.

Perhaps the most worrying criticism of brief therapy is that many gamblers would rejoice in and take advantage of the spouse's change of attitude. It may be the case that many heavy gamblers desire resigned acceptance by their spouse. Of course, this point of view challenges the central assertion of brief therapy that the gambling is being maintained by the attempts of the spouse to have it stop.

E. Win therapy

According to Sartin (1988), the real pathology in pathological gambling is loss of money — not an obsessive-compulsive personality, not a defective relationship with the spouse, and not a disease from which the gambler will never fully recover. Sartin's view of pathological gambling leads to a radically different approach to treatment. Win therapy has the straightforward aim of converting losing gamblers into winning gamblers.

Win therapy applies to horse racing and not to other forms of gambling. The gambler contracts to avoid gambling again until he or she has received sufficient training in handicapping. The details of the handicapping methods are not supplied by Sartin although he has indicated that furlong times (the speed with which a horse completes each furlong in a race) play a central role (Sartin, 1984). When a losing gambler has mastered the methods of handicapping, he or she can now proceed to gamble with less risk.

Sartin reports having treated 1387 gamblers by win therapy. Only 1.8% of the gamblers appear to have a pathology that goes beyond the fact of losing and the consequences that follow. Seventy-two percent of the sample have been able to resume gambling in a healthy, profitable way. A further six percent resumed gambling but relapsed into heavy, losing gambling and are counted as failures. The remainder of the sample were still in training at the time of the Seventh International Conference on Gambling and Risk Taking in Reno in 1987, at which Sartin's study was presented. Sartin offers no follow-up data other than to state that, in relation to the successful group, "Under regular monitoring they continue to manifest a healthy psychological protocol" (Sartin, 1988, p. 367).

If the criterion for effective treatment of pathological gambling is long-term abstinence, then Win Therapy can be seen to be quite ineffective. However, with regard to this, Sartin's view is clear:

> Like most psychiatrists, I have done a lot of work with patients/clients with behavioral manifestations that are rooted in sexual problems characterized by "Disorders of impulse control." Were I, or any other practitioner, to prescribe ABSTINENCE in lieu of cure for such problems, I would be laughed out of practice by patients and peers alike (Sartin, 1988, p. 383).

ABSTINENCE OR CONTROL AS THE GOAL OF TREATMENT

According to the doctrine of Gamblers Anonymous, control as a treatment goal for compulsive gambling is an absurdity. Since the compulsive gambler cannot control his or her urges to gamble, controlled gambling is a contradiction of terms. The unacceptability of controlled gambling as a treatment goal is endorsed by most groups working within the medical model of pathological gambling. However, it can be seen that for many programs, control and abstinence are equally valid alternatives (see, for example, behavior therapy or minimal intervention) and that for some approaches, controlled gambling is the only acceptable goal (as is the case for win therapy). Furthermore, the abstinence rate at follow-up declines rapidly as the period of time to follow-up increases from six months to two years.

Table 8 shows figures derived from the reports of major programs treating pathological gambling with abstention as the major criterion for success. The major omissions from Table 8 are the results of the studies published by: Greenberg and Rankin (1982) where the aim appears to have been control rather than abstention; Sartin (1988) where the aim was re-education rather than abstention; and a number of studies where the follow-up data has not yet been published in full (this includes the work of Blackman, Simone and Thoms, 1986 and Dickerson, 1987).

TABLE 8

Comparison of the effectiveness as measured by abstinence of four treatment approaches to pathological gambling

Broad therapeutic strategy follow-up	*Study reported by*	*Gamblers treated* N	*Percentage abstaining from gambling at* 6 months	1 year	2 years
Gamblers Anonymous	Brown	114	—	—	15
Psychotherapy	Taber et al.	66	48		
	Franklin et al.; Russo et al.	204	—	31	—
Psychoanalysis	Bergler	60	75	—	—
Behavior therapy	Mixed	53	—	23	—
	Blaszczynski; Barker & Miller	93	—	—	14

High rates of abstention are reported six months after the completion of treatment although the 75% cited for psychoanalysis may be inflated by an undisclosed number of gamblers who were seen but not accepted into analysis and by the fact that systematic follow-ups were not reported by Bergler. Thus, a best guess of effectiveness of treatment generally after six months have elapsed is about 50%. One year after completion of treatment, the abstinence rate has fallen to approximately 29% and by the two-year follow-up, abstinence has dropped further to about 15%.

While a decline in abstinence rates would be expected as the period since treatment increases, the rapid decline shown by these figures suggests that the long term effectiveness of treatment for pathological gambling is low independent of the type of treatment offered. There are three possible explanations for the rapid decline in abstention from gambling following treatment:

1. Pathological gambling is an illness from which most people so afflicted do not recover. Gambling may cease for a time, but unless vigilance is maintained, possibly for the rest of one's life, a relapse is very likely to occur and to reoccur. This explanation is essentially the view of Gamblers Anonymous.

2. Treatments reviewed do not deal with the central cause of gambling problems. Most pathological gamblers cannot continue gambling after treatment because they have no money with which to do so. However, many of the gamblers treated are simply serving time until they can again try their luck. The decline in abstention occurs because eventually most gamblers will reach a financial position where they can again begin to gamble. It is the contention of this analysis that the neglected factor in the treatment of pathological gamblers is the irrational thinking which gamblers use in the gambling activity.

3. Abstention from gambling is an unrealistic goal. In areas such as the United States of America and Western Europe, most people gamble at some time each year and gambling is widely promoted as a recreational activity. Gambling itself is not pathological. Therefore, the problem which everyone faces when gambling is self-control. Thus, the objective of treatment should be controlled gambling and not abstaining from gambling altogether. With control as the criterion, many of the treatments reviewed will be seen to be highly effective.

The following discussion compares treatment strategies again but with controlled gambling as the criterion rather than the absence of gambling. Table 9 shows the reported rates of controlled gambling for the treatment programs reviewed. Controlled gambling includes all levels of gambling that are no longer a problem to the person involved and therefore includes abstention from gambling.

There are several observations to be made about the data entered in Table 9. First of all, some gamblers have been followed up after a greater period than two years; this applies in particular to the studies conducted by Blaszczynski (1988). Secondly, what counts as controlled gambling is not well defined.

TABLE 9

Comparison of the effectiveness as measured by controlled gambling of different treatment approaches to pathological gambling

Broad therapeutic strategy	*Study reported by*	*Date*	*Gamblers treated*	*Number in control of their gambling after*		
			N	6 mths	1 year	2 years
Gamblers Anonymous	Brown	1987	114			17
		Total	*114*			*15%*
Psychotherapy	Russo et al.	1984	124		46	
	Franklin & Richardson	1988	80		54	
	Taber et al.	1987	66	38		
	Bolen & Boyd	1968	10	8		
		Total	*280*	*60%*	*49%*	
Psychoanalysis	Bergler	1958	60	45		
		Total	*60*	*75%*		
Behavior therapy	Blaszczynski	1988	120			42
	Barker & Miller	1968	3			3
	Rankin	1982	1			1
	Seager	1970	16		8	
	Aversion case studies		2		2	
	Dickerson and Weekes	1979	1		1	
	Greenberg & Rankin	1982	26	12		
	Koller	1972	12	6		
	Peck and Ashcroft	1972	5	4		
		Total	*186*	*51%*	*58%*	*37%*
Cognitive therapy	Bannister	1977	1		1	
Brief therapy	Walker	1985	1		1	
Win therapy	Sartin	1988	1387	999		
Hypnotherapy	Griffiths	1982	1	1		
Logotherapy	Victor and Krug	1967	1	1		
	Grand total control	*6 months*	*1568*	*72*		
		1 year	*225*	*50*		
		2 years	*237*	*27*		

For example, it is not immediately clear what is meant, in relation to gambling, by terms such as: "markedly reduced" (McConaghy et al., 1983); "variable control" (Greenberg and Rankin, 1982); and, "binge gambling" (Franklin and Richardson, 1988). Thirdly, where follow-ups occurred over different periods of time — for example six months to two years for Koller (1972) — all the results are placed at the shorter end of the range. Finally, the overall figures are heavily biased by two results: Brown (1987) for Gamblers Anonymous and Sartin (1988) for Win Therapy. The data for Gamblers Anonymous does not include the unknown number of former G.A. members who returned to controlled gambling but did not continue attending meetings. Thus the 15% figure for Gamblers Anonymous is undoubtedly an underestimate with respect to a criterion of controlled gambling. Sartin's large sample dominates the data for the six-month follow-up. However, the figure for the early follow-up fortunately remains constant at 72% whether or not Sartin's data is included.

Table 10 reveals that the same rapid decline in controlled gambling is evident that was observed for the abstinence criterion in Table 8. The high level of controlled gambling after six months (72%) drops to 50% after one year and to 27% after two years. However, if the Gamblers Anonymous data are omitted, on the grounds that they may be a serious underestimate of reality, then the level of controlled gambling after two years is 37%. Thus, although the picture remains unclear, there is weak evidence that controlled gambling may be maintained in as many as one in three pathological gamblers receiving treatment. Again, this level of success is no basis for satisfaction.

TABLE 10

Summary of treatment effectiveness with control as the criterion

Broad Therapeutic Strategy	*Gamblers treated*	*Number in control of their gambling after*			*% in control of their gambling after*		
	N	6 mths	1 year	2 years	6 mths	1 year	2 years
Gamblers Anonymous	114			17			15
Psychotherapy	204		100			49	
	76	46			60		
Psychoanalysis	60	45			75		
Behavior therapy	124		46				37
	19		11			58	
	43	22			51		
Win therapy	1387	999			72		
Case studies	4	2	2				
Totals					**72**	**50**	**27**

REFERENCES

Adkins, B.J., Taber, J.I. and Russo, A.M. (1985). The spoken autobiography: A powerful tool in group psychotherapy. *Social Work*, 435-439.

Allcock, C.C. and Dickerson, M.G. (1986). *The guide to good gambling*. Australia: Social Sciences Press.

Barker, J.C. and Miller, M. (1966). Aversive therapy for compulsive gambling. *Lancet*, February 26:1, 491-492.

Barker, J.C. and Miller, M. (1968). Aversion therapy for compulsive gambling. *The Journal of Nervous and Mental Disease*, 146, 285-302.

Baucum, D. (1985). Arguments for self-controlled gambling as an alternative to abstention. In W.R. Eadington (ed.), *The Gambling Studies:*

Proceedings of the Sixth National Conference on Gambling and Risk Taking, 5, 199-204. Reno, NV: University of Nevada, Reno.

Bergler, E. (1970). *The Psychology of Gambling*. London: International Universities Press. (First published in New York: Hill and Wang, 1957).

Blackman, S., Simone, R.V. and Thoms, D.R. (1986). Treatment of gamblers. *Hospital and Community Psychiatry*, 37, 404.

Blaszczynski, A.P. (1985). A winning bet: Treatment for compulsive gambling. *Psychology Today*, 19, 38-46.

Blaszczynski, A.P. (1988). Doctoral Dissertation. University of New South Wales.

Boyd, W.H. and Bolen, D.W. (1970). The compulsive gambler and spouse in group psychotherapy. *International Journal of Group Psychotherapy*, 20, 77-90.

Brown, R.I.F. (1985). The effectiveness of gamblers anonymous. In W.R. Eadington (ed.), *The Gambling Studies: Proceedings of the Sixth National Conference on Gambling and Risk Taking*, 5, 258-284. Reno, NV: University of Nevada, Reno.

Brown, R.I.F. (1987). Dropouts and continuers in Gamblers Anonymous: Part 2. Analysis of free-style accounts of experiences with GA. *Journal of Gambling Behavior*, 3, 68-79.

Brown, R.I.F. (1987). Dropouts and continuers in Gamblers Anonymous: Part 3. Some possible specific reasons for dropout. *Journal of Gambling Behavior*, 3, 137-151.

Brown, R.I.F. (1987). Dropouts and continuers in Gamblers Anonymous: Part 4. Evaluation and summary. *Journal of Gambling Behavior*, 3, 202-210.

Cotler, S.B. (1971). The use of different behavioral techniques in treating a case of compulsive gambling. *Behavior Therapy*, 2, 579-584.

Cromer, G. (1978). Gamblers anonymous in Israel: A participant observation study of a self-help group. *The International Journal of the Addictions*, 13, 1069-1077.

Custer, R.L. and Milt, H. (1985). *When Luck Runs Out*. New York: Warner Books.

Dickerson, M.G. (1983). *A self-help guide to people wanting to stop or cut-back on the amount they spend on gambling.* Paper presented at a one-day seminar, Rozelle Hospital.

Dickerson, M.G. (1984). *Compulsive gamblers.* London: Longman.

Dickerson, M.G. and Weekes, D. (1979). Controlled gambling as a therapeutic technique for compulsive gamblers. *Journal of Behavior Therapy and Experimental Psychiatry*, 10, 139-141.

Frankl, V.E. (1967). *Psychotherapy and Existentialism.* Middlesex, England: Penguin.

Franklin, J. and Richardson, R. (1988). A treatment outcome study with pathological gamblers: Preliminary findings and strategies. In W.R. Eadington (ed.), *Gambling Research: Proceedings of the Seventh International Conference on Gambling and Risk Taking*, 5, 392-407. Reno, NV: University of Nevada, Reno.

Goorney, A.B. (1968). Treatment of a compulsive horse race gambler by aversion therapy. *British Journal of Psychiatry*, 114, 329-333.

Greenberg, D. and Rankin, H. (1982). Compulsive gamblers in treatment. *British Journal of Psychiatry*, 140, 364-366.

Griffiths, F.V. (1982). A case of compulsive gambling treated by hypnosis. *International Journal of Clinical and Experimental Hypnosis*, 30, 195.

Koller, K.M. (1972). Treatment of poker-machine addicts by aversion therapy. *The Medical Journal of Australia*, 1, 742-745.

McConaghy, N., Armstrong, M.S., Blaszczynski, A. and Allcock, C. (1983). Controlled comparison of aversive therapy and imaginal desensitization in compulsive gambling. *British Journal of Psychiatry*, 142, 366-372.

Maurer, C.D. (1985). An outpatient approach to the treatment of pathological gambling. In W.R. Eadington (ed.), *The Gambling Studies: Proceedings of the Sixth National Conference on Gambling and Risk Taking*, 5, 205-217. Reno, NV: University of Nevada, Reno.

Russo, A.M., Taber, J.I., McCormick, R.A. and Ramirez, L.F. (1984). An outcome study of an inpatient treatment program for pathological gamblers. *Hospital and Community Psychiatry*, 35, 823-827.

Salzmann, M.M. (1982). Treatment of compulsive gambling. *British Journal of Psychiatry*, 141, 318-219.

Sartin, H.G. (1988). Win therapy: An alternative diagnostic and treatment procedure for problem gamblers. In W.R. Eadington (ed.), *Gambling Research: Proceedings of the Seventh International Conference on Gambling and Risk Taking*, 5, 365-390. Reno, NV: University of Nevada, Reno.

Seager, C.P. (1970). Treatment of compulsive gamblers by electrical aversion. *British Journal of Psychiatry*, 117, 545-553.

Spanier, D. (1987). *Easy Money: Inside the Gambler's Mind.* London: Secker and Warburg.

Taber, J.I., McCormick, R.A., Russo, A.M., Adkins, B.J. and Ramirez, L.F. (1987). Follow-up of pathological gamblers after treatment. *American Journal of Psychiatry*, 144, 757-761.

Taber, J.I. and Chaplin, M.P. (1988). Group psychotherapy with pathological gamblers. *Journal of Gambling Behavior*, 4, 183-196.

Tepperman, J.H. (1985). The effectiveness of short-term group therapy upon the pathological gambler and wife. In W.R. Eadington (ed.), *The Gambling Studies: Proceedings of the Sixth National Conference on Gambling and Risk Taking*, 5, 185-198. Reno, NV: University of Nevada, Reno.

Walker, G. (1985). The brief therapy of a compulsive gambler. *Journal of Family Therapy*, 7, 1-8.

Problem Gaming: Any Business of a Casino?

Gary J. Scrimgeour

In 1989, for the first time in American history, a major casino corporation moved to recognize, and to operationally address, the addictive behavior known as problem gambling. This effort, undertaken by Harrah's Hotels and Casinos, raises interesting and practical questions:

- Should a leisure industry be concerned about the abusers of its product among customers and employees?
- Won't a casino lose money by discouraging the custom of problem gamblers? and
- Is it any business of a casino whether anyone is a problem gambler or not?

To answer these questions, Harrah's President, Phil Satre, appointed an Employee Task Force and provided it with a consultant in the social control of addictive behavior. In brief he said he wanted to know whether Harrah's should do something about problem gambling, and if so, what. The Task Force met for a year and came up with numerous findings and recommendations.

Their answers to the above questions were clear and unqualified:

- Yes, problem gambling does affect all aspects of a casino's business: often in unexpected ways and with more cost than profit.
- No, a casino will make rather than lose money by discouraging problem gamblers among employees and customers.
- And yes, it is very much a casino's business to know whether a person is a problem gambler or not.

In sum, it is in a corporation's self-interest to acknowledge problem gambling.

THE TASK FORCE

The members of the Task Force (which continues to function) are all middle managers; that is, those who supervise many people and who are in constant touch with the customers. They showed their expertise at the first meeting in four crucial matters.

First, they all agreed that problem gaming affects all of a casino's operations. Most significant, they said that line employees and their managers already routinely try to prevent customers from suffering the worst consequences of their problem gambling. The employees' only doubt, they said, is whether the corporation approves of their intervening with customers.

Second, they all agreed that problem gamblers are a measurable proportion among three different groups: customers, employees, and employees' families. They agreed intervention should occur with all three groups. They all strongly urged that intervention with customers be extremely cautious and not moralistic.

Third, they agreed that casinos should not espouse either a soft or a moralistic approach to problem gambling. Because they were dealing with a business environment, they had to make it functionally easy for any employee to determine whether any behavior is or is not a problem. They began to formulate their own definition of problem gambling. Eventually it would become as follows:

> "Problem gambling is that casino gaming behavior which both (a) has elements of compulsiveness, and (b) interferes with business operations or employee performance."

Fourth, they all saw a single major reason for a casino corporation to respond to problem gaming: good business now and in the future. With the expansion of lotteries during the 1980s, problem gambling became a widespread public issue. If the casino industry is to expand to during the 1990s, it will have to anticipate this concern when new geographical areas make decisions. Respectability and responsibility will be key words. In other words, they saw "market positioning" as a major advantage to the effort, well in line with Harrah's reputation as a corporate good citizen.

The seven Task Force members undertook to discuss these four issues with other employees to validate or correct their own opinions. Since they came from all five Harrah's properties in two states (Nevada and New Jersey), they were well positioned to question anybody, from the General Manager to line employees.

This process continued throughout the year over which the Task Force met. They also interviewed members of Gamblers Anonymous, treatment experts, the Nevada Council on Compulsive Gambling, security personnel, collections agents, and others.

The kind of questions which the Task Force raised give an idea of its scope. Here are some examples:

- Were lawsuits by compulsive gamblers a major reason for the corporation being responsible in this area? (Answer: Not at Harrah's, and not so far, despite their increasing frequency.)
- What proportions of customers and employees are problem gamblers? (Answer: This is unknown but the incidence is significant and should be investigated by experts.)
- Can we trace specific expenditures and losses to problem gamblers? (Answer: Very clearly, especially in credit operations, collections, and employee theft.)
- Are high rollers problem gamblers? (Answer: Not in terms of the Task Force definition.)
- Do problem gamblers contribute a substantial proportion of the income of casinos? Do casinos actively encourage problem gaming? Would they be smart to encourage more problem gaming? (Answers: A resounding "no" in each case).

- Do certain policies or practices toward employees encourage problem gaming amongst them and their families? (Answer: Clearly, yes.)

Many other questions did not lend themselves to a yes or no answer. Here are some examples:

- Should casinos ignore problem gambling among their customers but counteract it among their employees, or should they proceed more or less equally against both, and if so, how? And if not, how not?
- Do some specific kinds of gaming encourage problem gaming among certain social groups and if so, what should the corporation do?
- Since gaming is a leisure industry, whose customers like the freedom, the risk, and the element of chance, can the industry legitimately regulate them or save them from themselves?
- Do existing state regulations mandate a response to problem gaming?
- What policies or procedures should the corporation clearly avoid?

After a year of steady work, the Task Force submitted a report containing detailed recommendations, most of which were very specific. All of these recommendations have been accepted by senior managers and are currently being implemented in all Harrah's properties. Implementation is slowly but steadily resulting in many changes within corporate practices. In other words, the Task Force met with success when its recommendations were screened by the business people who operate casinos on a daily basis.

IMPLICATIONS FOR THE CASINO INDUSTRY

This success leads to some observations useful to other casino corporations. First, wherever they seek to expand, casinos must respond to the probable charge that their presence will increase problem gaming in that area. Especially in a current social climate that disapproves of all kinds of compulsive behavior, gaming will be more closely scrutinized than ever before. The industry must make a real and not a token response to the charge if it is to expand.

Second, there is plenty of room for choice as to what a corporation does about problem gambling. In some jurisdictions, regulations mandate attention to it. In others, nobody cares. It is clear that casinos should take certain steps, and that they may take others if they wish. Equally, they would be well-advised to avoid certain policies or procedures.

Third, self-regulation is the alternative to state regulation. As the tobacco and liquor industries have discovered, willful blindness to the dangers associated with a product invites a strong outside reaction which includes decline in the use of the product.

Fourth and finally, taking issue with problem gambling makes good business sense. Problem gaming costs the casino industry significant money, probably much greater sums than are known. The dilemma is how to cultivate responsibility and common sense without becoming moralistic. The solution lies in careful attention to details.

Whenever an industry or a corporation sets out to deal with any problem of compulsive personal behavior, it is sailing into dangerous waters. Whether facing drug use, alcohol abuse, poor health practices, or gaming, it is contesting deeply held personal beliefs which result in ingrained behavior that individuals find highly pleasurable.

In this regard, the President of Harrah's had an observation. "We must proceed very carefully in this area," he said. "In particular, we must say exactly what we do and do exactly what we say." This is an observation with which the Task Force found itself in very strong agreement and offers as essential advice to any interested corporation.

Control of problem gambling will never be achieved by a single casino corporation. Even strong state control finds the job difficult. Eventually (and soon) state and private controls will combine in some way and have already done so in other countries besides the United States. This makes specially interesting the Employee Task Force's clear opinion that there is no downside to a responsible approach by a casino to problem gambling undertaken with caution and tact. That advice suggests the way is open for a mutually beneficial and negotiated approach by the industry and its regulators.

The Selective Adaptation of the Alcoholics Anonymous Program by Gamblers Anonymous©

Basil R. Browne

In the 1980s there has been a dramatic increase in support groups. Levoy (1989) and Leerhsen, et al. (1990) report 500,000 weekly meetings attended by 15 million people in the United States. "In the last 10 years, the number of these self-help organizations has quadrupled, and the topics they cover have been expanded . . ." (Leerhsen, 1990, p. 50). A major form of support group is twelve-step recovery programs, the model for which is Alcoholics Anonymous; this article will focus on only this form of support group. The terms self-help and mutual-aid are used interchangeably with support groups.

© A revised version of this article has been published in the *Journal of Gambling Studies* (1991), 7(3), 187-206. New York: Human Sciences Press. Permission to reprint has been granted by the author and publisher.

A popular belief is that all twelve-step programs are basically the same. This assumption is also made in the academic community; Preston and Smith (1985), for example, argue that:

> "With minor alterations and adjustments, the G.A. program is the same as that of A.A.. The 'Unity Program' is exactly as the '12 Traditions' of A.A. while changes in the '12 Steps' of the program of recovery may be more a reflection of the time in which they were written than any conscious deviation" (Preston and Smith, 1985, p. 99).

Although some twelve-step programs develop their own materials, most twelve-step programs use Alcoholic Anonymous materials such as the *A.A. Big Book* and merely substitute their particular addiction for alcohol or alcoholism while using that material. This is not the case with Gamblers Anonymous' adaptation. Others, Lesieur (1990) for example, have pointed to some differences between A.A. and G.A. and to some of the negative implications of those differences. Lesieur (1990) argues:

> "First, it would be easy to believe that GA is a clone of AA. However, those who are familiar with AA will notice that the Twelve Steps are different in GA. God and spirituality are de-emphasized in GA's steps and in the overall program, and the Lord's Prayer is not said at the end of each meeting. One consequence is that there are fewer step meetings in GA, which, in the author's experience, works to the detriment of GA members because it is typically at step meetings that members of self-help groups come to express their feelings. (In GA, old-timers who have not been to step meetings frequently still appear to be "big shots.") Thus, some GA groups, especially those whose GA members also belong to AA, tend to hold more step meetings and discuss feelings" (Lesieur, 1990, p. 242).

Unlike Preston and Smith (1985) who see A.A. and G.A. as basically the same, but much more forceful than Lesieur (1990), in this article it will be argued that Gamblers Anonymous is qualitatively different from Alcoholics Anonymous in organization structure and practice and in member consciousness.

DATA

The Gamblers Anonymous-Alcoholics Anonymous comparative study lasted a year; ten months of which was spent doing observational work. The author attended approximately 200 meetings of Alcoholics Anonymous and Gamblers Anonymous. In addition to the 1989/1990 study, this analysis draws upon my year-long observation of Gamblers Anonymous rooms and the nine formal interviews conducted three years ago. This time around, the author conducted eleven formal G.A. interviews, averaging about three hours in length, the shortest one being two hours and the longest five and one-half hours.

The interviews were semi-structured; they began by asking for standard biographical information, followed by a more open ended portion in which the subjects were asked to relate in their own words their gambling or alcohol stories and their experiences with Gamblers Anonymous and/or Alcoholics Anonymous. They were interrupted only for clarification. The interviews were tape recorded and at the end of the stories, interviewees were asked about apparent contradictions, for elaboration, and for further clarification of the related experience.

The author also conducted five formal Alcoholics Anonymous interviews, which averaged 1.5 hours. Four of the Gamblers Anonymous interviewees were also members of other twelve-step programs. The author primarily attended open meetings, but also observed three closed A.A. meetings and was invited to four or five closed G.A. meetings. The author was not allowed to observe one closed G.A. meeting, and left two A.A. open meetings because the chairs, the person who tells their story, were uncomfortable with my presence.

As required by human subject protocol, I informed the secretary of the meeting of my presence and the nature of my study. Initially, the secretaries at G.A. meetings typically announced my presence and I was asked to say what my study was about. However, as I continued to attend, I was only introduced when there were possible new members in the room. The secretaries at A.A. meetings typically introduced me to the chair of the meeting but did not inform the open meetings of my presence and I was not asked to tell the membership about my study. Only in the few closed meetings, where a group conscience was taken, was I asked to give a short description of my study.

I attended meetings at different times and in various Northern California locations. Field notes were taken after the meetings, most of which were written up within a day of the meeting. At first I attended many meetings, but in the latter half of the study I regularly attended three open G.A. meetings and three open A.A. meetings. The A.A. meetings were all a part of one fellowship;

the meetings were chosen as representative of the various A.A. meetings in the area.

FINDINGS

As Lesieur (1990) points out, Gamblers Anonymous is not a clone of Alcoholics Anonymous. But, there are a number of similarities. First, they are both self-help groups that practice the principle of anonymity; thus the similarities in their names. Second, both use the disease model of addiction and advocate abstinence as their goal.

On closer inspection of Gamblers Anonymous and Alcoholics Anonymous, there are several differences. First, except for celebration meetings, Gamblers Anonymous meetings are considerably smaller than Alcoholics Anonymous meetings. Although the size may vary by location, the average G.A. meeting I attended had about seven members, whereas the average A.A. meeting had about 40 members. The smallest A.A. meeting I attended had 18 members. Gamblers Anonymous started 22 years after Alcoholics Anonymous, which was founded in 1935, so, one might expect A.A. to be larger than G.A. In 1982 A.A. had an estimated 50,000 groups, while G.A. in 1988 had about 1,000 groups; that makes A.A. 50 times larger than G.A. At the same age, however, A.A. was 13 times larger; in 1967, A.A. had 13,279 groups. One should not conclude from these numbers that A.A. is a better (more effective) program than G.A. because that evaluation would require analysis of several complex variables; this analysis does not seek to answer that question. The growth or lack of growth of G.A. is a continuing problem for the organization (Preston & Smith, 1985). Gambling in modern society is growing rapidly while G.A. is growing slowly if it is growing at all.

Lesieur (1990) gives the following growth trajectory for G.A.: In 1960 there were 16 chapters, in 1970 there were 130 chapters and in 1988 there were 600 chapters. In Northern California, the number of G.A. chapters remained about the same between 1987 and 1990, but the size of the meetings dropped considerably. Informal discussion with informants in other parts of the country suggests that retention and/or growth is a problem for Gamblers Anonymous even while there has been a rapid growth in twelve-step fellowship across the country. A further look at the other differences between A.A. and G.A. may shed some light on this problem.

There are several minor differences between the two groups that are apparent on closer inspection. First, Gamblers Anonymous meetings are generally longer than A.A. meetings; depending on the type of meeting, A.A. meetings are either one hour or an hour and a half normally, while G.A. meetings can last from an hour for a small group to as long as four hours. This is in large part due to the practice in G.A. of giving everyone a chance to give "therapy," in G.A. lexicon, or to "share," in A.A. lexicon. Alcoholics Anonymous also has many meetings per week and throughout the day. In the Northern California area, which runs from Santa Cruz to Sacramento, there are approximately 20 weekly G.A. meetings. For A.A., the East Bay, which only includes Oakland, Alameda, Emeryville, Berkeley and El Cerrito, there are over 300 meetings per week. Gam-Anon meetings are usually held on the same night and location as the Gamblers Anonymous meetings, while in A.A., Alanon meetings were not typically held at the same time and location as A.A. meetings.

Second, there are several lexicon differences. As already mentioned, in G.A. one gives therapy while in A.A. one shares. Another difference is that one "jumps", while in A.A. one "has a slip" or returns to drinking. Third, like Debtors Anonymous, G.A. has a pressure relief group that Alcoholics Anonymous does not have. A pressure relief group is given by G.A. members, called *Trusted Servants*, and is referred to as "the moment of truth." Members are supposed to reveal their entire financial situation and other personal, employment and legal problems they have as a result of their gambling careers. Although the meeting is supposed to have more than a financial focus, the primary advise given at such meetings is financial, how to budget one's money, and how to approach loan sharks or institutions one owes a lot of money with a manageable repayment plan. Problems, especially financial problems that appeared to be unmanageable, are made manageable with the help of G.A.

Finally, Gamblers Anonymous has relatively few step meetings. Like Lesieur (1990), it is the author's belief that this is important and may work to the detriment of the members. Whereas the steps are the central focus of Alcoholics Anonymous in that they are the primary tools passed along from one member to another, in G.A. they do not hold that central place.

SIGNIFICANT DIFFERENCES

There are three areas of significant differences between A.A. and Gamblers Anonymous, but before discussing them it is useful to note the differences in the steps and traditions of the two programs. As stated before, there is a de-emphasis of God and spirituality with G.A. But there are other differences. The following list presents the A.A. steps and the corresponding G.A. steps. In referring to their steps and traditions, G.A. uses "the recovery program" for the steps and "the unity program" for the traditions.

The 12 steps of A.A.	*The 12 Steps of G.A.*
1. We admitted we were powerless over **alcohol**—that our lives had become unmanageable.	1. We admitted we were powerless over **gambling** — that our lives had become unmanageable.
2. Came to **believe** that a Power greater than ourselves could restore us to **sanity**.	2. Came to **believe** that a Power greater than ourselves could restore us to **a normal way of thinking and living**.
3. Made a decision to turn our will and our lives over to the care of **God, as we understand Him**.	3. Made a decision to turn our will and our lives over to the care of **this Power of our own understanding**.
4. Made a searching and fearless **moral inventory of ourselves.**	4. Made a searching and fearless **moral and financial inventory of ourselves**.
5. Admitted to **God, to ourselves**, and to another human being the exact nature of our wrongs.	5. Admitted **to ourselves** and to another human being the exact nature of our wrongs.
6. Were entirely ready to have **God remove all these defects of character**.	6. Were entirely ready to have **these defects of character removed**.
7. Humbly asked **Him** to remove our shortcomings.	7. Humbly asked **God (of our understanding)** to remove our shortcomings.
8. Made a list of all persons we had harmed and became willing to make amends to them all.	8. Made a list of all persons we had harmed and became willing to make amends to them all.
9. Made direct amends to such people whenever possible, except when to do so would injure them or others.	9. Made direct amends to such people whenever possible, except when to do so would injure them or others.
10. Continued to take personal inventory and when we were wrong promptly admitted it.	10. Continued to take personal inventory and when we were wrong, promptly admitted it.

continued on next page . . .

. . . continued from previous page

The 12 steps of A.A.	*The 12 Steps of G.A.*
11. Sought through prayer and meditation to improve our conscious contact with **God, as we understood Him**, praying only for knowledge of His will for us and the power to carry that out.	11. Sought through prayer and meditation to improve our conscious contact with **God as we understood Him**, praying only for knowledge of His will for us and the power to carry that out.
12. Having **had a spiritual awakening as the result of these steps**, we tried to carry this message to **alcoholics**, and to practice these principles in all our affairs.	12. Having **made an effort to practice these principles in all our affairs**, we tried to carry this message to **other compulsive gamblers**.

12 Traditions of A.A.	*12 Steps of Unity of G.A.*
1. Our common welfare should come first; personal recovery depends upon **A.A. unity**.	1. Our common welfare should come first; personal recovery depends upon **group unity**.
2. **For our group purpose there is but one ultimate authority — a loving God as He may express Himself in our group conscience.** Our leaders are but trusted servants; they do not govern.	2. Our leaders are but trusted servants; they do not govern.
3. The only requirement for **A.A.** membership is a desire to stop **drinking**.	3. The only requirement for **Gamblers Anonymous** membership is a desire to stop **gambling**.
4. Each **group** should be **autonomous** except in matters affecting other groups or **A.A.** as a whole.	4. Each **Group** should be **self-governing** except in matters affecting other groups or **Gamblers Anonymous** as a whole.
5. **Each group** has but one primary purpose — to carry its message to the **alcoholic** who still suffers.	5. **Gamblers Anonymous** has but one primary purpose — to carry its message to the **compulsive gambler** who still suffers.

. . . continued on next page

. . .continued from previous page

12 Traditions of A.A.	*12 Steps of Unity of G.A.*
6. **An A.A. group** ought never endorse, finance, or lend the **A.A.** name to any related facility or outside enterprise, lest problems of money, property, and prestige divert us from our primary purpose.	6. **Gamblers Anonymous** ought never endorse, finance or lend the **Gamblers Anonymous** name to any related facility or outside enterprise, lest problems of money, property and prestige divert us from our primary purpose.
7. Every **A.A. group** ought to be fully self-supporting, declining outside contributions.	7. Every **Gamblers Anonymous Group** ought to be fully self-supporting, declining outside contributions.
8. **Alcoholics Anonymous** should remain forever **nonprofessional**, but our service centers may employ special workers.	8. **Gamblers Anonymous**, as such, ought never be organized; but we may create service boards or committees directly responsible to those they serve
9. **A.A.**, as such, ought never be organized; but we may create service boards or committees directly responsible to those they serve.	9. **Gamblers Anonymous**, as such, ought never be organized; but we may create service boards or committees directly responsible to those they serve.
10. **Alcoholics** Anonymous has no **opinion** on outside issues; hence the **A.A.** name ought never be drawn into public controversy.	10. **Gamblers** Anonymous has no **opinions** on outside issues; hence the **Gamblers Anonymous** name ought never be drawn into public controversy.
11. Our public relations policy is based on attraction rather than promotion; we need always maintain personal anonymity at the **level of press, radio, and films**.	11. Our public relations policy is based on attraction rather than promotion; we need always maintain personal anonymity at the **level of press, radio, films and television**.
12. Anonymity is the spiritual foundation **of all our traditions**, ever reminding us to place principles before personalities.	12. Anonymity is the spiritual foundation **of the Gamblers Anonymous program**, ever reminding us to place principles before personalities.

Sources: A.A. Grapevine, Inc. (1984); Gamblers Anonymous (Revised 1988)

Gamblers Anonymous is significantly different from Alcoholics Anonymous in three areas: in organization, in their respective conception of the problem of the addiction, and in the nature of members' consciousness.

A. Organizational Structure

Perhaps the most significant change Gamblers Anonymous made in the twelve-steps, twelve-traditions is tradition two. Gamblers Anonymous' second tradition or "steps of unity" states that "our leaders are but trusted servants; they do not govern," whereas A.A.'s second tradition states, "For our group purpose there is but one ultimate authority — a loving God as He may express Himself in our group conscience. Our leaders are but trusted servants; they do not govern." Gamblers Anonymous leaves out the idea that the ultimate authority for the group is God as He may express Himself in our group conscience. In A.A. this idea translates into an organizational structure that A.A. members describe as an inverted pyramid where the power lies with each group and those in service or leadership positions merely administer the wish of the groups. The organizational structure is set up to guard against the leaders getting too powerful. Term in office, for example, is limited, and it is very difficult to change the basic tenets of the organization.

The organizational structure in Gamblers Anonymous is top-heavy. G.A. members, those in service and trustees, point out that Gamblers Anonymous is like any other organization. In G.A. the leadership positions are very political and powerful positions. Power and status pervades the organization.

Another important point stemming from the second tradition is the different notions of group conscience each organization holds. In Gamblers Anonymous, a group conscience requires all members to agree, whereas in A.A., although there is some variation, a group conscience does not require unanimity, although it requires substantial agreement. This difference highlights the potentially political nature of Gamblers Anonymous. At the group level this works to the detriment of the group. If one member disagrees with something that the rest of the group thinks is useful to the group, he or she can get their way, thus submitting the group to his or her will. In A.A., on the other hand, care is taken to assure that one member does not impose their will and way on the group. In fact, for A.A., "self will run riot" is at the root of the addict's problem. This difference has the consequence of exclusion in Gamblers Anonymous and inclusion in A.A.

In Alcoholics Anonymous, the group conscience process has a more didactic purpose. The discussion proceeds by looking at all the possibilities or sides of an issue or problem. Members who will vote for an issue will argue the downside to make sure all aspects of the issue are covered and also to educate the newcomers to the fact that they have choices. This is not to say that the A.A. process is devoid of any politics; this is merely to point out that A.A.'s structure guards against one person imposing their will on the group and at the same time allowing many point of views to be expressed, while G.A.'s conception of group conscience does not guard against this possibility. In A.A., having the higher power as ultimate arbiter unexpectedly allows minority positions to be voiced.

B. Conception of the Problem

The second major difference between G.A. and A.A. is their conception of the problem, of the addiction that members confront. In G.A., the dominant position is that gambling is the problem. And although some hold the view that gambling is merely a symptom of the real problem, it is not the dominant view. In A.A., on the other hand, the dominant position is that although alcohol is important, it is not the major problem the alcoholic has. Alcohol, for A.A., is an epiphenomenon; the real problem is the self-centered, self-loathing or self-praising self. Initially, there is focus on alcohol but as the member remains abstinent, there is a shift of focus to the self-centered self.

C. Members' Consciousness

The final significant difference between A.A. and G.A. is the nature of member's consciousness. In A.A., members have twelve-step consciousness, whereas in G.A., members have "page 17" consciousness. In Gamblers Anonymous, many long time members tell newcomers that the program basically boils down to following page 17 of the "combo book." That book is read in almost all Gamblers Anonymous meetings from cover to cover; it is in effect G.A.'s "bible." The combo book is a short, pocket sized, summary of the G.A. program. Many members carry this pamphlet with them. Page 17 reads as follows:

TO ALL GAMBLERS ANONYMOUS MEMBERS, PARTICULARLY THE NEW GAMBLERS ANONYMOUS MEMBERS:

1. Attend as many meetings as possible, but at least one meeting per week.
2. Telephone other members as often as possible between meetings. Use the Telephone List!

3. Don't tempt or test yourself. Don't associate with acquaintances who gamble. Don't go in or near gambling establishments. Don't gamble for anything. This includes buying from the stock market, commodities and options, buying or playing lottery tickets, raffle tickets, flipping a coin, or entering the office sports pool.
4. Live the Gamblers Anonymous Program ONE DAY AT A TIME. Don't try to solve all your problems at once.
5. Read the recovery and unity steps often and continuously review the Twenty Questions. Follow the steps in your daily affairs. These steps are the basis for the entire Gamblers Anonymous Program and practicing them is the key to your growth. If you have any questions, ask them of your Trusted Servants and Sponsors.
6. When you are ready, the Trusted Servants will conduct a Pressure Relief Group meeting or evaluation for you and your spouse (if married), and adherence to it will aid in your recovery.
7. Be patient! The days and weeks will pass soon enough, and as you continue to attend meetings and abstain from gambling your recovery will really accelerate (Gamblers Anonymous, 1987, p. 17).

The combo book used to be also known as the "white book," or now also as the "yellow book." Although there is a minority of G.A. members with twelve-step consciousness, which most got from going to other twelve-step groups or being sponsored by someone in G.A. that belongs to another twelve-step group, the dominant consciousness of G.A.'s members is page 17 consciousness.

Page 17 is very practical advice focussed on helping the gambler stop gambling. Page 17 assumes that the primary problem the gambler faces is gambling. And although members are advised to read the steps often and follow them in their daily lives, Gamblers Anonymous has few step meetings or other means of incorporating the steps into members' lives and consciousness.

In A.A., the steps hold a central place in a member's way of life and consciousness once they take to the program. There are many step meetings, members refer to the steps frequently in their stories and shares, and the primary role of one's sponsor is someone to work the steps with. Old timers in A.A. advise newcomers that the key to the A.A. program is working the steps. In G.A., on the other hand, the sponsor is more of a friend and confidant.

In the author's opinion, twelve-step consciousness is basically transmitted through working the steps the way the Alcoholics Anonymous big book suggests. Gamblers Anonymous, at one point in its history, made use of A.A.'s literature on the steps; G.A. used material from the *Twelve Steps and Twelve Traditions* (the "12 by 12"). The "12 by 12," however, is the advanced "course" on the steps and traditions and presupposes that members have done the steps the way the A.A. big book suggests. So, G.A. "took" the graduate course without taking the undergraduate course.

In my opinion, the key step in the transmission of twelve-step consciousness is step 4. It is in working the steps, writing out one's moral inventory with one's sponsor's direction, and listening to other members share their experience, strength and hope that members are socialized into the twelve-step perspective and consciousness.

TWELVE STEP CONSCIOUSNESS

There are four elements to twelve-step consciousness as discerned from listening to the shares of members "who have got it." First, the problem, any problem that is being dealt with, is located in the self-centered self. This can either be the self-loathing or self-praising self. Second, the member elaborates on the emotional aspects of their reaction, and the attribution that fear is the root cause of the problem is made. The model for locating one's problems in the emotional self-centered, self-loathing or self-praising self is found in the Alcoholics Anonymous big book. In the chapter, "How it Works," members are instructed on how to write a "searching and fearless moral inventory." It is not unusual to see members with pads or note books writing out this inventory. In A.A. it is typically written with suggestions from one's sponsor. Members lists their resentments, what they think the cause of that resentment is, and how it affects them. The following item is the first example listed in A.A.'s big book:

I'm resentful at:	*The Cause*:	*Affects my*:
Mr. Brown	His attention to my wife.	Sex relations. Self-esteem (fear)
	Told my wife of my mistress.	Sex relations. Self-esteem (fear)
	Brown may get my job at the office.	Security. Self-esteem (fear)

(Alcoholics Anonymous, 1976, p. 65)

Members in A.A., with the assistance and support of their sponsors, write out their moral inventory and in the process learn to locate problems in the self-centered emotional self. Members gain distance on their own reactions and learn to distrust their first reaction, their alcoholic reaction to problems. Members also gain this perspective just by being present in meetings during which others share their experience, strength and hope. While sharing in meetings, members "who have got it" unconsciously frame their comments, their shares with twelve-step consciousness. They locate problems in the emotional self-centered self.

The last two elements of twelve step consciousness could be summarized as the process of getting out of that emotional self-centered self through two means, through a spiritual means and through an action means. In A.A. the spiritual means is broadly defined, although the underlying process is similar for each form of spirituality. There are at least three forms of spiritual: the traditional God, the group, and the "true self" or "inner child." The underlying process is one of turning over or surrendering of the alcoholic self. Surrendering to the traditional God is sometimes fairly passive but can have an active component, that is, one should do the "footwork" before turning it over or surrendering.

The other two forms are more active. With the group as God, one has to tell the group or members of the group one's problems and be willing to do what is suggested. Members have to seek out and consult other members or share one's problem at a meeting. The action is talking it out. Twelve step groups have suggested that members having difficulty with the traditional God use the group as God initially. The assumption was that the person would eventually embrace a traditional conception of God. This author believes that the "group as God" has become a permanent spiritual tradition, as many members do not embrace a traditional God.

The third spiritual notion is more psychological. Members get in touch with and operate under the influence of the "inner child" or true self. This is in contrast to the alcoholic self. And members frequently go to other groups and/or therapy in order to get in touch with this true self. Like the group as God tradition, the inner child as God tradition is growing in A.A. The growth and development of these latter traditions in A.A. is in part responsible for the continued growth of A.A.

The fourth and final element of A.A. or twelve step consciousness is taking action. This is the final step of getting out of the emotional self-centered self. The program is not only an intellectual program; it is also a practical one. Members have to take action; tell their story, follow up on what is suggested to them, do the footwork, make amends. Twelve step consciousness can be summarized as locating any problem in the emotional self-centered self and getting out of that self spiritually and practically.

GAMBLERS ANONYMOUS CONSCIOUSNESS

As stated earlier, G.A. consciousness is basically page 17 consciousness. It is claimed here that G.A. consciousness is markedly different from A.A. and other twelve-step groups in the nature of the members' consciousness. In G.A., members make relatively more use of the disease conception of addiction and typically do not locate their problems in the emotional self-centered self. In fact, those who locate problems in that emotional self-centered self are ostracized by the group. G.A. members do not talk about their feelings as is the common practice in other twelve-step groups. The dominant, page 17 group is quite dogmatic and intolerant of other paths to recovery. They frequently comment that they got better using page 17, and if it is good enough for them, it is good enough for others. Members who express twelve-step consciousness as described above are labelled as trying to be saints.

Another element of G.A. consciousness which is captured in the de-emphasis of God in the G.A. steps and traditions is its notion of spirituality. G.A. rejects two of the three conceptions used by A.A. — the traditional conception of God and the "inner child" conception — for what appears to be a more humanistic conception. G.A. uses the "group as God" spiritual conception the way it was traditionally used by A.A., that is, as a temporary conception. Gamblers Anonymous defines spirituality in the combo book as follows:

> The word spiritual can be said to describe those characteristics of the human mind that represent the highest and finest qualities such as kindness, generosity, honesty and humility (Gamblers Anonymous, 1987, p. 1).

Gamblers Anonymous appears to have a humanist and social conception of spirituality. The irony is that that conception is dogmatically and rigidly enforced. G.A. members forcefully reject the traditional conception of God, but they employ a more liberal conception dogmatically. Like the G.A.

members with twelve-step consciousness, the traditional God folks are also marginalized.

Gamblers Anonymous frames gambling as the problem and total abstinence as the solution. They use the disease conception of the problem that A.A. and other twelve-step groups also use, but they do not have an epiphenomena conception of addiction as other twelve-step groups do. As a result, G.A. members, in their practice, try to link or locate all their problems to gambling and they are quite confused when they are abstinent from gambling and they still have many problems. Gamblers Anonymous does not have a language of the emotional self-centered self. This, in the author's opinion, is in part why G.A. has problems retaining members. Members make use of the disease conception to remove the stigma of their problem and abstinence from gambling makes their situation temporarily better, but G.A. has problems dealing with the continuing problems the abstinent gamblers have.

In A.A. and other twelve-step programs, members embrace a conception of problems that allows continuing self-management regardless of the problem. In G.A., on the other hand, members have difficulty framing their continuing social, psychological, and life problems with gambling. Many give up after a while. The different ways of handling or framing problems is quite evident in members' shares or therapies. In field work, I have frequently observed members of A.A. and of G.A. deal with the same or similar problem. The A.A. member applies twelve-step consciousness and proceeds with tackling the problem and other aspects of their life, whereas the G.A. members appear to spin their wheels or go in circles. G.A. members will tell their problem to the group in great detail week after week trying in vain to link the problem to gambling. They typically do not accept responsibility for their part of the problem; instead, they try to link it to gambling. And since they are abstinent, they eventually conclude that G.A. must not be very helpful for other problems.

A.A. and other twelve-step groups provide a framework that can be used for any problem while G.A.'s is specific to gambling. I contend that in A.A. (and other twelve-step groups), members are taught and socialized to distrust their first reaction — their alcoholic reaction — and are encouraged to develop and act on a second reaction, a non-alcoholic reaction, a non-alcoholic self. The conception of a tainted self and the development of a functional self is at the root of the process. Gamblers Anonymous uses the disease conception of addiction to take away the stigma of the tainted self, but does not have an effective program of developing a functional self.

This difference can be seen in the wording of step 2. A.A.'s step states, "Came to believe that a Power greater than ourselves could restore us to sanity," whereas G.A.'s step states, "Came to believe that a Power greater than ourselves could restore us to a normal way of thinking and living." A.A.'s step 2 assumes a state of insanity on the part of the alcoholic, which is a very personal, relatively permanent, or at least a difficult to overcome state, whereas G.A.'s step 2 assumes an abnormal way of thinking and living, a partly personal, more social state that appears to be relatively easier to overcome. The personal element is merely an abnormal way of thinking that is caused by gambling; it is not deeply rooted in the self. It is also much easier to define a normal way of thinking and living than it is to define sanity. What happens in G.A. is that each member defines "normal way of thinking" and "living their way," and there are numerous ways of doing that. A popular one is that if one is relatively happy, that is a normal way of thinking and living.

This is not an evaluation of the effectiveness of A.A., G.A. or other twelve-step programs, and this is not claiming that A.A. is better than G.A. Rather, I am merely pointing to the central place a language of the self plays in A.A. and not in G.A., as well as pointing to some of the consequences for the members and for the organizations.

ROOTS OF SIGNIFICANT DIFFERENCES

How and why is Gamblers Anonymous so different from A.A. and other twelve-step groups? What are the roots of these significant differences?

Gamblers Anonymous' structure is partly rooted in the circumstances of its founding. However, many structural and, consequently, consciousness changes have occurred in Gamblers Anonymous that the circumstances of its founding do not explain. Gamblers Anonymous' structure was not imprinted at its founding. This necessitates a historical organizational analysis that the author has undertaken but which is far from complete.

Contrary to what Gamblers Anonymous's official literature states, the fellowship is not simply the outgrowth of a chance meeting between two men in the month of January 1957. The history of Gamblers Anonymous is much more complex, and a lot of pertinent information is presently not known or has never been researched.

The present Gamblers Anonymous was officially formed on Friday, September 13th, 1957. But the first Gamblers Anonymous, which is not directly connected to the present Gamblers Anonymous, was formed in 1949. Deland (1950) documents:

> As in the case of liquor addiction, many independent efforts are being made to "cure" addiction to gambling. Fashioned somewhat after Alcoholics Anonymous, a group, suffering in the pocketbook from gambling, organized Gamblers Anonymous in California in January 1949 (Deland, 1950, p. 27).

The original Gamblers Anonymous started with twenty-one members and, according to Deland (1950, p. 28), grew to "thousands in and outside of California." It was a mutual-help group "with the purpose of encouraging people to cure themselves of the betting habit." Little is known about this group that tried to get a petition onto the November 1950 ballot that would amend the state constitution to abolish horse racing in California. Deland, however, speaks of their optimism in "establishing branches in other cities, and in due time they expect to put anti-racing bills on the ballot in New York, Florida, Illinois, and Maryland" (1950, p. 28). Little is known of the circumstances surrounding the failure of that first effort.

Unlike the first Gamblers Anonymous, the present Gamblers Anonymous is not prohibitionist in their orientation. Jim W., Gamblers Anonymous' number one man, tried and failed several times to get the organization off the ground. The frustration from those failures appeared to have played a role in the present form of the twelve steps used by Gamblers Anonymous. Jim W. was a member of Alcoholics Anonymous and his wife, Sybil, was the manager of A.A.'s central office. The first meeting between Gamblers Anonymous' number one and number two members was not a "chance" meeting. Sam J. (not Sam F.) was referred by Sybil after Sam had called Alcoholics Anonymous' central office. Again, little is know about the interaction between the two except that they would meet and talk and neither had returned to gambling. One source (Frank, 1962) states that Jim had been abstinent from gambling since 1954.

What we do know, however, is that at the first official meeting of Gamblers Anonymous on 13th September, 1957, A.A.'s twelve steps had already been changed. The only later change in Gamblers Anonymous' twelve-steps would be to step four, to which would be added a financial inventory. So, the other changes can be attributed to be the result of the interaction between G.A.'s number one and number two men. Reliable sources point to the fact that Sam J. was an atheist in explaining why Jim W. de-emphasized the spiritual aspects of the A.A. steps.

At that first meeting, the G.A. twelve steps were presented to the group of thirteen. There were two wives, four A.A. members who did not have a gambling problem, six male gamblers, and one female gambler.

Sam J. did not remain long with the organization, but his pressure to remove God from the steps and the program are preserved in the G.A. twelve steps. The structure and consciousness of Gamblers Anonymous were not imprinted at its first meeting; Gamblers Anonymous would undergo many more structural, organizational and consciousness changes in the next 33 years, but again our knowledge of what happened is incomplete. What we do know, however, is that the present organization is quite different from what Jim W. envisioned. His vision of G.A. is drawn by the author from the Gamblers Anonymous "combo" book, the "bible" of Gamblers Anonymous. Jim W. wrote the first combo book; it was first published in June, 1962. Changes from that first edition and the present 1988 version embody the changes in the organization.

It is my contention that the first combo book represents Jim W.'s vision of the organization, and that vision is much closer to the structure, organization and consciousness of Alcoholics Anonymous than the present Gamblers Anonymous. There are several important changes that have occurred in the combo book. First, there is a systematic changing of the male centered style of the first combo book. Second, spirituality has been de-emphasized through the book; Jim W.'s vision was of a much more spiritual program. Third, the importance of the steps has been left out. Jim W. saw the steps as the foundation of the program. After laying out the twelve steps, he writes:

> "No one claims these steps are in any way original with G.A. They reflect practical experience and application of spiritual insights as recorded by thoughtful men in many ages. Their greatest importance lies in the fact that they work. They enable us and thousands of others to lead happy productive lives. They represent the foundation upon

> which our society has been built. They were given to us freely, for which we are grateful" (Gamblers Anonymous, 1962).

This passage has been removed from the present combo book.

Fourth, the twelve steps are not the same as they were presented at the first meeting. As stated previously, step four was changed to include a financial inventory. Unlike most of the other changes, there is information on this change. The fifth change is in the vision of the organization's structure. The first combo book's vision of the organizational structure of G.A. was more like A.A.'s structure than the present Gamblers Anonymous structure. Jim W. writes, in response to the question, *Who Runs G.A.?*, the following:

> "G.A. is a unique spiritual movement having no central government and but little formal organization. There are no officers or executives who wield authority over the fellowship or the individual. Even though G.A. is an informal organization, certain jobs have to be done. In the local group someone has to be responsible for the meeting place, keep an accounting of the group finances, arrange for refreshments and keep in touch with local and national service centers. This means that a group needs responsible people to perform these duties. In accepting these responsibilities a member may acquire a title, but titles in G.A. are used only to designate areas of service. Those who accept these responsibilities are directly accountable to those they serve" (Gamblers Anonymous, 1962).

Contrary to this organizational image, the present G.A. has officers or executives who wield authority over the fellowship.

The other changes between the 1962 and 1988 combo book are additions rather than deletions. The minor additions are a history and a preamble. The major and significant additions are the Twenty Questions and page 17. The details of when these additions were made are yet to be researched, but their importance to the present consciousness of Gamblers Anonymous is quite evident. Page 17, from my observations, has become the centerpiece of G.A. consciousness; it has replaced the twelve steps as the foundation of the program and the consciousness of its members. The de-emphasis on spirituality and the addition of the twenty question, I think, are signs of the medicalization of the organization (Rosecrance, 1985).

DISCUSSION AND CONCLUSION

There is clearly a need for further research on Gamblers Anonymous. How did these important structural and organizational changes come about? Is page 17 consciousness the dominant one in other areas of the country or world? Are the small group dynamics centered around the old-timers and the newcomers, as Turner and Sanders (1990) argue, or around the page 17 proponents and the twelve step fellowship proponents as I argue?

What is clear from this study is the fact that Gamblers Anonymous is markedly different from other twelve-step fellowships in organizational structure and the consciousness of the respective members. Gamblers Anonymous is more of a mutual help abstinence club than a twelve-step fellowship. Gamblers Anonymous largely lacks twelve-step consciousness, is hierarchically structured, and status practices pervade the organization. These features, in the author's opinion, help to explain the relatively slow growth of the organization when other twelve-step fellowships are growing dramatically. Organizational practices, especially the status practices, also hinder the retention of women and minority groups in the organization.

This study also confirms or adds to the gambling literature (Brown, 1985; Turner and Saunders, 1990) that argues that the basic process in Gamblers Anonymous is a transformation of the self. Brown (1985) argues that this transformation is quite similar to a religious conversion, and Turner and Saunders (1990) argue that this construction is done through a medical relabeling process.

I think that both are on target. In addition, however, I would like to point out not only that the transformation of the self is the basic process in twelve-step fellowships, but also that Gamblers Anonymous's particular adaptation of the twelve steps limits the choice of the new self by emphasizing one path, a secular, more medical path, while denouncing other paths.

REFERENCES

A.A. Grapevine, Inc. (1984). *This is A.A.* New York: Alcoholics Anonymous World Services, Inc.

Alcoholics Anonymous (1976). *Alcoholics Anonymous: The Story of How Many Thousands of Men and Women have Recovered from Alcoholism*, third edition. New York City: Alcoholics Anonymous World Services, Inc.

Brown, R.I.F. (1985). Parallels between behaviour change processes in addiction recovery and in conversion experiences. *Contact: The Interdisciplinary Journal of Pastoral Studies*, 86, 20-22.

Brown, R.I.F. (1986). Dropouts and continuers in Gamblers Anonymous: Life-context and other factors. *Journal of Gambling Behavior*, 2:2, 130-140.

Brown, R.I.F. (1987a). Dropouts and continuers in Gamblers Anonymous, Part 2: Analysis of free-style accounts of experiences with GA. *Journal of Gambling Behavior*, 3:1, 68-79.

Brown, R.I.F. (1987b). Dropouts and continuers in Gamblers Anonymous, Part 3: Some possible specific reasons for dropout. *Journal of Gambling Behavior*, 3:2, 137-151.

Brown, R.I.F. (1987c). Dropouts and continuers in Gamblers Anonymous, Part Four: Evaluation and summary. *Journal of Gambling Behavior*, 3:3, 202-210.

Deland, P.S. (1950). The facilitation of gambling. *The Annals of the American Academy of Political and Social Science*, 269, 21-29.

Frank, S. (1962). Gamblers Anonymous: Modeled after Alcoholics Anonymous, this new organization succeeds where psychiatrists fail in helping compulsive gamblers lick the habit. *Saturday Evening Post*, 235, 44-46.

Gamblers Anonymous (1962). *Gamblers Anonymous: Questions and answers about the program of compulsive gambling and the G.A. recovery program.* Los Angeles, CA: G.A. Publishing Co.

Gamblers Anonymous (1987; Revised 1988). *Gamblers Anonymous.* Los Angeles, CA: G.A. Publishing Co.

Leerhsen, C., Lewis, S.D., Pomper, S., Davenport, L. and Nelson, M. (1990). Unite and conquer: America's crazy for support groups. Or maybe support groups keep America from going crazy. *Newsweek*, February 5, 50-55.

Lesieur, H.R. (1990). Working with and understanding Gamblers Anonymous. In T.J. Powell (ed.), *Working with Self-Help* (237-253). Silver Spring, MD: NASW Press.

Levoy, G. (1989). A place to belong. *Health Magazine*, February, 54-57.

McCormick, A. and Brown, R.I.F. (1988). Gamblers Anonymous as medicine, as religion and as addiction recovery process. In W.R. Eadington (ed.), *Gambling Research: Proceedings of the Seventh International Conference on Gambling and Risk Taking* (pp. 344-364). Reno, NV: University of Nevada.

Preston, F.W. and Smith, R.W. (1985). Delabeling and relabeling in Gamblers Anonymous: Problems with transferring the Alcoholics Anonymous paradigm. *Journal of Gambling Behavior*, 1:2, 97-105.

Rosecrance, J. (1985). Compulsive gambling and the medicalization of deviance. *Social Problems*, 32:3, 275-284.

Turner, D.N. and Saunders, D. (1990). Medical relabeling in Gamblers Anonymous: The construction of an ideal member. *Small Group Research*, 21:1, 59-78.

ACKNOWLEDGEMENT

This research was supported by NIAAA post-doctoral grant, 2 T32 AA07240-11, at the Alcohol Research Group, Berkeley, California. I would like to thank Mary Phillips, Ron Roizen, Kim Bloomfield, Robin Room, Laura Schmidt, Connie Weisner, Ron Rothbart, Andrew Treno, Chris Vourakis, John Rumbarger and Mike Hilton, all connected with ARG, for the wonderfully supportive and intellectually stimulating atmosphere at ARG.

Compulsive Gambling: Structured Family Intervention

Mary Heineman

Family members are confronting compulsive gamblers about the consequences of their gambling all the time. Unfortunately, these confrontations are often nothing more than empty threats. When these encounters take place, they are usually done on a one on one basis — the concerned person alone with the gambler — and, as a result, the effort is futile because the gambler is a well seasoned manipulator, and as such, the one doing the confronting is put off or ignored.

Another fault of self-directed interventions is that the concerned persons have not been trained by a professional as to what to say and how to say it. These interventions have only one goal: to get the identified patient (the compulsive gambler) into treatment. This type of intervention is a "hit or miss" operation rather than a process which evolves over time. These ineffective interventions often result in painful negative emotions for the loved ones leaving them feeling more discouraged, more disappointed and more helpless than before. In addition, the family continues being affected by a disease they do not understand but which they continue to try to control. These loved ones do not know that they too need help and that effective treatment is available. Their belief that, "I will be fine as soon as the gambling stops," is erroneous.

Professional preparation for those seeking to confront a compulsive gambler is being made available in mental health/addiction treatment agencies across the country. These professionally conducted interventions are done in such a way that the afflicted is not criticized, put down, lectured or blamed for the gambling nor for its consequences. The compulsive gambler is confronted in a loving and supportive manner, while hearing, often for the first time, that compulsive gambling is a disease, and therefore cannot be controlled, only arrested.

The disease of compulsive gambling is an emotional illness which leads the afflicted to believe the answer to all existing problems, financial or emotional, is to "hit it big" one more time. This child-like thinking often keeps the compulsive gambler active in his disease until the very late stages. In the meantime, the family and friends are continually affected by a behavior they cannot control and do not understand. As a result, the family may be more affected, emotionally and physically, than the compulsive gambler. Because this disease can be completely hidden for so long, the family too often has no knowledge as to the depth of the illness until the late stages. The most important goal of a professionally conducted family intervention is to get *someone* into treatment.

In order to help some of the affected (family members and friends) who are hurting from this disorder, it is, at times, necessary to "hook" them into treatment through the intervention door. Once the concerned others have an understanding of this disease, are supporting each other, and agree to a common goal of no future "bailouts" for the compulsive gambler, intervention into this illness has begun. It can never be emphasized enough that in order to interrupt the progression of any addiction, it is often most advisable to start with the affected, as opposed to the afflicted, because they are better able to hear about the nature of the illness and the necessary steps to take in order to arrest it.

PROCEDURE

Most family interventions begin with a phone call to a treatment agency from a family member or friend of a compulsive gambler. The gathering of information about the gambler and the effects of the gambling begins with this call. There are specific questions the counselor will ask over the phone. It is important for the counselor to know: the age and sex of the compulsive gambler; the ages and sexes of the gambler's children; with whom the gambler is living; and whether or not the gambler has ever gone for help (Gamblers Anonymous and/or professional counseling). It is also important to ask the caller: how the compulsive gambler is related to him/her; and how long the caller feels the gambling has been a problem. The final question to ask the caller is, "Exactly what precipitated this call?" Because the compulsive gambling has most likely been a problem for some time, it can be expected that the disease has progressed further and the latest incident has resulted in greater fear on the part of the caller.

After the counselor collects the information needed over the phone, the focus becomes the emotional state of the caller. The caller may be feeling very guilty for having "betrayed" a loved one. The caller may have been told by the compulsive gambler that he/she is the cause of the out-of-control gambling. The professional can expect the caller to be filled with many painful feelings having made the call in the first place. It is important to listen to the caller's feelings and concerns, and support their decision to intervene.

Once the preliminary information is collected and the caller has been heard and supported, an appointment is made for a consultation. The caller is asked to bring one other concerned person to the consultation session. The purpose of inviting a second party to the consultation is twofold; first, as a support for the initiator of the intervention, and second, because the additional party will confirm (or deny) the information given by the caller.

THE CONSULTATION

This session is a continuation of the conversation between the caller and the counselor. The counselor will continue to collect information from the caller and the accompanying individual in order to determine whether or not the family is appropriate for family intervention.

The counselor will need additional information about the identified patient (the compulsive gambler). It is important to ask about the identified patient's (the I.P.'s) physical and mental health; whether or not the I.P. has a history of mental illness; and whether or not the I.P. is under the care of a medical doctor or a psychotherapist. If the I.P. is under the care of a doctor or a therapist, it is recommended that the family contact this primary caretaker and advise him/her of their plan to carry out a structured family intervention with the I.P. and ask whether there is an objection of the part of the primary caretaker.

Most important to ask the two people at the consultation is whether or not the I.P. has ever attempted suicide. Should the answer be in the affirmative, it is necessary for the family to request input from the attending physician regarding the I.P.'s mental status before carrying out the intervention. Some agencies will refuse to facilitate a structured family intervention if the I.P. has ever attempted suicide. This point should be discussed and seriously considered before any family intervention commences.

Once all the meaningful data about the I.P. have been obtained, the consultation will proceed to help the concerned persons determine exactly who will be attending the preparation sessions. The family will be directed to invite anyone who knows about the I.P.'s problem gambling, anyone who has been affected by it, and anyone who is sincerely concerned about how the gambling is affecting the I.P.'s life. The family is not to go home and inform others about the problem gambling and elicit their support. They are to approach only those who already aware of the seriousness of the I.P.'s gambling.

Should some concerned persons live out of town, they too can be included in the intervention by being informed as to what is taking place at each preparation session and, if possible, by being in attendance on the day of the intervention. Should this be impossible, they can still write down how they are being affected by the gambling and forward it to the professional or to a family member, so that it can be read to the I.P. at the intervention.

Should there be children and/or elderly family members who have been affected by the gambling, they too shall be invited to attend the preparation sessions.

The final issue addressed at the consultation is to have each of the individuals in attendance express just how they have been affected by the gambling. By so doing, they have a chance to get in touch with their pain, verbalize their feelings, and be supported by the counselor and their companion. At the same time, the counselor will direct each of them to GamAnon (a self help program for family members of compulsive gamblers) where they can be further educated and supported.

THE FIRST PREPARATION SESSION

This is the first session where all the concerned persons come together and share their common problem. The session begins with introductions and with each member present sharing their perception of the I.P.'s gambling. As each responds, the professional listens attentively for evidence of denial in any member of the group. When there is evidence of denial, the professional does not confront it until each member has had a chance to speak. Then the counselor will return to the individual exhibiting denial and feed back some of the views offered by other family members which clearly depicts the extent of the I.P.'s gambling and the seriousness of it.

At this point the counselor will again address the concept of compulsive gambling being a family disease. Based on what each group member has shared, the idea of them getting involved in a self-help program should be introduced again. A few minutes is spent explaining the fellowship of GamAnon, and dispensing schedules of meetings.

Following this, the counselor will direct each group member to write, in letter form, how the I.P.'s gambling has been affecting him/her so that it can be read directly to the I.P. at the intervention. The counselor will explain the importance of writing down what they want to say is so that they are not thrown off course should the I.P. try to do that. In addition, should the concerned person or the I.P. become emotional and need to pause for a moment, the reading can continue without losing the thought or feeling being expressed before the interruption. In other words, nothing important or significant will go unsaid.

It is advisable that these letters follow a particular format. Each letter is to cover very specific points; i.e., why they sought the help of a professional; what changes they have seen over the last few months or years; an incident or two involving the I.P.'s gambling and how they were affected by it; how their relationship has changed because of the gambling; what they fear will happen if help is not sought; and what they hope for once the gambling stops.

When writing their letters, each participant will speak from a personal position. They will use the pronoun "I" and not "we," i.e., "I am concerned about you"; "I love you." These letters are to be written as though the gambler and the family member are the only two people involved. No other person is to be mentioned in any one letter. The letter is to focus on the writer's feelings in direct relationship to the I.P.'s gambling. They are not to include any criticisms of the gambler, nor put downs, nor are they to be in the form of a lecture. Each letter is to end with the writer asking the gambler to accept help so the gambling can be arrested.

Should the gambler refuse to accept help, then, and only then, will the writer tell the I.P. how their relationship will change because in the eyes of the concerned person the gambling is more important to the I.P. than the relationship between the two of them.

Participants are then instructed to return home and begin to write down exactly what they intend to say to the I.P. on the day of the intervention. They are also instructed to return with any questions that might arise before their next session. In addition, out-of-town family members who have also been affected by the gambling are to be contacted and asked to write their own letter to the I.P. The procedure is explained to them by the contact person and they are asked to call the counselor some time during the week so any questions they have may be answered.

SECOND PREPARATION SESSION

Any new participants are introduced and a summary of the proceedings covered in session one are repeated. Then the reading of the letters commences. As each person reads what they have written, all other group members are asked to close their eyes, listen attentively and pretend they are the I.P. These concerned persons know the I.P. better than the counselor; therefore, they are the ones most appropriate to determine what the I.P. will hear, and what reactions to expect.

The professional listens to each reading while making notes to remove anything condescending or of a lecturing nature. In addition, the counselor helps each to identify their feelings which surface as they read how the I.P.'s gambling has affected them.

Following each reading, the group will share how they felt as they listened and how they believe the I.P. will react to what was read. Because the letters are focused on the writer's emotions there is less likelihood of the I.P. becoming defensive. The bottom line is: "Your gambling is causing you to distance from me and I miss you. I want you back in my life."

Following the critique of each letter, the group is directed to return home to edit and revise what they have written remembering to focus on their feelings and nothing else. Before the group leaves the office, the counselor again spends time reinforcing the family disease concept which the group can now better understand after listening to the pain expressed in the letters just read. The professional again directs each concerned person to start attending GamAnon if they have not already begun to do so.

THE THIRD PREPARATION SESSION

All new questions are answered. Then the counselor asks the group how many attended a GamAnon meeting during the week. Again the professional encourages and supports each family member obtaining help for the effects of the gambling disease upon them. It is important to reinforce each concerned person's need for support to survive this disease whether or not the I.P. accepts treatment.

At this point in treatment, the family is usually cohesive and supportive of each other and feels bonded and united for the first time in many years or perhaps ever.

Next, each letter is re-read using the same procedure as carried out in session two. Should any letter still be on an intellectual level, the counselor will give further guidance by helping the writer to identify the feelings behind the incidents described. By so doing, the professional is helping each family member to share the pain they have been carrying within.

Although family members have given money to the afflicted individual time and time again, the incidents involving money are minimized in their letters in order that they can express the painful emotions they feel as a direct result of the I.P.'s gambling. The letters focus in on the amount of time the gambler spends feeding the addiction, how much the gambler is missed, and how hurt they are that the gambler is not there for them emotionally.

The latter part of the third session is spent discussing how the group will get the I.P. to attend the following session. Most important in arranging the I.P.'s presence at that session is not to fabricate any untruth to accomplish it. The counselor will suggest one member of the group tell the I.P. that he/she has been going for counseling because of the way he/she has been affected by the gambling. This family member will then tell the I.P. that the next session will take place in a few days and that the counselor would like the I.P. to attend that session. Should the I.P. refuse to attend, an alternate plan will be put into effect. The alternate plan consists of the intervention taking place in the home of one of the concerned persons who attended each of the preparation sessions.

Should the intervention take place anywhere but the counselor's office, a spokesperson shall be chosen from the group to see to it that the confrontation is carried out as planned. The spokesperson who is chosen by the intervention group is rarely the spouse or the I.P.'s enabling parent. In the case of parents, it is common that one parent has become enmeshed with the I.P. while the other parent has distanced. The distant parent has long since made the decision to cease giving the I.P. money to pay bills or to cover gambling debts. This "hard" parent makes a good spokesperson because this is the parent who has had little interaction with the I.P. as a result of the progression of the disease. Because there has been silence between them, the I.P. is likely to listen when this parent speaks. However, because the group knows the I.P. best, they are the ones to decide which person is most likely to command the attention of the I.P.

It is most preferable to have the intervention take place in the counselor's office. However, if that is not possible, it can be conducted successfully in another setting.

Once the spokesperson is chosen, the group begins rehearsing the intervention in full. Decisions are made as to where each person will sit, who will read their letter first, and what part the professional will play throughout the intervention session.

The last part of this session is spent once again pointing out to the family how strongly they have been affected by the I.P.'s compulsive gambling and how important it is for each of them to become part of a self-help group so they can continue to learn about this disease and so they can begin to gain strength, feel supported and hopeful.

THE FOURTH PREPARATION SESSION

It is to be expected that the I.P. will be present at this session. If it is conducted in the counselor's office, the counselor will guide and orchestrate the confrontation so that it is carried out with dignity and support for the family as well as for the I.P.

After each member has read their prepared statement, the counselor will summarize what has been said and ask the I.P. to accept treatment for the gambling problem. The definition of treatment is explained to the I.P. and options are offered so that the I.P. can take part in the decision as to which road to travel to recovery.

Should the I.P. agree to treatment, a determination is made as to which course of action to take and exactly what treatment will consist of. It is possible the I.P. will agree to start attending Gamblers Anonymous meetings and arrest the disease. Some may agree to include professional counseling in addition to self-help. In some cases, if the I.P. is obviously very depressed, a psychiatric evaluation may be in order and, should the doctor so determine, treatment at an in-patient facility may be recommended. Regardless of the I.P.'s decision, the family is asked to return for one more session together, and once again is directed to continue their own self-help recovery program.

THE FIFTH SESSION

The purpose of this session is to allow the group to process the feelings they experienced during the confrontation and to share those feelings with the other group members. Following this, each concerned person is asked how the group will continue to support each other as the effects of the I.P.'s disease progresses or as the recovery period begins.

CONCLUSION

The primary purpose of a professionally led structured family intervention is to get *someone* into treatment. Should only one member of an intervention group continue in treatment following the confrontation, the intervention is successful. It takes only one person to intervene in the progression of this disease. Fortunately, in most situations, more than one individual continues with their own treatment following a professionally conducted family intervention.

Many compulsive gamblers enter treatment following the ongoing recovery of one of their loved ones. When one family member begins to recover, the whole family is affected, just as when one member of a family begins to gamble compulsively, the ripple effects touch everyone who cares.

Compulsive Gambling Hotline: A Source for Help and Information

Valerie C. Lorenz

The Compulsive Gambling Hotline of Maryland is the only national, 24-hour live hotline, dedicated specifically for issues relating to compulsive gambling. Started in December 1987, its purpose is to furnish information on compulsive gambling, make referrals to professional treatment providers and self-help groups, and to conduct crisis counseling and intervention for callers in distress. The Hotline is funded in part by the Maryland Department of Health and Mental Hygiene.

In 1978, the Maryland state legislature became the first in the United States to publicly acknowledge through legislative action that compulsive gambling causes a serious economic and social impact upon its citizens and upon the state. Thus the Department of Health and Mental Hygiene (DHMH), Alcohol and Drug Abuse Administration, began providing funds for the nation's first public treatment program, which included the implementation of a compulsive gambling hotline. The hotline was funded for four years. By 1985, the DHMH had diverted all of its attention and its fiscal support to combat drug and alcohol abuse. Compulsive gamblers were advised to go to a drug treatment center for their gambling addiction, and all further funding for treatment ceased at that time.

This paper presents a historical perspective of the development and growth of our Compulsive Gambling Hotline, cost and funding issues, research data, problems, unexpected findings, and future directions.

SCOPE AND FUNDING OF THE HOTLINE

In November 1987, the DHMH issued a Request For Proposal (RFP) for the establishment of a statewide, 24-hour live compulsive gambling hotline. Three organizations responded, and the contract for $7,038 was awarded to the National Center for Pathological Gambling, Inc. (now the Compulsive Gambling Center, Inc.) in Baltimore.

The Center is a not-for-profit agency started in February 1986, under the direction of the author. Its goals are to provide treatment for the gambler and family members, conduct research into this disorder, to train mental health and allied professionals, to educate the community about compulsive gambling, and to establish prevention programs.

The targeted start-up date for the Hotline was December 1, 1987. The services of various long-distance telephone carriers were reviewed. The specific service chosen was done so because the costs of nationwide service and local service were virtually identical. In its proposal, the Center had argued that gambling, both legal and illegal, is pervasive throughout the country, that American society is transient, and that family members were scattered. Thus a citizen of Maryland who might have lost all his money at a casino and finds himself stranded in Nevada, could receive help through this national hotline. The type of help offered by this Hotline would also be available to a parent (or family member, friend, or employer) living in other parts of the country whose son or daughter might reside in the state of Maryland. The DHMH agreed and a national hotline was implemented. (Note: This national perspective was consistent with the DHMH's view in 1978 in funding the first treatment program.)

The Center had presented some secondary goals to the DHMH. By virtue of the hotline, the Center hoped to establish a national network of treatment providers, while also gathering national data on these potential callers, to determine which differences might exist between compulsive gamblers in

Maryland and those throughout the country. This information should be of benefit to treatment providers as well as to local and national policy makers.

The Hotline is only an incoming telephone line; thus it was necessary to get a second telephone line for outgoing calls. Cost for this was minimal; the standard rate for a single business phone. Further, although the Hotline was set up to be answered by Center staff, it was deemed advisable to purchase an answering machine as an emergency back-up for when staff might be unavailable.

A caller intake form was developed after reviewing those of other hotlines, incorporating the needs of the DHMH and the goals of the Center. For instance, the DHMH had gone on record in 1985 stating that compulsive gamblers have sufficient health insurance or money to pay for treatment and, therefore, did not require DHMH funding support. The DHMH was also of the opinion that most compulsive gamblers did not need therapy other than the support group of Gamblers Anonymous. Thus the intake form reflects questions to be asked of the caller with respect to the gambler's job, type of health insurance, other major problems, such as past or present alcohol or drug abuse, depression, legal problems or suicidal intent, in order to determine funding and treatment needs.

During the first contract period, the Hotline was operational for the remainder of fiscal year 1988, from December 1, 1987, to June 30, 1988. As was to be expected with two new telephone lines, there were quite a few wrong numbers initially, which abated over time. There were 651 legitimate calls. (Wrong numbers or hang-ups are not included in these figures.)

The following year, the DHMH again issued a RFP for the continuation of the Hotline, this time for $7,500 for the full fiscal year. Again the Center competed and won the contract, and it was able to expand its public relations efforts, resulting in 971 appropriate calls for the fiscal year.

The Center was automatically awarded a continuation of the contract for Fiscal Year (FY) 1990, in the amount of $10,000. There were 1243 "appropriate" calls during this period and over 10,500 calls requesting lottery information. These "lottery" calls were attributed to the Hotline phone number being printed on lottery tickets. Because the volume of calls was so totally unanticipated, the DHMH granted an additional $9,000 to the Center, for a total of $19,000 for FY 1990.

In 1990, the DHMH and the Center signed a three-year contract for $20,000 for FY 1991, $22,000 for 1992 and $24,000 for 1993. However, it is anticipated that these funds will need to be supplemented either by the DHMH, the Maryland State Lottery, or the General Fund as the number of calls continue to increase. It is to be noted that phone charges are based on the distance of the caller, length of call, and time of day that the call is made. (The DHMH granted an additional $5,000 at the end of FY 1991.)

LOGISTICAL RESULTS

In order to plan for staffing and promotion of the Hotline, the intake form included data collection on the date of the call, time of call, length of call, which staffer took the call, nature of call, and how the caller learned about the Hotline number. Nature of Call includes information on compulsive gambling, referral to Gamblers Anonymous or professionals, caller giving the Hotline information, caller was in need of strong support or assistance, crisis or suicide, complaint, information on the Hotline, other problems not necessarily related to compulsive gambling, administrative, prank, threat, research, or media request for information, Task Force, lottery, or follow-up calls.

It was found that both in Maryland and in the U.S. the months with the largest volume of calls were winter months of January, February and March (33% in Maryland, 36% for the entire country). August was the heaviest summer month for all three years.

During 1988, 22% of the calls were made in the evenings or on weekends. (All period references are to the fiscal year.) By FY 1990, this had increased to 30%. During the week, Mondays appeared to be the busiest days. Initially, most calls came in between 9 a.m. and 10 a.m., and between 2 p.m. and 4 p.m. However, as the Hotline was promoted nationally, this spread became larger. Most serious calls, those in which the gambler was suicidal or at serious financial or legal risk, come in at night or on weekends, both in Maryland and nationally.

Thus an initial review of the *frequency* of calls would suggest that daytime staffing is sufficient, and would allow for the use of volunteers or an answering machine for nighttime and weekend calls; however, the *nature* of the calls suggest the contrary. These more serious calls also take longer. While 50% of the calls take five minutes or less, more serious calls take 45 minutes or longer. Media interviews average a half hour.

DEMOGRAPHIC FINDINGS

In each of the three years, the vast majority of the identified compulsive gamblers were male, although some differences exist between national and Maryland gamblers. Male compulsive gamblers made up 83% in FY 1988 and FY 1989, and dropped to 81% in FY 1990. In Maryland, in FY 1989, 83% were male, and in FY 1990, only 75% were male. The reasons for this increase in the percentage of female compulsive gamblers in Maryland could be many; however, in view of the prevalence of the many "smaller" games of chance, such as the state lottery, tip jars, bingo, and poker machines, one might attribute the availability and ready accessibility of such forms of gambling as contributing factors to the larger number of female gambling addicts.

A major difference is seen in the ages of the compulsive gamblers, as indicated in Table 1. Initially, Maryland callers were younger than throughout the country. However, even nationwide there are now more teenage gambling addicts. This certainly supports the contention of researchers, such as Jacobs (1992) and others (Ladouceur & Mireault, 1988; Lesieur, 1988; and Lorenz, 1990), that there is an increase in teenage compulsive gamblers. In view of the many forms of gambling available in Maryland and other states, especially those with lotteries, this would also be suggestive of an environmental influence in the increase of compulsive gambling. Gambling addiction as a whole is striking a younger population.

Staffers attempt to identify the race of the compulsive gambler, either by direct questioning or through voice inflection. The gamblers are categorized as white, black, hispanic, asian/oriental, or other. During FY 1988, from the national Hotline, six percent of the compulsive gamblers were judged to be black. In FY 1989 this number doubled, to 12%, and in FY 1990, 13% of the callers were thought to be black. In Maryland, there was a 4% increase between FY 1989 and FY 1990, from 12% to 16%, among callers considered to be black.

The question of co-addiction or serial addiction has been of concern to both treatment providers and to policy makers. With these callers, some differences are apparent, which were a function of both the increased promotion of the Hotline on a national basis, and more precise questioning by the staff with respect to present and past abuse of alcohol or illicit drugs. In FY 1988 only 4% of the compulsive gamblers said that alcohol was a problem for them. In FY 1989, 6% indicated alcohol-related problems, and in FY 1990, 11%

admitted to such difficulties, on a national level. In Maryland, the percentage was slightly higher — 13% during FY 1990. Figures were slightly higher in FY 1991.

TABLE 1

Age of Hotline Compulsive Gamblers in the U.S. and Maryland

Fiscal Year	*Age Group*	*U.S.*	*Maryland*
FY 1988	in their forties	35%	35%
	in their thirties	29%	29%
	in their teens	1%	3%
FY 1989	in their thirties	34%	28%
	in their forties	25%	35%
	in their teens	2%	1%
FY 1990	in their thirties	31%	33%
	in their twenties	19%	28%
	in their teens	2%	4%
FY 1991	in their thirties	29%	33%
	in their twenties	24%	27%
	in their teens	4%	3%

Drug problems, past or present, among these callers were quite rare. In FY 1988 and FY 1989, one percent or less admitted to abusing drugs. This number rose to 5% in FY 1990, but dropped in FY 1991.

In FY 1990, approximately 10% of Hotline callers admitted to difficulties with depression, crime, and suicidal attempts. In FY 1990, staffers were more specific in their questioning, and it was found that 3% of Hotline callers were suicidal at the time of calling, and another 2% had been suicidal in the past; 1% were subjected to violent physical abuse; 18% were considered to be seriously depressed requiring immediate care; and 16% had current legal problems. Maryland and national figures turned out to be fairly similar on these measures.

Maryland compulsive gamblers were more likely to be employed than national callers. In Maryland, 73% had full-time jobs, while nationally, only 66% were so employed. Not surprisingly, not too many of the compulsive gamblers, either in Maryland or nationally, had the money or health insurance to pay for treatment. Approximately 30% carry Blue Cross/Blue Shield or similar health insurance, as opposed to a slightly higher number who were insured through Health Maintenance Organizations (HMOs), and there was a similar number who had no insurance at all. The balance were either on medical assistance or had military or veterans benefits. In short, the vast majority of callers need supplemental funding from state departments of health in order to pay for their gambling addiction treatment. Of those who did have at least some health insurance, it was learned that the majority gambled at casinos or race tracks, and more typically represented white, middle class males who had full time employment.

Callers were also asked how they learned of the Hotline phone number. This was deemed of value in determining how limited funds or time could be spent most judiciously in reaching the largest possible number of people. The Hotline is listed in all Maryland Yellow Page phone directories; 29% of the callers learned of the Hotline through the phone book. Other callers learned of the number through the 800 telephone operator.

Newspaper stories, radio talk shows, or television shows often result in a large number of calls, but these tend to taper off after a few days. Thus, on a more consistent basis, the phone book or operator are the major sources for learning about the Hotline phone number. The other major source is Maryland State Lottery tickets or brochures which list the Hotline number.

GAMBLING PREFERENCES

Callers were asked about their gambling habits and to name their first and second preference of type of gambling. Because of the rather stark differences in gambling activity between Maryland compulsive gamblers and those from other states, results from both groups for FY 1990 are listed in Table 2.

The numbers for second choice of gambling are small; however, even these numbers are suggestive that gambling patterns of compulsive gamblers in Maryland may differ from gamblers in other states, which is suggestive of environmental factors contributing to compulsive gambling. These results are presented in Table 3.

TABLE 2

First Gambling Preference			
Maryland (n=322)		*National (n=757)*	
Lottery	22%	Casinos	19%
Poker machines	19%	Poker machines	15%
Horse racing	13%	Horse racing	15%
Sports	13%	Sports	14%
Casinos	12%	Lottery	13%
Cards	6%	Cards	9%
Tip jar, pulltab	4%	Tip jar, pulltab	3%
Compulsive spender	5%	Everything	3%
Bingo	2%	Dog racing	2%
Slot machines	1%	Bingo	2%
All others total	3%	All others total	5%

Also noteworthy is the increase of lottery addicts in FY 1990 when compared with previous figures. Nationally, there was a 6% increase, from 7% to 13%, while in Maryland there was a 15% increase, from 7% to 22%. Explanations for this increase could be either an increase of lottery addicts, or the greater ease which lottery players have in locating the 1-800 Hotline number, which since February, FY 1990 has been printed on Maryland lottery tickets. Such Hotline information was not available at Maryland's race tracks, casinos, bingo parlors, or other gambling sites.

TABLE 3

Second Gambling Preference			
Maryland (N=92)		*National (N=192)*	
Poker machines	21%	Casinos	17%
Lottery	15%	Sports	15%
Casinos	14%	Horses	15%
Sports	13%	Lottery	12%
Cards	8%	Poker machines	12%
Horses	7%	Cards	11%
Dice	5%	Everything	6%
Everything	4%	Slot machines	5%
Options, commodities	4%	Options, commodities.	3%
Bingo	2%	Bingo	2%
Tip jar, pulltabs	2%	Dice	2%

REFERRALS

Several criteria are used to determine where to send a compulsive gambler or family member for help. When the caller is referred to Gamblers Anonymous, in Maryland, at least two meeting times are provided. The caller is first given the location of a meeting held the same day or the next day; then the caller is referred to a meeting closest to the caller's home or place of employment. The caller's age, sex, and type of gambling are also considered when a third meeting is suggested.

For Gamblers Anonymous meetings outside of the state of Maryland the caller is given the meeting times and addresses of at least two meetings and phone numbers of individual members of Gamblers Anonymous in that area who are willing to serve in the capacity of first contact. Callers are also given the phone number of the Gamblers Anonymous International Service Office in

Los Angeles. Family members are given the phone number of the GamAnon International Service Office. If the caller lives in a state which has a state affiliate of the National Council on Problem Gambling, Inc., a referral is made to that organization as well.

Professional referrals in Maryland are based on location of the compulsive gambler, seriousness of the presenting problem, and the ability to pay. The first determination is location. The caller is always referred to a provider or a center specializing or experienced in treating compulsive gamblers which is closest to the caller. If, on the other hand, the caller is assessed to be suicidal, a referral is made to the nearest hospital. If a caller has only military or Veterans Administration (VA) benefits, the referral is made to a VA medical center identified as having a gambling treatment program, which may be out of state, in addition to also being referred to a provider closer to the caller's home. Callers who lack the ability to pay for treatment are referred to a local community mental health center and are also advised of gambling treatment providers nearest them.

It is not unusual for the Center to receive requests from mental health counselors for information on treatment approaches with compulsive gamblers. These calls tend to be helpful in expanding the network of providers.

In at least 25% of the cases, the caller faces legal complications or the caller may be threatened by a bookmaker or loanshark. On such occasions, the caller may be referred to a private attorney, the U.S. attorney's office, or to the FBI.

Compulsive gamblers who are in jeopardy of losing their jobs are referred to their Employee Assistance Program counselor, whenever possible. Callers complaining about legalized gambling are referred to their local legislator or to the specific agency involved with that gambling, such as the state lottery.

On occasion, the Center receives calls about the Hotline, such as funding base, staffing, and services. These questions are answered by the staff and may also be referred to the Maryland Department of Health and Mental Hygiene.

Finally, callers such as students or the media may request statistical and general information on compulsive gambling. Center staff provide such information and also make referrals to other treatment providers and researchers in the field, the National Council on Problem Gambling, or to its state affiliates.

MARKETING OF THE HOTLINE

Due to the lack of funding, advertising expenses for the Hotline have had to be kept to an absolute minimum. During the first year, all promotion was kept within the state of Maryland. Listings were taken out in the Yellow Page directories, starting with the more populated areas of the state. When the contract was renewed for the second year, a listing was placed in all Yellow Page directories. The cost of such placement amounted to approximately $200 per month. In FY 1992, Yellow Page advertising was expanded to select cities in the U.S.

By the end of the first contract period, the State's Department of Health and Mental Hygiene gave permission to expand promotion of the number. Thus, it was included in all media press releases, news shows and interviews. It was also given as the contact number for radio or television talk shows.

For another marketing approach, stickers were designed consisting of a bright orange one inch by three inch label, inscribed simply "1-800-332-0402" on one line and "Compulsive Gambling Hotline" below that. These labels were included in all the Center's mailings, and were distributed as well at conferences. A third marketing item was a pencil with the Center's name and the Hotline number on it. In FY 1990, when the Center's brochures needed to be updated, the Hotline number was also printed on them. Costs for a special Hotline brochure were too prohibitive, given the inadequate funding support, so Hotline brochures were not printed until FY 1993.

Maryland legislators have received *Final Reports* from the Center regarding the Hotline at the end of contract periods, and information from Hotline data was presented at legislative hearings. This has not, however, resulted in any additional funding for the Hotline.

The Center has also approached radio stations in the state to air 15 or 30-second public service announcements. While these public service announcements are free of charge, they do require time and effort — thus limited resources — which are not covered by the monies allotted in the contract.

In February 1990, the Maryland legislature told the State Lottery to warn lottery players about compulsive gambling. As a result, the Hotline number was printed on lottery brochures and on the back of lottery tickets. The message is at the bottom of the lottery ticket, boxed, and reads: "Compulsive gambling is a treatable disorder. For help call toll-free 1-800-332-0402." The advertising agency for the lottery is currently planning a 30-second public service announcement for television, hoping to use renowned athletes and movie stars known to be compulsive gamblers, in this effort.

PROBLEMS AND MORE PROBLEMS

As in any new project, one expects the unexpected. This was true also of the Compulsive Gambling Hotline.

A. Lack of Adequate Funding

Shortage of funding was known to be an issue from the onset. The Center was faced with providing maximum services, with trained mental health counselors, 24 hours per day. If it increased its promotional activities, telephone costs would go up and so would the use of staff time. This shortage has continued to the time of this writing. The allotment from DHMH in FY 1990 was $20,000, while the cost is over $100,000. The Center has thus sought funds from private sources to offset this shortfall. Its success is limited.

B. Breakdown in Communication

Center staff were not aware of the slow bureaucratic process in receiving state funds. What was expected within a week or two, in actuality took over two months. Further, when the second contract was negotiated, the Center was made keenly aware that funding is based on the date of *signing* the contract, which itself was often delayed due to bureaucratic procedures. Thus, there was no contract from July 1, 1988 to October 1, 1988, and no funds were provided for that interim period. The Center was faced with the choice of terminating the Hotline or continuing it at the Center's expense. The latter course of action was taken. Since that experience, contract negotiations are started at least three months in advance to avoid a repetition of this funding complication.

C. Breakdown in Equipment

The Hotline telephones were located in three sites in the Center's offices. Three phones were purchased, one with an answering machine. Within three years, five phones had broken down, and every answering machine had to be replaced. The Hotline eventually shifted to a separate answering machine rather than a combination phone/answering machine.

D. Unpredictable Events

At one time, Hotline calls were coming in at the rate of about three calls a day, with an occasional wrong number, when the pattern took a sudden new direction. A call would come in, there would be ten to 25 seconds of silence, and the line would be disconnected. Most of these calls came in the mornings, generally between 9 a.m. and noon. This kept up for five continuous working days. By the time the local police, the FBI in Baltimore and Massachusetts, and phone security personnel from the three phone companies involved were able to tap into the lines, over three hundred calls had been received. The source of the problem was traced to an error made by a bank employee who had punched the Compulsive Gambling Hotline number into the bank credit line computer data bank. The Center was forced to cancel appointments with patients because of these constant disruptions. The bank made reimbursement to the Center for the costs that were incurred.

E. Unpredictable Volume

The Center expected an increase in calls in response to media promotion. However, the intensity and duration of increased volume were not predictable since there were no similar services that the Center could turn to for guidance. Through experience, the Center has implemented some basic procedures to handle a sudden increase in volume and types of calls. When the Pete Rose story broke in 1989, for instance, there was an increase in calls over a period of several months from media reporters who wanted to know more about compulsive gambling. This took more time from clinical staff members, with each call usually lasting a minimum of thirty minutes. It also increased the volume of materials which was sent to these callers, thus escalating staff, postage, and printing costs.

On the other hand, when project staff appear on popular radio or television shows, especially if it is a national show, there might be over 100 calls a day for several days. Newspaper articles or magazine stories on compulsive gambling tend to result in a slight increase of daily calls, but these calls tend to come in over a longer period of time. Many people may read an article about the Hotline and not make a call until several months later.

Another problem in this area was not knowing when a television, radio or printed story would be aired, and often staff was caught unprepared for the sudden upsurge in volume. As a matter of procedure, staff now makes it a policy to learn when a story is scheduled for release, so that extra clinical team members, staff and volunteers can be called upon to cover the phones.

UNEXPECTED MARKETING EVENTS

An increase of calls per month was desired and expected; however, the staff did not anticipate the avalanche of calls that came in on different occasions. The Hotline was averaging about 150 calls per month when there was a sudden upsurge of calls in November 1989. This was due to the ongoing publicity about baseball hero Pete Rose and his alleged sports gambling. Media interest was exceptionally high, and requests for information on compulsive gambling came from all over the country.

On another occasion ESPN, the sports television network, aired a three minute segment on compulsive gambling and U.S. professional football's championship game, the Super Bowl. Within three days, over 400 compulsive gamblers who were sports bettors called in requesting assistance. These callers had a variety of problems, such as wanting to know what to do when bookies or loansharks threatened them with physical harm, whether they should pay off their bookies, or making requests for help with their emotional problems that had arisen due to sports betting, such as failing classes in school and dealing with stress from debts. The vast majority of these sports bettors ranged in ages from 12 to 20, and all of them were males. They described sports betting as common among high school students, and bookmaking operations were often found to be located on college campuses. Almost all were deeply in debt and their school grades were suffering. Some were forced to drop out of school because they were unable to continue functioning. New literature geared to the teenage gambler had to be developed to accommodate these young callers.

Legislative activity also created an increase in calls, in particular, when Oregon voted on the NFL Lottery and when riverboat gambling became a hotly debated issue in several states. In the midst of this activity, calls quadrupled within one month. Again, many of these calls were from the media, requesting information on the potential impact of additional legalized gambling on compulsive gambling and on the community in terms of illegal gambling and costs.

In January 1990, Jim Bohannan invited this author to join him on the Larry King radio talk show, which was aired not only once, but twice, nationally.

This resulted in over 125 calls from gambling addicts or family members within the following 12-hour period. A temporary staff member had to be hired to help with the phones and to respond to the many requests for literature on compulsive gambling.

The Hotline was averaging over 300 calls per month at the beginning of 1990 when yet another unexpected upsurge occurred, resulting in a peak of over 3,500 calls in a one-month period. This surge was attributed to when the Maryland State Lottery began printing warning notices and the 1-800 number on lottery tickets and promotional materials; thus, most of the calls were unrelated to compulsive gambling issues.

A by-product of this situation resulted in the accumulation of considerable unexpected data on buyers of Maryland lottery tickets. Approximately 10,500 calls came in during the five-month period of February and June, 1990. Of these, 4485 were entered onto the computer and analyzed according to national and Maryland data. Calls came in from 45 states, including Hawaii and Alaska, but just over two-thirds of the calls analyzed originated in Maryland. Over 97% of the calls were less than one minute in duration. The gender of Maryland and national callers was 52% males.

Unfortunately, the Lottery did not first consult with the Center, about printing the Hotline number on lottery tickets, and the results for the Center's normal operations were disruptive and costly. Since then, the State Lottery has assigned a liaison to work with the Center, which has improved the working relationship between the two organizations. The Lottery and the Center consult on issues relating to compulsive gambling, lottery advertisement, and public service announcements. The Center is also advised when a new type of lottery game is implemented, so that the staff is prepared to handle the anticipated increase in calls. More recently, the state lottery and the Center printed a lottery vendor's guide to compulsive gambling, the first of its kind in the country.

Not surprisingly, there was a cost overrun of the Hotline budget in FY 1990 as a result of this experience. Thus the DHMH allocated an additional emergency grant of $9,000 for the Hotline, representing a total of $19,000 for the fiscal year. Nearly 12,000 calls were received on the Hotline during FY 1990, of which slightly over 1,300 were related to compulsive gambling. The remainder were what were dubbed "lottery" calls — calls from people who wanted some information on winning lottery numbers, where to get winning tickets cashed, how to buy subscriptions, how much is paid on certain winning lotto tickets, etc.

The Center was able to capitalize on this opportunity to inform callers about the services of the Hotline and that compulsive gambling is a treatable disorder. The Center was thus reaching an unprecedented and unanticipated number of bettors in Maryland and throughout the United States.

The Center systematically recruits volunteers. One source of new "volunteers" has been through the Office of U.S. Probation and Parole. These volunteers are offenders who were ordered by federal courts to perform community service. This appears to be a mutually satisfactory relationship, and the Center expanded this working relationship to the city and state probation and parole offices. Ideally, the majority of volunteers would be recovering gamblers, so that there can be a natural empathy. In reality, they are not. GA and Gam-Anon members tend to respond negatively to requests for volunteers.

FUTURE DIRECTIONS

In 1990, the Center signed a three-year contract with the Department of Health and Mental Hygiene for continuation of the Compulsive Gambling Hotline through FY 1993. During this contract period, the Center will continue to promote the Hotline through media interviews nationally.

An ongoing strategy of the Center is to make greater efforts to have feature articles on compulsive gambling and its impact on the family and community in the smaller newspapers which serve local communities in Maryland, especially if a local compulsive gambler's story is included. Also, a special Hotline brochure is included in all mailings, and will be distributed at conferences, libraries, community mental health centers, and state legislatures. Efforts will also be put forth to obtain private funding for expansion of the Hotline staff. Volunteers alone cannot provide the services that are needed for a crisis line with such an array of stressful and potentially dangerous situations. It is anticipated that the Hotline will need to hire several paid staff members in the near future.

Historically, immediate response to a high stress or high risk call has resulted in effective diffusion of the stress or crisis, and when necessary, interception and transportation to a hospital; however, additional phone lines had to be added so that callers in distress would not encounter a busy signal or a recording.

As additional funds become available, they will be used for promotional materials for distribution in other states. It is also anticipated that research endeavors will be expanded to other states. Up to FY 1990, data were analyzed on the basis of Maryland and national data. Future research is likely to look at data from specific states, perhaps starting with those states that were included in the Volberg and Steadman (1989) study. Current data suggests regional differences — more legal problems in New Jersey, more drug problems in Calfornia, more female gamblers in Minnesota, etc. The Center will attempt to establish a uniform data collection form for use by *all* compulsive gambling hotlines.

SUMMARY AND CONCLUSIONS

The Compulsive Gambling Hotline has provided, and continues to provide, a valuable service to individuals, families, and communities who are suffering from the effects of compulsive gambling. It offers immediate crisis counseling and makes referrals to self-help groups and professional therapists who are trained in treating this disorder. It provides ongoing education to communities throughout the country via its many media interviews and through its lottery calls. Its network of therapists has grown, and it has encouraged training of mental health providers in treating this illness. Locales with illegal gambling activities have been identified, for the benefit of local and federal law enforcement and legislative bodies. And it is helping convicted offenders make amends by giving them an opportunity to give to the community rather than to take from it, by way of service to the community in working on the Hotline.

Through Hotline data, it has been possible to identify the variances within gambling groups, by age, sex, race, and type of gambling. It was learned that many compulsive gamblers lack adequate mental health insurance, thus making it virtually impossible for them to receive the professional treatment they may need. The Hotline has also identified gaps in service providers, which further complicates the gambling addict's efforts at recovery.

In spite of increased targeted promotional efforts, blacks and ethnic minorities are under-represented among gambling addicts using this line. On the other hand, blacks and ethnic minorities are over-represented among lottery calls.

The Hotline has also been able to identify shifts in types of gambling. For instance, from our calls from FY 1988 to FY 1992, there was an increase in lottery and poker machine addicts in Maryland, while there was a decrease in race track and casino addicts. This is not a reflection of the observed national trends, however, and may be a consequence of the types of gambling available in Maryland. This would reinforce the position that availability and accessibility of gambling are contributing factors in the development of compulsive gambling, thus leading to an increase in these types of gambling addiction.

The Hotline has also been able to identify pockets of illegal gambling, such as tip jars in rural areas, after-hours card clubs in cities, and slot machines or video poker machines in fraternal organizations, which appear to be on the rise. Bookmakers, as a rule, tend to be verbally abusive by threatening harm to the gambling addict or family members. More recently, a worrisome trend of actual physical violence perpetrated by members within this gambling subculture was noted.

Lottery calls provide indicators of popular types of lottery games as they are introduced, while also reflecting the types of people who buy lottery tickets. With the compulsive gambling Hotline number printed on lottery tickets and on promotional materials, lottery addicts now have direct access to a crisis line phone number, and these lottery addicts are, in fact, calling for help.

In short, the Compulsive Gambling Hotline is an excellent means of supplying information to people who want to know more about this devastating and treatable psychiatric disorder.

APPENDIX

TYPES OF CALLS

The Compulsive Gambling Hotline receives a wide array of calls. The following are a sampling of these calls.

A husband knows he needs help but fears that if he goes for counseling, his wife will find out how much he owes.

A fifteen-year military serviceman wrote bad checks to support his gambling habit. He made them all good, but got "kicked out." He wants to get back in the service.

Her husband's gambling escalated after his best friend committed suicide. He lost their savings and their tax refund at the track.

A news service wants background information after learning about Pete Rose's suspension.

A widow with a son who is a compulsive gambler is angry. She says the state lottery gives gambling credibility, and makes it harder on single parents to raise children.

The caller wants to go to a Gambler's Anonymous (GA) meeting but has no car or money for transportation.

A distraught wife found out her husband lied to her. "He owes $5,000 to the bookies. He told me he owed $500."

Her husband has a grocery store with a lottery machine in it. He owes the state $30,000 due to his lottery addiction.

The caller wants to file a complaint of skimming by a bingo parlor.

A recovering compulsive gambler called back to thank the Hotline staff. He is in treatment, has a new job, and is doing fine.

A 17-year old is flunking college. He stays up all night playing cards.

Her husband beat her up after finding out she gambled away mortgage payments. The bank wants to foreclose.

Her husband forged her name on her life insurance policy and used the cash value for gambling at the casino. Should she press charges?

Where are Gamblers Anonymous and GamAnon meetings held?

The bookie is threatening to break his son's legs. His wife is seriously ill. He does not want to pay, but fears for his wife's health and son's life.

He went to a state-funded drug program for his gambling problems, and was told the first appointment available is in two months. He needs help now.

A ministry student wants information on chaplaincy at the race track.

He is divorcing his wife because she will not quit gambling.

She has tried everywhere for help. Now she wants to kill herself.

She saw a one-hour television show on compulsive gambling. It was very helpful. Thank you.

She saw a television show on compulsive gambling and learned new ways to get money to feed her habit.

Her husband, a colonel, just died. She no longer has to worry about his debts and losing his military career due to his gambling.

An employer has several employees who have gambling problems.

What are the Twenty Questions of Gamblers Anonymous? What are the early warning signs of compulsive gambling?

Her son is married to a bingo addict. The four grandchildren are being neglected.

A psychologist would like training in treating this disorder.

A military officer is gambling at Indian reservation casinos. He lost $22,000 last year. He was driving back to his base and needed someone to talk with.

Why are teenagers allowed to go to race tracks?

The wife of a police officer hocked his gun to play the video machines.

What does the Bible say about gambling? Is playing bingo in church a sin?

He is filing bankruptcy to get rid of gambling debts.

A police officer knows he is addicted to lotteries. He and his partner also go to the casinos after work.

A sergeant in military intelligence started gambling on slot machines, during a "really bad tour of duty," while overseas.

The caller thought the bookie was his best friend even though he owes him $7,500. "He always calls me."

Her husband found out about her gambling bills and tried to stab her.

He owes money to the bookie. The bookie threatened his boss. Now he might get fired.

A bar has had repeated convictions for having illegal poker machines. They are still there. Why are the police not doing anything?

He knows he needs help but does not want to go to Gamblers Anonymous. He is too well known.

He can't stop gambling. He has a gun, and keeps looking at the bullets on the table.

Can losing lottery tickets be used as a tax write-off?

A lawyer wants to know if the *Guilty but mentally ill* plea for gambling-related crimes has been used successfully in criminal cases.

She sells lottery tickets. Now she is addicted to lottery gambling. Should she quit her job?

His wife just filed for divorce because of his gambling. He stopped three years ago but she is still angry.

If tip jars are illegal, why are they in the VFWs and American Legions?

The *Army Times* wants to do a story on slot machines and gambling in the military.

A corrections officer is thinking of using his weapon to get money for gambling.

A lottery addict feels lucky. He has 2,000 losing tickets and Virginia is having a special losing ticket lottery.

The FBI broke up an organized crime family heavy into bookmaking. The defendants are using compulsive gambling as a defense.

He is sentenced to jail for gambling-related crimes. He sat all night by the river, wanting to throw himself in.

A 10-year-old boy called, crying. "Mom left. I'm afraid of Dad. He looks funny. He got fired because he plays cards. My little brother's scared, too."

REFERENCES

Jacobs, D. (1989). Illegal and undocumented: A review fo teenage gambling and the plight of children of problem gamblers in America. In Shaffer, H., Stein, S.A., Gambino, B., and Cummings, T. (eds.), *Compulsive Gambling: Theory, Research & Practice* (pp. 249-292). Lexington, MA: Lexington Books.

Jacobs, D. (1992). *Teenage compulsive gambling in Virginia and California.* Paper presented at the Annual Conference of the National Council on Problem Gambling, Inc., Cleveland, OH.

Ladouceur, R. and Mireault, C. (1988). Gambling behaviors among high school students in the Québec area. *Journal of Gambling Behavior*, 4:1, 3-12.

Lesieur, H.R. and Kline, R. (1987). Pathological gambling among high school students. *Addictive Behaviors*, 12, 129-135.

Lorenz, V.C. (1990). *An Overview of Pathological Gambling.* Baltimore, MD: Compulsive Gambling Center, Inc.

Volberg, R. and Steadman, H. (1989, December). Prevalence estimates of pathological gambling in New Jersey and Maryland. *American Journal of Psychiatry*, 1618-1619.

For further information on the Compulsive Gambling Hotline, contact Dr. Valerie Lorenz at the Compulsive Gambling Center, Inc., 924 East Baltimore Street, Baltimore, MD 21202.

The Role of Support in Recovery from Compulsive Gambling

Sharon A. Stein*

Compulsive gambling, or "pathological gambling" as referred to by the *Diagnostic and Statistical Manual of Mental Disorders*, is characterized by "a chronic and progressive failure to resist impulses to gamble, and gambling behavior that compromises, disrupts or damages personal, family, or vocational pursuits" (American Psychiatric Association, 1987). Throughout this paper, the term "compulsive gambling" will be used to identify destructive gambling behavior because that is the term used by members of Gamblers Anonymous, who as a group represent those

* Preparation of this paper was supported, in part, by a contract (#2322905893) from the Massachusetts Department of Public Health through the Massachusetts Council on Compulsive Gambling and the Norman E. Zinberg Center for Addiction Studies.
Requests for more information or comments should be sent to Sharon Stein, Cognitive Behavior Therapy Unit, McLean Hospital, 115 Mill Street, Belmont, MA, 02178, USA.

most effected by the behavior. Gamblers Anonymous is a self-help program open to anyone who feels as if their gambling behavior has gone beyond their emotional control (Gamblers Anonymous Publishing, 1984).

Most of the research on compulsive gambling to date has been focussed on finding the cause of compulsive gambling. As a review of the research on compulsive gambling by Dickerson (1989) points out, most of the studies assume that there is a qualitative difference between compulsive gamblers and non-compulsive gamblers, and this basic assumption never really becomes tested. Most research on compulsive gambling begins with an *a'priori* premise that there is a biological, psychological, social, or behavioral cause that will account for the difference between compulsive gamblers and non compulsive gamblers.

The only way to satisfactorily answer the question, "Are there factors which account for differences between those who develop compulsive gambling and those who do not?" would be to conduct a prospective longitudinal study, in which large numbers of people were tracked for a long period of time and observed on hundreds of variables to determine which characteristics identified those who became compulsive gamblers. Although this type of study could be important to conduct, it would be very expensive and time consuming.

So far, researchers have picked certain variables that seem plausible and conducted studies using their favorite predictors. As Burglass and Shaffer (1980) point out for the field of addictions research, there are many more mini-theories with interesting results stemming from researchers' interests in promoting a certain paradigm than there are comprehensive theories that combine one or more theoretical outlooks. Shaffer (1989) has noted that the field of compulsive gambling research is subject to a conceptual crisis similar to that of addictions research in general, because there is no theoretical agreement about where to look for the causes of compulsive gambling behavior.

There are four main areas in which researchers have looked for the causes of compulsive gambling: psychological, sociological, behavioral, and biological. Psychological studies have examined internal psychological processes, such as the personality of the gambler following Freud (1928) and Bergler (1957); sociological studies have examined the socio-economic class of compulsive gamblers, as well as the social milieu of the casino or racetrack (Lesieur, 1984; Rosecrance, 1988); behavioral studies look at the reinforcement contingencies and illusion of control over outcomes that compulsive gamblers exhibit

(Dickerson, 1979; Frank and Smith, 1989) and lastly, the biological approach, has looked for the causes of compulsive gambling in the gamblers' brain (Goldstein, Manowitz, Nora, Swartzburg and Carlton, 1985) adrenal system (Roy, Adinoff, Roehrich, Lamparski, Custer, Lorenz, Barbaccia, Guidotti, Costa, and Linnoila, 1988) or some other physiological process (Dickerson and Adcock, 1987; Carlton, and Goldstein, 1987).

One of the most fascinating things about this field is that the published studies show significant differences between compulsive gamblers and non-compulsive gamblers in every single one of these areas. The research shows strong evidence that individuals who meet the DSM-III-R criteria for compulsive gambling at the time they are measured appear different than controls in every one of these areas.

The common factor among these various studies is that compulsive gamblers appear deviant, differing from normal gamblers in the extent of their gambling behavior, their self-control, their personality (often showing anti-social or narcissistic personality disorder according to some studies) as well as even physiologically responding differently to gambling than non-compulsive gamblers do. These findings make it seem as if the assumption about the difference between compulsive and non-compulsive gamblers is correct. However, all of the studies reported here looked at the differences between compulsive gamblers and non-compulsive gamblers retrospectively in order to infer a causal factor. The real question that is not addressed by any of the retrospective studies is whether each of these "areas of deviance" is a result or a cause of the compulsive gambling behavior.

Compulsive gamblers in the midst of the "chase" as Lesieur (1984) has depicted are isolated and lonely even while surrounded by tremendous activity. Sometimes the gambling is even a socially engaging activity. Lesieur's (1979) image of the ever tightening spiral of options and involvement portrays the way that a compulsive gambler becomes isolated as individuals who were former social, financial, and emotional supports cut off contact with the gambler. Rosenthal (1986) discusses the compulsive gambler's isolation in a system of self deception. Reality becomes distorted as the compulsive gambler creates a world based on the hope of the future or the dreams of the past, rather than looking at the present.

The compulsive gambler may even become isolated from his or her own knowledge of what is happening during the game. Browne (1989) conducted a study of the concept of going "on tilt" with frequent poker players. He found that those who go on tilt often were likely to become compulsive gamblers. The subjective experience for gamblers who go "on tilt" include blackouts, memory loss, dissociative states, or simply playing mindlessly without thinking of strategy. The situations that spark episodes of "going on tilt" are often feeling ashamed and losing face in front of fellow gamblers or by being provoked and criticized by fellow gamblers. Although several authors (Rosecrance, 1988; Abt, Smith, and Christiansen, 1985) have written of the social benefits of gambling, the benefits of honest, intimate friendships in the gambling arena do not seem to apply to compulsive gamblers.

The observation that compulsive gamblers tend to be isolated, lonely, and labeled deviant even by fellow gamblers, led this author to wonder about the role of social support in the recovery of compulsive gambling. If isolation and deviance is the common thread among all the symptoms of the disorder, might not connection, relatedness and building a social support network facilitate recovery?

Rather than searching for the causes of compulsive gambling, the purpose of this study was to understand how individuals who formerly were obsessed with gambling managed to choose not to gamble for periods of weeks, months, and years. The repeated daily choice to abstain from gambling over a period of time, when one formerly behaved in an opposite manner, is a drastic lifestyle change. This study investigates the relationship between feeling supported for making the change to not gambling and the length of time one has remained abstinent.

There is consistent evidence from studies of Gamblers Anonymous (Custer and Custer, 1978) and outcome measures of treatment programs (Taber, McCormick, Russo, Adkins and Ramirez, 1987) that individuals who at one time in their lives exhibited the signs and symptoms of compulsive gambling behavior eventually learn to either abstain or control their compulsive gambling behavior. There is much controversy in the field regarding the concept of whether individuals who once appeared to be compulsive gamblers can actually return to social gambling. This study did not look at that question, but rather focussed on the processes of change that individuals go through as they continually make the decision to abstain from gambling.

There were two questions posed in the analysis of the data to be presented. The first is, "What factors are associated with the length of abstinence time for recovering compulsive gamblers?" The second is more specifically looking at, "What is the relationship between a recovering compulsive gambler's perception of social support and his or her length of time in abstinence from gambling?" Does the perception of social support relate strongly to the probability of continuing to abstain from gambling? This study was exploratory in nature and not confirmatory. Given the limited research on the process of quitting compulsive gambling, this study was conducted only with compulsive gamblers who had chosen to abstain from gambling rather than using control groups of individuals who had learned to control their gambling or who considered themselves to gamble non-compulsively.

METHOD

A. Subjects

Subjects were 47 individuals who identified themselves as either formerly or currently having a problem with excessive gambling. The sample consisted of 15 females and 32 males. Subjects were mainly from either the Massachusetts area or the Nevada area of the United States. Subjects were recruited on a volunteer basis through various organizations: Gambler's Anonymous meetings in Massachusetts and Nevada, the Massachusetts Council on Compulsive Gambling, the Nevada Council on Compulsive Gambling, therapists treating compulsive gamblers, the V.A. hospital in Boston, and members of G.A. who helped recruit volunteers in California, Nevada, and New Jersey, as well as the Massachusetts area. All of the women in the sample came from the Las Vegas, Nevada region.

B. Procedure

Subjects were given a questionnaire called the Compulsive Gambling Recovery Survey, with a stamped return envelope attached. Subjects were asked by the contact person, either directly or through the mail, to fill out and mail back the completed questionnaire. Subjects typically either filled out the questionnaire and mailed it back or handed it back to the researcher at a later GA meeting which was pre-arranged. The return rate for those who actually filled out the questionnaires that they were given was about 15% in general. The return rate was near 50% in Nevada, perhaps because the researcher had more contact with participants.

C. Dependent Measure

The dependent measure in this study is the reported length of time that a former compulsive gambler has abstained from gambling. This measure was obtained by simply asking in two places on the questionnaire, "What was the date of the last time you gambled for money?" In a second question, subjects were asked, "How long have you abstained from gambling." In all cases, these two lengths of time matched very closely. Subjects were also asked if the last time they gambled was only a small slip or whether it was a long binge. In the few cases in which subjects reported a small slip, there was not more than two months time difference, so the official date of the last time they gambled was used. Although to the author's knowledge there have been no studies of the reliability of self report on lengths of abstinence in recovering compulsive gamblers, there is high social pressure among Gambler's Anonymous members to be accurate in reporting abstinence dates. The GA groups in Nevada hold "birthday" parties for members, and the GA groups in Massachusetts hold "anniversary" parties, both celebrating the date that abstinence from gambling begins.

For the sample of 47 subjects, the time abstinent from gambling ranged from 1 week to 29 years, with 50% of the sample having two years or less of abstinent time. As shown in Table 1, the mean time abstinent for this sample was 4 years, but the median was 2 years. Because the distribution was skewed, this variable was transformed using log e in the data analysis.

TABLE 1

Demographic Information from Sample of Recovering Compulsive Gamblers

N = 47

VARIABLE	*RANGE*	*MEAN*
Time abstinent from gambling	1 wk. to 29 yrs.	4 yrs. (median 2 yrs.)
Age	21 to 81	44
Perception of support for not gambling	26 to 50	44
Gender	Male — 32 (68%)	Female — 15 (32%)
Had treatment for gambling problem	Yes — 21 (45%)	No— 26 (55%)

In Table 1, several demographic variables are also presented. There were no significant differences between men and women for the variables of length of time in recovery or perceived level of social support. As will be discussed later, whether one had been in treatment for gambling or not was significantly correlated with the variable of length of time abstinent from gambling.

D. Independent Measures

Several independent measures were collected in the overall study; but for this paper, only the measure of social support for recovery as an independent variable is presented. Because this study was conducted through self-report, the variable "social support" is really a measure of the subject's perception of social support. A social support score was calculated by adding together the scores on all ten items. Those questions which were phrased in the negative were reversed, so as to make the highest score possible a 50 and the lowest score possible a 10. As shown in Table 1, subjects scored on a range of 26 to 50 with a mean score of 44.

Social support information was collected in two parts. First, subjects were asked to list who the people were that they felt were supportive in their recovery. Second, subjects were asked 10 questions regarding how supported they felt for making the change to not gamble. Table 2 shows the format that was used to collect this data. The questionnaire was shortened for this presentation in that under each of the numbers the meaning of the scale was reprinted each time.

E. Results and Discussion

The first question posed by this study is "What factors are associated with the length of abstinence time for recovering compulsive gamblers?" When the data were collected and analyzed, it turned out that several variables were correlated with the outcome variable of time abstinent from gambling. These variables and their correlations are shown in Table 3.

Table 3 shows that the variables of age, treatment for gambling problems, and perceived support are all significantly correlated with length of time abstinent from gambling. The relationship between age and time abstinent makes sense intuitively, in that the older one becomes from the time one has quit gambling, the more likely one is to have more time in recovery if one does not gamble again. However, this is the weakest of the three significant correlations. The fact that age and abstinence time are not more highly correlated points to the fact that individuals may be relapsing and gambling again. This question cannot be answered from the data collected in this study alone. But the question could be answered in a study in which repeated measures were taken to track individuals over their time in recovery.

TABLE 2

Change Support System Questionnaire

Directions: Take a few minutes to think about who has given you support to *change your gambling behavior*. It may be your friends, family, your Gambler's Anonymous group, a psychologist or a therapy group. Please check here, the types of people or groups who have helped you change. If there is no one, leave this part blank.

Gambler's Anonymous group ☐

Sponsor ☐

Therapist ☐

Family ☐

Spouse ☐

Friends ☐

Therapy group ☐

Other ☐ ________________________

Please indicate below the extent to which you tend to agree or disagree with each statement. In each case, make your choice in terms of how you feel *right now*, not what you have felt in the past or what you would like to feel. There are five possible responses to each of the items in the questionnaire:

①—Strongly Disagree

②—Disagree

③—Undecided

④—Agree

⑤—Strongly Agree

Please circle the number that best describes how much you agree or disagree with each statement.

1. There are people who will really try to help me resist when I feel like gambling.
   1 2 3 4 5

continued . . .

2. There are people whom I can trust to really listen when I am upset.
   1 2 3 4 5

3. No one really cares whether I gamble or not.
   1 2 3 4 5

4. There are people in my life that I have fun with.
   1 2 3 4 5

5. There are people in my life that help me sort out problems that bother me.
   1 2 3 4 5

6. If I disappeared for a while, no one would ever call to find out what happened.
   1 2 3 4 5

7. There are people who would stick by me in a crisis.
   1 2 3 4 5

8. There are people who would loan me money if I needed it.
   1 2 3 4 5

9. There are people who depend on me to be supportive when they need help.
   1 2 3 4 5

10. I talk to people about my recovery on at least a weekly basis.
    1 2 3 4 5

TABLE 3

Simple Correlations of Variables With Gambling Abstinence Time

N = 47

	TIME ABSTINENT FROM GAMBLING		
	r	p value	df
Age	0.29	< .05	46
Had Gambling Treatment (0 = No treatment 1 = treatment)	-0.35	< .01	46
Perceived Support	0.37	< .01	46

The second correlation of gambling treatment and length of time abstinent is negative, meaning that those who have had treatment for gambling are likely to have less time in recovery than those who have not. This is probably a byproduct of the newness of gambling treatment more than an intrinsic relationship between gambling treatment and recovery. Since treatment specifically for gambling problems has only become available in the past 10 years, with the majority of gambling treatment programs starting up in the past five years (Gambino and Cummings, 1989), it makes sense that those who have had gambling treatment would be likely to have less time in recovery than those who did not.

The second question asked above was, "What is the relationship between a recovering compulsive gambler's perception of social support and his or her length of time in abstinence from gambling?" As the third correlation in Table 3 shows, there is a statistically significant relationship between the perception of social support and the length of time one has been abstinent from gambling.

Further analysis shows that there is a definite trend between how supported the recovering compulsive gamblers feel for quitting gambling and the length of time in recovery. The relationship between support and length of time in recovery from compulsive gambling becomes more heterogeneous when one feels more supported or has a lot of time in recovery. One interpretation of this relationship is that feeling supported for changing is an important factor in maintaining recovery from compulsive gambling for some people, and for others, feeling supported was a precipitant to beginning the recovery process. A further analysis following recovering compulsive gamblers over time would be necessary to tell whether those recovering gamblers who do not feel as supported are more likely to relapse.

An additional question that could be addressed by this study is whether it matters how much support a person actually has, or is it just how supported they feel that relates significantly to time in recovery? To answer this question, the author added up the numbers of people that each subject listed as being part of a support network. There appears to be no relationship between how many people the recovering gamblers had as a support network for recovery, but simply how supported they felt that related significantly to time in recovery. This was verified by running a regression analysis in which the addition of the variable SUPNET, the numbers of people in the support network, was not a significant predictor of time in recovery in a model which already included support.

CONCLUSION

This exploratory study gives evidence for the notion that feeling supported for change is significantly related to the length of time compulsive gamblers are able to maintain abstinence from gambling. It is not possible to infer from this study that perception of support is causally related to time in recovery. However, further studies which follow recovering compulsive gamblers over time may be able to determine whether lack of perceived social support is a factor in relapse. Certainly clinical data and data from members of Gambler's Anonymous gives evidence for the notion that those recovering compulsive gamblers who isolate themselves and do not discuss thoughts and feelings with others are more likely to fall back into compulsive gambling or other addictive behavior.

The finding that compulsive gamblers who feel supported in their recovery are more likely to have a longer period of recovery may have implications for preventing relapses for compulsive gamblers. More research is needed on the factors affecting both the process of becoming a compulsive gambler and recovering from it. By viewing compulsive gambling behavior as a problem that develops and becomes arrested or recovered from over the lifespan, it may be possible for researchers to see factors which can prevent its occurrence (Stein, 1989). The feeling of being supported and connected to one's peers may be a factor contributing to the recovery from other addictive behaviors as well.

Further research on addictive behavior will be most integrative across disciplines if the variable of time is used to track the onset, progression and final outcome of individual's addictive behavior. Following Vaillant (1987), researchers in the addictions need to take a bigger chunk of time information in the gathering of data on addictive behavior. It may be necessary to look across the lifespan of individuals to be able to see the patterns that result in individuals' eventual destruction by or recovery from addictive behaviors.

REFERENCES

Abt, V., Smith, J.F. and Christiansen E.G. (1985). *The Business of Risk: Commercial Gambling in Mainstream America.* Lawrence, KS: University Press of Kansas.

American Psychiatric Association (1987). *Diagnostic and Statistical Manual of Mental Disorders*, 3rd edition, revised. Washington D.C.: American Psychiatric Association.

Bergler, H. (1958). *The Psychology of Gambling.* New York: International University Press.

Browne, B.R. (1989). Going on tilt: Frequent poker players and control. *Journal of Gambling Behavior*, 5:1, 3-21.

Burglass, M.E. and Shaffer, H.J. (1981). Introduction: The natural history of ideas in the treatment of the addictions. In H. Shaffer and M. Burglass (eds.), *Classic Contributions in the Addictions.* New York: Brunner/Mazel.

Carlton, P.L. and Goldstein, L. (1987). Physiological determinants of pathological gambling. In T. Galski (ed.), *The Handbook of Pathological Gambling* (pp. 111-122). Springfield, IL: Charles C. Thomas.

Custer, R.L. and Custer, L.F. (1978, December). *Characteristics of the recovering compulsive gambler: A survey of 150 members of Gamblers Anonymous.* Paper presented at the Fourth National Conference on Gambling, Reno, Nevada.

Dickerson, M. and Adcock, S. (1987). Mood, arousal, and cognitions in persistent gambling: Preliminary investigations of a theoretical model. *Journal of Gambling Behavior*, 3:1, 3-15.

Dickerson, M.G. (1979). FI schedules and persistence at gambling in the U.K. betting office. *Journal of Applied Behavior Analysis*, 12, 315-23.

Dickerson, M.G. (1989). Gambling: A dependence without a drug. *International Review of Psychiatry*, 1, 157-172.

Frank, M.L. and Smith, C. (1989). Illusion of control and gambling in children. *Journal of Gambling Behavior*, 5:2, 127-136.

Freud, S. (1928). Doestoevsky and parricide. In J. Strachey (ed. and translator), *The Complete Psychological Works of Sigmund Freud*, Standard Edition (1961, XIX, 157-170). London: Hogarth Press.

Gambino, B. and Cummings, T. (1989). Treatment for compulsive gambling: Where are we now? In H. Shaffer, S. Stein, B. Gambino and T. Cummings (eds.), *Compulsive Gambling: Theory, Research and Practice* (pp. 315-335). Lexington, MA: Lexington Books.

Gamblers Anonymous (1984). Los Angeles: G.A. Publishing.

Goldstein, L., Manowitz, P., Nora, R., Swartzburg, M. and Carlton, P. (1985). *Biological Psychiatry*, 20, 1232-1234.

Lesieur, H. (1984). *The Chase: Career of the Compulsive Gambler.* Cambridge, MA: Schenkman Books.

Lesieur, H. (1979). The compulsive gambler's spiral of options and involvement. *Psychiatry: Journal for the Study of Interpersonal Processes*, 42, 79-87.

Rosecrance, J. (1988). *Gambling without guilt: The Legitimation of an American Pastime.* Pacific Grove, CA: Brooks/Cole Publishing.

Rosenthal, R.J. (1986). The pathological gambler's system for self-deception. *Journal of Gambling Behavior*, 2:2, 108-120.

Roy, A., Adinoff, B., Roehrich, L., Lamparski, D., Custer, R., Lorenz, V., Barbaccia, M., Guidotti, A., Costa E. and Linnoila, M. (1988). Pathological gambling: A psychobiological study. *Archives of General Psychiatry*, 45, 369-373.

Shaffer, H.J. (1989). Conceptual crises in the addictions: The role of models in the field of compulsive gambling. In H. Shaffer, S. Stein, B. Gambino and T. Cummings (eds.), *Compulsive Gambling: Theory, Research and Practice.* Lexington, MA: Lexington Books.

Stein, S.A. (1989). A developmental approach to understanding compulsive gambling behavior. In H. Shaffer, S. Stein, B. Gambino, and T. Cummings (eds.), *Compulsive Gambling: Theory, Research and Practice.* Lexington, MA: Lexington Books.

Taber, J.I., Russo, A.M., Adkins, B.J. and McCormick, R. A. (1986). Ego strength and achievement motivation in pathological gamblers. *Journal of Gambling Behavior*, 2:2, 69-80.

Vaillant, G. (1987). Time: An important dimension of psychiatric epidemiology. In B. Cooper (ed.), *The Epidemiology of Psychiatric Disorders*. Philadelphia: Johns Hopkins University Press.

Proposed Criteria for Suspending Acute and Rehabilitative Care for Chronic Mental Patients

Julian I. Taber, James R. Smith and Michael D. Boston

Although rationing health care is an unpopular topic, selective restrictions on the amount of mental health care allotted to individuals is frequently mandated by limited resources and increasing case loads. The mental health system will continue to limit the care given to chronic patients by default if it does not develop scientifically sound and legally defensible criteria for suspension of active care. This paper suggests simple, objective behavioral criteria for determining when to suspend acute and rehabilitative mental health care in individual cases in which practical, cost effective benefits may not reasonably be anticipated. A typical illustrative case history is given, thirteen criteria for the suspension of active treatment are outlined, and some implications for treatment and policy are discussed.

In general medicine the criteria for clinical death and brain death, although not free from controversy, have by now been rather clearly specified, and these criteria have serious implications in medicine, law and sociology. They are among the most important issues in medical ethics (Gonda, 1989; Veatch, 1983; Jonsen, Siegler and Winslade, 1986; Showalter and Andrew, 1984; Culver and Gert, 1986; Cohen, 1988). Experience teaches that it is far better to have objective and universal death criteria, criteria which facilitate important end-stage treatment, than to allow events to be determined by individual biases.

In like manner, the mental health professions need universal, testable and objective criteria to assist in making decisions about what level or intensity of care to offer in cases of end-stage or irreversible mental illness. The mental health care system seems vulnerable in as much as it lacks objective and generally accepted criteria. Thus, the literature of general medicine is not irrelevant to the question of when to suspend or withhold active treatment for the mentally ill and we shall review some important issues once we have outlined a typical case history and presented our proposed criteria.

In the struggle to rationalize the distribution of scarce resources between responsive and refractory mental patients, care suspension criteria should be reliable, valid and humane. Only then can such criteria be defended against the inevitable attacks of those who would, because of idealism or special interest, admit to no limits on health care of any sort.

The case history to be presented is one that seems to fit all of the proposed criteria and, in fact, is the case which finally stimulated the authors to try to formalize ideas which had been under discussion for a long time. This particular individual was first seen as a relatively simple case of pathological gambling, but as the case workup was developed it began to appear that the subject was an "end-stage" pathological gambler for whom none of the usual treatment methods were likely to work since he had already been exposed to all kinds of programs and treatments. It soon became clear that the patient was a problem gambler and a great deal more. Ultimately, it was concluded that the patient was a rather typical refractory end-stage mental patient and decided that it would be inappropriate to treat him without considering the full range of his physical and mental problems. The authors have seen many other similar end-stage mental cases in our own public sector practices, the arena perhaps most likely to receive such cases and to require the criteria we propose here.

END-STAGE MENTAL ILLNESS

These discouraging end-stage cases appear to be essentially "dead" psychologically in as much of any continued personal growth seems most unlikely and, hence, the authors coined the term "Psychothanatoid Syndrome" to refer to similar end-stage mental patients. Historical and philosophical concepts of death include, in fact, a similar notion that biological life and even social life might continue following the "departure of the soul" (Veatch, 1983). Thus, it seems, there has been some previous recognition of psychological death. The use of any term such as psychothanatoid, however, opens the discussion to distracting and irrelevant debate. It is now preferable to use the phrase "End-stage Mental Illness" (EMI) to refer collectively to the proposed criteria.

Our formulation is of a "condition of being" rather than that of a disorder, disease or illness. We believe that the diagnostic criteria for EMI, unlike those for mental disorders, should all be met in making the diagnosis since termination of treatment can be a drastic step. Suspension of treatment, of course, ought not imply the end of caring or concern. When we speak of suspending or withholding treatment, we refer to acute care interventions and rehabilitative or remediation efforts, efforts directed toward producing important and lasting changes in thinking and behavior. We do not, of course, suggest withholding supportive care, necessary medications, attention to physical conditions, proper diet and so forth. We suggest only that we recognize the incurability of some patients, accept their permanent limitations and subsequently spare both patient and society the additional pain and expense of intensive treatment. This by no means implies any kind of passive euthanasia (Rachels, 1983) or a right to abandon a patient (Pozgar, 1987; Holder, 1983) without arranging appropriate supportive care.

In the following case history, identifying data have been changed to protect the patient's identity; these details do not affect the conclusions drawn in this paper, nor do they change substantially the clinical features of the case.

CASE HISTORY

The subject (S) was a 57 year old Caucasian male who served a number of years in a uniformed military service of the United States and received a "less than honorable" discharge for "sexual misconduct" with another male. He held a college degree and had done additional graduate work which equipped him for the profession he followed earlier in life after military service. He was the second of three siblings raised by the natural parents. S presented himself in interview as somewhat distant but friendly and relatively well groomed. He was clearly overweight, and he was polite and mild mannered showing good attention and concentration. There were no intrusive thoughts, no history of hallucinations or delusional thinking. There was a good fund of knowledge available to S with no interference or rambling. This patient was referred to the first author because S had been noted to be a pathological gambler and confirmation of this diagnosis was sought. There was the hope that this could be treated and that life would be better for S if he could stop gambling.

DEVELOPMENTAL FEATURES

S's earliest memories were generally of negative experiences and arose from ages four and five. He recalled his mother and father fighting verbally, and his own fear that these fights would result in catastrophic destruction of the family. The father was distant emotionally with frequent outbursts of anger. S always felt that he could not please the father and was fearful of him since the father's expectations seemed impossible for S to meet. The father was a laborer and apparently alcoholic.

The mother was reported to have been very emotional. She did not use alcohol and appeared to S to be very religious. He reported that she used various illnesses to get her way and that she liked being the center of attention. In most matters, the mother was the buffer between the father and S. Nevertheless, S appears to have lacked trust and confidence in his mother.

Both of S's siblings were reported to have developed alcohol problems and S had not had contact with any of his family for many years.

S began school at age five and was accelerated one grade at age eight; thus, he found himself too small to engage effectively in sports until his senior high school year at which time he played varsity sports. He reported that he was never close to anyone individual during his developmental years, although his older brother was perhaps a close ally.

There was no reported physical abuse, gross neglect or nutritional deprivation. There were no unusual childhood accidents, traumas or illnesses. He finished high school at age sixteen and college at age twenty. He remembers getting drunk on wine at age five. School was generally a rewarding period and drinking came to be an increasing problem during college years. He became an officer in the military holding responsible positions. Following military service, he took up a business career that was increasingly disrupted by alcohol abuse. His longest job, aside from military service, lasted two and a half years. S never married and seems to have recognized a homosexual preference during his military service. He never had children. There was, at the time of last interview, a strongly expressed preference for the sexual companionship of much younger men.

ADDICTIVE BEHAVIOR

During most of S's adult life, drinking and the results of drinking were major controlling factors. Concomitant with frequent intoxication were heavy gambling and homosexual activity. By the time S had reached late maturity, a well developed pattern had been formed: Restlessness and sexual tension led S to visit parts of town such as the local bus station where he could find younger men who would engage in sexual activity for money and gifts. S would typically bring the young man home to his apartment hoping to maintain a prolonged relationship only to find his friend equally restless and generally disloyal.

Attempting to prolong each relationship, S would take his friend to gamble in casinos and provide gambling money from his small disability allowance, an income based on medical problems. He himself gambled heavily at dollar slot machines, but the gambling seemed secondary to alcohol use and the excitement of the sexual encounter. S reported with considerable delight that on many occasions he had won sizable amounts and had used his winnings to buy presents for his companions. Unfortunately, inevitable losses and a loosening of the relationship with the current friend always led to more drinking. Alcohol, of course, was supplied free of charge in the casinos to frequent players.

Thus, S would relapse at the end of each cycle to chronic alcoholism, neglecting responsibilities and self-care while exacerbating his medical problems. This cycle, initiated by sexual desire and ending in loss of control of both alcohol and gambling, had repeated itself many times over a 20 year period.

During one interview, S made suggestions that he intended to stop smoking. He made equally promising (but unsolicited) statements about returning to Alcoholics Anonymous and about giving up his old lifestyle. These were seen as very superficial and well practiced devices for pleasing a therapist and, on one occasion, the therapist supplied S with a list of self-help meetings and encouraged him to return to Gamblers Anonymous only to find S, five minutes later, playing cards in the ward dayroom.

TREATMENT HISTORY

The authors were able to obtain summaries of many of S's medical records for the twenty years prior to his most recent admission to our facility although some private hospital records from earlier years were not available. He was treated beginning about age thirty-two in state hospitals for depression and alcoholism. He was hospitalized on psychiatric units in his mid-30s and had frequent episodes of depression. He was successfully operated for cancer of a major organ system at about age thirty-five. It is interesting to note that some of the oldest records indicate that S was observed as neat, alert and fully oriented with memory intact. There was never, in any of the records, a suggestion of any psychotic process or of disturbed thinking. S is reported to have presented himself, for the most part, with little overt feeling and had never complained of suicidal ideation or serious suicide attempts. He had repeatedly shown superficial concern regarding his guilt and his failure in life, but never made any permanent changes. He seldom, if ever, presented evidence of anxiety or generalized tension. An enlarged liver was noted on several admissions and it was frequently noted that he displayed little real motivation for change. He had been given a number of psychiatric diagnoses, beginning at age thirty-six, with sociopathic personality disorder (sic), sexual deviation (sic), and chronic alcoholism.

At age 50, he presented again during one of his many admissions with reported marijuana abuse and depression. He had been repeatedly placed in halfway houses, alcohol programs and city mission facilities. At age 53, during one admission, he reported that he had been given approximately 20 electro-convulsive shock treatments at a state hospital in earlier years. In his 30s and 40s he was repeatedly arrested for driving under the influence of alcohol. There was also a history of pancreatitis and pneumonia. S described himself at various points as a loner and a drifter with no close friends. Other than the reported marijuana use, there was no history of drug abuse.

In one examination a physician noted that genital examination revealed bilaterally small testes. He was found by various physicians to have hypertension, peptic ulcer, chronic obstructive pulmonary disease and glucose intolerance. S frequently reported the classic signs of alcohol withdrawal including delirium tremens and blackouts. At several points it is noted that S was discharged from alcoholism treatment for drinking during treatment, an event which he tended to see as unimportant. He was diagnosed as obese, but never followed a diet for weight reduction. On several occasions he was placed on disulfurium (i.e., antibuse) with great confidence expressed by S and his physicians only to be readmitted for drinking within a few weeks. During one admission it was suggested that he might have a Bipolar disorder although strong clinical signs of depression or of hyperactivity had never been noted in the record. There were no records of prolonged depressed mood, suicidal thinking, early morning wakefulness, anhedonia, etc. One physician did note that S had attempted suicide at age 35 with an overdose of medication, but the event was poorly documented and appears to have been an inference made by the examiner.

He was repeatedly referred over the years to rehabilitation medicine services, stop-smoking clinics, alcohol and substance abuse programs and psychiatric units in endless efforts to help him or simply to be rid of him.

Traumatic injuries were associated with intoxication and included a skull fracture at age 30 and surgery for nasal septal deviation. At age 55 he was noted to have had a cervical radiculopathy that had been repaired with laminectomy. He was reported at the same time to have adult onset diabetes millitus but took no medical treatment.

S completed our Addictive Disorders Treatment Program and was sent to a veterans' home at his request; while there, however, he found there were no suitable young, sexually active men available and began to make frequent trips from the veterans' home to a larger city where he could find willing sexual companions. Invariably, however, on these trips S became intoxicated and was eventually forced to leave the veterans' home.

Thereafter, he reported back to a Department of Veterans Affairs Medical Center and was again admitted for detoxification on a psychiatry ward. From here he was referred to an outpatient mental health clinic where he was seen for individual psychotherapy by one of the authors. Problems to be addressed in therapy were his own expressed discomfort with his lifestyle, his drinking and his gambling. He was seen for three sessions and the therapist asked S if he might want to give up looking for young sexual companions on the streets since this seemed to be a key factor in his relapse. It was suggested that he might find a man of his own age with whom he could be compatible. S agreed that he might have a more settled relationship with such a companion. Within days S was readmitted to inpatient psychiatry for detoxification and was seen on the ward with a young male visitor who was running errands for him. S's primary goal at the moment was to get a check cashed so that he could supply money to his young friend. S superficially agreed once again to his need to attend A.A. and to make major changes.

PSYCHOMETRIC FINDINGS

During his last inpatient admission a full psychometric battery was done. On the Minnesota Multiphasic Personality Inventory (MMPI) a valid profile showed significant elevations on numerous clinical scales. The patient appeared to have, at the time of testing, a relatively low energy level and to be emotionally isolated. Essentially, the MMPI profile was not different from those commonly observed in a psychiatric population or a hospitalized alcoholic population. S's score on masculinity-femininity was also significantly elevated and the profile was that of a depressed, emotionally isolated, introverted and self-preoccupied individual. Ego-strength was minimal as measured by that sub-scale.

S was able to write out a detailed life history in response to specific standard questions which showed detailed memory for recent and remote events.

S was referred for neuropsychological testing and willingly completed a Wechsler Adult Intelligence Scale, Revised Form (WAIS-R) which showed a Verbal I.Q. of 101, a performance I.Q. of 111 and a Full Scale I.Q. of 106. On WAIS-R sub-tests of general information and arithmetic, S scored in the high average range. His attention, social judgment and reasoning, as well as verbal abstract reasoning, were in the average range. Performance on sub-tests measuring constructional abilities and visual perceptual organization were in the high average range. Performance sub-tests scores for social reasoning, planning and visual organization were in the average range. On a measure of motor speed and new learning his score was in the average range. The examiner, a qualified neuropsychologist, in his report concluded, "These results suggest the patient was able to sustain attention to detail and has no deficits for encoding and memory." S also took the Rey Complex Figures Test which is a nonverbal test of memory; his score suggested some slight deficits in basic visual-perceptual abilities. However, his reproduction was done in an organized manner suggesting good planning. Immediate and delayed recall for the figure on the Rey Test were both significantly better than his reproduction score. Results suggest that visual-constructional abilities might have been better than basic visual-perceptual skills.

On the Audio-Verbal Learning Test (AVLT) performance was average to high average for S's age group in the areas of immediate and delayed recall as well as recognition. A normal learning curve on this test was noted.

In summary, the examiner concluded that S's overall performance was in the average range of intellectual functioning. Fund of information and mathematical development were in the high average range. All other measures were in the average range for this patient's age. There were no defects in verbal or nonverbal memory.

CASE DISCUSSION

It would be impossible to give any accurate estimate of the dollar value of all of S's failed treatments which involved over thirty admissions to acute care facilities with the multitudes of associated examinations, tests, special therapies, consultations and referrals. Then there were the many sheltered living arrangements paid for by federal, state and local funds. Certainly these costs would be in the hundreds of thousands of dollars, and S may still have twenty or more years to live. Dozens of similar cases are seen every year by clinicians.

Although this patient had many emotional problems as suggested by the MMPI, neither personality, performance, perceptual or intellectual measures explain S's long history of treatment failure and non-compliance. Other patients with similar test results might very well be excellent prospects for remediation efforts. Current psychometric technology does not seem to promise any easy way to discriminate between responsive and refractory EMI patients except in cases of severe psychosis or gross neurological deficit.

Some clinicians working in substance abuse programs would tend to see S as merely one more relapsing alcoholic and might be tempted therefore to continue working on the alcoholism, the overeating, the gambling or the smoking depending on the specialty of the clinician. Other clinicians would argue in favor of some underlying disorder such as a bipolar condition or an as yet undiagnosed thought disorder to account for his many problems. Perhaps some Axis II personality disorder should be invoked since S does, after all, show signs of the schizotypal, antisocial, borderline, passive aggressive and dependent personality.

Scholars outside the mental health field, and some within, might take a simple libertarian view that S is no more than willfully disobedient to society's standards of normal conduct; his behavior, after all, was purposeful and pleasure oriented. Thus, it could be argued, he deserves to live with the consequences of his misbehavior, that he has no mental illness at all, and that he does not belong in the health care system except when in need emergency life-saving interventions (Szasz, 1983a, 1983b). The purely libertarian view would relegate the management of people like S, if there were to be any management at all, to civil, political and economic agencies, and perhaps to the criminal justice system as well. It is this view which may, in part, explain why multitudes of homeless now make their onerous intrusions into the lives of ordinary citizens.

People like S live desperate lives full of pain and risk and the extent of their success in pleasure seeking is in serious doubt. Certainly he is not a criminal, nor does he seem likely to live an independent life without the need for constant rescue. He is as much a social problem as a medical one, but society seems unlikely to formulate a real solution without the guidance of the mental health community.

If, as we believe, the case presented fits a pattern of frequent treatment failure commonly seen among chronic mental patients, the need for criteria to justify withholding further intensive and costly treatment efforts seems urgent. Possible explanations for this chronic patient's refractory behavioral pattern are many, but they may not really be relevant to treatment planning.

A number of critical ethical issues are brought forward when we consider what to do with EMI patients the first of which may be the right to care (Telfer, 1983). Does the EMI patient have the same right to all forms of care commonly given to responsive mental patients, and if not, then how do we limit our liability and rationally distribute the care that is available? The success of "right to treatment" legal cases (Sade, 1983; Gert and Culver, 1983) has led to the imposition of strictly monitored care standards, and clinicians are now sometimes in the position of having to write detailed treatment plans for patients who are essentially untreatable with current technology.

In general medicine it seems to be well established that the provider may suspend or withhold care that is predictably ineffective without exposure to punitive legal liability (Showalter, 1984); likewise, the provider may legally withhold treatment from the noncompliant patient (Sade, 1983).

If we decide to offer only supportive care, rather than active treatment, we must deal with issues of paternalism (Gert and Culver, 1983), the right to be cared for in the least restrictive environment (Pozgar, 1987), respect for patient autonomy (Beauchamp and Childress, 1983), problems of civil commitment (Szasz, 1986; Livermore, Malmquist and Meehl, 1986) and, of course, society's judgment of and willingness to pay for any proposed alternative maintenance care. Whether we accept the hands-off libertarian view or, on the other extreme, decide to set up special camps or holding centers like the huge mental hospitals of the past, we will need universal, objective and legally acceptable criteria for deciding when the individual chronic patient has become an EMI patient.

Treatment suspension could be based on the patient's ability to pay (Evans, 1986), but this raises the ethical problem of taking money for treatments that are not likely to be successful and ignores the indigent patient. The imposition of lifetime dollar limits to mental health care is another financial tool, but since the EMI patient seldom has health insurance and "the system" has no good way of tracking patients who wander from one public facility to another, such strategies seem irrelevant. The development of any national patient tracking system raises what seem to be fatal objections based on well established principles of a patient's right to privacy. Economic and demographic criteria simply do not define the EMI patient and will not provide for his or her welfare.

Allocating treatment on a "social worth" basis means treating individuals differently depending on their perceived past or potential contributions to society, e.g., limiting dialysis or transplant surgery to patients under age 55. Social worth allocation raises special problems in fairness of allocation and is an "elitist" approach that is objectionable to many. One egalitarian view would allocate resources on a "first come, first served" basis, but this is a limited view which closes its eyes to social consequences and does not remove the clinician's responsibilities. Yet another important consideration which sometimes overrides the rights of the individual patient is concern for public welfare and safety, but just how harmful to society — aside from cost — the EMI patient is remains questionable. Most do little real harm except to themselves. They tend to be isolated drifters or reclusive street people who, at worst, commit petty crimes and are seen as public nuisances.

Our position is that the decision to suspend treatment for the untreatable would be best if it were based upon behavioral criteria which the patient himself presents in examination. Potential behavioral criteria are carried and displayed by the patient in every situation he or she enters. If research were to show that these behavioral criteria are both reliable and valid, many of the legal and ethical questions involved in the suspension of treatment would be rendered irrelevant since a positive diagnosis could lead to a constructive plan for supportive maintenance and offer a potential umbrella to shield the clinician from liability. However, if the clinician continues to employ the usual mental illness diagnostic labels, he or she might reasonably be expected to continue to apply the usual costly interventions.

PROPOSED CRITERIA FOR END-STAGE MENTAL ILLNESS

The following proposed criteria are based on the authors' experiences in many years of practice with large numbers of late stage mental patients. The criteria represent a first attempt to provide rigorous, objective and useful criteria for withholding acute and rehabilitative care. They are presented not for immediate use, but with the intent of stimulating discussion and research aimed at testing their reliability and validity. The proposed criteria are as follows:

1. Mentation and attention are narrowly focused upon personally selected and immediate hedonistic goals;

2. Concurrent with criteria 1, there is a somatic insensitivity or functional anesthesia for other physical and environmental conditions which observers would judge to be painful and/or intolerable;

3. There is a persistent and generalized lack of any real emotional sensitivity to the condition of others as well as continuing failure of empathic bonding beyond mere lip service.

4. There is an absence of any significant, internal ego structure or personal organizing principles beyond selective pleasure giving activities;

5. Mood is chronically dysphoric and shows no significant swings or alterations: If the negative effect is explained by the patient at all, it is attributed to external causes;

6. Consistent with criteria 5, there is a pervasive and continuing external locus of control (19) in which any sense of personal responsibility for one's present situation or actions is absent;

7. Consistent with criteria 5 and 6, there is profoundly reduced insight into, or concern with, personal dynamics or into the effects one's behavior may have on self or others;

8. There is a pervasive phobia-like rejection of "normal" and socially accepted performance in any sphere of activity;

9. There is notable pseudo-impulsivity which is often seen in schizotypal personality disorder, an impulsivity that is really practiced eccentricity;

10. There are present one or more advanced addictive disorders;

11. There is a rebellious, chronic and generally ineffective independence which leads to a continuing failure to thrive when left without social and material support systems;

12. Except for concrete adaptations to specific environmental changes, there is a continuing absence of any new learning of an abstract nature as well as a worsening of the condition proportional to the intensity of efforts to induce change; and

13. There is no focused, persistent or vindictive rage or anger, no criminal harmfulness, and no suicidal impulse or plan.

FURTHER DISCUSSION OF THE CRITERIA

The EMI "condition of being" is intended to describe a functional or acquired condition with no known organic basis. Many physical and neurological conditions can produce similar behavior; when there is a known etiology, the appropriate diagnosis should be retained. In like manner, when there is a clearly documented history of a functional mental illness being held in full or partial remission with ongoing treatment, the traditional diagnosis should be retained.

The functional anesthesia referred to in criterion 2 seems to be explained by the single mindedness with which the EMI patient pursues a specific personal goal at any given time. In the case above, S tolerated poor diet, inadequate clothing and miserable living conditions — things to which most people would assign a first priority — in order to pursue his major activities in the areas of sex, gambling and alcohol.

One of the present authors remembers an interview with a classic "street person" who was referred for admission to an alcohol program; the patient, who seemed to meet the criteria for EMI, was obsessed with getting a bus ticket from the social worker in order to return to the downtown area and retrieve his "bundle" from a dumpster where it was hidden. When the patient crossed his legs a maggot was observed to fall from a festering wound on his ankle. He refused medical attention and left the facility before an intervention could be arranged. In another case, a physician was explaining the discovery in x-ray of a major lung mass, but the patient's only question during a pause was, "You got a cigarette, Doc?" There was no real appreciation of the significance of what the patient had just heard.

Such patients may live for extended periods with scabies, infections, fractures, frostbite and other painful conditions complaining only about quite irrelevant issues.

The absence of ego structure referred to in criterion 4 may suggest a schizoid-like process, but the other common signs of schizophrenia are generally absent.

The chronic dysphoric mood (referred to in criterion 5) is not accompanied with the usual signs of major depression but, if the patient has been responsive to antidepressant medications in the past, the EMI diagnosis may be withheld pending a trial of chemotherapy.

We have come to think of the fear of having to conform to "normal" standards of conduct (criterion 8) as "normophobia." There seems to be an ingrained value system that places the individual outside the usual expectations for average, usual and acceptably moderate conduct. This idiosyncratic and rebellious alienation from normal social roles is no doubt related to criterion 12 in which it was noted that focused therapeutic change efforts will usually make the EMI patient even more eccentric and rebellious; normally effective therapies seem to force the individual to retreat even further into the pattern described.

Whether or not the specific criteria for the EMI diagnosis survive the tests of rigorous research, the need for such a classification seems great. Like death itself, the end-stage, untreatable mental patient presents the clinician with a personal dilemma for which there usually has been little preparation in training.

It is a situation in which "less is more," a situation which calls for surrender to a harsh reality. This inevitable surrender, however, need not be seen as a personal defeat for the clinician and can, instead, be the opportunity for better case management.

REFERENCES

Beauchamp, T.L. and Childress, J.F. (1983). The principle of autonomy. In N. Abrams and M.D. Bucker (eds.), *Medical Ethics*. Cambridge, MA: Massachusetts Institute of Technology.

Cohen, C.B. (1988). *Casebook on the Termination of Life-Sustaining Treatment and the Care of the Dying*. Bloomington, IN: University.

Culver, C.M. and Gert, B. (1986). The definition and criterion of death. In T.A. Mappes and J.S. Zembaty (eds.), *Biomedical Ethics*, 2nd edition. New York: McGraw-Hill.

Evans, R.W. (1986). Health care technology and the inevitability of resource allocation. In T.A. Mappes and J.S. Zembaty (eds.), *Biomedical Ethics*, 2nd edition. New York: McGraw-Hill.

Gert, B. and Culver, C.M. (1983). The justification of paternalism. In N. Abrams and M.D. Bucker (eds.), *Medical Ethics*. Cambridge, MA: Massachusetts Institute of Technology.

Gonda, T.A. (1989). Death, dying and bereavement. In H.I. Kaplan and B.J. Sadock (eds.), *Comprehensive Textbook of Psychiatry*, 5th edition, vol. 2. Baltimore: Williams and Wilkins.

Holder, A.R. (1983). The duty to care. In N. Abrams and M.D. Buckner (eds.), *Medical Ethics*. Cambridge MA: Massachusetts Institute of Technology.

Jonsen, A.R., Siegler, M. and Winslade, W.J. (1986). *Clinical Ethics*. New York: Macmillian.

Livermore, J.M., Malmquist, C.P. and Meehl, P.E. (1986). On the justification for civil commitment. In T.A. Mappes and J.S. Zembaty (eds.), *Biomedical Ethics*, 2nd edition. New York: McGraw-Hill.

Pozgar, G.D. (1987). *Legal Aspects of Health Care Administration*, 3rd edition. Rockville: Aspen.

Rachels, J. (1983). Active and passive euthanasia. In N. Abrams and M.D. Buckner (eds.), *Medical Ethics*. Cambridge, MA: Massachusetts Institute of Technology.

Rotter, J.B. (1982). *The Development and Applications of Social Learning Theory*. New York: Praeger.

Sade, R.M. (1983). Medical care as a right. In N. Abrams and M.D. Bucker (eds.), *Medical Ethics*. Cambridge, MA: Massachusetts Institute of Technology.

Showalter, J.S. and Andrew, B.L. (1984). *To Treat or Not to Treat*. St. Louis: Catholic Health Association of the United States.

Szasz, T.S. (1983). The illogic and immorality of involuntary psychiatric interventions. In N. Abrams and M.D. Buckner (eds.), *Medical Ethics*. Cambridge, MA: Massachusetts Institute of Technology.

Szasz, T.S. (1983). Reagan should let the jurors judge Hinckley. In N. Abrams and M.D. Buckner (eds.), *Medical Ethics*. Cambridge, MA: Massachusetts Institute of Technology.

Szasz, T.S. (1986). The myth of mental illness. In T.A. Mappes and J.S. Zembaty (eds.), *Biomedical Ethics*, 2nd edition. New York: McGraw-Hill.

Telfer, E. (1983). Justice, welfare, and health care. In N. Abrams and M.D. Bucker (eds.), *Medical Ethics*. Cambridge, MA: Massachusetts Institute of Technology.

Veatch, M. (1983). The definition of death: Ethical, philosophical, and policy confusion. In N. Abrams and M.D. Buckner (eds.), *Medical Ethics*. Cambridge MA: Massachusetts Institute of Technology.

ACKNOWLEDGEMENT

The opinions expressed in this paper are those of the authors and do not represent those of the Department of Veterans Affairs. The authors thank Ted Young, Ph.D. and Sarah L. Fitzpatrick for their help. A version of this paper was read at the Eight International Conference on Risk and Gambling which was held in London, England, August 15 through 17, 1990.

Models Explaining Gambling Severity among Patients undergoing Treatment in Maryland: 1983 through 1989

Robert A. Yaffee, Valerie C. Lorenz, and Robert M. Politzer

In 1989, the State of Maryland Department of Health and Mental Hygiene convened a task force to investigate the nature of the gambling problem within its territory. With a view toward providing new and useful information for policy-makers and legislators, the task force investigated the types of gambling preferred and the intensity with which gambling was pursued by compulsive gamblers undergoing clinical treatment in Maryland between 1983 and 1989. In addition to the profile of preferences on the part of these patients, two models explaining the severity of the gambling problem, based on the population of clinical patients, were developed. The gambling problem severity scale is a key variable linked to the compulsive nature of gambling. The findings from this analysis have serious implications for understanding the nature of the problem, treating the problem, and formulating regulatory policy. These models are the subject of this presentation.

THE DATA AND THEIR SOURCES

The data for this analysis come from a survey of patients undergoing therapy for this psychiatric illness. These data were offered by the three treatment centers in State of Maryland that have clinical programs dedicated to the treatment of pathological gambling. These data were provided by The National Center for Pathological Gambling, Inc., the Washington Center for Pathological Gambling, Inc., and Taylor Manor Hospital, in a fashion such that the identity of the patients was kept from the analysts of the data.

The time frame within which these data were collected dates from the inception of these programs until the summer of 1989. The Taylor Manor Hospital program began in 1983; the National Center for Pathological Gambling data collection started in 1985; and the Washington Center for Pathological Gambling data come from patients treated at that facility since 1983. Overall, these data come from approximately four to six years of treatment of patients in Maryland during the 1980s.

For this analysis the data were culled from at least two treatment centers. The number of Maryland residents in the National Center for Pathological Gambling to 1989 was 94. The number of Maryland residents at Taylor Manor was 93, and the number in the Washington Center for Pathological Gambling clinical program was 59. If all three clinical surveys asked a question, the data from all questionnaires were included as long as the coding of the question was consistent. If all three treatment centers asked the question but the coding of the particular variable from only two treatment centers were consistent, then the data were culled from those programs with consistent coding. If only one treatment center asked a question, the question was, as a rule, not included in this analysis.[1] The total number of possible observations was therefore 246, but instances of missing data often limited the number of observations to less than 246. Missing data came from persons refusing to answer, perhaps because the question was not applicable. The larger sample size permitted analyses that otherwise could not have been performed.

Moreover, after coding to prevent duplication of cases within the treatment subpopulations, traces of respondent identification were eliminated. Thus, the identity and anonymity of the respondents were guaranteed to the fullest extent possible. In keeping these confidences, this task force has complied with ethical obligations of researchers and clinicians. The patients will thus find that they have reason to confide in the task force, to help policy makers formulate policy in the public and patient interest.

RESEARCH QUESTIONS

The severity of the gambling problem among compulsive gamblers undergoing treatment in Maryland may be a key to understanding the etiology of compulsive gambling. If the intensity of this compulsion could be significantly reduced, this pathological condition could be attenuated. If the severity could be reduced substantially, the condition might be rendered manageable. The more severe the problem is, the more uncontrollable the illness will be. If the factors that contribute to the severity of the problem are understood, then indicators of the problem, clues to understanding the illness, and therapies for dealing with it may be developed. Hence, this article attempts to examine the severity of the gambling problem among compulsive gambling patients in Maryland.

STATISTICAL TECHNIQUES

As background to the addiction severity models, frequency distributions of the favored types of gambling and the component variables of the model are given. Presentation of these distributions of first and second gambling preference are given in percentages of respondents. When these presentations are given as approximate values, they are rounded to the nearest percent. The size given in the parenthesis is that of the size of the Table, not the count of that percentage.

A particular type of categorical data analysis — *logit analysis* — was selected for this general modeling building for a variety of reasons. Logit analysis can be construed as a kind of analysis of variance, utilizing the logit transformation of a dependent variable. The logit transformation is merely the natural log of the odds ratio. The odds ratio is the probability of an event happening divided by the probability of it not happening. These probabilities can be assessed by proportions or percentages in a cross-tabulation. Logit analyses are appropriate when the dependent variable is categorical or ordinal in nature, and most of the variables in this study are categorical or ordinal in nature.

Logit modeling has the advantage of being able to accommodate a larger multi-variable model by which it is possible to assess the significance and magnitude of the main effects of more components as well as their respective interactions in the model. This allows a better way to examine the nature of catalyzing or suppressing main effects as well as interactions. The more elaborate logit model allows examination of a multitude of effects that may be antecedent to or intervening in a simple bivariate cross-classification analysis.

Even if the dependent variable were a collapsed continuous ratio, logit analyses using nominal or ordinal dependent variables are generally more robust than commonly used techniques such as classical regression analysis or discriminant analysis in that their validity is dependent on fewer assumptions.[2] The maximum-likelihood estimation of the techniques is not as susceptible, with large samples, to problems of misestimation, heteroskedasticity, and nonnormality as are ordinary least squares estimation procedures found in the classical regression analyses. They are more robust than discriminant function analyses because they can handle interaction effects and do not dependent on such assumptions as multivariate normality and homogeneity of the error covariance matrices. Because the logit model is a more robust, elaborate, and elegant analytic approach to these data, it is used to assess the nature of the severity of the gambling problem among Maryland's patient gamblers for the time frame of the study.

It might be objected that one could use classical regression analysis with a dichotomous dependent variable to obtain a similar results. Using ordinary least squares estimation, the classical regression model would tend to overpredict and underpredict the values of the dependent variable, leading to bias. If the dependent variable is dichotomous, coded zero and one, ordinary regression would produce predictions higher than the one and lower than the zero value. It would also predict a lot of values between the two values of the dichotomous dependent variable. If the dependent variable has a few ordered values, ordinary regression would similarly mispredict the values of the dependent variable. If the dependent variable is unordered and polytomous, classical regression would be inappropriate. The errors would not be normally or homogeneously distributed. The F tests for significance testing would not work and there would be no clear way to determine whether the predictors should be included in the model. The coefficient of determination, the *R-square*, would not work either, leaving no reliable way to assess the strength of the overall model.

With a dependent ordered typology, such as the severity level of the gambling problem, the use of a logit analysis with cumulative logits is the appropriate technique to use. The cumulative logit makes use of the ordering in the dependent variable and is tantamount to a series of binary logits with cut points for the odds ratios at the demarcations of levels of the ordinal dependent variable. For this purpose, the *Statistical Analysis System* (SAS) LOGIST procedure, part of the SAS User's Group International Supplementary Library, was chosen. This procedure uses maximum likelihood estimation and cumulative logits formed from the ordering in the dependent variable.

When using a binary coded, rather than an ordered polytomous dependent variable, binary logit (logistic regression) analysis was employed. The transformation of the dependent variable here is a simple logistic one. The regression of the natural log of the odds ratio of the moderate or heavy gambling severity to the lower level of gambling severity is performed on the predictor variables. Logistic regression, with maximum likelihood estimation, is appropriate here. To provide for criterion validation of the results of the programming and analysis where logistic regression as the statistical technique was selected, analyses using the categorical modeling procedure in SAS, the logistic regression procedure in SPSS/pc[3], and the logit procedure in LIMDEP[4] were employed in developing this model. These binary logistic regression programs produced the same regression coefficients and significance test results.[5]

FINDINGS

A. Demographic Characteristics of the Patients

Before reporting findings, it might be of some interest to describe very briefly the nature of the demographic background, socioeconomic characteristics, and familial and personal histories of the population. Demographically, these patients were mostly married, middle-aged, male caucasians from families with two brothers or sisters. Approximately 40 percent (n=226)[6] of these respondents noted that they were between 30 and 39 years of age. Another 27 percent reported being between 40 and 49 years old. Almost 16 percent described themselves as being between 20 and 29. About 12 percent of them were between 50 and 60. Smaller percentages were teenagers or senior citizens. Thus, these patients were largely middle-aged.

The patients were largely male caucasians. Eighty-five percent (n=246) were male and 15 percent were female. More than 86 percent (n=217) were white. Twelve percent reported being black. Less than one percent reported Hispanic

(0.5 percent), Asian (0.9 percent), or of other (0.5 percent) racial characterization.

Most (58.9%, n=241) of these patients were married. Seventeen percent reported being divorced and 12 percent reported being single. About 7 percent noted being widowed and almost four percent said that they were separated. Less than two percent told of living together with a partner.

The families from which they come are not large. Almost 24 percent (n=159) came from families with two siblings. About 18 percent come from families with three brothers or sisters. Almost three-fourths of these patients come from families with three or fewer siblings.

B. Socio-Economic Characteristics of the Patients

In general, these patients are fully-employed, clerical or sales persons, with at least a high-school education, and earning less than $30,000 a year. Of the 239 persons responding to the question concerning their employment status, 83.3 percent reported that they were fully employed, 2.9 percent indicated that they were part-time employed, and 13 percent noted that they were unemployed. Less than one percent of these patients suggested that they were retired or students.

A plurality of patients were clerical or sales persons, with smaller portions of this population having come from management/executive positions and the professions. Of the 229 patients answering this question, 43.7 percent noted that they had clerical or sales occupations. Almost 38 percent indicated that they held executive or management positions. Almost 14 percent indicated that they were in the professions. Slightly more than four percent said that they were in business. Less than one percent maintained that they were housewives or students.

The educational level of these patients was not high. When asked how many years of school the respondents completed, the patients indicated that about a quarter of them had dropped out of high school and more than half had completed 12 years of schooling. If one can assume that the respondents had not repeated years of school and had not skipped grades, some inferences can be made about the level of educational attainment. A little more than one-fourth (26 percent, n=246) had dropped out of high school. More than half (52.4 percent) had graduated high school. Another 4.1 percent had some college, while another 11.8 percent had two through four years of college. Approximately six percent had gone to graduate school.[7]

The income level of these patients is characterized by a fairly flat income distribution across the income spectrum, trailing off a little at the upper end. Approximately 27 percent (n=239) reported making $10,000 per year or less. Another 21.8 percent maintained that they earned between $11,000 and $20,000 per annum. Nearly 27 percent claimed that they made between $20,001 and $30,000. About 13 percent asserted that they made between $30,001 and $40,000. Less than twelve percent affirmed that they made more than $40,000 per year.

C. History of Parental Abuse and Loss

These patients come from families with a substantial amount of parental abuse of alcohol, gambling, and early demise. In a considerable portion of cases, the father had a problem with alcohol or gambling. In a significant percentage of cases, the mother had passed away before the patient had turned 18 years of age. Of the 169 patients answering the question of whether one of the parents had an alcohol problem, 37.9 percent stated that their parents were plagued by such a problem. Some 37.3 percent of the fathers (n=75) were said to have had an alcohol problem. Slightly more than eight percent (n=170) of the mothers and 23.7 percent (n=170) of the fathers were reported to have had a gambling problem.

A large portion of the parents of these patients had died before the patient had turned 18 years of age. Surprisingly, 50.3 percent (n=169) of the mothers and 14.2 percent of the fathers (n=169) had died before the patient was 18 years old. This history may indicate inadequate resistance to indulgence and early loss of parental support and guidance.

D. History of Personal Abuse and Consequences

Many of the patients have been abused, and many do overindulge themselves. This behavior has led large proportions of them to undergo treatment and incarceration. Over 41 percent (n=168) were subjected to physical or sexual abuse in earlier years. More than 26 percent (n=187) have had or do have a drug problem, while 50.8 percent (n=187) have had or do have an alcohol problem. Fifteen percent (n=187) report overeating of one sort or another, such as indulging sweets, salts, or quantities. More than 25 percent of the patients have attempted suicide (n=167). Many of these patients (48 percent, n=173) have been outpatients before. More than 22 percent (n=172) have been inpatients before. More than 20 percent had pending legal problems (n=153). Approximately 13 percent (n=174) have found themselves in jail or prison. Sizeable portions of this patient population have experienced other abuses and their consequences.

THE NATURE OF THE GAMBLING PROBLEM: FAVORED TYPES OF GAMBLING

What are the gambling preferences of these patients? The patients may have had some difficulty deciding which category properly characterized their preference. The favorite gambling preference indicated was horse or dog racing (which means horses because there are no dog tracks in Maryland); second is poker machines; third is casinos; and fourth is sports wagering. Among the second most favorite kind of gambling, the lottery is pre-eminent, followed by casino and then cards. Fourth place for the second preference was tied by poker machines, horses/dogs, and sports. These preferences are presented in more detail in Tables 1 and 2.

The most favored form of gambling was presented in Table 1 (N=144). Over thirty percent of the patients stated that their favorite type of gambling was the races. Almost 21 percent of the patients maintained that their favorite type of gambling was poker machines. Sixteen percent of the patients stated that their favorite type of gambling was some form of casino betting.

The distribution of the second favorite type of gambling was also examined and is found in Table 2. Primary among the second most favored type of gambling was the lottery/numbers. About thirty-six percent of the patients reported that this was their second favored type of gambling. The casino again reappears on the list of second most favored preferences for approximately 16 percent of the cases.

The horses, poker machines, casinos and lotteries are the major forms of gambling among Maryland patients between 1983 and 1989. Yet, the nature of the gambling problem comprises a question of intensity as well.

TABLE 1

First Gambling Preference		
1ST PREFERENCE	FREQUENCY	PERCENT
Missing	9	
Bingo	1	0.7
Cards	14	9.7
Casino	23	16.0
Dice, Bar Boot	1	0.7
Horse/Dogs	44	30.6
Lottery/Numbs	8	5.6
Poker Machines	30	20.8
Pool	1	0.7
Sports	19	13.2
Stocks/Options	1	0.7
Anything	2	1.4

TABLE 2

Second Gambling Preference		
2ND PREFERENCE	FREQUENCY	PERCENT
Missing or none	44	
Bingo	1	0.9
Business	1	0.9
Cards	14	12.8
Casino	17	15.6
Dice, Bar Boot	2	1.8
Horse/Dogs	10	9.2
Lottery/Numbs	39	35.8
Poker Machines	10	9.2
Pool	1	0.9
Slot Machines	1	0.9
Sports	10	9.2
Stocks/Options	2	1.8
Anything	1	0.9

THE NATURE OF THE GAMBLING PROBLEM: AN ORDINAL LOGIT MODEL OF THE SEVERITY OF THE GAMBLING PROBLEM

As a simple yet elegant quantitative measure of addiction severity, a gambling problem severity scale, was constructed and used as the basis for the logit analysis. Preliminary bivariate screening was conducted. Candidate predictors were selected and crosstabulated with a collapsed verson of the gambling problem severity ratio. The relationships found to have significance levels of .10 or less qualified the predictor for inclusion in the right hand side of the logit model. The dependent variable construction, selection of predictor variables, explanation of the model, assessment of its fit, and the interpretation of its coefficients are now examined.

The gambling problem severity scale was constructed by dividing the size of the gambling debt by the annual income of the patient. The higher the ratio, the more severe was the gambling problem. This ratio was trichotomized into low, medium and high levels. The low level extended from 0 to 0.233, the medium level ranged from 0.233 to 0.8667, and the high level spanned the region above 0.868 to the maximum of 58.8. Because this collapsed gambling problem severity measure is an ordered typology, a logit analysis utilizing cumulative logits was selected for the analysis.

A logit is the natural log of the odds ratio of the collapsed version gambling problem severity variable. The natural log of one is 0, and the natural log of 0 is undefined. For example, the natural log of 10 is 2.303; when 2.718 is raised to the power of 2.303, one obtains the result of 10. The odds ratio is the probability of being characterized by one of the categories (levels) of the gambling problem variable divided by the probability of not being characterized by that level. The probability of being in a group may be empirically obtained by the proportion of total cases in that group, as long as the observations are independent of one another. The categories are mutually exclusive and collectively exhaustive. Thus, the odds ratio is the probability of having a addiction at one of the three levels of the gambling problem severity scale divided by the probability of having an addiction at either of the other levels.

With cumulative logits on an ordered trichotomy, we examine the cumulative logits of the gambling problem severity scale. This gives us two formulae. The first formula utilizes the natural log of the odds ratio of either of the top two levels compared to the bottom level. The second formula utilizes the natural log of the odds ratio of the top level compared to either of the two lower levels. These transformations of the severity of gambling problem ratio become the dependent variable in this analysis. Cumulative logits provide us with two dependent variables:

$$\text{logit1} = LN \left[\frac{\text{Probability (Gambling prob severity ratio level 2 or 3)}}{\text{Probability (Gambling prob severity ratio level 1)}} \right]$$

$$\text{logit2} = LN \left[\frac{\text{Probability (Gambling prob severity ratio level 3)}}{\text{Probability (Gambling prob severity ratio level 1 or 2)}} \right]$$

The single formula provided is a summary combination of variables that contribute to the explanation of logit1 and logit2. Alpha1 may be construed as the intercept with logit1 as a dependent variable, and alpha2 as the intercept used with logit2 as the dependent variable. The generic formula of the cumulative logit is as follows:

$$\text{Cum logit} = \alpha_i + B_1X_1 + B_2X_2 + \ldots + B_nX_n$$

$$= \ln\left(\frac{prob(x_i)}{1 - prob(x_i)}\right) = \alpha_i + B_1X_1 + \ldots + B_nX_n$$

where

α_i *= intercept above cut point i*

$prob(x_i)$ *= probability of gambling severity above level i*

The Bs here are logistic regression coefficients of their respective variables (Xs) in the formulae. They are the coefficients expressing the change in the logit that accompanies a unit change in the variable under consideration. The values of the other variables are held constant during this process. To obtain the change in the odds ratio associated with a unit change in the independent variable, merely exponentiate its regression coefficient. That is,

to obtain odds take B_i *to the* e^{B_i}

The percentage change in the odds of the collapsed gambling severity ratio associated with a unit change in the independent variable is:

$$\textit{\% change in odds of the dependent variable} = (e^{B} - 1) * 100$$

The estimation process is accomplished by a maximum likelihood algorithm. The observed values of the dependent variable are compared to the fitted values of the model. The model estimates the parameters for the alpha and Bs which maximize the probability of obtaining the observed set of data. This may be done by calculating the estimated likelihood function and taking the partial derivatives with respect to the Bs or alpha. The resulting formula may be set to 0 for computation of the maximum. The values of the coefficients which maximize this likelihood function are then used as the coefficients in the formula. More specifically, the Gauss-Newton maximum likelihood algorithm utilizing step halving with the Gauss increment was utilized.[8] This method is robust to the violation of several ordinary least squares regression assumptions.[9]

The fitting strategy employed involved selection of candidate predictors from significant cross-tabulations with the trichotomized dependent variable, testing the null model, the main effects model, a model with two-way interactions, and models with higher order interactions. Before proceeding with the testing of interaction models, nonsignificant main effects were pruned from the model. The testing of a model with interactions was obviated by the lack of improvement in the fit when the all first order-interactions were found to be non-significant. Higher order interactions (three-variable) were tested but encountered an excessive number of empty cells in the cross-tabulations formed; hence, these were abandoned. Then the model was fine-tuned by collapsing categories of the predictor variables to improve the fit between the observed and predicted models.

This final recoding of scores yielded the same variables coded as follows: Education was defined as having at least graduated from high school. This variable was coded as zero for having been a high school dropout and as one for having at least graduated from high school. Whether the mother died before the patient was 18, whether the patient has or has had physical or sexual abuse, and whether the patient has or has had a problem with drug abuse, are similarly coded dummy variables: a one indicated presence of the characteristic and a zero indicated absence of it.

Among the patients, it was found that these variables significantly discriminated among the levels of severity of the gambling problem. Together these variables with the Gauss-Newton maximum likelihood estimation, yielded the results in Table 3, where the Bs (the regression coefficient in the ordinal logit analysis), their standard errors, the Wald Chi-square statistics (the quantity of [the B divided by its standard error] squared), and the significance levels of the Wald statistic (which is distributed as a Chi-square with one degree of freedom) are presented.

TABLE 3

Ordinal Logit Analysis

Variable	*B*	Std Error	Chi-square Wald Statistic	*p*
Alpha1	-3.021	.600	25.29	0.000**
Alpha2	-4.178	.647	41.70	0.000**
Mom died early	2.144	.432	24.68	0.000***
Physical & sexual abuse	1.132	.380	8.86	0.003**
Drug Problem	-1.598	.608	6.90	0.009**
Education	1.104	.463	5.68	0.017*

Null Model - 2 Likelihood Ratio = 292.42 p=0.00
-2 log likelihood of Model w/variables = 233.09
Model Likelihood Ratio Chi-square = 59.33, 4 df, p=0.00
Somers' Dyx = .608 Gamma = .674
Significance levels:
*p < .05
**p < .01
***p < .001

The influence on the odds of the gambling severity problem on the part of a unit increase in the particular variable, controlling for the influence of all other variables, can be discovered by examining the change in odds ratios in Table 4. The change in the odds of being in either of the top two levels (over being in the lower category) of the gambling severity problem as a result of a unit change in the respective variable is provided from the table above, using equation 1. The change in the odds of being in the top level (over being in either of the other levels) per unit change of the variable in the model is provided from Table 4, using equation 2.

Among these covariates, the most powerful association with the change in the severity of the gambling problem is the death of the mother before the patient was 18 years of age. The second most powerful relationship with this odds ratio is that of the physical or sexual abuse of the patient. The education of the patient has approximately the same magnitude of an effect on the odds ratio, while the existence of a drug problem is the only other addiction which has a negative influence on the severity of the gambling problem. The existence of a drug problem is inversely related to the increased severity of the gambling problem.

The strength of the model is indicated by nonparametric correlation coefficients with magnitudes extending from 0 to 1.0 and signs of plus or minus. The Somers' D of .608 and a Gamma of .674 represent the correlation between the observed a predicted values, corrected for ties and the correlation not corrected for ties, respectively. However, this is not a perfect fit, as the significance level of the likelihood ratio Chi-square would indicate.

TABLE 4

Regression Coefficients (*B*s) and Odds Change for Model[10] Associated with Each Variable

	EQUATION 1 MODERATE TO VY SEVERE COMPARED TO LOW LEVELS	EQUATION 2 VERY SEVERE COMPARED TO LOWER LEVELS		
Variable	*B*	*B*	*Odds exp(B)*	*% chge of odds*
Intercept	-3.021	-4.18		
Mom died early	2.144	2.144	8.534	753.4
Physical & sexual abuse	1.132	1.132	3.102	210.2
Drug problem	-1.598	-1.598	.202	-79.8
High school graduate	1.104	1.104	3.016	20.2

The relative strength of the variables in increasing the odds of being in either of upper levels of the severity of the gambling problem are, in decreasing order, the demise of the mother before the age of 18, whether the patient was a high school graduate, the experience of past physical or sexual abuse, and lastly whether or not the patient has or had a drug problem. The past or present existence of a drug problem was negatively related to the increased severity of the gambling problem. Even so, the odds change linked to a unit increase in drug problem was significant, albeit small.

BINARY LOGIT (LOGISTIC REGRESSION) MODEL

There are several reasons for which a newer version of this model is fit. This model is fit better when it is reduced to a binary logistic regression. In the ordinal logit, the counts in the middle and upper two levels of the gambling severity problem were 27 and 30, respectively. In a binary logit, we have a larger sample size in the collapsed category and the asymptotic estimates are more precise. We may improve the fit of the model by collapsing these upper two levels into a medium/high severity problem. That measure of fit, - 2*log likelihood goes from 233.09 with the ordinal logit model to 152.34 with the binary logistic model.

The prediction is improved. With the new model we are able to attain a 77.7 percent correct prediction. The sensitivity is 73.7 percent and the specificity is 79.8 percent. The false negative rate is 14.7 percent and the false positive rate is 34.4 percent. Correlations between the observed and predicted scores increase. The Somer's D jumps from .608 to .673 and the Gamma jumps from .674 to .735, when a binary logistic regression of this newly collapsed gambling severity problem is performed.

The model is changed somewhat. Most coefficients have approximately the same magnitudes, directions, and significance levels in the binary as they had in the ordinal logit model. Yet the dependent variable has been modified and hence the model is somewhat different. To be sure, education appears to be more powerfully associated here than in the ordinal model. Being a high school graduate appears more strongly associated with the more serious gambling problems than before. This model is presented in Table 5. Only past or present drug problem, among all of these significantly related variables, is inversely related to the logit of the severity of the gambling problem.

TABLE 5

Binary Logistic Regression Analysis				
Variable	*B*	Std Error	Chi-square Wald Statistic	*p*
Intercept	-3.133	.649	23.28	0.000***
Mother died early	2.371	.450	27.73	0.000***
High school graduate	1.188	.503	5.58	0.018*
Physical & sexual abuse	1.014	.431	5.80	0.016*
Drug problem	-1.789	.626	8.01	0.005**
Significance levels: *p < .05, **p < .01, ***p < .001				

TABLE 6

Regression coefficients, odds change, and percentage change for Binary Logistic Regression Model			
Variable	*B*	Odds change exp(*B*)	% Change in Odds (exp(b)-1)*100
Intercept	-3.313		
Mom died early	2.371	10.71	970.8%
High school graduate	1.188	3.28	228.1
Physical & sexual abuse	1.014	2.76	176.6
Drug Problem	-1.789	0.167	-83.3

DISCUSSION

The ordinal logit model for a severity of the gambling problem is nicely formulated into high, medium, and low severities. If we collapse the high and medium gambling severity into one category, and use this binary split, into "low" and "higher than low" gambling severity, then we obtain a binary logit model which fits the data even better than the ordinal logit model. We improve our correct prediction rate to 77.7 percent. This model has high predictive validity for these patients and hence appears to have much utility.

What factors explain the gambling problem severity? The death of the mother is the most powerfully related influence on the severity of the gambling compulsion. If the mother died at an early age, then the associated severity is likely to be worse. It could be speculated that the earlier the emotional bond is broken, the more the gambler may have been deprived of early emotional support, and the more the gambler may have a need to find a source of security, be it financial or otherwise. If the gambling patient had been or is being physically or sexually abused, then the odds are higher that the patient has a more severe gambling problem. Gambling may be seen as an attempt to recoup lost esteem. High school graduates among these patients are more likely to be more compulsive in gambling than those who did not graduate. Such patients appear to be more venturesome and risk-seeking than those who did not attain that educational level.

Surprisingly, the existence of a past or present drug problem appears to be negatively related to the severity of the gambling problem. The more the gambler gets involved with drugs, the more befogged the person's focus of attention becomes, the more detached from the reality of the gambling, and the less the ability to get highly involved with serious gambling. Serious gamblers require clarity of mind and control. They prefer to spend their money for gambling rather than for buying drugs. Those patients with the more severe gambling problems tend to steer clear of drug usage and dependence.

This model has implications for the theory of the addictive personality syndrome, as advanced by Durand F. Jacobs (1986). The addictive personality theory postulates a unified theory of addiction. Persons may try to lump compulsive gambling into a theoretical construct including other addictions, whereby they would treat one addictive malady as they would another. From analysis of frequency distributions alone, persons might be inclined to link compulsive gambling to other kinds of addictions in this way.

Our logit findings reveal that frequencies analyzed by themselves may yield deceptively simple results. Some of the clinical interviews unfortunately lumped past and present tense together when inquiring as to drug or alcohol dependency. Although about 50 percent claimed past or present alcohol abuse, the logit analyses among these patients yielded no significant relationship between such alcohol abuse and the severity of the gambling problem. Even though 26.7 percent of the patients claimed to have had or have a drug problem, the logit analyses reveal an inverse relationship between the severity of the gambling problem and the past or present drug abuse. These findings call into question the notion of the addictive personality, insofar as it refers to concurrent or simultaneous addiction.

If this addictive personality syndrome has any meaning, the co-addictive tendencies, among these patients, are simultaneous or serial/sequential. That 50.3 percent of these patients have had or do have an alcohol problem is interesting. The lack of any significant relationship between the severity of the gambling problem and alcohol dependency, whether past or present, moves one to question the notion that general addictive predispositions apply to both kinds of addiction. As the incidence of alcohol addiction does not seem to be related to the gambling problem severity, different types of treatment modalities might apply to those afflicted with each alcohol and gambling addiction.

The negative relationship between the present drug problem and the compulsive gambling problem makes intuitive sense. There seems to be a zero-sum situation between simultaneous compulsive gambling and drug abuse. The clarity of mind and control required for serious gambling is undermined by compulsive drug usage. The spending of money to satisfy the need for drugs depletes the compulsive gambler of his means for satisfying his gambling addiction. The needs of the drug and the gambling addict compete and conflict. They are difficult to satisfy simultaneously. This fact could account for the negative relationship between the severity of the gambling problem and drug abuse.

The question arises as to whether the addictive tendencies obtain, so that an addictive personality displaces or replaces one addiction with another. Although there could be an inverse relationship between the severity of the gambling problem and present drug use, that is not to say there could not be a more or less sequential singular addiction tendency, with gambling replacing the drug problem. If this sequential addiction holds, it could attenuate or suppress the stronger inverse effect of the negative relationship between the simultaneous drug abuse and gambling abuse. The result would be a muted negative main effect of drug abuse on the severity of the gambling problem. This suppression could attenuate the magnitude of the simultaneous effect. Is there a practical limit to the number of addictions that can afflict a victim? If it is common for such persons to roller-coaster from one to another addiction, then the inverse tendencies between drug and gambling addiction at the same time are probably more intense than indicated. Dual addiction would be more sequential than concurrent, and the treatment modalities indicated would have to be specially tailored to the type of addiction. Under these circumstances, it would be a mistake to treat gambling addiction as if it were another form of drug or alcohol addiction.

These findings are limited in geographical scope and time. What characterizes the population of Maryland patients from 1983 to 1989 need not hold for all other States, regions, or times. Replication is needed to provide a firm basis for generalization.

Further research and analysis is underway with Gamblers Anonymous patients to explore co-addiction further. Nonetheless, enough evidence exists to disconfirm any universality of the notion of the addictive personality as assuredly one of simultaneous as well as serial addiction. More research on co-addiction is clearly needed.

ENDNOTES

[1] An exception to this rule was the query about insurance. Only one treatment center, the National Center for Pathological Gambling, Inc., asked this question. The frequency distribution of the answers to this question was deemed important for policy makers, for which reason this item was included.

[2] The logit analyses depend on a sufficiently large sample size and few zero cell counts in the multiple cross-classifications involved. In contrast, an ordinary least squares regression depends on distributional assumptions that are more difficult to attain for generalization: Equality of variance, normal distribution of errors, non-correlation of errors, and linearity of the relationship. Because we are dealing not with sample data, but with the population itself, we are not unduly dependent on all of these assumptions. But the moment we wish to generalize from the Maryland population to a larger population at one point in time or to generalize beyond the current time frame of 1983 through 1989, we have to take care not to seriously violate these assumptions.

[3] SPSS/pc is a package written and distributed by Statistical Package for the Social Sciences, Inc. in Chicago, Illinois. Release 3.1 of the personal computer package has a logistic regression procedure within it.

[4] LIMDEP, *Limited Dependent Variable Analysis*, is a flexible computer program written by Professor William H. Greene at New York University.

[5] SAS/pc produced coefficients with the opposite signs only because it was basing its calculations on the lower rather than the upper probability level.

[6] All subsequent samples sizes (N's) pertain to the specific sample size from the variable or relationship between variables being discussed.

[7] Missing values were treated as 12 or fewer years of school in this question.

[8] For a detailed treatment of the Gauss-Newton algorithm, see Douglas Bates and Donald Watts, *Nonlinear Regression Analysis and Its Implications*, (New York: John Wiley and Sons, 1988), pp. 40ff. This is an asymptotic estimation process, where the smallest number of observations per variable was more than 41.

[9] The assumption of equality of variance along the predicted line is relaxed. There should, however, be no substantial correlation among the independent variables. The highest intercorrelation among these indepenent variables was .24. The average absolute interitem correlation was .136, yielding no substantial evidence of multicollinearity.

[10] This is the odds of the model due to inclusion of the variable. This is the contribution to the model odds, where the intercept is factored into the calculation, not a partial odds contribution where only the *B* is exponentiated. To calculate the model odds, the alpha is added to the *B* before this express is exponentiated.

REFERENCES

Agresti, A. (1984). *Analysis of Ordinal Categorial Data.* New York: John Wiley and Sons, Inc.

Harrell, F.E., Jr. (1986). The Logist Procedure. *SUGI Supplemental Library User's Guide*, Version 5, 269-294. Cary, NC: SAS Institute, Inc.

Jacobs, D.F. (1986). A general theory of addictions: A new theoretical model. *Journal of Gambling Behavior*, Spring/Summer, 15-31.

Magidson, J. (1988). Progression beyond regression. Reprinted from *DMA Research Council Newsletter*, Winter/Spring/Autumn.

ACKNOWLEDGEMENTS

We would like to express our gratitude to the directors of the three Maryland clinical treatment centers, Dr. Valerie C. Lorenz, of the Compulsive Gambling Center, Inc., Clark Hudak, of The Washington Center for Pathological Gambling, Inc. and Dr. Joseph Ciarrocchi, of Taylor Manor Hospital, for sharing with us anonymous patient data for this analysis of compulsive gamblers. Moreover, we would like to thank Edi Franceschini, Deputy Director of New York University's Academic Computing Center, for permission to run this analysis on the IBM® mainframe.

TRADEMARK ACKNOWLEDGEMENT